MATHEMATICAL FOUNDATIONS FOR DESIGN:
Civil Engineering Systems

MATHEMATICAL FOUNDATIONS FOR DESIGN:
Civil Engineering Systems

Robert M. Stark
Robert L. Nicholls
University of Delaware

McGraw-Hill Book Company

New York   St. Louis   San Francisco   Düsseldorf   Johannesburg
Kuala Lumpur   London   Mexico   Montreal   New Delhi
Panama   Rio de Janeiro   Singapore   Sydney   Toronto

Mathematical Foundations for Design:
Civil Engineering Systems

Library of Congress Catalog Card Number 70–138859

07–060857–1

234567890MAMM798765432

This book was set in Times Roman, and was printed and bound by The Maple Press Company. The designer was Merrill Haber; the drawings were done by John Cordes, J. & R. Technical Services, Inc. The editors were B. J. Clark and Diane Drobnis. Adam Jacobs supervised production.

Contents

Preface

This text develops techniques commonly associated with operations research and systems engineering which are applicable to the design and operation of systems that concern civil engineers. Following an introductory chapter on methodology, six chapters deal with optimization, and the final five chapters with applied probability. The techniques developed are used to solve problems in transportation design, traffic control, water-resource design and operation, structural design, and construction management.

Chapter 1 delineates methodology of problem formulation, classification, choosing a value criterion, and constructing a model. A section on the time value of money compares alternative measures of a sum, an essential element for design and operating decisions.

Chapters 2, *3*, and *4* deal with the optimization of a linear function subject to linear constraints, i.e., linear programming. Chapter 2 is an informal introduction to the simplex method of linear programming. It is not essential to have a rigorous mathematical grasp to use linear programming effectively. Chapter 3 illustrates several engineering applications and provides an extensive list of references. Portions of the work in earlier references have been superseded. However, they can provide perspective for a developing subject. Chapter 4 contains additional linear techniques for solving engineering design and operational problems. These techniques provide for increased computational efficiency, for uncertainties in parameter values, and for integer valued variables. The chapter sections are mutually independent, except for Sections 4-3 and 4-5, but require a mastery of Chapter 2.

Chapter 5 deals with nonlinear optimization, a subject of current research interest. The first three sections extend elementary calculus optimization to include constraints. The rather comprehensive treatment of geometric programming in Section 5-4 reflects its promise for engineering design. Sections 5-2 to 5-4 are more mathematical, but the remainder of the book is largely independent of them. Sections 5-5 to 5-7 introduce search techniques, the representation of some nonlinear problems by linear ones, and graphical optimization, respectively.

Chapter 6 is a series of elementary examples which illustrate the formulation of dynamic-programming problems and the principle of optimality. The examples illustrate applications in mechanics, management, and design. They are independent of each other and of the preceding chapters.

Chapter 7 is divided into three parts: sequencing, routing, and scheduling. Sequencing and routing problems are not as well known to civil engineers as scheduling problems. Part III is an introduction to critical path scheduling. The parts are largely independent of each other and of the earlier chapters.

Chapter 8 is the first of five chapters on applied probability. A knowledge of the chapter is required in succeeding chapters. While the material is basic, those not having some familiarity with probability will find it helpful to use a supplementary text.

Chapter 9 emphasizes the formulation of fundamental random models and provides the means for formulating more advanced ones. Random models have important applications so we emphasize them more than usual.

Chapter 10 illustrates with diverse examples the extensive use of expectation for engineering decisions and design criteria. A brief section indicates the use of expectation for the analysis of random phenomena. The sections are independent of each other and of subsequent chapters.

Chapter 11 extends and applies the theory in Chapters 8 and 9. The first section, on reliability, is purposely brief. Applications to civil systems are more recent and not as well developed as in electrical engineering, for example, where quality control, environmental conditions, and failure modes are better defined. Sections 11-2 and 11-3 contain brief introductions to random walk and Markov chains and suggest engineering applications. Sections 11-4 and 11-5 provide a comprehensive introduction to queueing. The study of queueing enhances one's competence in applying probability to design and operational problems—as, for example, in transportation facilities. Portions of these two sections are advanced. Many of the topics are self-contained.

Chapter 12 introduces operational techniques for sums, products, and their combinations of independent random variables. These techniques are useful for more complex random models. Their study can follow Chapter 9.

The appendices provide techniques and information useful to the study of the text.

Appendix 1 summarizes a methodology and techniques for curve fitting. *Appendix 2* discusses how to perform the inductive proofs, and *Appendix 3* contains rates-of-return tables. *Appendix 4* contains probability tables and summarizes properties of frequently used probability functions, *Appendix 5* provides techniques for solving difference equations.

The book has been written for advanced undergraduate and beginning graduate students. It should also be useful to advanced students and practicing engineers. A one semester systems course could include most sections of Chapters 1 to 3 and 6 to 9 and selected sections of other chapters. If courses in probability and optimization are pre-requisites, then sections of Chapters 4 and 5 or 10 to 12 can be added, and the remaining sections used for a second semester course.

Applications of most of the topics to civil engineering are quite recent· The many examples in the text illustrate possibilities, and the selections were made primarily to illustrate techniques rather than to solve real problems. Interested readers can improve some examples and devise more imaginative applications.

Valid cases can be made for several alternatives to our choice of topics and levels of treatment. The emphasis is in those areas where civil engineering applications are already, or have promise of becoming, established in the profession. However, we considered simulation only briefly, and the computer plays a disguised role in spite of its obvious importance. Similarly, statistics and statistical decision theory receive scant attention.

It is a pleasure to acknowledge the many important contributions that Robert H. Mayer, Jr., and Farrokh Neghabat made to this text while they were graduate students. As reviewers, Hatem Khalil, William Mandery, Erik Vanmarcke, and Alvin R. Vincent were very helpful. The many students who managed with our notes in varying stages of imperfection deserve our greatest appreciation. Finally, Mrs. Frances Phillips' expert typing aided us immeasurably.

ROBERT M. STARK
ROBERT L. NICHOLLS

1
Methodology

The succeeding chapters of this book emphasize analytic techniques which have been or have promise of being useful in engineering design. This chapter differs from the rest in its main concern for methodology, i.e., the manner in which problems are viewed. Also, since economic comparisons are basic to engineering decision making, a section on the time value of money is included. We hope that this chapter places the remaining ones in better perspective.

Many of the facilities designed or managed by civil engineers are interacting components of a larger system. Dams and freeways, for example, are often links in a regional water resource or transportation system. The expanding character of the modern environment and the increased mobility of its inhabitants give rise to problems of regional scope. These problems usually involve considerations which cross interdisciplinary boundaries, and new research methods have had to be developed. Hall, in his "A Methodology for Systems Engineering" [12], writes:

Increasingly complex systems are undoubtedly important in the evolution of systems engineering, although the concept of a complex system is elusive and has not yet been given numerical or scientific definition.   The term must be understood informally by example, although complexity refers in part to the number and kinds of components in the system, and in part to the number of kinds of relations between the components.

Increasing complexity can be sensed from the increasing number of interactions between the members of a rising population, the accelerating division of labor and specialization of function, the increasing use of machines over manual labor, with consequent rise in productivity, and the increasing speed and volume of communications and transportation.   It is hard to say whether increasing complexity is the cause or the effect of man's effort to cope with his expanding environment.   In either case a central feature of the trend has been the development of large and very complex systems which tie together modern society. These systems include abstract or nonphysical systems, such as government and the economic system.   They also include large physical systems like pipeline and power distribution systems, transportation and electrical communication systems.

The growth of these systems has increased the need not only for over-all planning, but also for long-range development of the systems. This need has increased interest in the methods by which efficient planning and design can be accomplished in complex situations where no one scientific discipline can account for all the factors.

Two similar disciplines which emerged about the time of World War II to cope with these problems are called *systems engineering* and *operations research*.   Many definitions have been given these disciplines.   It has been suggested that operations research is oriented toward the management of operating systems and systems engineering toward their design—in other words, that operations research tends to deal with tactical (limited scope or duration) problems and systems engineering with strategic ones.   For our purpose, it is more pertinent to ask what these disciplines have in common. First, there is in both a system (executive) orientation; second, both tend to use interdisciplinary teams; and third, both involve the application of the scientific method[1] to problems of control and design.

These three characteristics are, of course, not new; they have been a part of sound engineering practice for many years.   What is new is the recent development and recognition of techniques to better achieve desired goals. The system orientation and the interdisciplinary team provide the counteraction to specialization.   As knowledge has expanded and challenged the capacity of the brain, specialties have formed.   As recently as a century ago,

---

[1] The components of the scientific method are (1) to observe, (2) to hypothesize, (3) to test, and (4) to conclude.

natural science was divided into physics and chemistry. Later, biology and psychology were identified, and in this century, the social sciences as well. Ackoff and Sasieni, in "Fundamentals of Operations Research" [2], write:

> We have become so accustomed to classifying knowledge in a way that corresponds to the departmental structure of universities that we act as though nature were also so structured. Nothing could be further from the truth. There are no such things as physical problems, biological problems, ... and so on. There are only problems; *the disciplines of science represent different ways of looking at them.* Any problem can be looked at through the eyes of every discipline. But, of course, it is not always fruitful to do so.

While this book is essentially one of mathematical techniques, this does not mean that methodology is less important. Indeed, it may be more important. However, methodology is better appreciated after one has learned some techniques and has attempted to solve practical problems with them. In the next six sections we consider the formulation and classification of problems, measurement, the choice of a value theory, and the construction of models for problem solution.

1-1 PROBLEM FORMULATION

A problem can be said to exist when (1) some objective(s) is to be accomplished, (2) there are alternative ways to accomplish it, and (3) the optimal way or combination of ways is not readily apparent.

To formulate a problem we should ask:

1. What are the objectives? While the objectives frequently undergo revision during the study, some statements are needed at the outset. From them we derive a *measure of performance* against which alternative designs are evaluated.
2. Which aspects of the system are subject to the designer's control (controllable variables)? The permissible ranges of control variables comprise the problem *constraints.*
3. Which aspects of the environment are beyond the designer's control? We must probe to ascertain how these uncontrollable variables affect the outcomes.

"A problem well put is a problem half-solved," runs an old saw. It is particularly apt in system design, where one seeks the *form* of a problem whose *content* may be rather unfamiliar. For example, Hooke's law and an iso-volumic Boyle's law both have a linear form but different content. Actually, the formulation of problems is a dynamic rather than a static process. As answers are obtained, it is possible to improve the precision of the problem formulation. This is why exercises in textbooks are clearly stated, as compared with those arising in practice.

The emphasis upon precision in formulating problems must be weighed against the danger of inhibiting the generality of the problem statement. The greater the generality, particularly at the outset, the greater is the potential for finding a desirable solution which might otherwise have been undiscovered. Hall [12] quotes Arnold as follows:

> The first thing to do, however, is to make sure that we know exactly what need we are trying to fill, what goal we are trying to reach. I think that we can decide right at the start that our goal is not to have a path beaten to our door, but it might not be quite so easy to decide that our goal might not be building a better mousetrap either. Actually, our prime goal is to get rid of mice in some way or another, and when stated in this way we don't care whether we trap them, electrocute them, drown them, or scare them to death—anything to get rid of them. The basic goal usually defines the *general, long-range* problem, in this case, devise a better means of getting rid of mice. The words that you use in defining the general problem have to be chosen very carefully so that the referents of these words or their connotations do not limit the thinking of yourself or the designer to whom you assign this task. The wrong word can unintentionally predispose the thinking of the designer to follow a limited number of paths and preclude his investigation of other equally desirable and fruitful ones. I said "get rid of" rather than "kill" or "exterminate." We don't want any mice around, so in addition to thinking up ways and means of killing them we might profitably consider how we might get them all to emigrate to the South Pole or to commit mass suicide like the lemmings of Scandinavia. In the same way, exterminating, to me at least, connotes poisoning by gas or in the food and is therefore limiting.

1-2 PROBLEM TYPES

The criterion of "best" solution is expressed by the *objective function* of the problem, which is, in turn, expressed as a function of the selected measure of performance. The type of objective function depends upon the available knowledge of the various outcomes. The available knowledge can be classified in three ways, by so-called "problem types":

1. *Certainty*: each course of action is assumed to result in a definite outcome.
2. *Risk*: each course of action results in one of several outcomes. The

particular outcome is not known until "after the fact," but the chance (probability) of each outcome is known.
3. *Uncertainty*: each course of action leads to outcomes which are not explicitly known, and hence probabilities cannot be assigned.

Problems of certainty and uncertainty can be regarded as limiting cases of risk problems. While every practical problem is, strictly speaking, one of uncertainty, for the most part engineers have represented their problems as ones of certainty. Because problems of certainty are usually easier to model than their probabilistic counterparts, they are often used in a heuristic way, i.e., as devices to explore the structure of the problem. However, risk-type problems attract much current research. The techniques for problems of uncertainty have also attracted interest [1]. About one-half of this text is devoted to techniques for problems of certainty. The second half develops topics in applied probability to enable the engineer to formulate risk-type problems. Techniques for problems of uncertainty are beyond our scope, and the interested reader is referred to the literature of statistical decision theory ([9], [11], and [20]).

1-3 SCALES OF MEASUREMENT

The effectiveness of our endeavors is a direct consequence of our ability to measure and to tailor our responses according to the result of the measurement. The simplest and least powerful measurements involve no more than discriminating between objects. The most powerful measurements assign numbers on a scale which possesses an absolute zero, e.g., time or weight. Less powerful measurement scales arise frequently in the behavioral and social sciences. The increasing importance of these sciences to engineering design suggests that we briefly describe other scales of measurement.

Campbell [5] and Stevens [16] distinguish four scales of measurement: *nominal, ordinal, interval,* and *ratio scales.*

1. *Nominal scales.* A nominal scale is the least powerful measurement scale. It serves only to distinguish between objects, individuals, or categories. It associates no values or specific differences with this distinction.
2. *Ordinal scales.* An ordinal scale not only distinguishes between objects but also implies whether an object has more, the same, or less of the attribute in question. An ordinal scale can be likened to a nonlinear elastic ruler. The order of the numbers is maintained, but the distance between them is not meaningful. That is, an ordinal scale cannot indicate *by how much* an attribute is more or less than some other attribute. The Mohs scale of mineral hardness is an ordinal scale. Measurements in the social and behavioral sciences are frequently on nominal or ordinal scales.

3. *Interval scales.* On an interval scale, equal intervals imply equal differences in the attribute being measured. The Fahrenheit and centigrade scales are of the interval type since equal intervals correspond to equal volumes of the liquid column. An interval scale is more powerful than either a nominal or an ordinal scale, and where only *relative* measurements are significant, it is equal to the more powerful ratio scale. The interval scale is not the most powerful scale because its zero is arbitrary. For this reason, the Fahrenheit and centrigrade scales are not the most favored for scientific measurement. One cannot say that 40°F is twice as "hot" as 20°F (although the number 40 is twice the number 20).

4. *Ratio scales.* When an absolute zero is added to the properties of an interval scale, it defines the ratio scale. Measurements on the ratio scale are perhaps the most common to engineers.

1-4 MEASURES OF VALUE

The *objective function* of a problem expresses the value criterion in terms of a measure of performance. Multidimensional objectives are a condition of life for the civil engineer. For example, he seeks a structure having "maximum safety," "optimum weight," and "minimum cost." These are conflicting objectives and require *trade-off* functions and *value theories* for adequate consideration. Trade-off functions translate values on one scale (e.g., weight or safety) into values on another scale (e.g., dollars). There are several theories of value, although engineers usually seek an economic one. For perspective, we briefly describe some value theories.

Economic value   Two closely related concepts of value in economics are *value-in-exchange* and *value-in-use.* Value-in-exchange is the quantity of other goods (or money) which can be obtained in exchange, i.e., the market value. Value-in-use is the relative importance placed upon an item by its user or owner. For example, the market value of a bolt may be quite different from its value as part of a bridge.

The profit criterion is one of maximizing the difference between revenues and costs. The units need not be dollars—any common scale of value will do. An oversight in the choice of criteria is to speak of either "minimizing costs" or "maximizing returns"—or, what is impossible, of "maximizing returns while minimizing costs" [15]. In textbook situations, constant returns are implicitly assumed when a minimum-cost objective is chosen. However, in practical problems the engineer must carefully assess the influence upon returns of policies which promise to minimize costs. The profit criterion can be extended to conditions of risk—a so-called "expected profit," which is the basis for sections of Chap. 10.

Frequently one must choose between two alternate designs, one requiring a large initial cost and small maintenance costs and another requiring small initial cost and large periodic costs. Cost comparisons must reflect time as well as magnitude. A dollar invested now will be worth $(1 + i)$ dollars a year from now and $(1 + i)^n$ dollars in n years, where i is the interest rate. Conversely, a payment of \$1 n years from now is equivalent to a payment now of $(1 + i)^{-n}$. The term $(1 + i)^{-n}$ is called the *present-worth factor*. The derivation and use of economic formulas are the subjects of the next section.

Psychologic value The psychologic theory of value holds that value resides in an appreciation or pleasure afforded by an object. That is, value is a feeling and the measure of value is the intensity of feeling.

Psychologic values help us to solve problems by guiding us toward choosing good objectives. The beauty of many structures attests to the observation that designers employ more than a single-value objective.

Psychologic measurement, called *psychometrics*, is still crude as compared with economic measures. Psychometric scales have been devised by Von Neumann and Morgenstern [21] and by Churchman and Ackoff [6]. Combining individual preferences into group preferences is a challenging assignment. It is one which the civil engineer frequently faces.

Precedent value Precedence, often a basis for legal decisions, is commonly used by engineers. It must be applied with discrimination, and only after asking oneself: (1) Was the prior decision an optimal or successful one? and (2) Are the assumptions for the current problem sufficiently similar to the historical one to justify using the same decision? Hall refers to this as the casuistic theory of value [12].

1-5 TIME VALUE OF MONEY

Economic problems are an integral part of engineering. Engineers are sensitive to the direct cost of a design and anticipate maintenance and operating costs. Besides magnitudes, it is pertinent to consider time factors, i.e., when costs arise. This section provides various measures of a sum of money to enable comparisons of alternative designs.

Consider an investment of P dollars which returns i dollars per dollar per period. The return at the end of the first period is iP, and the original investment has increased to $(1 + i)P$. This sum is reinvested and returns $i(1 + i)P$ at the end of the next period, so that the original amount is worth $(1 + i)^2 P$, etc. One can conclude inductively (see Appendix 2) that an original investment P will increase after n periods to the sum S_n, given by

$$S_n = (1 + i)^n P = [\text{spcaf}\,(i,n)]\,P$$

where spcaf (i,n) is called the *single-payment compound-amount factor*.

Similarly, a future payment S_n has an equivalent present worth P, given by

$$P = (1 + i)^{-n} S_n = [\text{sppwf } (i,n)] S_n \tag{1}$$

where sppwf (i,n) is the *single-payment present-worth factor*. The factor $\rho = (1 + i)^{-1}$ is called the *discount factor*.

Consider a sequence of n uniform periodic payments, R. The first payment earns interest over $n - 1$ periods and is equivalent to an amount $(1 - i)^{n-1} R$ after n periods; the second earns interest over $n - 2$ periods and is worth $(1 + i)^{n-2} R$ after n periods; and so on. This sequence of payments is equivalent to a sum S_n, given by the finite geometric series,

$$S_n = (1 + i)^{n-1} R + \cdots + (1 + i) R + R$$

$$= \frac{(1 + i)^n - 1}{i} R = [\text{uscaf } (i,n)] R \tag{2}$$

where uscaf (i,n) is the *uniform-series compound-amount factor*. Likewise, a future sum S_n can be expressed as an equivalent series of uniform payments, R; that is,

$$R = \frac{i}{(1 + i)^n - 1} S_n = [\text{sfdf } (i,n)] S_n$$

where sfdf (i,n) is the *sinking-fund deposit factor*.

The sequence of n uniform payments, R, can also be expressed as a present worth P. Combining Eqs. (1) and (2) yields

$$P = \frac{(1 + i)^n - 1}{i(1 + i)^n} R = [\text{uspwf } (i,n)] R$$

where uspwf (i,n) is the *uniform-series present-worth factor*.

Table 1-1   Interest factors

Given	Find	By multiplying with the	
P	S_n	Single-payment compound-amount factor (spcaf),	$(1 + i)^n$
S_n	P	Single-payment present-worth factor (sppwf),	$(1 + i)^{-n}$
R	S_n	Uniform-series compound-amount factor (uscaf),	$\dfrac{(1 + i)^n - 1}{i}$
S_n	R	Sinking-fund deposit factor (sfdf),	$\dfrac{i}{(1 + i)^n - 1}$
R	P	Uniform-series present-worth factor (uspwf),	$\dfrac{(1 + i)^n - 1}{i(1 + i)^n}$
P	R	Capital-recovery factor (crf),	$\dfrac{i(1 + i)^n}{(1 + i)^n - 1}$

Finally, expressing a present amount P as an equivalent sequence of n uniform payments gives

$$R = \frac{i(1+i)^n}{(1+i)^n - 1} P = [\text{crf } (i,n)] P$$

where crf (i,n) is the *capital-recovery factor*.

These formulas are summarized in Table 1-1. The interest factors in Table 1-1 are tabulated for various values of i and n in Appendix 3. Since interest factors are often cumbersome to evaluate for large values of n, it is helpful to consider *instantaneous* or *continuous compounding*. An interest rate of i dollars per dollar per period yields a return of $i \, \Delta t$ dollars per dollar when the compounding interval is Δt. Each dollar is equivalent to $(1 + i \, \Delta t)^n$ dollars after n periods. As $\Delta t \to 0$ and $n \to \infty$ such that the limit of $n \, \Delta t$ is finite, we have, using the definition of the exponential function,

$$\lim_{\substack{n \to \infty \\ \Delta t \to 0}} (1 + i \, \Delta t)^n \to e^{it}$$

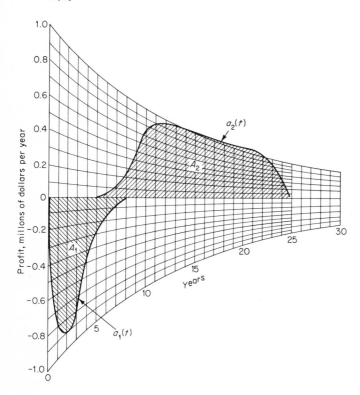

Fig. 1-1   Present-worth plotting paper. 7% interest compounded annually.   (*Reprinted from Hall [12].*)

Finally, we mention the availability of present-worth plotting paper (Fig. 1-1). In this figure $a_1(t)$ and $a_2(t)$ indicate estimated future expenses and income, respectively. The present worth is represented by the sum $A_1 + A_2$.

ECONOMIC BASES FOR COMPARISON

The above rate-of-return formulas are employed in making economic comparisons of alternatives. Three methods of comparison commonly used are the annual-base, present-worth, and benefit-cost–ratio methods. We briefly consider each.

1. *Annual-base comparisons.* An annual-base comparison reduces all revenues and expenditures over the selected time to an equivalent annual value. Examples 1-1 and 1-2 illustrate this comparison.

Example 1-1   Alternative pipelines   A 30-in. pipeline can be installed for $90,000. Annual operating and maintenance cost (including pumping) is estimated at $20,000. An alternative, 24-in. line can be installed for $70,000. Its associated operating and maintenance cost is estimated at $26,000 per year. Either line is expected to serve for 25 years, with 5% salvage when replaced. We compare the two pipelines on an annual-cost basis assuming a 15% rate of return.

For the 30-in. line, the annual cost, AC_{30}, is

$$AC_{30} = 90{,}000 \text{ crf } (15\%,25\text{yr}) - (0.05)(90{,}000) \text{ sfdf } (15\%,25\text{yr}) + 20{,}000 = \$33{,}970$$

since crf $(15\%,25\text{yr}) = 0.155$ and sfdf $(15\%,25\text{yr}) = 0.0047$.

For the 24-in. line, the annual cost, AC_{24}, is

$$\begin{aligned} AC_{24} &= 70{,}000 \text{ crf } (15\%,25\text{yr}) - (0.05)(70{,}000) \text{ sfdf } (15\%,25\text{yr}) \\ &\quad + 26{,}000 \\ &= \$36{,}870 \end{aligned}$$

On this basis, the 30-in. line is the better investment.

Example 1-2   An unspecified alternative investment   A rail siding crosses a street within a chemical plant complex. Tank cars frequently delay crossing vehicles, and management is considering construction of a grade separation to eliminate delays. Proponents of the grade separation argue that delays cost $40 per day over a 245-day working year. The grade separation is estimated to cost $90,000, with an economic life of 30 years. Maintenance cost of the structure is estimated at $800 per year. The company is experiencing a rapid growth, so that competition for the firm's capital is keen enough for management to seek a 15% return.

The annual (245 days) cost of delays at \$40 per day is \$9,800, which is considerably less than the annual cost of construction,

90,000 crf (15%,30 yr) + 800 = \$14,480

where crf (15%,30yr) = 0.152 (Appendix 3). Therefore, construction of the grade separation is not warranted.

2. *Present-worth comparisons.* In present-worth comparisons, all anticipated revenues and expenditures are expressed by their equivalent present values. Consider an example.

Example 1-3 Alternative water systems A city plans to enlarge its water system. One proposal calls for the construction of a storage dam and treatment plant which would cost \$480,000 and would satisfy estimated demand over the next 12 years. The expected annual operating cost would be \$30,000. After 12 years, a second dam and additional treatment facilities would be constructed for \$550,000, with an additional annual operating cost of \$25,000.

The alternate plan is to build a single large storage dam now, which, together with a new treatment plant, would cost \$620,000. The annual operating cost would be \$26,000 for the first 12 years. After 12 years, additional treatment facilities would be added for \$50,000 and annual operating costs would be expected to increase to \$32,000. We compare the alternative plans using a present-worth analysis with an interest rate of 8%.

For the first plan, the present worth of all future expenditures, PW_1, is

$$PW_1 = 480,000 + 550,000 \text{ sppwf } (8\%,12 \text{ yr}) + 30,000 \text{ uspwf } (8\%,12 \text{ yr})$$
$$+ 55,000 \text{ uspwf } (8\%,\infty) \text{ sppwf } (8\%,12 \text{ yr}) = \$1,198,00$$

since sppwf (8%,12 yr) = 0.379, uspwf (8%,12 yr) = 7.54, and uspwf (8%,∞) = 12.5. We have assumed that the system will operate indefinitely without expansion (or contraction) after the twelfth-year construction. Thus the \$55,000 annual cost starting 12 years hence and continuing indefinitely is converted to a single payment at 12 years (uspwf) and then to a single payment at present (sppwf).

For the second plan, the present worth PW_2 is

$$PW_2 = 620,000 + 26,000 \text{ uspwf } (8\%,12 \text{ yr}) + [32,000 \text{ uspwf } (8\%,\infty)$$
$$+ 50,000] \text{ sppwf } (8\%,12 \text{ yr})$$
$$= \$994,850$$

The second plan is the lower-cost alternative.

3. *Benefit-cost–ratio comparisons.* The *benefit-cost ratio* (BCR) is a useful measure for comparing alternative public projects. In corporate finance, the fundamental equation is

Profit = revenue − cost

An implicit assumption is that costs and profits accrue to the same party. In public projects, however, the citizens who bear the cost are not always those who derive the benefit, as returns from public expenditures might be termed. For this reason, a benefit-cost ratio often provides a more meaningful comparison than the "revenue-cost" relation. Specifically,

$$BCR = \frac{AW}{AC}$$

where AW is the annual worth of benefits to users and AC is the total annual cost (to those who pay). A present-worth benefit-cost analysis may also be pertinent. The justification for an expenditure is suggested by a benefit-cost ratio of at least unity.

Example 1-4   A benefit-cost comparison[2]   A bridge connects two highways, A and B, parallel to a river. The bridge is a connecting link in a highway, C, perpendicular to the river. Traffic lights at the intersection of Routes A and C and at the intersection of Routes B and C control the flow of traffic on these highways.

The daily vehicular traffic on Route A averages 10,000; on Route B, 3,000; and on Route C, 6,000, with average speeds of 50 mph. Fifteen percent of the vehicles are commercial.

The value of time for a commercial vehicle is estimated at $5 per hour, and for a private vehicle at $2 per hour. The stop-and-start costs are estimated at 0.5 cent and 0.25 cent, respectively. About 50% of the traffic on each route is delayed at a traffic light, and the average idle time is 0.78 min on Route A, 1.6 min on Route B, and 1.30 min on Route C.

There have been 4 fatal and 75 nonfatal accidents at the intersection of Routes A and C in the past 5 years because of failure to heed traffic signals. The record at the intersection of Routes B and C is 3 fatal and 60 nonfatal accidents. Insurance claims have averaged $50,000 per fatal accident and $800 per nonfatal accident.

The cost of operating a traffic signal is $1,200 a year. In addition, one crossing guard is stationed at the junction of Routes A and C for 8 hr each day and another at Routes B and C for 4 hr each day. A crossing guard is paid $5,000 per year for 300 eight-hour days.

[2] Examples 1-4 and 1-5 are adapted from "Managerial and Engineering Economy" by G. A. Taylor, 1964, by permission of Van Nostrand Reinhold Company.

Overpasses and underpasses to permit continuous traffic flow can be constructed on both sides of the bridge. At the A and C junction, the cost is $1,100,000, and at the B and C junction, it is $1,200,000. The added annual cost of road maintenance and repair is estimated at $5,000, and 0.4 mile has been added to the travel for about 35% of the traffic. The operating cost of commercial vehicles is estimated at $0.24 per mile, and for noncommercial vehicles, it is $0.06 per mile. The new system eliminates the need for traffic signals and crossing guards and will reduce accidents by an estimated 90%. The estimated economic life is 20 years with no salvage value.

Misapplication of the benefit-cost ratio can arise when alternatives are aggregated rather than evaluated separately. We determine a separate benefit-cost ratio for the proposed construction at each junction, using an interest rate of 6%.

Junction A-C

Annual time cost saved:

$$0.5(10,000)\frac{0.78}{60}(365)[0.15(5) + 0.85(2)]$$

$$+ (0.5)(6,000)\frac{1.30}{60}(365)[0.15(5) + 0.85(2)] \quad = \$116,000$$

Annual start-and-stop cost saved:

$$0.5(10,000)(365)[0.15(0.005) + 0.85(0.00250)](1.0 + 0.6) \quad = 8,490$$

Annual accident cost saved:

$$0.9\left[\frac{4}{5}(50,000) + \frac{75}{5}(800)\right] \qquad\qquad = 46,800$$

Cost of time for added mileage:

$$0.35(10,000)\frac{0.4}{50}(365)[0.15(5) + 0.85(2)](1.0 + 0.6) \qquad = -40,100$$

Cost of operation for added mileage:

$$0.35(10,000)(0.4)(365)[0.15(0.25) + 0.85(0.06)](1.0 + 0.6) \quad = -71,100$$

$$\textit{Net benefits} = \$60,090$$

Added annual cost to the public:

$$1,100,000 \text{ crf } (6\%,20\text{yr}) - 1,200 - \frac{365}{300}(5,000) + 5,000 \qquad = \$93,600$$

since crf $(6\%,20\text{yr}) = 0.0872$.

$$\text{BCR} = \frac{60,090}{93,600} = 0.65$$

Junction B-C
Annual time cost saved:

$$0.5(3,000)\frac{1.6}{60}(365)\,[0.15(5)+0.85(2)]+0.5(6,000)$$

$$+\frac{1.30}{60}(365)\,[0.15(5)+0.85(2)]=\$93,900$$

Annual start-and-stop cost saved:

$$0.5(3,000)(365)\,[0.15(0.005)+0.85(0.0025)]\,(1.0+2.0)\qquad=4,730$$

Annual accident cost saved:

$$9\left[\frac{3}{5}(50,000)+\frac{60}{5}(800)\right]\qquad\qquad\qquad=35,640$$

Cost of time for added mileage:

$$0.35(3,000)\frac{0.4}{50}(365)\,[0.15(5)+0.85(2)]\,(1.0+2.0)\qquad=-22,500$$

Cost of operation for added mileage:

$$0.35(3,000)(0.4)(365)\,[0.15(0.24)+0.85(0.06)]\,(1.0+2.0)\qquad=-40,000$$

$$Net\ benefits=\$71,770$$

Added annual cost to the public:

$$1,200,000\ \text{crf}\ (6\%,20\text{yr})-1,200+5,000-\frac{4(365)}{8(300)}(5,000)\qquad=\$105,400$$

$$\text{BCR}=\frac{71,770}{105,400}=0.68$$

Since both BCRs are less than unity, one can argue against either construction.

A benefit-cost ratio is convenient for making comparisons among pairs of alternatives. If two alternatives, a and b, are such that $\text{AC}_a>\text{AC}_b$, the BCR formula can be written

$$\text{BCR}_{a-b}=\frac{\text{AW}_a-\text{AW}_b}{\text{AC}_a-\text{AC}_b}=\frac{\text{AUC}_b-\text{AUC}_a}{\text{AC}_a-\text{AC}_b}$$

where AUC denotes the annual user cost. For $\text{BCR}_{a-b}>1$, alternative a is preferred to b.

Example 1-5 Another benefit-cost comparison   Two alternate routes are being considered for a section of a thruway—a river route and a mountain route.   The river route is 20 miles long and has a predicted initial cost of \$4,750,000.   The annual cost of maintenance and operation will be \$2,000 a mile.   Major resurfacing will be required every 10 years at a cost of \$850,000.

The mountain route is only 15 miles long but would cost \$7,375,000 due to the expense of establishing acceptable grades, and so on.   Major resurfacing is estimated for every 10 years at \$650,000.   The annual cost of maintenance will be \$2,500 a mile.

An average speed of 50 mph is anticipated for either highway, and the average daily traffic is predicted to be 5,000 vehicles, including about 1,000 commercial vehicles.   The value of travel time for commercial and non-commercial traffic is given in Example 1-4.   Travel costs are 15% higher than in Example 1-4 on the grades of the mountain route.   Both highways are estimated to have a 30-year life with zero salvage.   The cost of capital is taken as 7%.

River route   The annual cost to the public for construction and maintenance is

$$\{4,750,000 + 850,000[\text{sppwf }(7\%,10\text{yr}) + \text{sppwf }(7\%,20\text{yr})]\}\text{ crf }(7\%,30\text{yr})$$
$$+ 2,000(20) = \$475,300$$

where sppwf $(7\%,10\text{yr}) = 0.508$, sppwf $(7\%,20\text{yr}) = 0.258$, and crf $(7\%,30\text{yr})$ $= 0.0806$.

The annual user costs are

Time: $[(5,000)(365)\frac{20}{50}][0.2(5.00) + 0.8(2.00)]$ $=$ 1,898,000

Distance: $[(5,000)(365)(20)][0.2(0.25) + 0.8(0.06)] =$ $\underline{3,577,000}$

$$\textit{Total user cost} = \$5,475,000$$

Mountain route   The annual cost to the public for construction and maintenance is

$$\{7,375,000 + 650,000[\text{sppwf }(7\%,10\text{yr}) + \text{sppwf }(7\%,20\text{yr})]\}$$
$$\text{crf }(7\%,30\text{yr}) + 2,500(15) = \$671,600$$

The annual user costs are

Time: $[(5,000)(365)\frac{15}{50}][0.2(5.00) + 0.8(2.00)]$ $=$ 1,424,000

Distance: $[(5,000)(365)(15)][0.2(0.25) + 0.8(0.06)](1.15) =$ $\underline{3,090,000}$

$$\textit{Total user cost} = \$4,514,000$$

$$\text{BCR}_{m-r} = \frac{\text{AUC}_r - \text{AUC}_m}{\text{AC}_m - \text{AC}_r}$$

$$= \frac{5,475,000 - 4,514,000}{671,600 - 475,300} = 4.90 > 1$$

This provides a basis for choosing the more expensive mountain route.

Three bases for comparing monies have been indicated. However, they are not exhaustive. The discounted-cash-flow comparison, for example, compares the interest rates earned by various alternatives [17]. It is important to consider which cash-flow comparison to use since different types of comparisons may result in different rankings of the alternatives. If the proposed project is to be financed from annual taxes, an annual-cost comparison may be suggested. In the case of the unbalanced bid in Chap. 3, a present-worth objective seemed appropriate.

1-6 MODEL CONSTRUCTION

Models are representations of reality in somewhat the sense that a painting is a representation of a photograph. The modeler seeks the simplest model which will predict and explain phenomena with an accuracy adequate to his purpose. Three common types are iconic, analog, and symbolic models.

Iconic models are scaled versions of the real thing. Relevant properties of the system are represented by the same properties in the model. Laboratory models of bridges and buildings for the study of complex structural behavior are examples of iconic models. The modulus of elasticity of the bridge material, for example, is represented by the same modulus in the model material.

Analog models use one set of properties to represent another set. Electric current can represent heat or fluid flow; fluid systems can represent traffic flow; soap films, torsional stress; contour or equipotential lines, ground elevation; and so on.

Symbolic models use symbols to represent variables and relationships between them. Their generality and abstractness make them easy to manipulate.

A problem can sometimes be represented better by more than one model, in combination or in sequence. In other cases, where the model of a problem is inconvenient to solve, it is sometimes possible to decompose the model into components, which can be solved more conveniently. The output of one model then serves as the input for another. Such methods appear, for example, for symbolic models in Chap. 4.

Sometimes a symbolic model is difficult to construct but a similarity is perceived between the system under study and one that is better known. For example, suppose that a contractor working at several sites in a remote area wishes to connect them with a road of minimum total length so that equipment can be moved among the sites (Fig. 1-2). The problem, called *Steiner's problem* [8], is not easy to represent symbolically, and analytic solutions are quite recent [10]. However, there is a simple analog. If pins are placed in a board to represent the construction sites and if the board is immersed in a soap solution and carefully withdrawn, a soap film will span the pins and its

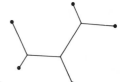

Fig. 1-2 Minimum total path.

total length will be a minimum.[3]   The known property of a soap film to achieve a configuration which minimizes the potential energy is exploited to obtain an experimental solution.

The aptness of a model reflects the abilities of its creators and sometimes their luck.   Although some patterns emerge, very few nonobvious rules can be cited for model building, and not much has been written about models in general [4 and 9].   Modeling requires the resolution of conflicting objectives; the model should be accurate, but the solution should be easy to achieve. These considerations are pertinent in the examples of Chap. 3.

A general optimization model may be represented by

Maximize: $z = f(\mathbf{x}, \mathbf{y})$

subject to the constraints

$$g_i(\mathbf{x}, \mathbf{y}) \geqslant 0 \qquad i = 1, \ldots, n$$

where $\mathbf{x}$ and $\mathbf{y}$ represent vectors of controllable and uncontrollable variables, respectively.   The solution is the value(s) of $\mathbf{x}$ as a function of $\mathbf{y}$ which maximizes z subject to the n constraints $g_i(\mathbf{x}, \mathbf{y}) \geqslant 0$.   In almost all instances, solutions to models in the text will be achieved by analytic (including enumerative) means.

A model, like a problem statement, should be continuously tested throughout its formulation.   Common model deficiencies are:

1.   It includes irrelevant variables.
2.   It excludes relevant variables.
3.   One or more relevant variables are evaluated inaccurately.
4.   It contains incorrect functions or functional forms.

Variables can frequently be manipulated to reduce computational effort without sacrificing accuracy.   For example, the similarity between two variables may be sufficient to aggregate them as a single variable.   Variables having ranges of values in which the solution is not sensitive may be treated as constants by assigning average values to them.   Variables to which the solution is believed to be insensitive are ignored in preliminary models.

---

[3] A second (transparent) surface placed on top of the pins helps prevent collapse of the soap film.

Later, it is desirable to explore the sensitivity of the solution to these variables (as in Secs. 4-5 and 5-1, for example). Sometimes computational efficiency is achieved by treating discrete variables as continuous ones, and vice versa. Models can sometimes be simplified by modifying their functional form, e.g., by approximating nonlinear functions with piecewise linear segments or transforming expressions involving products of variables into linear expressions using logarithms. Occasionally, a model can be simplified by removing or altering constraints. A problem may be solved ignoring constraints and testing whether the solution satisfies them. If it does not, methods may be available or devised for introducing the constraints gradually or for identifying the "binding" constraint.

Suitable models of practical problems may be too complex for symbolic representation. Three methods for "forcing" solutions are simulation, gaming, and experimentation.

Simulation is an imitation of reality. Simulations may be based upon iconic, analog, or symbolic models. For example, if one were to move the pins in the above soap-film model to ascertain the effect upon total path length, he would be simulating movement of the construction sites. The simulation of symbolic models is usually carried out on a high-speed computer. This permits experiments on the "paper" system which would be impractical to perform on the real system because of time or financial limitations. A year's traffic, for example, may be simulated on a computer in a few minutes.

Gaming is a simulation in which decisions are made by live decision makers. Gaming, not to be confused with game theory, is used in complex military, international, and industrial decisions where models are virtually nonexistent. A *game* of bidding strategy in the construction industry developed by William Park and marketed under the name "Entelek" is an example of *gaming*.

Experimental optimization is used whenever a system is too complex or too poorly understood to be adequately modeled or when a model can be constructed but no convenient technique is available for obtaining a solution. Experiments can be conducted on the system to locate an optimal solution. An example of an experiment on a real system is a search for the operational variables in a cement plant or petroleum refinery which permit a given production rate of specified products at least cost. Experimental (search) techniques for symbolic models are described in Chap. 5.

Each of these techniques is of interest to the engineer, especially the rapidly developing subject of simulation. References [7], [13], [18], and [19] provide more detailed information.

Wilde and Beightler [22] have observed:

Optimization is only the last of three steps needed to reach a rational decision. The first two, description of the system and adoption of a measure of effectiveness, are absolute prerequisites for the third.   Therefore in taking the time to apply optimization theory, one cannot neglect more conventional engineering and economic phases of a problem without risking ultimate failure.   Optimization theory should be regarded not as an isolated specialty to be applied only by detached consultants, but rather as a valuable addition to the existing professional knowledge of the practicing economist, operations analyst, engineer, or administrator.   In most industrial problems the work expended on defining the decision problem mathematically, gathering reliable data, and agreeing on objectives far exceeds the effort needed for mathematical optimization.   True, a decision without optimization is as unfinished as an arch without a keystone.   But optimization, like a keystone, is only a small part of the total structure and consequently cannot compensate for shoddy workmanship or faulty materials elsewhere in the project.

A methodologic self-consciousness coupled with an ability to define, to measure, and to call upon a variety of statistical techniques is the ingredient for achieving useful solutions to problems.   A decision maker advised by the civil engineer is frequently not able (due to lack of training or time) to understand the technical details.   However, he can usually grasp the logic if the engineer adequately exposes it to him—as, for example, to a jury or a municipal planning commission.   The confidence engendered in the decision maker is essential to the implementation of even the best conceived designs.

PROBLEMS   (Solutions to problems with ♦ appear at back of book)

1-1.   The purchases of Manhattan Island from the Indians, the Louisiana Territory from France, and Alaska from Russia were outstanding bargains.   But were they as outstanding as it appears?   Compute the present worth of each purchase price if it had been invested at a compound interest rate of 6%.

Purchase	Year	Price	Present worth at 6%
Manhattan Island	1626	$ 24	
Louisiana Territory	1803	15,000,000	
Alaska	1867	7,200,000	

1-2.   A community can provide for its water-storage needs with a high-elevated steel tan in town (tank A) or a low-elevated tank (tank B) on a nearby hill.   Tank A will cost $90,000, and tank B $80,000.   Annual operating and maintenance will be $300 for tank A and $700 for tank B.   Using the annual-cost method of comparison, with 6% interest, which tank should be chosen if both have 50-year life with no salvage?

1-3.   A railway overpass must be rebuilt due to structural deterioration and limited load capacity.   Alternatives include replacing the present bridge with a new superstructure placed on the existing abutments or replacing it with a corrugated-pipe tunnel and embankment. Compare the two designs by a present-worth analysis, using the data below and assuming a 4% interest rate. Both designs have an economic life of 30 years with no salvage value.

	Bridge	Tunnel
First cost	$40,000	$50,000
Annual maintenance	1,500	500

1-4. A trunk-line telephone cable can be routed either around (Route A) or beneath (Route B) a lake. The associated costs are:

	First cost	Annual maintenance cost
Route A	$ 80,000	$4,000
Route B	110,000	2,000

Assume a 40-year life, with zero salvage for either route. Choose the best route, using present-worth comparison with 8% interest.

1-5. A temporary waterline is required for 4 years to supply a construction camp at a large dam. Which of the following designs should be used, by present-worth comparison, if an 8% return is required and if all pipe and pumps can be resold after 4 years for 30% of initial cost?

| | Pipe size, in. | | |
	6	8	10
Initial cost, pipe and pumps	$5,000	$6,000	$7,500
Annual pumping cost	2,500	2,000	1,800

1-6. A wood products manufacturer can purchase either of two tracts of timber. Tract A costs $300,000, is estimated to last 12 years, and would have a land-salvage value after 12 years of $60,000. Logging and shipping operations for this tract would cost $25,000 per year. Tract B costs $450,000, would last 20 years, and would have a salvage value of $30,000. Logging and shipping would cost $20,000 per year. Which tract should be purchased? Use a present-worth comparison with a required interest rate of 15%. Assume that similar tracts will be available in the future. ◆

1-7. A municipal storm-drainage culvert several blocks in length has become inadequate due to commercial development, which has caused higher storm runoff factors and higher damage costs from flooding. The city engineer's office has developed three alternate solutions: (*a*) Replace the existing 36-in. corrugated pipe with a 54-in. pipe. (*b*) Replace the pipe with a small box culvert consisting of concrete base, concrete-block walls, and precast concrete plank roof. (c) Add a parallel 36-in. corrugated pipe and retain the existing one. The construction costs are (a) $35,000, (b) $50,000, and (c) $25,000, respectively. All alternatives have no salvage value and have identical annual maintenance costs. New construction has a useful life of 60 years, but the existing 36-in. pipe would have to be replaced in 20 years at a projected cost of $40,000. Its salvage value 60 years from now would be $10,000. Which of the three designs should be constructed, assuming a 4% interest?

1-8. A Portland cement company has options on two properties for the construction of a new plant. The production capacity of the plant will be the same regardless of which site is chosen, but initial plant costs will vary because of differences in topography, foundation conditions, etc. Production costs will also vary between the two sites because of differences in costs of raw materials, energy requirements for the crushing of raw materials, etc.

The characteristics of each site are tabulated below.

	Site A	Site B
Property cost[1]	$10,000,000	$15,000,000
Plant construction cost[2]	7,000,000	6,000,000
Unit production cost[2]	$1.75/bbl	$1.50/bbl
Raw-materials sources:[3]		
Limestone available	3,000,000 tons at $0.75/T	5,000,000 tons at $0.55/T
	6,000,000 tons at 1.10/T	5,000,000 tons at 1.20/T
Shale available	75,000 tons at 0.35/T	225,000 tons at 0.40/T
	150,000 tons at 0.45/T	450,000 tons at 0.65/T
	300,000 tons at 0.80/T	
Iron-ore concentrate available	Unlimited, at $11.00/T	Unlimited, at $10.00/T
Coal available	Unlimited, at $10.00/T	Unlimited, at $9.00/T
Est. average market price at plant[4]	$5.25/bbl	$4.90/T

[1] Includes adjacent limestone source.
[2] All operating costs exclusive of raw-materials cost.
[3] Costs are for quarrying, transportation to plant.
[4] Varies with average transportation distances to market areas.

Annual plant capacity will be 700,000 bbl, and it is anticipated that 80% of plant capacity can be marketed regardless of the site. Raw-materials requirements per barrel of cement produced are 580 lb of limestone, 40 lb of shale, 10 lb of iron-ore concentrate, and 100 lb of coal. Assume that at each site the cheapest raw-materials source can be developed first and that each plant can operate until one of its raw materials is exhausted or for an anticipated life of 40 years, whichever is less.

Assuming the company requires 8% on investment, which site will yield the greatest return by the present-worth method of analysis?

1-9. Flood-protection levees are being designed for a river city. Four alternate plans have been proposed by the city engineer's office. Each plan is an extension of the previous one, with the levees longer and/or higher. Assuming that the city can raise sufficient funds, which of the four increments of flood protection should it buy?

Plan	Construction cost	Annual maintenance	Est. annual flood costs
A	$ 5,500,000	$ 92,000	$725,000
A + B	6,900,000	160,000	600,000
A + B + C	12,400,000	230,000	200,000
A + B + C + D	16,000,000	275,000	25,000

Assume a 50-year life, zero salvage value, and 4% acceptable interest rate. Use the benefit-cost–ratio comparison method.

1-10. Four roads (A, B, C, and D) are to be added to a highway network; the estimated benefits and costs for the various combinations are indicated below. If enough money is available to build only one road per year for the next 4 years, in what sequence should the roads be built? No construction is undertaken for a BCR of less than 1.

Combination	Projects	Benefit	Cost
1	0	0	0
2	A	10	20
3	AB	80	70
4	AC	60	60
5	AD	70	50
6	ABC	100	110
7	ABD	105	100
8	ACD	100	90
9	ABCD	150	140
10	B	50	50
11	BC	70	90
12	BD	80	80
13	BCD	120	120
14	C	45	40
15	CD	50	70
16	D	20	30

1-11.[4] A municipal ferry system crossing the bay at a coastal city handles an average daily volume of 2,000 vehicles, of which 20% are trucks and the remainder noncommercial. The crossing takes 15 min, and an average wait for the ferry is also 15 min. There is a $0.50 toll per vehicle. The annual operating disbursements for the ferry system (fuel,

[4] Adapted from "Managerial and Engineering Economy" by G. A. Taylor, 1964, by permission of Van Nostrand Reinhold Company.

maintenance, repairs, wages, etc.) total $450,000. The system could be sold, as is, to other communities for a total of $500,000. Otherwise, the remaining economic life is 30 years with zero salvage value.

The waiting time is estimated to be $4.50 per hour for commercial vehicles and $2.25 for noncommercial vehicles. The stop-and-start costs are estimated to be 0.7 cent for commercial vehicles and 0.45 cent for private vehicles, and the operating costs are 20 cents and 5 cents per mile, respectively.

A tunnel has been proposed to eliminate the ferry system. Cars could drive the 1-mile crossing at 40 mph without stopping. The total traffic is estimated at 4,000 vehicles, consisting of the 2,000 vehicles that use the ferry plus 2,000 private vehicles that presently avoid the ferry by driving 5 miles around the bay at an average speed of 20 mph. This route would include four traffic stops, each averaging 0.6 min.

The cost of the tunnel would be $20,000,000, with a 30-year economic life and zero salvage value. The annual maintenance and repair would total $50,000, with annual operating disbursements of $75,000. The toll charges for the tunnel would be $0.25 per car and $0.50 per commercial vehicle. If the cost of capital is 6%, what action should be taken based on a benefit-cost method of analysis?

1-12. Frequently the question is not "which alternative" but "what level of investment" is best. Problems in *incremental investments* may be solved by any of the usual comparison methods.

A logging company hopes to buy timber rights from several landowners. For how much of the total available land should rights be purchased? For a 20-year lease and minimum required return of 10%, which of the following incremental investments should be chosen, based on a discounted-cash-flow comparison? (For each *increment* of investment, compute the capital-recovery factor and find the corresponding interest rate from Appendix 3.)

		Land area		
	A	A + B	A + B + C	A + B + C + D
Investment	$380,000	$585,000	$675,000	$740,000
Net annual income	92,000	112,000	146,000	150,000

REFERENCES

1. Ackoff, R. L.: "Scientific Method: Optimizing Applied Research Decisions," John Wiley & Sons, Inc., New York, 1962.
2. Ackoff, R. L., and M. W. Sasieni: "Fundamentals of Operations Research," John Wiley & Sons, Inc., New York, 1968.
3. Barish, N. N.: "Economic Analysis for Engineering and Managerial Decision Making," McGraw-Hill Book Company, New York, 1962.
4. Beer, S.: "Decision and Control," John Wiley & Sons, Inc., New York, 1966.
5. Campbell, N. R.: "An Account of the Principles of Measurement and Calculation," Longmans, Green & Co., Ltd., London, 1928.
6. Churchman, C. W., and R. L. Ackoff: An Approximate Measure of Value, *Operations Res.*, vol. 2, pp. 172–180, 1954.
7. Cochran, W. G., and G. M. Cox: "Experimental Designs," 2d ed., John Wiley & Sons, Inc., New York, 1957.

8. Courant, R., and H. Robbins: "What Is Mathematics?" Oxford University Press, Fair Lawn, N.J., 1941.
9. Fishburn, P. C.: "Decision and Value Theory," John Wiley & Sons, Inc., New York, 1964.
10. Gilbert, E. N., and H. O. Pollak: Steiner Minimal Trees, *J. SIAM*, vol. 16, no. 1, January, 1968.
11. Gore, W. S., and F. S. Silander: A Biographical Essay on Decision-making, *Admin. Sci. Quart.*, vol. 4, pp. 97–121, 1959.
12. Hall, A. D.: "A Methodology for Systems Engineering," D. Van Nostrand Company, Inc., Princeton, N.J., 1962.
13. Morgenthaler, G. W.: The Theory and Application of Simulation in Operations Research, in R. L. Ackoff (ed.), "Progress in Operations Research," vol. I, John Wiley & Sons, Inc., New York, 1961.
14. Riggs, J. L.: "Economic Decision Models for Engineers and Managers," McGraw-Hill Book Company, New York, 1968.
15. Stark, R. M., and R. H. Mayer, Jr.: Discussion in *Proc. ASCE*, no. CO1, p. 131, July, 1969.
16. Stevens, S. S.: On the Theory of Scales of Measurements, *Science*, vol. 103, pp. 677–680, 1946.
17. Taylor, G. A.: "Managerial and Engineering Economy," D. Van Nostrand Company, Inc., Princeton, N.J., 1964.
18. Thomas, C. J., and W. L. Deemer, Jr.: The Role of Operational Gaming in Operations Research, *Operations Res.*, vol. 5, pp. 1–27, 1957.
19. Tocher, K. D.: "The Art of Simulation," D. Van Nostrand Company, Inc., Princeton, N.J., 1963.
20. Thrall, R. M., C. H. Coombs, and R. L. Davis (eds.): "Decision Processes," John Wiley & Sons, Inc., New York, 1954.
21. Von Neumann, J., and O. Morgenstern: "Theory of Games and Economic Behavior," 3d ed., Princeton University Press, Princeton, N.J., 1953.
22. Wilde, D. J., and C. S. Beightler: "Foundations of Optimization," Prentice-Hall, Inc., Englewood Cliffs, N.J., 1967.

2
Linear Programming

This and the following two chapters deal with linear programming. This chapter stresses the algebraic formulation and the simplex method of solution. The simplex method is useful for small problems, and its study exposes underlying principles of linear programming. Computer routines use modifications of the simplex method which are quite efficient.

The next chapter, Chap. 3, illustrates the wide variety of linear-programming applications and encourages the reader to formulate linear-programming problems "in the rough." It is more important, in our judgment, that the engineer recognize situations where linear programming might be useful than that he possess an up-to-date computational competence. Chapter 4 treats additional aspects of linear programming and related techniques.

We begin with an example:

A transit-mix company markets two concrete mixes, A and B. The company can produce up to 14 truckloads per hour of mix A or up to 7 loads per hour of mix B. The available trucks can haul up to 7 loads per hour of mix A and up to 12 loads per hour of mix B, due to the difference in delivery distances. The loading facility can handle not more than 8 truckloads per hour regardless of the mix. The company anticipates a profit of $5 per load on mix A and $10 per load on mix B. What number of loads per hour of each mix should the company produce?

The first step is to identify the variables. Let x and y be the production (in loads per hour) of mixes A and B, respectively. Equations (1') to (3') complete the formulation:

$$\text{Max:} \quad z' = 5x + 10y \tag{1'}$$

$$\text{Subject to:} \quad \frac{x}{14} + \frac{y}{7} \leqslant 1 \qquad \text{production} \tag{2a'}$$

$$\frac{x}{7} + \frac{y}{12} \leqslant 1 \qquad \text{delivery} \tag{2b'}$$

$$x + y \leqslant 8 \qquad \text{loading} \tag{2c'}$$

$$x, y \geqslant 0 \qquad \text{nonnegativity} \tag{3'}$$

In linear-programming parlance, Eq. (1'), the linear functional to be maximized (minimized), is called the *objective function*, the linear inequations (2a') to (2c') are called the *constraints*, and Eq. (3') is called the *nonnegativity condition* (although it is simply a constraint).

We shall return to this example. For the moment, we define the standard linear-programming form.

2-1 THE STANDARD LINEAR-PROGRAMMING FORM

When the objective and constraint functions are linear, the required optimization is said to belong to the linear-programming class. Specifically, the form

$$\text{Minimize:} \quad z = c_1 x_1 + \cdots + c_n x_n \tag{1}$$

subject to the constraints

$$a_{11} x_1 + a_{12} x_2 + \cdots + a_{1n} x_n = b_1$$
$$a_{21} x_1 + a_{22} x_2 + \cdots + a_{2n} x_n = b_2 \tag{2}$$
$$\dots\dots\dots\dots\dots\dots\dots\dots\dots\dots\dots\dots$$
$$a_{m1} x_1 + a_{m2} x_2 + \cdots + a_{mn} x_n = b_m$$

and

$$x_j \geqslant 0 \qquad j = 1, 2, \ldots, n \tag{3}$$

is called the *standard linear-programming form*. The quantities c_j, $b_i \geqslant 0$, and a_{ij} ($i = 1, \ldots, m$ and $j = 1, \ldots, n$) are assumed to be known constants, and m and n are positive integers.   The constants b_i are conventionally non-negative, and the c_j and a_{ij} are unrestricted in sign.

The formulation expressed by Eqs. (1) to (3) is more general than appears at first sight.   If the objective is to maximize, rather than minimize, one simply minimizes its negative.   That is, maximizing the linear functional $c_1 x_1 + \cdots + c_n x_n$ is equivalent to minimizing its negative, $-c_1 x_1 - \cdots - c_n x_n$.

Frequently a variable is unrestricted in sign; i.e., it may take either negative or nonnegative values.   The replacement of the unrestricted variable, say x_k, by the difference of two nonnegative variables—x_k^+, $x_k^- \geqslant 0$—enables one to satisfy the nonnegativity condition (3) because any negative number can be written as the difference of two nonnegative numbers, that is,

$$x_k = x_k^+ - x_k^- \tag{4}$$

If a negative sign appears on the right-hand side, one simply multiplies that constraint by -1.   Another important case arises when constraints express inequalities rather than equalities.   Consider the "less than" constraint

$$a_{k1} x_1 + a_{k2} x_2 + \cdots + a_{kn} x_n \leqslant b_k \tag{5}$$

Adding a so-called "slack variable," x_{n+1}, enables one to write inequation (5) as an equation:

$$a_{k1} x_1 + a_{k2} x_2 + \cdots + a_{kn} x_n + x_{n+1} = b_k \tag{5'}$$

Similarly, if the constraint is a "greater than" condition, then one subtracts a nonnegative "excess variable" to achieve an equality constraint. The constraint

$$a_{k1} x_1 + \cdots + a_{kn} x_n \geqslant b_k$$

can be transformed into the standard form

$$a_{k1} x_1 + \cdots + a_{kn} x_n - x_{n+1} = b_k$$

by subtracting the nonnegative "excess variable," x_{n+1}.   For example, consider the formulation

$$\text{Max:} \quad z' = x_1 - x_2$$
$$\text{Subject to:} \quad 2x_1 - 3x_2 + x_3 \leqslant 5$$
$$x_1 + x_2 - x_3 \geqslant 4$$
$$x_1, x_2 \geqslant 0$$
$$x_3 \text{ unrestricted in sign}$$

To place this in the standard form, we

1.   Replace x_3, which is unrestricted in sign, by $x_3^+ - x_3^-$, where $x_3^+, x_3^- \geqslant 0$

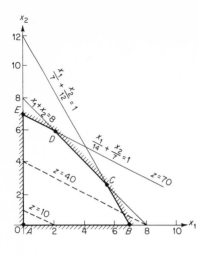

Fig. 2-1 Graphical solution of concrete-mix example.

2. Replace the objective function by its equivalent
    $$\text{Min: } z = -z' = -x_1 + x_2$$
3. Add a slack variable, x_4, to the first constraint and subtract an excess variable, x_5, from the second constraint.

Combining these, we have the standard form

$$\text{Min: } \quad z = -z' = -x_1 + x_2$$

$$\text{Subject to: } \quad 2x_1 - 3x_2 + x_3{}^+ - x_3{}^- + x_4 = 5$$
$$x_1 + x_2 - x_3{}^+ + x_3{}^- - x_5 = 4$$
$$x_1, x_2, x_3{}^+, x_3{}^-, x_4, x_5 \geqslant 0$$

The relaxed constraints [Eq. (2')] are plotted in Fig. 2-1 for the concrete-mix example. Each point in the region bounded by the pentagon ($ABCDE$) satisfies the constraints and the nonnegativity conditions. Also, a few iso-profit lines ($z = 10, 40, 70$) are indicated. Rewriting the problem in the standard form, and in more useful notation, we have

$$\text{Min: } \quad z = -z' = -5x_1 - 10x_2$$

$$\text{Subject to: } \quad \frac{x_1}{14} + \frac{x_2}{7} + x_3 = 1$$

$$\frac{x_1}{7} + \frac{x_2}{12} + x_4 = 1 \tag{6}$$

$$x_1 + x_2 + x_5 = 8$$

$$x_i \geqslant 0 \qquad i = 1, \ldots, 5$$

where x has been replaced by x_1 and y by x_2.

Table 2-1 Basic solutions for concrete-mix example

	1	2	3	4	5	6	7	8	9	10
x_1	[0]	[0]	[0]	[0]	14	7	8	70/17	2	28/5
x_2	[0]	7	12	8	[0]	[0]	[0]	84/17	6	12/5
x_3	1	[0]	−5/7	−1/7	[0]	1/2	3/7	[0]	[0]	9/35
x_4	1	5/12	[0]	1/3	−1	[0]	−1/7	[0]	3/14	[0]
x_5	8	1	−4	[0]	−6	1	[0]	−18/17	[0]	[0]
Location in										
Fig. 2-1	A	E				B			D	C

Since the number of variables exceeds the number of constraint equations, a unique simultaneous solution cannot exist. Suppose we set p variables equal to zero, where p is the difference between the number of variables, n, and the number of constraint equations, m. For example, $p = 2$ in the case of Eqs. (6). Then a unique simultaneous solution exists for each three-variable combination. Table 2-1 indicates the 10 possibilities. The two variables set equal to zero in each solution appear within brackets.

Note that of the 10 solutions, exactly 5 correspond to the coordinates of vertices of the pentagon and the remaining 5 violate the nonnegativity condition. By moving the objective line $z' = 5x_1 + 10x_2$ parallel to itself in Fig. 2-1, it is easy to conclude that the maximum value of z' is 70 and that the segment ED lies on the line $5x_1 + 10x_2 = 70$. Therefore, every point on that segment is an optimal solution. Thus, of the vast number of feasible solutions, i.e., those with coordinates within the pentagon $ABCDE$, only those on the segment ED are optimal. Had the objective function not been parallel to one side of the pentagon, only a single vertex would correspond to the optimal solution.

2-2 DEFINITIONS AND THEOREMS

The key to formulating more powerful methods for solving linear-programming problems is found in three theorems. To state these theorems properly requires the following vocabulary:

Segment If the coordinates of two points P_1 and P_2 are given by $x_j^{(1)}$ and $x_j^{(2)}$ $(j = 1, 2, \ldots, n)$, the segment joining P_1 and P_2 is the collection of points $P(\mu)$, whose coordinates are given by

$$x_j^{(\mu)} = (1 - \mu)x_j^{(1)} + \mu x_j^{(2)} \qquad j = 1, 2, \ldots, n$$

where $0 \leqslant \mu \leqslant 1$. In one dimension, for example, it is easy to see that the definition is in accord with our experience:

$$x^{(\mu)} - x^{(1)} = \mu(x^{(2)} - x^{(1)}) \qquad 0 \leqslant \mu \leqslant 1$$

whence

$$x^{(\mu)} = (1 - \mu) x^{(1)} + \mu x^{(2)}$$

Convex set　This is a collection of points such that if P_1 and P_2 are any two points in the collection, the segment joining them is also in the collection. For example, boundaries such as these

enclose convex sets. However, boundaries such as these

do not enclose convex sets because it is possible to choose at least one pair of points (as shown) such that not every point on the segment joining them belongs to the set.

Vertex (extreme point)　This is a point in the convex set which does not lie on a segment joining two other points of the set. Thus, for example, every point on the circumference of a circle and each vertex of the polygon satisfy the requirements for an extreme point.

Feasible solution　Any solution of the constraint equations satisfying the nonnegativity conditions is a feasible solution. In the concrete-mix example, every point bounded by the pentagon (convex set) is a feasible solution.

Basic solution　This is a solution of the constraint equations obtained by setting the "excess number," $n - m$, of variables to zero and solving the constraint equations simultaneously. In the concrete-mix example, each of the 10 solutions in Table 2-1 are basic solutions (but only A, B, C, D, and E are basic *and* feasible).

Basis　The collection of variables not set equal to zero to obtain the basic solution is the basis. In Table 2-1, for example, for the solution numbered 8, the basis is the collection (x_1, x_2, and x_5).

Basic feasible solution This is a basic solution which satisfies the nonnegativity conditions. As noted, solutions numbered 1, 2, 6, 9, and 10 in Table 2-1 are basic feasible solutions.

Optimal solution A feasible solution which satisfies the objective function is an optimal solution. Every point on the segment *ED* corresponds to an optimal solution.

Optimal basic solution This is a basic feasible solution for which the objective function is optimal. From Table 2-1 it is clear that solutions 2 and 9 are the only two which are optimal basic solutions.

The three basic theorems, mentioned earlier, can now be cited.

Theorem 2-1 *The collection of feasible solutions constitutes a convex set whose extreme points correspond to basic feasible solutions.*

This theorem tells us that we need be concerned only with convex sets since the only solutions of interest to us must be contained in the class of feasible solutions. Also, basic feasible solutions correspond to vertex points.

Theorem 2-2 *If a feasible solution exists, then a basic feasible solution exists.*

Theorem 2-1 assured us that the convex set contains all the feasible solutions. Now, if we find a feasible solution (say, by trial and error), then there must be at least one vertex to the convex set.

Theorem 2-3 *If the objective function possesses a finite minimum, then at least one optimal solution is a basic feasible solution.*

If the linear-programming problem has been properly formulated, it will satisfy the hypothesis of a finite minimum. This theorem assures us that at least one of the optimal solutions is a basic feasible solution. Therefore, our search for an optimal solution can be confined to the extreme points. This observation is of prime importance in the development of the simplex method to solve linear-programming problems.

The proofs of these theorems are not difficult and can be found in several of the references (e.g., [2] and [6]).

2-3 THE SIMPLEX METHOD

The standard form for the linear-programming problem was given in Eqs. (1) to (3). The basic feasible solutions correspond to the extreme points of the convex set of solutions (by Theorem 2-1). Hence the search for an optimal solution is narrowed to the extreme points since Theorem 2-3 guarantees that at least one extreme point must correspond to an optimal solution (if the problem possesses a solution). The simplex method is simply an iterative scheme for moving from one extreme point to an adjacent one until an optimal solution is identified.

We require:

1. A means of locating an initial extreme point from which to begin the journey about the convex set
2. A means of moving from one extreme point to another and preferably without backtracking
3. A means of identifying an optimal solution when it is reached and, if possible, without examining every extreme point

Each need is easily fulfilled. The first is accomplished using a clever trick. The second is, in essence, the simplex method; we shall see that there is no possibility of backtracking. Finally, an optimal solution plainly identifies itself, and one rarely examines every extreme point or even most of them.

1. THE CANONICAL FORM

For the moment, assume that an initial basic feasible solution is available. Let $x_1, \ldots, x_m$ denote the basic variables. The objective function and constraint equations, (1) and (2), can be written

$$\text{Min:} \quad z - z_0 = c'_{m+1} x_{m+1} + \cdots + c'_n x^n$$

$$
\begin{aligned}
\text{Subject to:} \quad x_1 + a'_{1,m+1} x_{m+1} + \cdots + a'_{1,n} x_n &= b'_1 \\
x_2 + a'_{2,m+1} x_{m+1} + \cdots + a'_{2,n} x_n &= b'_2 \\
\cdots\cdots\cdots\cdots\cdots\cdots\cdots\cdots\cdots\cdots\cdots\cdots\cdots &\qquad (7) \\
x_{m-1} + a'_{m-1,m+1} x_{m+1} + \cdots + a'_{m-1,n} x_n &= b'_{m-1} \\
x_m + a'_{m,m+1} x_{m+1} + \cdots + a'_{m,n} x_n &= b'_m \\
x_j \geqslant 0 \qquad j = 1, \ldots, n
\end{aligned}
$$

where the primes denote the new values of the coefficients as a result of the rearrangement and z_0 is a constant. Equations (7) are called the *canonical* equations for the basis $x_1, \ldots, x_m$. Note that the features of the canonical form are that (1) the basic variables have positive unit coefficients and only one of them (a different one) appears in each equation and (2) the objective function contains no basic variables.

2. MOVING TO AN ADJACENT EXTREME POINT (IMPROVING THE BASIS)

Having the coordinates of an extreme point, one obtains the coordinates of an *adjacent* extreme point by removing one variable from the basis and introducing one of the nonbasic variables into the basic set.

From one extreme point, we want to move to another for which z has a lower value. In the simplex method, movements are to adjacent extreme points. If this were not so, one might devise a scheme for moving to another (nonadjacent) and better extreme point and perhaps generalize it to move directly to an optimal point. No such scheme is available.

Since there may be several points adjacent to our momentary extreme point, we naturally wish to choose the one which makes the greatest improvement in z. If adjacent points make identical improvements in z, the choice is arbitrary. An improvement at each step ensures no backtracking.

How is the nonbasic variable that is tapped to join the basis chosen? A clue lies in the coefficients c'_j in the canonical form, Eqs. (7). In general, the coefficients c'_j may be positive, negative, or zero. If at least one of the c'_j is negative, by assigning a positive value to its associated nonbasic variable the value of z will be reduced. If more than one negative c'_j is present, a widely used rule of thumb is to choose the nonbasic variable associated with the smallest c'_j (that is, largest absolute value) to enter the basis. The value of z is given by $z_0 + c'_r x_r$, where c'_r is the smallest negative coefficient.

Two immediate questions arise. First, how large can we make x_r? Second, when x_r enters the basis, which variable is chosen to leave (since the number of basic variables is fixed at m)? To seek answers, rewrite Eqs. (7) after transposing every term containing x_r:

$$\text{Min:} \quad z - z_0 - c'_r x_r = c'_{m+1} x_{m+1} + \cdots + c'_n x_n$$

$$\text{Subject to:} \quad x_1 + a'_{1,m+1} x_{m+1} + \cdots + a'_{1,n} x_n = b'_1 - a'_{1,r} x_r$$
$$x_2 + a'_{2,m+1} x_{m+1} + \cdots + a'_{2,n} x_n = b'_2 - a'_{2,r} x_r$$
$$\cdots\cdots\cdots\cdots\cdots\cdots\cdots\cdots\cdots\cdots\cdots\cdots\cdots\cdots\cdots\cdots \quad (8)$$
$$x_m + a'_{m,m+1} x_{m+1} + \cdots + a'_{m,n} x_n = b'_m - a'_{m,r} x_r$$
$$x_i \geqslant 0 \qquad i = 1, \ldots, n$$

Any a'_{ir} which are nonpositive pose no limit on how much x_r can be increased. For positive a'_{ir}, x_r can be increased until one of the right-hand sides of the constraint set becomes zero. A further increase would violate the non-negativity condition (3). The maximum value that the incoming variable, x_r, can take is

$$\underset{\substack{i \\ a_{ir} > 0}}{\text{Min}} \frac{b_i}{a'_{ir}} = \frac{b'_s}{a'_{sr}} \qquad i = 1, \ldots, m \qquad (9)$$

where s is the index of the smallest ratio. In the event of a tie, the choice of s is arbitrary among the tying indices. Clearly, there is no motivation to assign a lower value to x_r. Now the answer to the second question is at hand since the basic variable, x_s, is zero in the equation which contributed the maximum ratio. Suppose that all the a'_{ir} are nonpositive. Then x_r can be increased indefinitely and the solution is unbounded. Any practical problem in which this is encountered has not been properly constrained.

3. IDENTIFYING AN OPTIMAL SOLUTION

We now know how to identify a nonbasic variable to which a positive value can be assigned to improve the value of z; we know how much that assignment should be; and we know which variable to remove from the basis to make room for the incoming variable. In short, we know how to move to an adjacent extreme point to improve the value of z. Equations (8) are now rearranged into a new canonical form, and the procedure is repeated. When do the iterations end? Recall that above we assumed at least one of the coefficients c'_j in the canonical objective function to be negative. Now suppose that there are no negative c'_j. Then the value of z cannot be further reduced and the solution is optimal. However, there may be alternate optima, i.e., other extreme points for the same value of z. If all the c'_j are positive, then

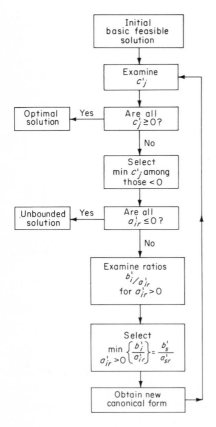

Fig. 2-2 Flow chart for simplex iterations.

the optimal solution is unique. If at least one c_j' is zero, then there are alternate optima. The extreme points corresponding to alternate optima can be obtained by introducing the variable associated with a zero cost coefficient into the basis according to the foregoing procedure. Of course, any point on the segment(s) joining optimal extreme points also corresponds to an optimum. Note that optima are global (as distinct from relative). A flow chart summarizes the procedure (Fig. 2-2).

We now illustrate the simplex procedure for the concrete-mix example:

Min: $z = -z' = -5x_1 - 10x_2$

Subject to: $\dfrac{x_1}{14} + \dfrac{x_2}{7} + x_3 = 1$

$$\dfrac{x_1}{7} + \dfrac{x_2}{12} + x_4 = 1 \tag{6}$$

$$x_1 + x_2 + x_5 = 8$$
$$x_i \geqslant 0 \qquad i = 1, \ldots, 5$$

1. In this instance, the standard form is also a canonical form (item 1). Whenever the original constraints are "less than" conditions, the addition of slack variables to achieve the standard form also yields the canonical form. Thus, the conversion of Eqs. (1) and (2) to Eqs. (7) is not necessary. The basic variables at the moment are x_3, x_4, and x_5 at respective values 1, 1, and 8.

2. To move to an adjacent extreme point, the coefficient -10 in the objective function fits the description in item 2. Thus, x_2 is tapped to enter the basis. How large can x_2 become? Using Eq. (9),

$$\frac{b_1}{a_{1,2}} = \frac{1}{1/7} = 7$$

$$\frac{b_2}{a_{2,2}} = \frac{1}{1/12} = 12$$

$$\frac{b_3}{a_{3,2}} = \frac{8}{1} = 8$$

and

$$\frac{b_s'}{a_{sr}'} = \min \frac{b_i'}{a_{ir}'} = \min (7, 12, 8) = 7$$

so that the index s corresponds to 1 (for the first constraint equation), which means that x_3 will leave the basis to make room for x_2. If x_2 is to be a basic variable, then its removal from the objective function and from the constraint equations (except for the first) becomes necessary. To obtain the new canonical form, as suggested in item 1, we divide the s row by $1/7$, which is the coefficient of the new nonzero variable x_2, to obtain

$$\frac{x_1}{2} + x_2 + 7x_3 = 7$$

and subtract suitable multiples of the resulting expression (-10, $1/12$, and 1) from the other equations to eliminate x_2 from them. For example, for the new second constraint equation, we have

$$\frac{x_1}{7} + \frac{x_2}{12} \qquad + x_4 \qquad = 1$$

$$\frac{-1}{12}\left[\frac{x_1}{2} + x_2 + 7x_3 \qquad\qquad = 7\right]$$

$$\overline{\rule{6cm}{0.4pt}}$$

$$= \frac{17x_1}{2} \qquad - 49x_3 + 84x_4 = 35$$

The new canonical form thus obtained is

Min: $\quad z = -70 + 70x_3$

Subject to: $\quad \dfrac{x_1}{2} + x_2 + 7x_3 = 7$

$17/168 x_1 - 7/12 x_3 + x_4 = 5/12$

$$\frac{x_1}{2} - 7x_3 + x_5 = 1$$

$$x_i \geqslant 0 \qquad i = 1, \ldots, 5$$

with the basis (x_2, x_4, x_5). The flow chart (Fig. 2-2) returns us to examining the c_j.

3. Since the coefficients in the objective function are all nonnegative, an optimal solution is at hand (item 3). Setting the nonbasic variables x_1 and x_3 equal to zero, we solve the preceding equations to obtain the optimal solution, $z_{\max} = 70$ and $(x_1, x_2, x_3, x_4, x_5) = (0, 7, 0, 5/12, 1)$, which corresponds to vertex E in Fig. 2-1.

However, note that the objective coefficient of the nonbasic variable x_1 is zero. This means that the optimal solution is not unique.

4. To obtain the alternate optima, we permit x_1 to become basic. Thus,

$$\frac{b_s'}{a_{s,1}'} = \min_{\substack{i \\ a_{i,1}' > 0}} \frac{b_i'}{a_{i,1}'} = \min(14, 70/17, 2) = 2$$

so that s is 3 (third equation "binds") and x_5 is the departing variable.

Table 2-2 Simplex tableaus

	b	x_1	x_2	x_3	x_4	x_5
	1	1/14	(1/7)	1		
	1	1/7	1/12		1	1
(0)	8	1	1			1
	$-z = 0$	-5	$*-10$			
	7	1/2	1	7		
	5/12	17/168	$-7/12$		1	
(1)	1	(1/2)		-7		1
	$-z = 70$	$*$		70		
	6		1	14		-1
	3/14			5/6	1	$-17/84$
(1′)	2	1		-14		2
	$-z = 70$			70		

The new canonical form is

Min: $z = -70 + 70x_3$

Subject to: $x_2 + 14x_3 - x_5 = 6$
$70x_3 + 84x_4 - 17x_5 = 18$
$x_1 - 14x_3 + 2x_5 = 2$
$x_i \geqslant 0 \quad i = 1, \ldots, 5$

This solution, $z'_{max} = 70$ and $(x_1,x_2,x_3,x_4,x_5) = (2,6,0,18,0)$, corresponds to vertex D in Fig. 2-1. Using the definition of a segment in Sec. 2-2, it is easy to generate the coordinates of every point on the segment DE of the convex set in Fig. 2-1.

A more efficient way to organize the solution is the simplex tableau of coefficients. The preceding iterations appear in Table 2-2. The asterisk denotes the minimum $c_j \leqslant 0$, while the pivot entry is circled. Multiplying the first row by 7 yields its canonical form. This is written in the first row of the next tableau. The arithmetic operations are exactly the same as for the equations, the principal economy being the elimination of repetitious writing of the symbols.

4. LOCATING AN INITIAL BASIC FEASIBLE SOLUTION

The foregoing sections describe the essential features of the simplex method starting with an initial basic feasible solution. One can always obtain such a starting solution by algebraic manipulation to convert the standard form into the canonical form. There is, however, a more clever way, using the simplex procedure itself; this is the so-called "phase I" routine.

If the problem consists solely of "less than" constraints, the addition of the slack variables yields a canonical form and the initial basic feasible solution is a gift. When one is not so lucky, a new and different nonnegative variable is added to each constraint equation which lacks canonical attire. Such variables are called *artificial variables*. In effect, the artificial variables have augmented the convex polygon of the original problem and the initial canonical form corresponds to an extreme point located in the new space. The problem now is to traverse extreme points until one is reached in the original space. When that occurs, and this will be apparent since all artificial variables will be nonbasic in the original space, the augmented space is literally removed so that future movements are among the extreme points of the original space until an optimum is obtained. In short, after creating artificial variables we eliminate them as promptly as possible. Instead of the original objective function z, consider a new objective function w equal to the sum of the artificial variables, that is, $w = x_{n+1} + \cdots + x_{n+m}$, where $x_{n+1}, \ldots, x_{n+m}$ are the artificial variables. We assume that one artificial variable is added to each constraint. Treat the original objective function as a constraint for the moment. Now, however, the canonical form is upset since the artificial variables, which are currently basic variables, appear in the new objective function. This is easily remedied by adding all the constraint equations in which artificial variables appear, solving for the sum of those variables, and setting the result equal to w to yield a canonical form. The (artificial) canonical form might appear as

$$w = \sum_{i=1}^{m} b_i - \sum_{j=1}^{n} \left[\sum_{i=1}^{m} a_{ij} \right] x_j$$

$$a_{11} x_1 + \cdots + a_{1m} x_n + x_{n+1} = b_1$$
$$\cdots\cdots\cdots\cdots\cdots\cdots\cdots\cdots\cdots\cdots\cdots\cdots$$
$$a_{m1} x_1 + \cdots + a_{mn} x_n + x_{n+m} = b_m$$
$$c_1 x_1 + \cdots + c_n x_n = z$$
$$x_j \geqslant 0 \qquad j = 1, \ldots, n+m$$

Now one employs the simplex procedure to minimize w. The minimum value of w is clearly zero since it is, however else it might appear, the sum of the nonnegative artificial variables. When $w = 0$, an extreme point on the

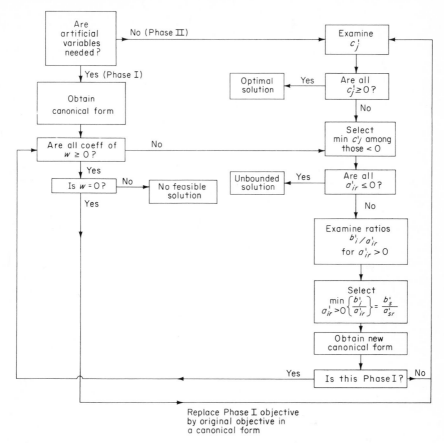

Fig. 2-3   Flow chart for simplex iterations with a phase I routine.

original convex set has been reached. w is then simply abandoned in favor of z, and the iterations continue until the optimal value of z is obtained. Suppose, however, that w refuses to be driven to zero.   This will be apparent when none of the coefficients is negative and yet w is greater than zero.   Clearly, this means that we cannot reach the original convex set and therefore no feasible solution exists for the original problem.

Again, a flow chart summarizes the procedure (Fig. 2-3).

The concrete-mix example yielded an immediate canonical form. Suppose, however, that there is an additional truckloading constraint,

$$2x_1 + x_2 \geqslant 2 \qquad\qquad (2d')$$

The standard form becomes

Min: $z = -5x_1 - 10x_2$

Subject to:
$$\frac{x_1}{14} + \frac{x_2}{7} + x_3 = 1$$

$$\frac{x_1}{7} + \frac{x_2}{12} + x_4 = 1$$

$$x_1 + x_2 + x_5 = 8$$
$$2x_1 + x_2 - x_6 = 2$$
$$x_i \geqslant 0 \qquad i = 1, \ldots, 6$$

Table 2-3 Simplex tableaus

	b	x_1	x_2	x_3	x_4	x_5	x_6	x_7
	1	1/14	1/7	1				
	1	1/7	1/12		1			
	8	1	1			1		
	2	②	1				−1	1
$-z =$	0	−5	−10					
$-w =$	−2	−2*	−1				1	
	13/14		3/28	1			1/28	−1/28
	6/7		1/84		1		1/4	−1/4
	7		1/2			1	1/2	−1/2
	1	1	①/②				−1/2	1/2
$-z =$	5		−15/2*				−5/2	5/2
$-w =$	0	0	0				0	
					End of phase I			
	5/7	−3/14		1			①/⑦	
	5/6	−1/42			1		1/12	
	6	−1				1	1	
	2	2		1			−1	
$-z =$	20	15					−10*	
	5	−3/2		7				1
	5/12	17/168		−7/12	1			
	1	1/2		−7		1		
	7	1/2		7				
$-z =$	70	0		70				

Since the form is not canonical, a phase I routine is used as follows from item 4. The calculations appear in Table 2-3. One artificial variable is needed for the final constraint and is denoted by x_7. The objective function for the phase I routine is $w = x_7 = 2 - 2x_1 - x_2 + x_6$. The canonical form for the phase I routine appears in the first tableau of Table 2-3. A single iteration brings w to zero and the solution to a vertex of the original convex set. Since the artificial variable can never again enter the basis, we delete the column for x_7 and the row for w. The third tableau continues the simplex technique for the original objective. The fourth and final tableau indicates optimality.

Comparing this optimal tableau with the one obtained previously without the additional truckloading constraint, one observes the same maximum profit. This can be clearly seen by plotting the additional truckloading constraint on the graph in Fig. 2-1. The constraint removes a triangular region from the lower left portion of the convex set and, hence, is not "active."

SUMMARY

This chapter introduced the linear class of mathematical programming problems. Definitions from linear algebra and the statement of three theorems were used to bridge the gap between the theory of convex sets and the solution to the linear-programming problem. A brief development of the simplex method and a means of obtaining a required initial basic feasible solution were outlined.

The simplex method is not computationally economic, and efficient modifications are available. References [1–4] and [7] are quite readable, while [6], [8], and [9] are more advanced. The two volumes (of a trilogy) by Hadley ([5] and [6]) are outstanding in their comprehensiveness.

PROBLEMS

2-1. Max: $z' = 5x_1 - 2x_2$

Subject to: $2x_1 + x_2 \leqslant 9$
$x_1 - 2x_2 \leqslant 2$
$-3x_1 + 2x_2 \leqslant 3$
$x_1, x_2 \geqslant 0$

2-2. Max: $z' = 2x_1 + 2x_2 - x_3 - x_4$

Subject to: $2x_1 + x_3 - 2x_4 \leqslant 6$
$2x_1 - 2x_2 - x_3 + x_4 \leqslant 8$
$x_1 + x_2 + 2x_4 \leqslant 5$
$x_i \geqslant 0 \qquad i = 1,\ldots,4$

2-3. Max: $z' = 3x_1 + x_2 - 2x_3$

Subject to: $x_1 - 2x_2 - x_3 \leqslant 10$
$2x_1 + x_2 + 2x_3 \leqslant 12$
$x_1 - x_2 + x_3 \leqslant 5$
$x_1, x_2, x_3 \geqslant 0$

2-4. Max: $z' = x_1 + x_2 + x_3 + 2x_4$

Subject to: $x_1 + x_3 + x_4 \leqslant 4$
$x_1 + x_2 + 2x_4 \leqslant 8$
$x_1 + 2x_2 - x_3 - x_4 \leqslant 6$
$-2x_1 - x_2 + x_3 + x_4 \leqslant 6$
$x_i \geqslant 0 \qquad i = 1, \ldots, 4$

2-5. Min: $z = x_1 + 2x_2 - x_3 + x_4$

Subject to: $x_1 - x_2 + x_3 \leqslant 4$
$x_1 + x_2 + 2x_4 \leqslant 6$
$x_2 - 2x_3 + x_4 \leqslant 2$
$-x_1 + 2x_2 + x_3 \leqslant 2$
$x_1, x_4 \geqslant 0$
x_2, x_3 unrestricted in sign

2-6. Max: $z' = 3x_1 + 2x_2 + x_3$

Subject to: $4x_1 + x_2 + x_3 = 8$
$3x_1 + 3x_2 + 2x_3 = 9$
$x_1, x_2, x_3 \geqslant 0$ ♦

2-7. Min: $z = x_1 - 2x_2 + x_3$

Subject to: $3x_1 - x_2 + x_3 \leqslant 4$
$x_1 - x_2 + x_3 \leqslant 2$
$-2x_1 + x_2 - x_3 \leqslant 4$
$x_1, x_2, x_3 \geqslant 0$

2-8. Min: $z = x_1 + 3x_2$

Subject to: $x_1 + 4x_2 \geqslant 48$
$5x_1 + x_2 \geqslant 50$
$x_1, x_2 \geqslant 0$

2-9. Max: $z' = 2x_1 - x_2 + 6x_3 + x_4$

Subject to: $4 \leqslant 2x_1 + 3x_3 + 2x_4 \leqslant 60$
$-3x_1 - x_4 \geqslant -50$
$x_1 + x_2 + x_3 + x_4 = 40$
$4x_1 + 6x_3 \geqslant 0$
$x_1, x_2, x_3 \geqslant 0$

x_4 unrestricted in sign

2-10. Max: $z' = x_1 + x_2 + 2x_3$

Subject to: $1 \leqslant x_1 \leqslant 4$
$3x_2 - 2x_3 = 6$
$-1 \leqslant x_3 \leqslant 2$
$x_2 \geqslant 0$

REFERENCES

1. Au, T., and T. E. Stelson: "Introduction to Systems Engineering," Addison-Wesley Publishing Company, Inc., Reading, Mass., 1969.
2. Garvin, W.: "Introduction to Linear Programming," McGraw-Hill Book Company, New York, 1960.

3. Gass, S. I.: "Linear Programming Methods and Applications," 2d ed., McGraw-Hill Book Company, New York, 1964.
4. Glickman, A. M.: "Linear Programming and the Theory of Games," John Wiley & Sons, Inc., New York, 1963.
5. Hadley, G.: "Linear Algebra," Addison-Wesley Publishing Company, Inc., Reading, Mass., 1961.
6. Hadley, G.: "Linear Programming," Addison-Wesley Publishing Company, Inc., Reading, Mass., 1962.
7. Llwellyn, R. W.: "Linear Programming," Holt, Rinehart and Winston, Inc., New York, 1964.
8. Orchard-Hays, William: "Advanced Linear Programming," McGraw-Hill Book Company, New York, 1968.
9. Simmonard, M.: "Linear Programming," Prentice-Hall, Inc., Englewood Cliffs, N.J., 1966.

3
Applications of Linear Programming

Linear-programming applications span a remarkable variety of subjects from agriculture to economics and petroleum refining to engineering. In areas of civil engineering—traffic control, structural design, water resources, construction management, etc.—there is widespread application. Most of the literature has originated in the past decade, and the potential for further application appears good, particularly for operational problems.

A series of examples comprises this chapter. The principal purpose of these examples is to provide experience in diagnosing situations where a linear-programming model can be useful. Models from which the engineer hopes to derive solutions are necessarily imperfect. At times, one can construct a model which closely represents the real situation but mathematical techniques to derive a solution may not be available. At other times, one can construct a model for which techniques are available but which is not a useful representation of the problem, so that the solution is of limited interest. Every useful model is a compromise between precision of representation and the expense which can be justified in deriving solutions. It is instructive to bear this compromise in mind when studying the examples. Perhaps no practical problem can be precisely represented by a linear-programming model. The question is whether the engineer constructing the model is resourceful (and lucky) enough to find a linear-programming representation from which he can gain relatively inexpensive insights. In order not to risk obscuring the foregoing considerations, we give scant attention to computational techniques in the examples. The interested reader can carry out some of the solutions by hand, by writing computer programs, or by using available routines.

The linear-programming model is well suited to *allocation* problems. For example, consider the following linear-programming form:

Max: $z = v_1 x_1 + \cdots + v_n x_n$

Subject to:
$$a_{11} x_1 + a_{12} x_2 + \cdots + a_{1n} x_n \leqslant b_1$$
$$a_{21} x_1 + a_{22} x_2 + \cdots + a_{2n} x_n \leqslant b_2$$
$$\ldots\ldots\ldots\ldots\ldots\ldots\ldots\ldots\ldots\ldots\ldots$$
$$a_{m1} x_1 + a_{m2} x_2 + \cdots + a_{mn} x_n \leqslant b_m$$
$$x_i \geqslant 0 \qquad i = 1, \ldots, n$$

Amounts $b_1, b_2, \ldots, b_m$ of m different inputs (or resources) are available to achieve the (to be determined) numbers $x_1, \ldots, x_n$ of n different outputs. Exactly a_{ij} units of resource i are necessary to produce one unit of output j ($i = 1, \ldots, m; j = 1, \ldots, n$). The value assigned to a single unit of output j is v_j. The allocation problem is to find how the inputs should be allocated to maximize the total output.

Many of the examples of this chapter can be viewed as linear allocation problems. However, some are usefully classified in other ways. Example 3-1 relates to structural engineering, Examples 3-2 and 3-3 to water-resource management, Example 3-4 to a traffic problem, and Examples 3-5 to 3-8 to construction management. Examples 3-6 and 3-8 lead to a standard linear-programming form whose properties will enable more efficient computational techniques (for the assignment and transportation problems in Chap. 4). Example 3-5 indicates how allocations can be "timed," and so on. Most of the examples in this chapter relate to operational problems. Some design problems appear in Chap. 4.

Example 3-1 Loading a structure An overhead crane (Fig. 3-1) is used to transport concrete from a mix plant to a casting yard. Lifting yokes facilitate placing concrete and moving cured members. What is the maximum concrete load ($W_1 + W_2 + W_3$) that can be carried in the three buckets at the positions shown? Cables 1 and 2 each have an 8-kip capacity, cables 3 and

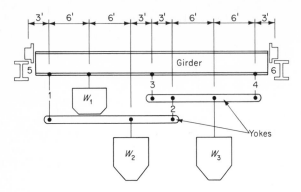

Fig. 3-1 An overhead crane.

4 each have a 16-kip capacity, and each crane rail (5 and 6) can support 20 kips. The crane girder and yokes are of negligible weight.

Let $F_1, F_2, \ldots, F_6$ represent the forces in cables 1, 2, 3, and 4 and supports 5 and 6, respectively. For equilibrium, we set the sums of the moments about each of the six support positions equal to zero. This yields

$$F_1 = 1/3W_2 \qquad\qquad F_4 = 2/15W_2 + 3/5W_3$$
$$F_2 = 2/3W_2 \qquad\qquad F_5 = 3/4W_1 + 7/12W_2 + 1/4W_3$$
$$F_3 = 8/15W_2 + 2/5W_3 \qquad F_6 = 1/4W_1 + 5/12W_2 + 3/4W_3$$

Hence, the linear-programming form:

Max: $W' = W_1 + W_2 + W_3$

Subject to: $1/3W_2 \leqslant 8$
$$2/3W_2 \leqslant 8$$
$$8/15W_2 + 2/5W_3 \leqslant 16$$
$$2/15W_2 + 3/5W_3 \leqslant 16$$
$$3/4W_1 + 7/12W_2 + 1/4W_3 \leqslant 20$$
$$1/4W_1 + 5/12W_2 + 3/4W_3 \leqslant 20$$
$$W_1, W_2, W_3 \geqslant 0$$

The second constraint clearly implies the first. Therefore, the second can be omitted and the number of constraints reduced to five. Generally, one need not worry about whether the constraints are independent. The simplex method, and most computer routines, do not require the removal of constraint dependencies.

Example 3-2 Regional water-quality management The following example is adapted from Deininger [31]. There are several related works, such as Lynn [37] and Day and Dolbear [30].

A number of communities, n, which discharge wastes into a stream are too distant for combined waste-treatment plants to be economical. We wish to determine the levels of treatment by each plant which satisfy the specified stream-quality criteria at minimum total cost.

We use the following notation:

$$p_j = BOD^1 \text{ discharge rate from city at } j; j = 1, 2, \ldots, n$$
$$x_j = BOD \text{ removal ratio at } j$$
$$p_j(1 - x_j) = BOD \text{ discharge rate into river at } j$$
$$p_{jk} = \text{decomposition ratio, fraction of waste from } j \text{ still present at } k$$
$$Q_j = \text{streamflow in the reach } j \text{ to } j + 1 \text{ (including wastes)}$$
$$B_j = \text{maximum allowable BOD loading in the reach } j \text{ to } j + 1$$
$$c_j = \text{unit cost of BOD removal at } j$$
$$d_j = c_j x_j p_j = \text{total cost per unit time for treatment at } j$$

Assumptions include:

1. Stream velocity is constant at 25 miles per day.
2. Streamflow is constant in the reach between adjacent pairs of cities. (Inflowing tributaries could be represented as "dummy" cities.)
3. Maximum BOD removal efficiency is 90% at any plant, and treatment cost is directly proportional to BOD removal.
4. BOD exertion of wastes follows the monomolecular equation, so that,

$$p_{jk} = \exp[-rt_{jk}]$$

   where r = deoxygenation rate and t_{jk} = passage time between cities j and k.
5. Pollution load limit B_j in BOD specified for the entire length of stream is 0.0012 lb per cu ft of streamflow.

The total-cost objective C may be written

$$\text{Min:} \quad C = \sum_{j=1}^{n} d_j$$

where n is the number of cities.

In terms of the BOD loading constraints, inequalities at the various cities can be written

$$\text{At city 1:} \quad \frac{p_1(1 - x_1)}{Q_1} \leqslant B_1$$

[1] Biochemical oxygen demand.

At city 2: $\dfrac{p_1(1-x_1)p_{12}+p_2(1-x_2)}{Q_2} \leqslant B_2$

. . . .

At city n: $\displaystyle\sum_{j=1}^{n}\dfrac{p_j(1-x_j)p_{jn}}{Q_n} \leqslant B_n$

A second set of constraints arises from the 90% maximum treatment efficiency:

$$0 \leqslant x_j \leqslant 0.90 \qquad j = 1, \ldots, n$$

This completes the linear-programming formulation. Typical data appear in Table 3-1.

Some variations and refinements which might be incorporated into the model are:

1. The specified pollution load limit might vary along the stream depending upon the requirements of various stream uses such as recreation, irrigation, fishing, and industry.
2. An upstream reservoir to augment low flows would reduce total treatment costs. Solving the problem for various increased minimum streamflows would indicate the corresponding reductions in treatment costs. This constitutes part of an economic study for reservoir sizing.
3. More than one water-quality parameter could be specified, e.g., total dissolved oxygen, bacterial count, etc. This leads to additional sets of linear constraints besides the set imposed by the BOD specification.
4. If treatment costs are convex functions of treatment efficiency (assumption 3), the problem might be considered using piecewise linear-programming techniques (Sec. 5-6).
5. If random variations in streamflow, waste quantity, and concentration are pertinent, stochastic programming (Sec. 10-1) or simulation techniques might be useful.

Table 3-1   Stream pollution and sewage treatment data

City	Mile point	BOD load p_j, lb/day	Deoxygenation rate r, days^{-1}	Treatment cost c_j, \$/lb of BOD	Streamflow Q_j, cfs
1 (upstream)	46	1,200	0.23	0.18	32.4
2	30	400	0.21	0.22	37.1
3	18	22,000	0.27	0.09	48.5
4 (downstream)	0	230	0.26	0.27	56.1

Example 3-3 Design of a water-resource system A reservoir is to be built to supply an irrigation district. The problem is to determine the capacity of the reservoir and the annual amount of water to release for irrigation.

The inflow to the reservoir (Fig. 3-2) is given in units of 10^6 acre-ft for the wet and dry seasons. The contributions of a tributary entering the stream below the reservoir are given as 0.6 unit and 0.4 unit, respectively, for the two seasons. Assume, as did R. Dorfman in Maass et al. [38], that the present worth of diverting an amount X of water each year to the irrigation district over the anticipated life of the project is given by the nonlinear function

$$2.1X + 36.8 \log(1 + 0.2X)$$

and the discounted capital cost of the reservoir, including operation and maintenance, is

$$43Y(1 + 0.2Y)^{-1}$$

where Y is the proposed reservoir capacity.

Assume that 40% of X is required during the wet season and 60% during the dry season.

If we assume that the reservoir is filled by the end of each wet season and emptied by the end of each dry season, the flows on two reaches of the river may be expressed as shown in the boxes in Fig. 3-2. Flow cannot be negative, and we have the nonlinear-programming problem:

Max: $z = 2.1X + 36.8 \log(1 + 0.2X) - 43Y(1 + 0.2Y)^{-1}$

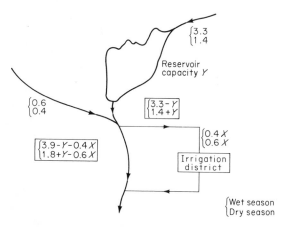

Fig. 3-2 Reservoir serving an irrigation district. (*Adapted from R. Dorfman in Maass et al. [38]*).

Subject to: $3.3 - Y \geqslant 0$
$3.9 - Y - 0.4X \geqslant 0$
$1.8 + Y - 0.6X \geqslant 0$
$X \geqslant 0 \qquad Y \geqslant 0$

As a first approximation, we replace the logarithm by its Taylor series through linear terms. A similar replacement is made for the expression $(1 + 0.2Y)^{-1}$. This yields a linear-programming approximation. Additional approximations may be achieved using piecewise linear programming (Sec. 5-6).

Example 3-4 Traffic-flow control Consider items which flow along several routes to a central processing center of fixed capacity. The flow on each route is a mix of several types of items. The problem is to control the route flow to optimize the mix of items in the processing center. For example, an ore-reduction plant can be fed by sources of ore with varying composition. The amount from each source to maximize plant profit is to be determined.

The model also suggests application to traffic systems. Some detailed examples of toll-pricing models appear in Wohl and Martin [26] and in Drew [21]. Here we use a simple and somewhat contrived example of the model for timing a traffic signal which regulates traffic to a toll facility.

The toll rates are type A, \$0.40; type B, \$0.85; type C, \$1.20. The toll facility has a capacity of 1,500 vehicles per hour. The traffic-light cycle should not exceed 3 min, and each route should have a green signal for at least 30 sec per cycle. We seek a timing for the traffic signal that maximizes the revenue per cycle. Only one route can empty into the toll area at a time, and excess traffic is shunted to alternate routes.

Let t_i be the "green time" on route i ($=$ I, II, III) in seconds. The objective function can be written

$$
\begin{aligned}
\text{Max:}\quad z &= [(0.50)(0.40) + (0.45)(0.85) + (0.05)(1.20)]\,792/3{,}600t_1 \\
&+ [(0.65)(0.40) + (0.25)(0.85) + (0.1)(1.20)]\,1{,}604/3{,}600t_2 \\
&+ [(0.35)(0.40) + (0.40)(0.85) + (0.25)(1.20)]\,612/3{,}600t_3 \\
&= 14.14t_1 + 26.39t_2 + 13.26t_3
\end{aligned}
$$

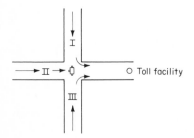

Fig. 3-3 Traffic-flow control.

Data

	Maximum flow rate		
Traffic mix	*Route I* 792 *vehicles/hr*	*Route II* 1,604 *vehicles/hr*	*Route III* 612 *vehicles/hr*
Type A	50%	65%	35%
Type B	45%	25%	40%
Type C	5%	10%	25%

subject to the constraints

$$792/3{,}600t_1 + 1{,}604/3{,}600t_2 + 612/3{,}600t_3 \leqslant 1{,}500/3{,}600(3)(60)$$

or

$0.53t_1 + 1.07t_2 + 0.41t_3 \leqslant 180$ capacity restriction

$t_1, t_2, t_3 \geqslant 30$ green-light restrictions

$t_1 + t_2 + t_3 \leqslant (3)(60) = 180$ cycle restrictions

This linear-programming problem can be solved "by hand" in five iterations and yields the solution

$t_1 = t_3 = 30$ sec $t_2 = 120$ sec

$z_{max} = \$37.18$ per cycle

Example 3-5 Unbalanced bidding

Much bidding, particularly in highway work, is conducted through unit-price proposals. A highway department advertises a proposal indicating the quantities of items (tons of gravel, square feet of trench sheeting, etc.) which it anticipates will be required. Bids are invited per unit of each item (unit bids), and the total bid is formed. The contract is usually awarded to the low bidder and provides for periodic (monthly) payments for the units completed during each period. Once the contract is awarded, the total bid becomes irrelevant because the proposed quantities usually differ from the actual quantities and the actual project cost seldom equals the total bid. A bidder can place relatively high unit bids on items to be completed early in the project and lower bids on later items. In this way, he obtains partial payment in advance, which can be used to finance subsequent stages of the contract.

A reasonable objective is the maximization of the present worth of all future revenue. Suppose that the proposal calls for unit bids on n items and the proposed completion time is k months. Let g_{jm} be the quantity of the mth item scheduled for completion (payment) in the jth month; $m = 1, \ldots, n$

and $j = 1, \ldots, k$ Also, let x_m be the (to be determined) unit bid for the mth item.   The revenue expected in the jth month from the completed units of the mth item is clearly $g_{jm} x_m$.   However, the sum will not be available to the contractor until the jth month, and therefore its present worth is $g_{jm} \rho^j x_m$, where ρ is the discount factor.   Clearly, the present worth of all future revenue, z', is

$$\text{Max:} \quad z' = \sum_{j=1}^{k} \sum_{m=1}^{n} g_{jm} \rho^j x_m$$

where the sum over j arises because the same item may be used in different time periods (e.g., the proposal calls for 6 tons of gravel, of which 4 tons are used in the second month and 2 tons in the fourth month).

There are various constraints to which the maximization is subject. First, the undiscounted sum of all revenue must not exceed the total bid B.   If a_m denotes the sponsor's proposed quantity of the mth item (that is, $a_m = \sum_{j=1}^{k} g_{jm}$), then

$$\sum_{m=1}^{n} a_m x_m \leqslant B \qquad \text{bid constraint}$$

Second, restrictions upon the unit bids are usually desirable.   Custom dictates, for example, that the unit bid for rock excavation, x_r, exceed that for earth excavation, x_e.   Thus

$$x_r - x_e \geqslant 0 \qquad \text{formality constraint}$$

Also, one can protect against a low unit bid (less than cost, say) by employing a constraint

$$x_m \geqslant C_{ml} \qquad \text{bounds constraint}$$

where C_{ml} is the desired lower bound on the unit bid.   Similarly, an upper bound may be desirable.

In addition to maximizing present worth, an unbalancing of a bid may assist in the timing of income (e.g., for tax purposes).   Thus, the revenue through the ith time period, $\sum_{m=1}^{n} \sum_{j=1}^{i} g_{jm} x_m$, may be set equal to $(i/kB\alpha)$, where α is a proportionality constant.   For example, if $\alpha = 1$, then the rate at which revenue accrues is equal to the time rate of project completion.

Thus the problem of unbalancing a bid is one of determining unit bids $x_1, \ldots, x_n$ for each item so that z' is a maximum and subject to appropriate constraints.   Since the objective function z' and the constraints are linear with respect to the unit bids, the required optimization is the solution of a linear-programming problem. Discussions of unbalanced bidding appear in [2] and [7].

Suppose that bids are solicited for the following simplified unit-price proposal:

Item. No.	Estimated No. of units	Item
1	25,000 sq yd	Clearing
2	60,000 cu yd	Earth excavation
3	40,000 cu yd	Rock excavation
4	25,000 sq yd	Cleanup

The bidder prepares the following (balanced) bid:

Item No.	Unit bid	Amount	Est. completion time, months
1	$2.00	$ 50,000	3
2	1.00	60,000	12
3	3.50	140,000	12
4	2.00	50,000	15
	Total bid	$300,000	

For simplicity, assume that payment at the unit bid price is made after each item is completed. If the cost of money is 1% per month, the present (or starting) worth of the balanced bid is

$$(\$50,000)(1.01)^{-3} + (\$60,000)(1.01)^{-12} + (\$140,000)(1.01)^{-12}$$
$$+ (\$50,000)(1.01)^{-15} = \$269,086$$

Now consider alternatives to increase the present worth:

1. We seek a set of unit bids which maximizes the present worth. Thus the objective is to maximize the linear functional

$$z' = (25,000)(1.01)^{-3} x_1 + (60,000)(1.01)^{-12} x_2 + (40,000)(1.01)^{-12} x_3$$
$$+ (25,000)(1.01)^{-15} x_4$$

where x_i is the (to be determined) unit bid on item i ($i = 1, \ldots, 4$). The maximization is subject to the bid constraint $25,000x_1 + 60,000x_2 + 40,000x_3 + 25,000 x_4 = 300,000$. In addition, suppose that we require that the unit bid for rock excavation be not less than that for earth excavation. Thus, we protect the formality of the tender with the constraint $x_2 - x_3 \leqslant 0$. The solution to this linear-programming problem (apparent by inspection) is

$x_1 = 12$, $x_2 = x_3 = x_4 = 0$, and $z'_{opt} = \$291{,}177$. Note an increased return of about 9%.

2. The above solution may not be satisfactory because of its call for unit bids at zero. Suppose we augment the constraint set as follows:

$$25x_1 + 60x_2 + 40x_3 + 25x_4 = 300$$
$$x_2 - x_3 \leqslant 0$$
$$1 \leqslant x_1 \leqslant 3$$
$$1 \leqslant x_2$$
$$1 \leqslant x_4 \leqslant 3$$

The solution to this linear-programming problem is $x_1 = 3$, $x_2 = x_3 = 2$, $x_4 = 1$, and $z'_{opt} = \$271{,}818$, a gain of about 1% in the present worth.

3. Suppose the bidder has investigated the proposed quantities and concludes that the actual quantities are more likely to be

Item 1: same as sponsor

Item 2: 50,000 cu yd

Item 3: 50,000 cu yd

Item 4: same as sponsor

The objective function using these estimates is

$$z' = (25{,}000)(1.01)^{-3} x_1 + (50{,}000)(1.01)^{-12} x_2 + (50{,}000)(1.01)^{-12} x_3$$
$$+ (25{,}000)(1.01)^{-15} x_4$$

The constraints remain as in alternative 2. The linear-programming solution yields $x_1 = x_2 = x_4 = 1$, $x_3 = 4.75$, and $z_{opt} = \$300{,}940$.

This should be compared with the \$269,086 which is the present worth of the contract without unbalancing (but using the bidder's estimates)—a gain of nearly \$30,000, or about 11%.

4. Finally, we illustrate the use of the linear-programming model to time income. On excavation items 2 and 3, let us assume that payments are made on the basis of completed units even if the entire excavation is incomplete. Also, suppose that the following time schedule has been devised:

Item	Required time, months	Begin	End
1	3	July 1, 1972	Sept. 30, 1972
2	9	Oct. 1, 1972	June 30, 1973
3	9	Oct. 1, 1972	June 30, 1973
4	3	July 1, 1973	Sept. 30, 1973

The bidder, let us say, prefers to defer most of the project income to 1973 for tax purposes and, specifically, wants to limit project income in 1972 to $125,000. First, we augment the constraints with

$$(25)\, x_1 + \tfrac{3}{9}(60)\, x_2 + \tfrac{3}{9}(40)\, x_3 \leqslant 125$$

in order to time the income. Otherwise, the model is as in alternative 2. Solving this linear-programming problem yields

$$x_1 = x_4 = \$3 \qquad x_2 = x_3 = \$1.50 \qquad \text{and} \qquad z_{opt} = \$270{,}513$$

This should be compared with $271,818, the optimal present worth without the rate constraint. Thus the cost of timing the income is about $1,300. The bidder can now decide whether the timing is worth that sum.

Additional discussion appears in [3].

Example 3-6   An assignment problem   A firm owns m cranes, and one is needed at each of n work sites, where $m \geqslant n$. The cranes vary in size, and the crane requirements vary from job to job. Management has constructed the following matrix:

$$\begin{bmatrix} w_{11} & w_{12} & \cdots & w_{1n} \\ w_{21} & w_{22} & \cdots & w_{2n} \\ \multicolumn{4}{c}{\dotfill} \\ w_{m1} & w_{m2} & \cdots & w_{mn} \end{bmatrix}$$

to represent the estimated returns w_{ij} from assigning the ith crane to the jth job. How should the cranes be allocated to jobs to maximize the total return?

Here it is convenient to use doubly subscripted quantities. Thus, let x_{ij} denote the fraction of the ith crane's time which should be allocated to the jth job. The objective function is

$$z' = w_{11} x_{11} + w_{12} x_{12} + \cdots + w_{1n} x_{1n} + w_{21} x_{21} + \cdots + w_{mn} x_{mn}$$

Constraints are required to ensure that no crane is assigned for more than 100% of its available time and that no job is assigned more than once. Specificially,

$$x_{i1} + x_{i2} + \cdots + x_{in} \leqslant 1 \qquad i = 1, \ldots, m$$

ensures that the ith crane is not assigned more than 100% of the time, and

$$x_{1j} + x_{2j} + \cdots + x_{mj} \leqslant 1 \qquad j = 1, \ldots, n$$

ensures that the assignment of cranes to the jth job does not exceed 100%.

The addition of the nonnegativity condition completes the formulation of the linear-programming problem. Actually, this is a linear-programming problem of a special type which enables one to achieve substantial computational efficiencies (see Sec. 4-2).

Example 3-7 A production problem A concrete-products manufacturer supplies hollow prestressed piles. The piles are processed in two successive stages: (1) casting and curing, and (2) prestressing. Production is being planned for the next 3 months. We wish to determine the number of piles to be processed through each of the two stages during regular time and overtime to satisfy demand at minimum cost. The data below are available.

| | | *Available production capacity, hr* | | | |
| | | *Casting-curing* | | *Prestressing* | |
Month	*Demand piles*	*Regular time*	*Overtime*	*Regular time*	*Overtime*
1	75	160	40	190	35
2	90	150	30	160	30
3	95	150	25	170	35

| | | *Cost per pile* | |
Stage	*Processing time per pile, hr*	*Regular time*	*Overtime*
Casting-curing	1.5	$ 800	$1,100
Prestressing	2.5	1,000	1,400

Stage	*Initial inventory, piles*	*Storage cost per pile per month*
Cast	7	$10
Cast and prestressed	5	8

We use the following notation:

d_j = demand for finished piles in month j; $j = 1, 2, 3$
x_{ij} = number of piles scheduled for regular time at stage i in month j
y_{ij} = number of piles scheduled for overtime at stage i in month j
a_{ij} = cost to produce one pile on regular time at stage i in month j
b_{ij} = cost to produce on overtime at stage i in month j
A_{ij} = regular-time production capacity (in piles) at stage i in month j
B_{ij} = overtime production capacity at stage i in month j

I_{1j} = in-process inventory at end of month j (initial inventory = I_{10})
I_{2j} = finished-piles inventory at end of month j (initial inventory = I_{20})
c_1 = cost of carrying one pile in in-process inventory from one month to the next
c_2 = cost of carrying one finished pile in inventory from one month to the next

The problem is to

Min: $\displaystyle\sum_{j=1}^{3}\sum_{i=1}^{2}(a_{ij}x_{ij}+b_{ij}y_{ij})+c_1\sum_{j=1}^{3}I_{1j}+c_2\sum_{j=1}^{3}I_{2j}$

Subject to: $x_{ij},y_{ij}\geqslant 0$
$\qquad\qquad x_{ij}\leqslant A_{ij}$
$\qquad\qquad y_{ij}\leqslant B_{ij}$ production capacities
$\qquad\qquad I_{2j}\geqslant 0$ no pile shortage
$\qquad\qquad I_{1j}\geqslant 0$ nonnegative in-process inventory
$\qquad\qquad i=1,2 \qquad j=1,2,3$

To express the objective function and the constraints in terms of the decision variables x_{ij} and y_{ij}, we observe that

$$I_{1j}=I_{10}+\sum_{n=1}^{j}(x_{1n}+y_{1n})-\sum_{n=1}^{j}(x_{2n}+y_{2n})$$

and

$$I_{2j}=I_{20}+\sum_{n=1}^{j}(x_{2n}+y_{2n})-\sum_{n=1}^{j}d_n$$

The reader can summarize this linear-programming problem in a simplex tableau.

Example 3-8 Minimizing cut-and-fill haul costs The cut-and-fill quantities for a 4-mile section of highway are shown in the profile of Fig. 3-4. The location of borrow pits appears on the plan, and haul costs are given per cubic yard-station. Haul costs are a function of grade (drawbar pull) and, therefore, vary with both location and direction of haul. Assume that excess cut can be discarded without cost.

To formulate the problem, we consider as origins the borrow pits and stations where earth is available and as destinations the stations requiring fill. The unit costs are obtained by computing unit transportation cost from each origin to each destination. To approximate haul costs, cut-and-fill quantities lying between adjacent stations are assumed to be at the lower

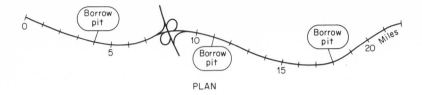

PLAN

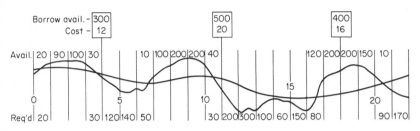

Distances, thousands of ft. Earth quantities, thousands of cu. yds.
Borrow pit costs, cents / cu yd.

PROFILE

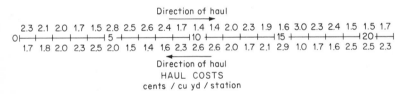

Fig. 3-4 Cut and fill for a highway.

station.   For example, the transportation cost from Sta 2 to Sta 5 is (2.0 + 1.7 + 1.5) = \$0.052 per cu yd, from Sta 5 to Sta 3 is (2.5 + 2.3) = \$0.048 per cu yd, and so on.

Let x_{ij} be the number of cubic yards of fill to be taken from Sta i to Sta j, and let c_{ij} be the unit cost.   For convenience, we consider only a portion of the highway, namely, the section from Sta 3 to Sta 7.   This section includes one borrow pit, denoted by B, that is, x_{Bj} is the amount of fill taken from the borrow pit at Sta 4 for transfer to Sta j.

The objective function is

$$\text{Min:}\quad z = 1.7x_{34} + 3.2x_{35} + 6.0x_{36} + 14.3x_{B3} + 12.0x_{B4} + 13.5x_{B5}$$
$$+ \; 16.3x_{B6} + 6.8x_{63} + 4.5x_{64} + 2.0x_{65} + 8.3x_{73} + 6.0x_{74} + 3.5x_{75} + 1.5x_{76}$$

Subject to: $\quad x_{33} + x_{34} + x_{35} + x_{36} \leqslant 30$
$$x_{B3} + x_{B4} + x_{B5} + x_{B6} \leqslant 300 \qquad \text{available fill}$$

$$x_{63} + x_{64} + x_{65} + x_{66} \leqslant 10$$
$$x_{73} + x_{74} + x_{75} + x_{76} \leqslant 100$$

$$x_{33} + x_{B3} + x_{63} + x_{73} = 30$$
$$x_{34} + x_{B4} + x_{64} + x_{74} = 120 \qquad \text{fill requirements}$$
$$x_{35} + x_{B5} + x_{65} + x_{75} = 140$$
$$x_{36} + x_{B6} + x_{66} + x_{76} = 50$$
$$x_{ij} \geqslant 0 \qquad \text{for all } i,j$$

This completes the linear-programming formulation. Note that the constraint coefficients are either zero or unity. In addition, the manner in which these 0s and 1s appear in the constraint equations enables one to classify this linear-programming form as a special type. It can be solved much more efficiently by techniques other than the simplex method (or its revisions). (See Sec. 4-1.)

PROBLEMS

3-1. The weekly demand for high-, medium-, and low-grade ores is 12, 8, and 24 thousand tons, respectively,. Two mines are in use. Mine A produces 6, 2, and 4 thousand tons of high-, medium-, and low-grade ore daily. Mine B's daily production is 2, 2, and 12 thousand tons, respectively. The daily operating cost of mine A is $200,000 and of mine B is $160,000. How should the mines be worked to meet the demand at lowest cost?

3-2. An airlines company is considering the purchase of new long-range, medium-range, and short-range jet passenger airplanes. The purchase price would be $6.7 million for each long-range plane, $5 million for each medium-range plane, and $3.5 million for each short-range plane. The board of directors has authorized a maximum commitment of $150 million for these purchases. Regardless of which airplanes are purchased, air travel of all distances is expected to be sufficiently large that these planes would be utilized at essentially maximum capacity. It is estimated that the net annual profit (after subtracting capital-recovery costs) would be $420,000 per long-range plane, $300,000 per medium-range plane, and $230,000 per short-range plane.

It is predicted that enough trained pilots will be available to the company to man 30 new airplanes. If only short-range planes were purchased, the maintenance facilities would be able to handle 40 new planes. However, in terms of the use of the maintenance facilities, each medium-range plane is equivalent to $1\frac{1}{3}$ short-range planes and each long-range plane is equivalent to $1\frac{2}{3}$ short-range planes.

The information given above was obtained by a preliminary analysis of the problem. A more detailed analysis will be conducted subsequently. However, using the above data as a first approximation, management wishes to know how many planes of each type should be purchased in order to maximize profit. Formulate the linear-programming model for this problem. Ignore the fact that the number of airplanes must be an integer.[2]

3-3. A petroleum company advertised for unit-cost bids on soil exploration at a refinery site. The contract will consist of land and offshore drilling for lighterage moors and pipelines. In the following table, the company's estimated quantities for different classes of drilling are shown adjacent to the quantities estimated by one of the bidders.

[2] This problem is reprinted from F. Hillier and G. Lieberman, "Introduction to Operations Research," Holden-Day, Inc., Publishers, San Francisco, 1967.

Location	Class of drilling	Client's quantity estimate, ft	Bidder's quantity estimate, ft	Bidder's normal unit price	Optimal unit price
Land	Soil	1,800	2,000	$ 4.00	
	3-in. undisturbed sample	45	60	10.00	
	Split-spoon sample	260	300	3.00	
	Tricone-bit drilling	400	300	6.00	
	NX rock coring	60	30	9.00	
Offshore	Soil auger	300	350	$ 5.50	
	3-in. undisturbed sample	15	25	14.00	
	Split-spoon sample	45	55	4.00	
	Tricone-bit drilling	80	40	8.00	
	NX rock coring	20	10	11.00	

The bidder decides upon a total bid of $16,000 based on the client's quantity estimates. How should he unbalance his bid? He believes he can raise or lower his normal prices by as much as 40%. Complete the final column of the table.

3-4. A contractor will submit a unit-price bid on the foundation work for a concrete dam. After reviewing the project and considering the potential competitive bidders, he sets his total bid at $750,000. The client's and bidder's quantity estimates are tabulated below. The last column is the bidder's estimate of the acceptable range within which he can submit unit prices. Given the estimated construction schedule (tabulated) and an interest rate of 8%, determine unit prices for the four construction items which will maximize the present worth of his income. ◆

Item	Quantity estimates Client's	Quantity estimates Bidder's	Bidder's estimated construction schedule, years 1	2	3	Allowable range for unit prices
Earth excavation, cu yd	400,000	350,000	250,000	100,000		$ 0.80–1.80
Rock excavation, cu yd	30,000	35,000	5,000	30,000		6.00–11.00
Drilling, ft	1,800	1,800		500	1,300	6.00–12.00
Grouting, cu yd	300	400			400	20.00–35.00

3-5. The contractor on a concrete dam has three potential aggregate sources: an island aggregate deposit, A; a point bar deposit, B, approximately 2 miles downstream from the dam; and river-dredged material, C, approximately 800 yd downstream. The estimated quantities and costs to produce and transport aggregate to the mix plant are:

Deposit	Estimated quantity, cu yd	Cost/cu yd
A	6,000	$3.00
B	4,000	3.50
C	13,000	4.00

The following aggregate blends from the three sources will produce material within the gradational limits specified for the three classes of concrete in the dam. The costs of cement, fly ash, and additives are:

Class of concrete	Specified limits	Cost/cu yd of concrete for cement, fly ash, additives
1	$A \geqslant 60\%$ $C \leqslant 20\%$	$3.50
2	$C \geqslant 60\%$ $A \leqslant 15\%$	3.00
3	$C \leqslant 50\%$	4.00

The contractor is paid $12 per cu yd regardless of class of concrete placed. To simplify, assume that 1 cu yd of aggregate makes 1 cu yd of concrete.

Write the initial simplex tableau to determine a production policy which maximizes the profit from the three aggregate sources.

3-6. An entrepreneur operates two limestone quarries several miles apart. Each quarry has three ledges of limestone interbedded with layers of shale. The upper ledge in each quarry is too soft for use as aggregate but is high in available calcium and can be pulverized and sold as agricultural lime. The intermediate ledge is not durable enough to meet the specifications for concrete work but can be sold for highway base-course material and secondary road surfacing. The bottom ledge is suitable for aggregate in bituminous and Portland cement concretes.

Since the depth of overburden and the thicknesses of the three ledges vary at the two quarries, the daily operating costs and production rates also vary, as follows:

Quarry	Daily operating cost	Average daily production, tons		
		Agricultural lime	Crushed stone	Aggregate
1	$1,400	30	150	225
2	2,400	35	90	450

Agricultural lime can be sold for $15 per ton, crushed stone for $3.10 per ton, and aggregate for $4.20 per ton. The operator estimates that in the approaching 9-month construction season, his market for the three classes of lime will be as follows:

Agricultural lime: 600 tons/month
Crushed stone: 4,000 tons/month
Aggregate: 9,000 tons/month

Since the quarries are open-pit operations, the overburden must be removed before material can be obtained from each strata. If, in order to expose a lower ledge of limestone, more material must be removed from an upper ledge than can be sold, the costs of pulverizing agricultural lime and/or crushing soft limestone can be saved. These savings from the daily operating costs are $6 per ton of agricultural lime not pulverized and $1 per ton of soft lime not crushed.

Formulate a linear-programming model to determine the number of days per month to operate the quarries for maximum profit during the 9-month period.

3-7. Consider the structural system shown below, in which wires 1 and 2 can support loads up to 300 lb each; wires 3 and 4, up to 100 lb each; and wires 5 and 6, up to 50 lb each. Neglect the weight of beams and wires and assume weights W_1, W_2, and W_3 at the positions indicated. What is the maximum total load, $W_1 + W_2 + W_3$, that the structure can support?

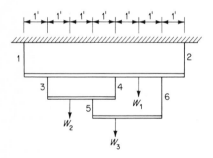

3-8. An aluminum reduction plant produces two grades of aluminum ingots, which it sells for $285 and $320 per ton. The company has two sources of bauxite available, with the following analyses and costs:

Ore	A	B	C	Cost/ton
1	40%	30%	30%	$15
2	10	70	20	20

The plant has a weekly smelting capacity of 200 tons of ore and has contracted to purchase from the mine a minimum of 50 tons per week each of ores 1 and 2. The $285-grade aluminum must have at least 30% of A and not more than 20% of either B or C. The $320 grade must have at least 40% of B and not more than 30% of either A or C. 80% of A and 90% of B and C are lost in the smelting process. What blend of the two ores will maximize profit?

REFERENCES

Construction management

1. Aguilar, R. J.: Decision Making in Building Planning, *Computers in Engineering Design Education*, vol. III, pp. 26–33, Civil Engineering, University of Michigan, Ann Arbor, 1966.
2. Gates, M.: Bidding Strategies and Probabilities, *Proc. ASCE*, vol. 93, no. CO2, pp. 75–107, March, 1967.
3. Mayer, R. H., Jr., R. M. Stark, and W. Fitzgerald: Unbalanced Bidding Models— Applications, *Univ. Delaware Tech. Rep.*, March, 1969.
4. Nicholls, R. L.: Operations Research in Construction Planning, *Proc. ASCE*, vol. 89, no. CO2, pp. 59–74, September, 1963.
5. Ritter, J. B., and L. R. Shaffer: Blending Natural Earth Deposits for Least Cost, *Proc. ASCE*, vol. 87, no. CO1, pp. 39–61, March, 1961.
6. Shaffer, L. R.: Planning a Grading Operation for Least Total Cost, *Proc. ASCE*, vol. 89, no. EM6, pp. 47–66, December, 1963.
7. Stark, R. M.: Unbalanced Bidding Models—Theory, *Proc. ASCE*, vol. 94, no. CO2, pp. 197–209, October, 1968.

Structural engineering

8. Bigelow, R. H., and E. H. Gaylord: Design of Steel Frames for Minimum Weight, *Proc. ASCE*, vol. 93, no. ST6, pp. 109–131, December, 1967.
9. Charnes, A., and H. J. Greenberg: "Plastic Collapse and Linear Programming Preliminary Report," paper presented at the summer meeting of the American Mathematical Society, September, 1951; abstracted in *Bull. AMS*, vol. 57, no. 6, p. 480, November, 1951.
10. Dorn, W. S., and H. J. Greenberg: Linear Programming and Structures, 30 pp. (including tables), *Tech. Rep.* 7, Carnegie Institute of Technology, Pittsburgh, Pa., August, 1955.
11. Douty, R.: Optimization of a Two-span Cover-plated Steel Beam, *Computers in Engineering Design Education*, vol. III, pp. 34–50, Civil Engineering, University of Michigan, Ann Arbor, 1966.
12. Heyman, J.: Plastic Design of Beams and Plane Frames for Minimum Material Consumption, *Quart. Appl. Math.*, vol. 8, no. 4, pp. 373–381, January, 1951.
13. Kany, M.: Theory and Applicability of Best Economical Dimensioning of Foundation Groups, *Proc. 6th Intern Conf. Soil Mech. Found. Eng.*, vol. II, p. 93, 1965.
14. Lewis, A. D.: Optimal Design of Structural Steel Framing for Tier-type Buildings, *Computers in Engineering Design Education*, vol. III, pp. 64–88, Civil Engineering, University of Michigan, Ann Arbor, 1966.
15. Moses, F.: Optimum Structural Design Using Linear Programming, *Proc. ASCE*, vol. 90, no. ST6, pp. 90–104, December, 1964.
16. Moses, F., and D. E. Kinser: Optimum Structural Design with Failure Probability Constraints, *Am. Inst. Aeron. Astronautics J.*, vol. 5, no. 6, pp. 1152–1158, June, 1967.
17. Ridha, R. A., and R. N. Wright: Minimum Cost of Frames, *Proc. ASCE*, vol. 93, no. ST4, pp. 165–183, August, 1967.
18. Reinschmidt, K. F., C. A. Cornell, and J. F. Brotchie: Iterative Design and Structural Optimization, *Proc. ASCE*, vol. 92, no. ST6, pp. 281–317, December, 1966.
19. Rubinstein, M. F., and J. Karagozian: Building Design Using Linear Programming, *Proc. ASCE*, vol. 92, no. ST6, pp. 223–245, 1966.
20. Rubinstein, M. F.: "New Concepts in Structural Design," American Iron and Steel Institute, New York, April, 1968.

Transportation engineering

21. Drew, D.: "Traffic Flow Theory and Control," McGraw-Hill Book Company, New York, 1968.
22. Hamberg, J. R., et al.: Linear Programming Test of Journey-to-work Minimization, *Highway Res. Record*, no. 102, pp. 67–75, 1965.
23. Hutchinson, B. G.: A Conceptual Framework for Pavement Design Decisions, *Highway Res. Record*, no. 121, pp. 1–14, 1966.
24. Lavalle, S. R.: "The Application of Linear Programming to the Problem of Scheduling Traffic Signals," paper presented at the seventh national meeting of the ORSA, Calif., Aug. 15–17, 1955; abstracted in *J. ORSA*, vol. 3, no. 4, p. 562, November, 1955.
25. Pinnell, C., and G. T. Satterly: Systems Analysis for Arterial Street Operation, *Proc. ASCE*, vol. 89, no. EM6, pp. 67–95, December, 1963.
26. Wohl, M., and B. V. Martin: "Traffic Systems Analysis," McGraw-Hill Book Company, New York, 1967.

Water resources management

27. Buras, N.: Conjunctive Operation of Dams and Aquifers, *Proc. ASCE*, vol. 89, no. HY6, pp. 111–131, November, 1963.
28. Castle, E. N.: Programming Structures in Watershed Development, in G. S. Tolley and F. E. Riggs, "Economics of Watershed Planning," chap. 12, pp. 167–178, The Iowa State University Press, Ames, 1961.
29. Chow, V. T.: "Handbook of Applied Hydrology," pp. 26–39, McGraw-Hill Book Company, New York, 1964.
30. Day, H. J., and F. Dolbear: Regional Water Quality Management, *Proc. 1st Annu. Meeting Am. Water Resources Assoc.*, University of Chicago, pp. 283–309, December, 1965.
31. Deininger, R. A.: Water Quality Management—The Planning of Economically Optimal Pollution Control Systems, *Proc. 1st Annu. Meeting Am. Water Resources Assoc.*, University of Chicago, pp. 254–282, December, 1965.
32. Dorfman, R.: Mathematical Analysis: Design of the Simple Valley Project, in G. S. Tolley and F. E. Riggs, "Economics of Watershed Planning," chap. 14-B, pp. 217–229, The Iowa State University Press, Ames, 1961.
33. Hall, W. A.: Aqueduct Capacity under an Optimum Benefit Policy, *Proc. ASCE*, vol. 87, no. IR3, pp. 1–11, September, 1961.
34. Heady, E. O.: Mathematical Analysis. Models for quantitative Application in Watershed Planning, in G. S. Tolley and F. E. Riggs, "Economics of Watershed Planning," chap. 14-A, pp. 197–216, The Iowa State University Press, Ames, 1961.
35. Lee, I. M.: Optimum Water Resources Development, *Giannini Found. Rep.* 206, University of California, Berkeley, 1958.
36. Loucks, D. P.: Wastewater Treatment Systems Analysis, *Conf. Preprint* 368, *ASCE Water Resources Eng. Conf.*, Denver, May 16–20, 1966.
37. Lynn, W. R.: Stage Development of Wastewater Treatment Works, *J. Water Pollution Control Federation*, pp. 722–751, June, 1964.
38. Maass, A., et al.: "Design of Water Resource Systems," Harvard University Press, Cambridge, Mass., 1962.
39. Masse, P., and R. Gibrat: Application of Linear Programming to Investments in the Electric Power Industry, *Management Sci.*, vol. 3, no. 2, pp. 149–166, January, 1957.
40. Masse, P.: "Optimal Investment Decision," translated from French by Scripla Technica, Inc., Prentice-Hall, Inc., Englewood Cliffs, N.J., 1962.

4
Additional Linear Methods

The merit of the simplex method developed in Chap. 2 is that it provides a grasp of how linear-programming problems can be solved. A principal reason for its inefficiency is that it requires the computation and retention of many numbers which may not be needed in subsequent iterations, e.g., a variable that will not enter the basis. Computer routines for revisions of the simplex method permit considerably more efficient solutions to linear-programming problems. We omit their consideration since they are readily available and do not particularly enhance our ability to formulate applications. There are, however, other aspects of linear-programming problems which may yield unusual computational efficiencies and/or insights. These are the subject of the six sections of this chapter.

To begin, a remark about *degeneracy* is pertinent. At a particular iteration, suppose that at least one of the basic variables has the value zero (see Prob. 2-4). Such variables are said to be degenerate. If a degenerate variable is designated to leave the basis in a subsequent iteration, the value of z is unchanged. This could be very unfortunate because it raises the possibility that a degenerate basis may repeat (cycle) and, hence, that successive iterations will not reduce z (even though an optimum has not yet been achieved). Fortunately, practical difficulties with degeneracy are not usually serious. While degeneracy is common, cycling is not, and procedures have been devised to "break" the cycle.

4-1 THE TRANSPORTATION PROBLEM

The introduction to Chap. 3 emphasized the resource-allocation aspect of linear programming. Imagine n job sites $J_1, J_2, \ldots, J_n$ which require a certain resource available from m sites $R_1, R_2, \ldots, R_m$. Let b_i represent the available amount at resource site $i(= 1, 2, \ldots, m)$; let a_j be the required amount at job site $j(= 1, 2, \ldots, n)$; and let c_{ij} be the unit cost of distribution from resource site i to job site j. This point of view suggests an allocation in the sense of *distribution of resources*. The matrix in Fig. 4-1 summarizes the data.

The problem is to determine the amounts x_{ij} at site R_i to be distributed to job site J_j such that the total cost is minimum. In symbols,

$$\text{Min:} \quad z = c_{11}x_{11} + c_{12}x_{12} + \cdots + c_{1n}x_{1n} + \cdots + c_{m1}x_{m1} + \cdots$$
$$+ c_{mn}x_{mn} \quad (1)$$

$$\text{Subject to:} \quad x_{11} + x_{12} + \cdots + x_{1n} \leqslant b_1 \qquad \text{use must not exceed}$$
$$\ldots\ldots\ldots\ldots\ldots\ldots\ldots\ldots \qquad \text{resource available} \quad (2)$$
$$x_{m1} + x_{m2} + \cdots + x_{mn} \leqslant b_m$$

$$x_{11} + x_{21} + \cdots + x_{m1} \geqslant a_1 \qquad \text{use must not be less}$$
$$\ldots\ldots\ldots\ldots\ldots\ldots\ldots\ldots \qquad \text{than resource} \quad (3)$$
$$x_{1n} + x_{2n} + \cdots + x_{mn} \geqslant a_n \qquad \text{required}$$

$$x_{ij} \geqslant 0 \qquad \text{all } i,j \quad (4)$$

		Job sites			Resources available
		J_1	J_2 $\bullet\bullet\bullet$	J_n	
	R_1	c_{11}	c_{12} $\bullet\bullet\bullet$	c_{1n}	b_1
Resource sites	R_2	c_{21}	c_{22} $\bullet\bullet\bullet$	c_{2n}	b_2
	$\vdots$		$\vdots$		$\vdots$
	R_m	c_{m1}	c_{m2} $\bullet\bullet\bullet$	c_{mn}	b_m
	Resources required	a_1	a_2	a_n	

Fig. 4-1 A resource-distribution matrix.

Equations (1) to (4) could be written more succinctly as

$$\text{Min:} \quad z = \sum_i \sum_j c_{ij} x_{ij}$$

$$\text{Subject to:} \quad \sum_j x_{ij} \leqslant b_i \qquad i = 1, \ldots, m$$

$$\sum_i x_{ij} \geqslant a_j \qquad j = 1, \ldots, n$$

$$x_{ij} \geqslant 0 \qquad \text{all } i, j$$

Clearly, this is a linear-programming form with a total of mn variables and $m + n$ constraints. The double-subscript notation should not obscure the similarity with the formulation in Chap. 2. It is convenient because it immediately suggests the origins and destinations involved.

Linear-programming problems which have the form of Eqs. (1) to (4) are called *transportation problems*. While linear-programming techniques are applicable, considerably more efficient techniques have been devised, as the following examples suggest.

Example 4-1   Subgrade distribution   A contractor working on several small county-highway relocations must transport quantities of select subgrade to each project from available borrow pits in the area. The entries in Table 4-1 give the haul distances and the select subgrade required and available in units of hundreds of truckloads.

For the corresponding linear-programming form of Eqs. (1) to (4), we seek the quantities x_{ij} which should be hauled from pit i to project j ($i = 1,2,3$; $j = 1,2,3,4$) such that the requirements are satisfied with a minimum total haul distance.

As in the simplex method, we seek an initial basic feasible solution. A simple procedure is the so-called "northwest-corner rule." Assign an amount

Table 4-1   Haul-distance matrix (in miles)

		1	2	3	4	Select subgrade available
			Project			
Pit	1	3	9	8	16	13
	2	15	1	7	17	16
	3	12	19	4	5	17
Select subgrade required		10	8	12	16	46

Table 4-2   Allocation by the northwest-corner rule

		Project			Select subgrade available
	1	2	3	4	
Pit 1	$x_{11} = 10$	$x_{12} = 3$			13
Pit 2		$x_{22} = 5$	$x_{23} = 11$		16
Pit 3			$x_{33} = 1$	$x_{34} = 16$	17
Select subgrade required	10	8	12	16	46

$x_{11} = \min (a_1, b_1) = \min (10,13) = 10$.   Hence, the resource requirement for project 1 is satisfied.   Three $(= 13 - 10)$ units of select subgrade are still available at pit 1 and are entered in the $(1,2)$ position in the matrix (see Table 4-2); that is, $x_{12} = \min (a_2, b_1 - x_{11}) = 3$.

Project 2 still requires $a_2 - x_{12} = 5$ units of subgrade.   Since pit 1 has been depleted, we examine the available subgrade at pit 2.   Of the 16 units available, we assign $5(= x_{22})$ to project 2.   The remaining 11 units available at pit 2 are assigned to project 3, that is, $x_{23} = 11$.   Continuing in this manner, we assign $x_{33} = 1$ and $x_{34} = 16$ to complete the initial feasible solution (Table 4-2).   Zero entries are assumed in the blank cells.   The solution in Table 4-2 results in a total of 223 hundreds of truckload miles.

Another, and often more desirable, initial solution can be obtained by the *minimum-cost rule*.   The first assignment is made to the cell with the lowest unit cost, and so on.

We next consider a simple procedure to test the initial basic feasible solution for optimality.

Consider one of the *nonbasic cells*, say $(1,3)$, that is, $x_{13} = 0$ for the current solution.   We permit x_{13} to enter the basis by forming a loop, as shown by the dashed lines in Table 4-2.   Beginning in the $(1,3)$ cell, we proceed to a sequence of *basic cells* (through a series of vertical and horizontal movements—$(1,2)$ to $(2,2)$ to $(2,3)$, returning to $(1,3)$.   If we increase the allocation in cell $(3,1)$ by unity, we must decrease the allocation in cell $(1,2)$ by unity, so that the row total is unchanged; this, in turn, requires an increase of unity in the allocation to cell $(2,2)$ to keep the same column total, etc.   The net change in cost for increasing the allocation to cell $(1,3)$ by unity, the *unit penalty*, is $c_{13} - c_{12} + c_{22} - c_{23} = 8 - 9 + 1 - 7 = -7$.   This means that for every unit increase in x_{13}, the total haul distance will be reduced by 7 units.   Appropriate loops and the corresponding unit penalties can be found for each of the nonbasic cells, as shown below.

Non-basic cell	Loop	Associated unit penalty
(1,3)	(1,3) → (1,2) → (2,2) → (2,3) → (1,3)	$8 - 9 + 1 - 7 = -7$
(1,4)	(1,4) → (3,4) → (3,3) → (2,3) → (2,2) → (1,2) → (1,4)	$16 - 5 + 4 - 7 + 1 - 9 = 0$
(2,1)	(2,1) → (2,2) → (1,2) → (1,1) → (2,1)	$15 - 1 + 9 - 3 = 20$
(2,4)	(2,4) → (3,4) → (3,3) → (2,3) → (2,4)	$17 - 5 + 4 - 7 = 9$
(3,1)	(3,1) → (1,1) → (1,2) → (2,2) → (2,3) → (3,3) → (3,1)	$12 - 3 + 9 - 1 + 7 - 4 = 20$
(3,2)	(3,2) → (3,3) → (2,3) → (2,2) → (3,2)	$19 - 4 + 7 - 1 = 21$

The positive outcomes associated with the last four nonbasic cells indicate that corresponding nonzero assignments will increase z from its current value of 223. The zero-unit-penalty cell (1,4) implies that z cannot be altered by an assignment to that cell. Therefore, cell (1,3) is chosen to enter the basis since it allows for the greatest improvement in total cost.

The largest assignment that can be made to cell (1,3) is the minimum of the assignments associated with the basic cells in the even positions of the respective loop (1,3). In the example, min $(x_{12},x_{23}) = x_{12} = 3$. A change in the allocation from pit 1 to project 3 necessitates changes in the other allocations of the corresponding loop. The result is shown in Table 4-3. Note that x_{13} has entered the basis at 3 while x_{12} is now nonbasic at zero.

The new value of z is $(3)(10) + (8)(3) + (1)(8) + (7)(8) + (4)(1) + (5)(16)$ $= 202$. Again, loops are formed for each nonbasic cell to find:

Nonbasic cell	Loop	Associated unit penalty
(1,2)	(1,2) → (1,3) → (2,3) → (2,2) → (1,2)	$9 - 8 + 7 - 1 = 7$
(1,4)	(1,4) → (3,4) → (3,3) → (1,3) → (1,4)	$16 - 5 + 4 - 8 = 7$
(2,1)	(2,1) → (1,1) → (1,3) → (2,3) → (2,1)	$15 - 3 + 8 - 7 = 13$
(2,4)	(2,4) → (2,3) → (3,3) → (3,4) → (2,4)	$17 - 7 + 4 - 5 = 9$
(3,1)	(3,1) → (3,3) → (1,3) → (1,1) → (3,1)	$12 - 4 + 8 - 3 = 13$
(3,2)	(3,2) → (3,3) → (2,3) → (2,2) → (3,2)	$19 - 4 + 7 - 1 = 21$

Since all the associated unit penalties are positive, the assignments of Table 4-3 constitute a unique optimal solution with a value $z_{opt} = 202$. If one or more of the associated unit penalties in the above tabulation had been zero, it would mean that alternate optima exist. These optimal solutions can be determined by making allocations to the associated cells.

A little reflection shows that when evaluating the associated unit penalties, the sense in which the loop is traversed is inconsequential. Also, the loop

Table 4-3   Allocations after first iteration

Project

		1	2	3	4	
	1	$x_{11} = 10$		$x_{13} = 3$		13
Pit	2		$x_{22} = 8$	$x_{23} = 8$		16
	3			$x_{33} = 1$	$x_{34} = 16$	17
		10	8	12	16	

associated with each nonbasic cell is unique, although these loops may be tricky to identify [15].   A technique for determining the associated penalties without specifically finding the loops is described in Ackoff and Sasieni [1, p. 130].   Also Prob. 5-8 suggests the derivation of another technique.

As in linear-programming problems, the solution of the transportation problem is marred by degeneracy (see [1, p. 135]).   Degeneracy can be recognized by a feasible solution with fewer than $m + n - 1$ positive-valued basic cells and may be encountered either when obtaining the initial feasible solution or at subsequent iterations.   With the northwest-corner rule, degeneracy occurs when the assignment to a cell [exception: cell (m,n)] satisfies both the required and the available quantities.   Assigning either of the adjacent cells (to the right or below) as a basic cell with a zero allocation resolves the difficulty.   When degeneracy occurs in an iteration, it is because there is a tie between the basic cells of the entering basic variable's loop.   Again, if it is assumed that all but one of these cells remain in the basis at zero value, the problem of degeneracy will be alleviated.

Transportation-type linear-programming problems are divided into two classes; *balanced* and *unbalanced*.   A balanced problem is one for which

$$\sum_{j=1}^{n} a_j = \sum_{i=1}^{m} b_i$$

that is, the total resource required equals the total of the resource available. The previous example is balanced since the two sums equal 46 (see Table 4-1). Unbalanced problems are transformed to balanced ones through the addition of a dummy row or column to absorb the imbalance.   For example, suppose that the required resources $a_1, \ldots, a_4$ in Table 4-1 are replaced by 10, 4, 12, and 11, respectively.   Now,

$$\sum_{j=1}^{4} a_j = 37 \quad \text{and} \quad \sum_{i=1}^{3} b_i = 46$$

Table 4-4　Balancing a transportation problem

Project

		1	2	3	4	*Dummy*	
	1	3	9	8	16	0	13
Pit	2	15	1	7	17	0	16
	3	12	19	4	5	0	17
		10	4	12	11	9	46

Table 4-4 includes a dummy (zero cost) column, which is used to balance the problem; the loop procedure is the same.

The next example suggests the solution to the haul-cost problem formulated in Example 3-8.

Example 4-2　Unbalanced transportation problem　Note that the transportation-type problem in Example 3-8 is unbalanced.　Using a dummy column, the data are expressed in the haul-cost matrix of Table 4-5.　The techniques of the preceding example are applicable, and the reader can verify the optimal solutions given in Chap. 3 (Prob. 4-3 at the end of this chapter).

It sometimes happens that the unit costs c_{ij} are not constant over the entire range of the decision variables x_{ij} as we have tacitly assumed.　This amounts to nonlinearities in the objective function, which for simple cases might be solved through a succession of transportation problems. Otherwise, integer linear programming (Sec. 4-6) or piecewise linear programming (Sec. 5-6) may be helpful.

Table 4-5　Haul-cost matrix for Example 3-8

To station

	Sta	3	4	5	6	*Dummy*	*Available*
	3	0	1.7	3.2	6.0	0	30
	B	14.3	12.0	13.5	16.3	0	300
From							
station	6	6.8	4.5	2.0	0	0	10
	7	8.3	6.0	3.5	1.5	0	100
Required		30	120	140	50	100	440

4-2 THE ASSIGNMENT PROBLEM

Allocations must sometimes be integral units, as in the assignment of men (or machines) to a like number of jobs with one man to a job. If $b_i = a_j = 1$ for all i and j and if $m = n$, then the transportation problem of the last section becomes an *assignment problem*. For this coefficient matrix, an even more efficient solution procedure has been devised. We illustrate the procedure with an example.

Example 4-3   Crew assignments   Four jobs are to be completed by four shop crews. The superintendent's estimates of the times the crews will require to complete the jobs are arranged in an *effectiveness* matrix:

Job	Crew 1	2	3	4
A	10	25	16	11
B	13	26	7	21
C	35	19	18	16
D	19	26	24	10

How should the jobs be assigned, one to a crew, to minimize the total time required?

The procedure for obtaining an optimal solution is a series of elementary matrix operations based upon the theorem [15, p. 186]:

> In an assignment problem, if a constant is added to (or subtracted from) every element of a row (or a column) in the effectiveness matrix, then the assignment that minimizes the effectiveness of the reduced matrix also minimizes the effectiveness of the original matrix.

For the given matrix, the smallest element of each row is subtracted from each element in that row and then the smallest element in each column is subtracted from each element in that column. The following results are obtained:

By operation on rows,

	1	2	3	4
A	0	15	6	1
B	6	19	0	14
C	19	3	2	0
D	9	16	14	0

And by operation on columns,

	1	2	3	4
A	⓪	12	6	1
B	6	16	⓪	14
C	19	⓪	2	0
D	9	13	14	⓪

From the last reduced matrix, the assignment with a total value of zero mini-mizes the reduced effectiveness matrix.   Thus

Job	Crew
A	1
B	3
C	2
D	4

According to the theorem cited, this assignment also minimizes the initial matrix.

When more than one 0 occurs in several of the columns or rows of the reduced matrix, the following procedure, outlined by Ackoff and Sasieni [1], may be used.

1.   Draw the minimum number of horizontal and vertical lines necessary to cover all zeros at least once; i.e., draw the line which covers the most zeros first, etc.   In an $n \times n$ matrix, fewer than n lines will cover all zeros only when there is no immediate solution at value zero among them. For example,

$$
\begin{array}{ccccc}
3 & 0 & 1 & 2 & 4 \\
0 & 2 & 4 & 0 & 3 \\
5 & 7 & 0 & 0 & 0 \\
0 & 2 & 1 & 3 & 2 \\
2 & 3 & 4 & 0 & 2
\end{array}
$$

4 lines, 5 × 5 matrix: no immediate optimal solution exists

2.   Find the smallest entry which does not have a line through it.   Here it is unity at (4,3).   Subtract this entry from all elements having no lines

through them. Also, add this value to each entry at the intersection of any two lines. The new matrix is

```
4 0 1 3 4
0 1 3 0 2
6 7 0 1 0
0 1 0 3 1
2 2 3 0 1
```

Note that this procedure has placed a zero at (4,3) and removed the zero at (3,4).

3. Is there a solution among the new zeros? If not, repeat steps 1 and 2 until a solution at value zero is achieved.

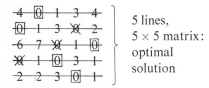

5 lines,
5×5 matrix:
optimal
solution

**Optimal
assignment**

Job	Crew
A	2
B	1
C	5
D	3
E	4

Alternative selections of lines yield the same solution as long as the minimum number of lines required to cover all zeros is used. With matrices of higher dimensionality, it sometimes happens that two (or more) zeros will occur in each of two (or more) columns and rows. In that case, the optimal solution is not unique and alternative optimal solutions exist.

Often, the number of origins (men) exceeds the number of destinations (jobs) while the coefficients a_i and b_i remain at unity. If there were m crews available for n jobs ($m > n$), the efficiency matrix would no longer be square. Situations of this type are handled by additions of *dummy* jobs at zero cost. The converted matrix is square, and the least efficient crew will be assigned the dummy task, i.e., the crew is not assigned.

Assignment problems requiring maximization or minimization are solved in a similar manner by first subtracting the largest element in the entire matrix from all elements. Neglecting the negative signs, this converts all values to "relative costs," and the solution proceeds. The total profit must be computed from values in the original matrix corresponding to the optimal assignments. Additional details appear in [2].

4-3 DUALITY

Associated with every linear-programming problem (the *primal*) is another linear-programming problem called its *dual*. If the primal involves n variables and m constraints, the dual involves n constraints and m variables. The solution to either is sufficient for readily obtaining the solution to the other. In fact, it is immaterial which is designated the primal since the dual of a dual is the primal. The proofs of these assertions appear in Hadley [9].

Suppose that the primal problem is

$$\text{Max:} \quad z'_p = c_1 x_1 + \cdots + c_n x_n \tag{5}$$

$$\text{Subject to:} \quad a_{11} x_1 + a_{12} x_2 + \cdots + a_{1n} x_n \leqslant b_1$$
$$\cdots\cdots\cdots\cdots\cdots\cdots\cdots\cdots\cdots\cdots\cdots \tag{6}$$
$$a_{m1} x_1 + a_{m2} x_2 + \cdots + a_{mn} x_n \leqslant b_m$$

$$x_j \geqslant 0 \quad j = 1, \ldots, n \tag{7}$$

The dual problem is defined by

$$\text{Min:} \quad z_d = b_1 y_1 + \cdots + b_m y_m \tag{8}$$

$$\text{Subject to:} \quad a_{11} y_1 + a_{21} y_2 + \cdots + a_{m1} y_m \geqslant c_1$$
$$\cdots\cdots\cdots\cdots\cdots\cdots\cdots\cdots\cdots\cdots\cdots \tag{9}$$
$$a_{1n} y_1 + a_{2n} y_2 + \cdots + a_{mn} y_m \geqslant c_n$$

$$y_i \geqslant 0 \quad i = 1, \ldots, m \tag{10}$$

The principal characteristics are:

1. The primal variables, Eq. (7), are replaced by m dual variables, Eq. (10).
2. The coefficient matrix of a_{ij}'s in Eqs. (6) is transposed to the a_{ji}'s of Eqs. (9).
3. The b_i and c_j in Eqs. (5) and (6) are interchanged in Eqs. (8) and (9).
4. The inequality signs in Eqs. (6) are reversed in Eqs. (9).
5. The maximization of objective (5) is replaced by a minimization in objective (8).

The dual representation of Eqs. (8) to (10) is called the *symmetric dual* and has the characteristics:

1. The primal constraints are of the forms

$$\sum_{j=1}^{n} a_{ij} x_j \geqslant b_i \qquad \text{minimization objective}$$

or

$$\sum_{j=1}^{n} a_{ij} x_j \leqslant b_i \qquad \text{maximization objective}$$

with corresponding dual constraints

$$\sum_{i=1}^{m} a_{ij} y_i \leqslant c_j \qquad \text{maximization objective}$$

or

$$\sum_{i=1}^{m} a_{ij} y_i \geqslant c_j \qquad \text{minimization objective}$$

respectively.

2. The nonnegativity condition applies to the dual variables as well as to the primal variables.

When required, equality constraints can be replaced by pairs of inequality constraints. For example, $3x_1 + x_2 = 4$ can be replaced by the pair $3x_1 + x_2 \geqslant 4$ and $3x_1 + x_2 \leqslant 4$. Multiplication of an inequation by -1 will reverse the inequality sign as appropriate. Therefore, conversion to a symmetric dual form is easily done and the simplex algorithm can be used to obtain solutions.

Consider the following illustration: The primal problem is

$$\text{Max:} \quad z'_p = x_1 + 4x_2$$
$$\text{Subject to:} \quad 3x_1 + 2x_2 \leqslant 6$$
$$2x_1 + x_2 = 5$$
$$x_1 - 3x_2 \geqslant 7$$
$$x_1, x_2 \geqslant 0$$

or, equivalently,

$$\text{Max:} \quad z'_p = x_1 + 4x_2$$
$$\text{Subject to:} \quad 3x_1 + 2x_2 \leqslant 6$$
$$2x_1 + x_2 \leqslant 5$$
$$-2x_1 - x_2 \leqslant -5$$
$$-x_1 + 3x_2 \leqslant -7$$
$$x_1, x_2 \geqslant 0$$

Note that the b_i in the primal need not be positive because we shall not solve the primal directly. The dual is written

Min: $z_d = 6y_1 + 5(y_2 - y_3) - 7y_4$

Subject to: $3y_1 + 2(y_2 - y_3) - y_4 \geqslant 1$
$2y_1 + (y_2 - y_3) + 3y_4 \geqslant 4$
$y_1, y_2, y_3, y_4 \geqslant 0$

Incidentally, it is not necessary to replace equality constraints by inequality pairs since the former will not affect the inequalities in the dual. However, if the ith constraint is left as an equality, then the ith variable of the dual is unrestricted in sign. Similarly, if the jth variable of the primal is unrestricted, the jth constraint of the dual is an equality. Hence, the dual of the previous example might be written, equivalently,

Min: $z_d = 6y_1 + 5y_5 - 7y_4$

Subject to: $3y_1 + 2y_5 - y_4 \geqslant 1$
$2y_1 + y_5 + 3y_4 \geqslant 4$
$y_1, y_4 \geqslant 0$
y_5 unrestricted in sign

It remains to determine how the optimal solution of the primal is obtained from the optimal solution of the dual. First, suppose that we multiply the successive inequalities (9) by $x_1, x_2, \ldots, x_n$, respectively, and add. Since the x_j's are restricted to be nonnegative, upon rearranging we obtain

$$y_1(a_{11} x_1 + a_{12} x_2 + \cdots + a_{1n} x_n) + y_2(a_{21} x_1 + a_{22} x_2 + \cdots + a_{2n} x_n)$$
$$+ \cdots + y_m(a_{m1} x_1 + a_{m2} x_2 + \cdots + a_{mn} x_n) \geqslant c_1 x_1 + c_2 x_2$$
$$+ \cdots + c_n x_n = z'_p \quad (11)$$

From inequations (6), each quantity in parentheses is less than its corresponding value of b, and it follows that

$$y_1 b_1 + y_2 b_2 + \cdots + y_m b_m \geqslant c_1 x_1 + c_2 x_2 + \cdots + c_n x_n$$

In other words, $z_d \geqslant z'_p$ for all $(x_1, \ldots, x_n)$ and $(y_1, \ldots, y_m)$ which satisfy Eqs. (5) to (10). Therefore, a set of x's and y's such that $z'_p = z_d$ maximizes z'_p while minimizing z_d; that is, the optimal (minimum) value of the dual is also the optimal (maximum) value of the primal.

Using a theorem due to Dantzig and Orden [9], the optimal values of the basic variables of the primal can be obtained from the solution to the dual. The theorem asserts that if the ith dual constraint is an inequation, then the corresponding ith primal variable is nonbasic, i.e., it vanishes. Also, if the ith dual variable is positive, then the ith primal constraint is satisfied at equality. Thus the values of primal variables are obtained by solving simultaneously the set of primal constraints for which the corresponding dual variables are positive.   A convenient way to obtain the primal variables utilizes the final dual tableau.   The ith primal variable equals the objective coefficient of the $(m + i)$th slack (or excess) variable in the final dual tableau [9].

Consider an example.

Example 4-4   Plastic analysis and weight minimization of a rigid frame
A three-member rigid frame is shown in Fig. 4-2.   Determine the plastic-moment capacities of the beam and columns (Mp_b and Mp_c) for minimum total frame weight.   Use limit analysis and assume a linear relationship between the plastic moments and the weight per unit length of the members.

A linear-programming solution for this class of problems was introduced by Prager [13].   Rubinstein and Karagozian [14] have extended the use of linear programming to the plastic-limit design of multistory buildings. The (linearized) weight w appears in the objective function

$$\text{Min:}\quad w = 40Mp_c + 30Mp_b$$

Figure 4-3 shows three possible collapse mechanisms and the six corresponding linear inequalities expressed in terms of the plastic moments in the columns and the beam.   The mechanism constraints are obtained using principles of virtual work.   The virtual work W and the maximum internal energy U are given in Fig. 4-3.

The problem is formulated as

$$\text{Min:}\quad w = 40Mp_c + 30Mp_b \tag{12}$$

$$\text{Subject to:}\qquad
\left.\begin{aligned}
4Mp_b &\geqslant 30\\
2Mp_c + 2Mp_b &\geqslant 30
\end{aligned}\right\}\quad \text{beam mechanisms}$$

$$\left.\begin{aligned}
2Mp_c + 2Mp_b &\geqslant 20\\
4Mp_c &\geqslant 20
\end{aligned}\right\}\quad \text{sway mechanisms} \tag{13}$$

$$\left.\begin{aligned}
2Mp_c + 4Mp_b &\geqslant 50\\
4Mp_c + 2Mp_b &\geqslant 50
\end{aligned}\right\}\quad \text{combined mechanisms}$$

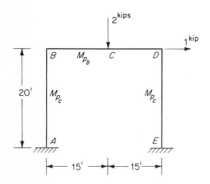

Fig. 4-2   Three-membered rigid frame.

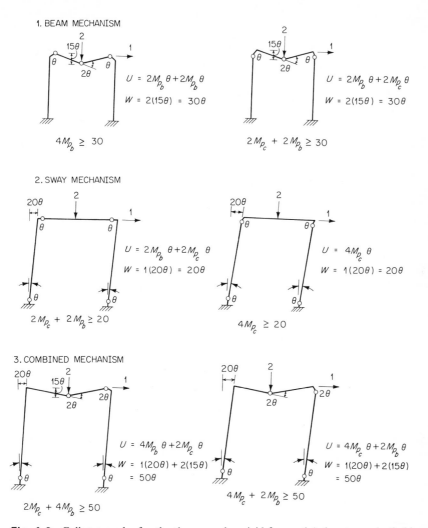

Fig. 4-3 Collapse modes for the three-member rigid frame; (o) denotes a plastic-hinge location.

$$Mp_c \text{ and } Mp_b \geqslant 0 \qquad (14)$$

Figure 4-4 illustrates the graphical solution to the problem.

To illustrate the duality theorem, we solve the dual of the above problem using the simplex technique. Considering expressions (12) to (14) as the primal problem, the dual problem can be formulated as

$$\text{Max:} \quad z'_d = 30y_1 + 30y_2 + 20y_3 + 20y_4 + 50y_5 + 50y_6 \qquad (15)$$

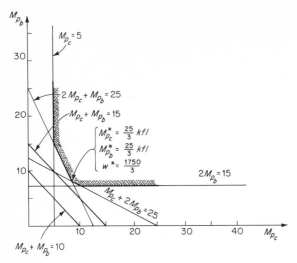

Fig. 4-4 Graphical solution.

Subject to:
$$2y_2 + 2y_3 + 4y_4 + 2y_5 + 4y_6 \leqslant 40$$
$$4y_1 + 2y_2 + 2y_3 + 4y_5 + 2y_6 \leqslant 30 \tag{16}$$
$$y_i \geqslant 0 \qquad i = 1, 2, \ldots, 6$$

Slack variables y_7 and y_8 are added to inequation (16) to obtain a canonical form. The resulting simplex tableaus are shown in Table 4-6.

Table 4-6 Simplex tableaus

		y_1	y_2	y_3	y_4	y_5	y_6	y_7	y_8
	40		2	2	4	2	4	1	
(0)	30	4	2	2		④	2		1
	0	−30	−30	−20	−20	−50	−50		
	25	−2	1	1	4		③	1	−1/2
(1)	15/2	1	1/2	1/2		1	1/2		1/4
	375	20	−5	5	−20		−25		25/2
	25/3	−2/3	1/3	1/3	4/3		1	1/3	−1/6
(2)	10/3	4/3	1/3	1/3	−2/3	1		−1/6	1/3
$z = \dfrac{1{,}750}{3}$		10/3	10/3	40/3	40/3			25/3	25/3

The solution obtained at the second iteration is $y_1 = y_2 = y_3 = y_4 = 0$, $y_5 = 10/3$, $y_6 = 25/3$, and $z_{max} = 1,750/3$ in agreement with $w^* = 1,750/3$ in Fig. 4-4. The solution to the primal problem can be obtained directly from the cost coefficients in the last tableau, i.e., corresponding to the slack variables y_7 and y_8, $Mp_c = 25/3$ and $Mp_b = 25/3$. Alternatively, corresponding to the basic dual variables y_5 and y_6, we must have equalities in the primal constraints, that is, $2Mp_c + 4Mp_b = 50$ and $4Mp_c + 2Mp_b = 50$. Solving this set of equations simultaneously yields the optimal solution.

This example illustrates the possibility of utilizing the dual to achieve computational efficiencies. As a rule of thumb, *an additional constraint requires more computational effort than an additional variable.* Thus, if the primal should have a large number of constraints and relatively few variables, its dual will probably require less computation since the numbers of variables and constraints are interchanged.

An economic interpretation of the dual problem is sometimes useful. The primal problem can be viewed as one of maximizing the volume (value) of the output (profit), z'_p, such that input limitations (resource availabilities) are not exceeded. The dual can be viewed as one of minimizing total input, z_d, subject to conditions which ensure that the value of each unit of output exceeds the corresponding value of the required inputs. Also, the optimal solution of the dual indicates the rate of change of z'_p with respect to the available resources b_i, $i = 1, \ldots, m$.

4-4 DECOMPOSITION

Large linear-programming problems, in numbers of variables and/or constraints, are quite common in practice. This section shares the motivation of the previous sections in the sense that certain properties of the constraint-coefficient matrix can be utilized to yield significant computational advantages. The decomposition principle of Dantzig and Wolfe ([4] and [5]) can, in appropriate circumstances, significantly reduce the number of constraint equations. Enormous computational gains stem from replacing the original problem by a series of smaller problems. Our discussion of decomposition will be facilitated by considering two preliminaries: the concept of a convex combination of points and a matrix notation for linear-programming problems.

A segment was defined in Sec. 2-2 as the collection of points $P(\mu)$ whose coordinates in an n-dimensional space are given by

$$x_j^{(\mu)} = \mu x_j^{(1)} + (1 - \mu) x_j^{(2)} \qquad 0 \leqslant \mu \leqslant 1; j = 1, 2, \ldots, n \qquad (17)$$

and joins the points $x_j^{(1)}$ and $x_j^{(2)}$. The generalization to a convex combination of r points $x_j^{(1)}, x_j^{(2)}, \ldots, x_j^{(r)}$ is written

$$x_j^{(\mu_j)} = \mu_{j1} x_j^{(1)} + \mu_{j2} x_j^{(2)} + \cdots + \mu_{jr} x_j^{(r)} \qquad (18)$$

where

$$\sum_{j=1}^{r} \mu_{jk} = 1 \quad \text{and} \quad 0 \leqslant \mu_{jk} \leqslant 1; j = 1, \ldots, n$$

This means that if the r points $x_j^{(1)}, \ldots, x_j^{(r)}$ belong to a convex set, then the convex combination $x_j^{(\mu_j)}$ is also a point in the convex set—in analogy with the definition of a segment.

Our interest in the convex combination stems from the fact that if the $x^{(k)}, k = 1, \ldots, r$, represent the coordinates of each of the r vertices of a convex set, then the convex combination can generate every point of the convex set by an appropriate choice of the μ_{jk}.

With respect to matrix notation, it is common to express the standard linear-programming form (Sec. 2-1) as

Min: $z = \mathbf{cx}$

Subject to: $\mathbf{Ax} = \mathbf{b}$ and $\mathbf{x} \geqslant 0$

where $\mathbf{A}$ denotes the $m \times n$ constraint-coefficient matrix

$$\begin{bmatrix} A_{11} & A_{12} & \cdots & A_{1n} \\ A_{21} & A_{22} & \cdots & A_{2n} \\ \vdots & & & \vdots \\ A_{m1} & A_{m2} & \cdots & A_{mn} \end{bmatrix}$$

$\mathbf{c}$ denotes the $1 \times n$ cost-coefficient matrix $(c_1 c_2 \ldots c_n)$, and $\mathbf{x}$ and $\mathbf{b}$ denote the $n \times 1$ and $m \times 1$ matrices

$$\begin{bmatrix} x_1 \\ \cdot \\ \cdot \\ \cdot \\ x_n \end{bmatrix} \quad \text{and} \quad \begin{bmatrix} b_1 \\ \cdot \\ \cdot \\ \cdot \\ b_m \end{bmatrix}$$

respectively.

The decomposition principle capitalizes upon a constraint-coefficient matrix $\mathbf{A}$ of the (partitioned) form

$$\mathbf{A} = \begin{bmatrix} \mathbf{A}_1 & \mathbf{A}_2 & \cdots & \cdots & \mathbf{A}_l \\ \boldsymbol{\beta}_1 & 0 & \cdots & \cdots & 0 \\ 0 & \boldsymbol{\beta}_2 & 0 & \cdots & 0 \\ \vdots & & & & \vdots \\ 0 & \cdots & \cdots & \cdots & \boldsymbol{\beta}_l \end{bmatrix} \tag{19}$$

where $\boldsymbol{\beta}_1, \ldots, \boldsymbol{\beta}_l$ are partitions of $\mathbf{A}$. Consider, as an illustration, the linear-programming problem

$$\text{Max:} \quad z' = 5x_1 + 3x_2 + 5x_3 + 2.5x_4$$

$$\begin{aligned}
\text{Subject to:} \quad 2x_1 + 3x_2 + 3x_3 + 2x_4 &\leqslant 15 \\
x_1 + x_2 &\leqslant 4 \\
2x_1 + x_2 &\leqslant 6 \\
2x_3 + 5x_4 &\leqslant 10 \\
x_3 &\leqslant 4 \quad \text{and} \quad x_j \geqslant 0; j = 1,2,3,4
\end{aligned}$$

The **A** matrix can conveniently be partitioned in the form

$$\mathbf{A} = \left[\begin{array}{cc:cc}
2 & 3 & 3 & 2 \\
1 & 1 & & \\
2 & 1 & \multicolumn{2}{c}{\mathbf{0}} \\ \hdashline
\multicolumn{2}{c:}{\mathbf{0}} & 2 & 5 \\
 & & 1 & 0
\end{array}\right]$$

In this case, $l = 1$ and

$$\mathbf{A}_1 = [2 \quad 3] \qquad \mathbf{A}_2 = [3 \quad 2]$$

$$\boldsymbol{\beta}_1 = \begin{bmatrix} 1 & 1 \\ 2 & 1 \end{bmatrix} \quad \text{and} \quad \boldsymbol{\beta}_2 = \begin{bmatrix} 2 & 5 \\ 1 & 0 \end{bmatrix}$$

Now, suppose one of the "rows" of the partitioned form, Eq. (19), containing a $\boldsymbol{\beta}$ matrix is postmultiplied (on the right) by the variable matrix **x** and set equal to the corresponding row(s) of the **b** matrix. We have a subset of constraint equations which, in conjunction with the nonnegativity condition and the objective function, defines a subsidiary linear-programming problem. There are exactly l such subsidiary constraint sets as

$$(0 \cdots 0 \, \boldsymbol{\beta}_t \, 0 \cdots 0) \, \mathbf{x} = \mathbf{b}_t \qquad t = 1,2,\ldots,l$$

where $\mathbf{b}_t$ is the corresponding "tth (partitioned) row" of the **b** matrix.

In the example, the common objective function is

$$\text{Max:} \quad z' = 5x_1 + 3x_2 + 5x_3 + 2.5x_4$$

The two subsidiary constraint sets are:

1. $\begin{aligned} x_1 + x_2 &\leqslant 4 \\ 2x_1 + x_2 &\leqslant 6 \end{aligned}$

    2. $\begin{aligned} 2x_3 + 5x_4 &\leqslant 10 \\ x_3 &\leqslant 4 \end{aligned}$

Now, for *every* subsidiary problem, we determine the coordinates of every vertex. Let r_1 be the number of vertices for the first subproblem, r_2 for the second, etc., and let $\mathbf{x}_1^{(1)},\ldots,\mathbf{x}_1^{(r_1)},\ldots,\mathbf{x}^{(r_l)}$ be the coordinates for each vertex of each of the l convex sets.

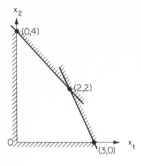

Fig. 4-5 Set of feasible solutions.

The set of feasible solutions for subproblem 1 of the example is shown in Fig. 4-5. The coordinate matrices corresponding to the vertices of the subsidiary convex set are

$$\begin{bmatrix} x_1 \\ x_2 \end{bmatrix} = \begin{bmatrix} 0 \\ 0 \end{bmatrix} \quad \text{and} \quad \begin{bmatrix} 3 \\ 0 \end{bmatrix} \quad \text{and} \quad \begin{bmatrix} 2 \\ 2 \end{bmatrix} \quad \text{and} \quad \begin{bmatrix} 0 \\ 4 \end{bmatrix}$$

Similarly, the coordinate matrices of the second subproblem are

$$\begin{bmatrix} x_3 \\ x_4 \end{bmatrix} = \begin{bmatrix} 0 \\ 0 \end{bmatrix} \quad \text{and} \quad \begin{bmatrix} 4 \\ 0 \end{bmatrix} \quad \text{and} \quad \begin{bmatrix} 4 \\ \frac{2}{5} \end{bmatrix} \quad \text{and} \quad \begin{bmatrix} 0 \\ 2 \end{bmatrix}$$

We now form a convex combination of the vertices for each of the subsidiary convex sets. These convex combinations are capable of representing every point of the respective convex set, as we mentioned earlier, according to the selection of the coefficients μ. An essential observation is that the optimal solution to the original (composed) problem must be consistent with the solutions to the subsidiary problems. More specifically, each set of points x_j, representing every point in the feasible region of the jth subsidiary problem, can be expressed as a convex combination of the coordinates of every vertex of the "composed" convex set.

Thus,

$$\mathbf{x}_j = \mu_{j1} \mathbf{x}_j^{(1)} + \mu_{j2} \mathbf{x}_j^{(2)} + \cdots + \mu_{jr_j} \mathbf{x}_j^{(r_j)} \qquad j = 1, 2, \ldots, l$$

where, again, there are r_j vertices in the jth convex set and n variables in the $\mathbf{x}$ matrix, $x_1, x_2, \ldots, x_n$, and the nonnegative coefficients μ_{jk} equal unity when summed over k.

For the example, we have

$$\mathbf{x}_1 = \begin{bmatrix} x_1 \\ x_2 \end{bmatrix} = \mu_{11} \begin{bmatrix} x_1^{(1)} \\ x_2^{(1)} \end{bmatrix} + \cdots + \mu_{1r_1} \begin{bmatrix} x_1^{(r_1)} \\ x_2^{(r_1)} \end{bmatrix}$$

with $r_1 = 4$, and so on.

Now, in the above expressions for x_j as convex combinations of vertex coordinates, *we can regard the μ's as variables.* Therefore, we can replace the original problem formulation with the following one:

1. Take the original objective function and substitute for each variable set x_j its convex combination. Thus the original objective is now expressed in terms of the variables μ.
2. Discard the portion of the original constraint set corresponding to the l subsidiary linear-programming problems. Retain only the portion

$$(A_1 A_2 \cdots A_l)(x) = (b_0)$$

where b_0 is the matrix corresponding to the first row $(A_1 \cdots A_l)$ of the partitioned b matrix, and replace x by the convex combinations used in step 1.
3. Augment the constraint set of step 2 by including the constraints that the μ's sum to unity.
4. Add the nonnegativity condition for all the μ's.

These steps define a new linear-programming problem whose solution enables us to calculate the solution to the original problem.

We write the above as:

1. $z' = \sum\limits_{j=1}^{2} \sum\limits_{k=1}^{r_j} \mu_{jk} c_j x_j^{(k)}$

2. $\sum\limits_{j=1}^{2} \sum\limits_{k=1}^{r_j} \mu_{jk} A_j x_j^{(k)} \leqslant b_0$

3. $\sum\limits_{k=1}^{r_j} \mu_{jk} = 1 \qquad j = 1, 2$

4. $\mu_{jk} \geqslant 0 \qquad$ all k and j

or, more explicitly,

Max: $z' = 0\mu_{11} + 15\mu_{12} + 16\mu_{13} + 12\mu_{14} + 0\mu_{21} + 20\mu_{22}$
$$+ 21\mu_{23} + 5\mu_{24}$$

Subject to: $6\mu_{12} + 10\mu_{13} + 12\mu_{14} + 12\mu_{22} + 12.8\mu_{23} + 4\mu_{24} \leqslant 15$
$$\mu_{11} + \mu_{12} + \mu_{13} + \mu_{14} = 1$$
$$\mu_{21} + \mu_{22} + \mu_{23} + \mu_{24} = 1$$
$$\mu_{ij} \geqslant 0 \qquad \text{all } i \text{ and } j$$

The optimal feasible solution to this linear-programming problem is

$$\mu_{12} = 1 \qquad \mu_{21} = \tfrac{1}{4} \qquad \mu_{22} = \tfrac{3}{4}$$
$$\mu_{11} = \mu_{13} = \mu_{14} = \mu_{23} = \mu_{24} = 0$$

and

$$z'_{max} = 30$$

The x_i's are computed as

$$\begin{bmatrix} x_1 \\ x_2 \end{bmatrix} = 0 \begin{bmatrix} 0 \\ 0 \end{bmatrix} + 1 \begin{bmatrix} 3 \\ 0 \end{bmatrix} + 0 \begin{bmatrix} 2 \\ 2 \end{bmatrix} + 0 \begin{bmatrix} 1 \\ 4 \end{bmatrix} = \begin{bmatrix} 3 \\ 0 \end{bmatrix}$$

and

$$\begin{bmatrix} x_3 \\ x_4 \end{bmatrix} = \tfrac{1}{4} \begin{bmatrix} 0 \\ 0 \end{bmatrix} + \tfrac{3}{4} \begin{bmatrix} 4 \\ 0 \end{bmatrix} + 0 \begin{bmatrix} 4 \\ \tfrac{2}{5} \end{bmatrix} + 0 \begin{bmatrix} 0 \\ 2 \end{bmatrix} = \begin{bmatrix} 3 \\ 0 \end{bmatrix}$$

The efficiency afforded by decomposition arises from the substantial reduction in the number of constraints. The increased costs arising from the increased number of variables is ordinarily very easily offset by the savings from a smaller constraint set. It is important to note that no matter how large the subsidiary problems may be, they can always be replaced by two constraints, one for the convex combination and the other to ensure that the μ's sum to unity.

There is another important point in connection with decomposition. We have said that one should determine the coordinates of every vertex in every subsidiary convex set. Fortunately, this is not necessary when the revised simplex method is used (although saying so helped clarify our discussion). Again, it is more pertinent for the engineer to recognize instances when the decomposition principle may be worthwhile than to have intimate familiarity with the computer routines. For small problems, however, it is feasible to simply enumerate the vertex coordinates and use the simplex method, as we have in the example.

The reader interested in further study of the decomposition principle should consult, in addition to [4] and [5], the work of Gass [7] and Simonnard [16]. Williams [17] provides a treatment for transportation-type problems.

Highway-network problems have recently been solved using decomposition. The following example is based upon a model by Pinnell and Satterly [12].

Example 4-5 Travel-time minimization in a highway network

Although traffic flow tends to seek equilibrium as individual drivers try to minimize their travel time, regulation (i.e., one-way routings, freeway ramp closures, etc.) can sometimes improve the efficiency of a network of arterial streets. The problem is to determine the optimal distribution of peak-hour

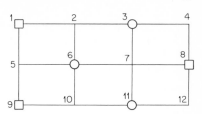

Fig. 4-6 An arterial street network.

traffic flow over an existing network such that individual trip desires are satisfied while the total travel time in the system is minimized.

Consider the arterial street network (Fig. 4-6), where circles represent origins and squares represent destinations. Origins and destinations could, of course, be located at every node in the network, but enough are shown to illustrate the solution technique.

Table 4-7 indicates travel times, c_{ij}, and branch capacities in vehicles per hour, b_{ij}, in the direction of travel from node i to node j.

Table 4-7 Travel times

i	j	c_{ij}	b_{ij}	c_{ji}	b_{ji}
1	2	8	50	9	50
1	5	6	40	8	60
2	3	6	30	·	·
2	6	5	·	·	·
3	4	·	·	·	·
3	·	·	·	8	30
·	·	·	40	11	40
·	·	9	30	13	50
·	10	7	30	12	50
10	11	7	40	10	60
11	12	13	50	10	30

Table 4-8 shows the hourly traffic volume originating at each origin and traveling to the three destinations during peak hours.

Table 4-8 Traffic volume

	Destination		
Origin	1	8	9
3	30	30	55
6	20	70	40
11	30	45	60

If one considers a single origin k, the traffic distribution problem can be written

$$\text{Min:} \quad z_k = \sum_{j=1}^{n} \sum_{i \in I_j} c_{ij} x_{ij}^{(k)} \tag{20}$$

$$\text{Subject to:} \quad \sum_{i \in I_j} x_{ij}^{(k)} - \sum_{i \in I_j} x_{ji}^{(k)} = b_j^{(k)} \tag{21}$$

$$j = 1, 2, \ldots, n$$

where $z_k =$ total traffic volume originating at k
  $x_{ij}^{(k)} =$ volume of traffic originating at k which travels branch $(i \rightarrow j)$
  $b_j^k =$ influx or efflux at jth node arising from origin k. Influx is considered positive, and efflux negative. (All nodes which are neither origins nor destinations for subproblem k will have $b_j^{(k)} = 0$.)
  $c_{ij} =$ travel time from node i to node j

Also, n is the total number of nodes, and the index $i \in I_j$ in Eqs. (20) and (21) indicates that the summation extends over those branches which meet at node j.

Constraint Eq. (21) is similar to Kirchhoff's law for electric current (the sum of vehicles into a node must equal the sum of vehicles out).

The capacity constraints of specific branches provide the "coupling constraints" which tie the subsidiary problems together. The total problem can then be formulated

$$\text{Min:} \quad z = \sum_{k=1}^{2} \sum_{j=1}^{n} \sum_{i \in I_j} c_{ij} x_{ij}^{k}$$

$$\text{Subject to:} \quad \sum_{k=1}^{3} x_{ij}^{k} \leqslant b_{ij} \qquad \text{all } j, k = 3, 6, 11$$

$$\sum_{k=1}^{3} \sum_{i \in I_j} x_{ij}^{k} - \sum_{i \in I_j} x_{ji}^{k} = b_j^{k} \qquad \text{all } j, k = 3, 6, 11$$

$$x_{ij}^{k} \geqslant 0 \qquad \text{all } i, j, k$$

Note that we related the subproblems to origins k rather than to destinations. The choice was arbitrary. If the number of destinations were less than the number of origins, it would be simpler to relate the subproblems to destinations. A similar example with a solution appears in [12].

A more realistic problem than the preceding arises when travel time on each branch is a function of flow volume, that is, $c_{ij}(x_{ij})$. Traffic studies have shown that traffic volume on freeways does not significantly increase travel time until some sharply defined critical volume is reached. For larger volumes, the delay time increases rapidly. On the other hand, travel time on arterial streets having signalized intersections is typically a nonlinear function of traffic volume for a wide range of volumes. The relationship can often be represented by a piecewise linear approximation of the volume–travel-time data for the various branches of the network. The use of piecewise linear approximations of nonlinear data is considered in Sec. 5-6.

4-5 PARAMETRIC LINEAR PROGRAMMING

In practical problems one is interested not only in the solution but also in how the solution changes when parameters change. Indeed, sometimes the latter is more important than the former. Change in the parameters may be either discrete (as, for example, when we are uncertain about which of several choices is the value of a particular parameter) or continuous, when the value of a parameter may be one in a continuum. The study of discrete parameter changes is often called a *sensitivity analysis*, and that of continuous changes is called *parametric programming*.

There are five basic types of parameter changes which affect the solution. They are:

1. Changes in the objective coefficients, c_j
2. Changes in the resource limits, b_i
3. Changes in the constraint coefficients, a_{ij}
4. The effect of including additional constraints
5. The effect of including additional variables

A thorough discussion of these changes, while not necessarily difficult, is beyond our scope. In principle, one could imagine solving a new problem for every change one wishes to explore. Fortunately, for small numbers of changes there are useful shortcuts. Computer programs are available for exploring more extensive problems, but they appear to be neither abundant nor always efficient. Indeed, the subject of parametric programming is still of research interest.

We illustrate a few parametric-programming ideas for the transit-mix example of Chap. 2. Recall that the objective function was $z = 5x_1 + 10x_2$. Suppose that we would like to know by how much the coefficient of x_1 can vary before the optimal solution ($x_1 = 2$, $x_2 = 6$) changes. The dual relationship of Sec. 4-3 furnishes the means. The corresponding dual constraints for this problem are

$$\tfrac{1}{14}y_1 + \tfrac{1}{7}y_2 + y_3 \geqslant 5$$
$$\tfrac{1}{7}y_1 + \tfrac{1}{12}y_2 + y_3 \geqslant 10$$

Since $x_1 = 2$ and $x_2 = 6$, the dual constraints are actually equalities. Also, the second primal constraint is an inequality for this solution, so that $y_2 = 0$. Therefore, the above dual constraints can be rewritten as

$$\tfrac{1}{14}y_1 + y_3 = \tfrac{1}{8}C$$
$$\tfrac{1}{7}y_1 + y_3 = 10$$

Note that the primal objective coefficient of x_1 is the right-hand side of the first equation. Suppose we were to replace this coefficient by a symbol, say C, and solve for y_1 and y_3. For optimality, y_1 and y_3 must be nonnegative; hence, we obtain

$$y_1 = 140 - 14C \geqslant 0 \qquad \text{or} \qquad C \leqslant 10$$

and

$$y_3 = 2C - 10 \geqslant 0 \qquad \text{or} \qquad C \geqslant 5$$

These relations suggest that for $5 \leqslant C \leqslant 10$, the solution $x_1 = 2$, $x_2 = 6$ remains optimal. Suppose, however, that the resource limit C is outside this interval. How might we study the effect upon the optimal solution? Simply by carrying C in the simplex iterations! For example, consider the initial tableau.

Arbitrary C in initial tableau

	x_1	x_2	x_3	x_4	x_5
1	1/14	(1/7)	1		
1	1/7	1/12		1	
8	1	1			1
0	$-C$	-10			

First, suppose we assume that $C < 10$. Therefore, x_2 is chosen to enter the basis with 1/7 as the pivot element. Carrying out the iteration yields the following tableau.

Optimal tableau : $-\infty < C \leqslant 5$

	x_1	x_2	x_3	x_4	x_5
7	1/2	1	7		
5/12	17/168		$-7/12$	1	
1	(1/2)		-7		1
70	$5 - C$		70		

This tableau happens to be optimal provided that $C \leqslant 5$, that is, that cost coefficients are nonnegative. If $C < 5$, the solution is unique; whereas if $C = 5$, alternate optima exist.

If C exceeds 5 (but is less than 10), the previous tableau is nonoptimal and x_1 is marked to enter the basis with 1/2 as the pivot element. Carrying out the next iteration yields:

Optimal tableau: $5 \leqslant C \leqslant 10$

	x_1	x_2	x_3	x_4	x_5
6		1	14		−1
3/14			⑤/⑥	1	−17/84
2	1		−14		2
$60 + 2C$			$140 - 14C$		$-10 + 2C$

which happens to be optimal provided $5 \leqslant C \leqslant 10$. Note, again, the alternate optima for $C = 5$ and $C = 10$. Incidentally, this solution agrees with the dual solution above.

Now suppose that C exceeds 10. Therefore, x_3 is marked to enter the basis with 5/6 as the pivot element. A further iteration yields:

Optimal tableau: $10 \leqslant C < 120/7$

	x_1	x_2	x_3	x_4	x_5
12/5		1		−84/5	12/5
9/35			1	6/5	−17/70
28/5	1			84/5	−7/5
$24 + \dfrac{28}{5}C$				$-168 + \dfrac{84}{5}C$	$24 - \dfrac{7C}{5}$

which is optimal for $10 \leqslant C \leqslant 120/7$.

Now suppose that C exceeds 120/7. Then x_5 enters the basis with 12/5 as the pivot element, and we have:

Optimal tableau: $120/7 \leqslant C < \infty$

	x_1	x_2	x_3	x_4	x_5
1		5/12		-7	1
1/2		17/168	1	$-1/2$	
7C	1			7	
7C	1	$-10 + \dfrac{7C}{12}$		7C	

which is optimal for $C \geqslant 120/7$.

In summary, the optimal solution(s) can be tabulated as:

C	x_1	x_2	z
$-\infty < C \leqslant 5$	0	7	70
$5 \leqslant C \leqslant 10$	2	6	$60 + 2C$
$10 \leqslant C < 120/7$	28/5	12/5	$24 + 28/5C$
$120/7 \leqslant C$	7	0	7C

Having explored the effect of changes in a cost coefficient, we next consider the resource limits. A clever observation reveals that changes in the resource limits can be treated in the same manner as changes in the cost coefficients. Specifically, note that changing the b_i's is equivalent to changing the cost coefficients of the dual. Thus the technique of the preceding paragraphs, when applied to the dual, yields the effect of changes in the resource limits.

Since it is sometimes inconvenient to work with the dual, an alternative means of analysis is useful. Our approach is to express the b_i's as linear functions of a parameter λ and to seek optimal solutions for its various values. Suppose that the estimates of the maximum number of truckloads per hour (resource limits) in the transit-mix example are to be revised. The constraints might be written [see Eqs. (2a') to (3') of Chap. 2]

$$\tfrac{1}{14}x_1 + \tfrac{1}{7}x_2 + x_3 = 1 + \lambda$$
$$\tfrac{1}{7}x_1 + \tfrac{1}{12}x_2 + x_4 = 1 + 2\lambda$$
$$x_1 + x_2 + x_5 = 8 + \lambda$$

where λ denotes the unit of increment in the revised estimates. We wish to know how the solution varies with respect to λ. For the initial tableau, we have:

Arbitrary λ in initial tableau

	x_1	x_2	x_3	x_4	x_5
$1 + \lambda$	1/14	(1/7)	1		
$1 + 2\lambda$	1/7	1/12		1	
$8 + \lambda$	1	1			1
0	-5	-10			

and the next iteration is:

Optimal tableau: $-5/17 \leqslant \lambda \leqslant 1/6$

	x_1	x_2	x_3	x_4	x_5
$7 + 7\lambda$	1/2	1	7		
$5/12 + (17/12)\lambda$	17/168		$-7/12$	1	
$1 - 6\lambda$	1/2		-7		1
$70 + 70\lambda$			70		

This tableau is optimal provided λ is chosen so that there are no infeasibilities. The values of λ for which the resource limits are negative (infeasible) are $\lambda < -1$, $\lambda < -5/17$, and $\lambda > 1/6$, respectively. Clearly, the limits upon λ for which this solution remains feasible are $-5/17 \leqslant \lambda \leqslant 1/6$.

The effect of changes outside these limits is desired next. Specifically, for $-1 < \lambda < -5/17$, an infeasibility exists in the second constraint. Therefore, we multiply the second constraint by -1, and then, to rescue the canonical form, we further multiply that constraint by $12/7$ and eliminate x_3 from the other two constraints. Clearly, x_3 is the only choice for a basic variable. Thus we have the tableau:

Optimal tableau: $-1/2 \leqslant \lambda \leqslant -5/17$

	x_1	x_2	x_3	x_4	x_5
$12 + 24\lambda$	12/7	1		12	
$-5/7 - (17/7)\lambda$	$-17/98$		1	$-12/7$	
$-4 - 23\lambda$	$-5/7$			-12	1
$120 + 240\lambda$	85/7			120	

which can be shown to be optimal for $-1/2 \leqslant \lambda \leqslant -5/17$.

Now suppose that $\lambda > -1/2$. Since the first constraint is limiting, we multiply it by -1 to seek a new canonical form. We obtain

$$-12/7x_1 - x_2 - 12x_4 = -12 - 24\lambda$$

Since the right side is positive and since the coefficients on the left are negative, there is no variable which can be made both basic and nonnegative. Thus, no optimal solution exists for $\lambda < -1/2$.

Now suppose that $\lambda > 1/6$. Returning to the second tableau (for which the objective-function value is $70 + 70\lambda$), we identify the third constraint as limiting. We multiply by $-1/7$ and achieve the canonical form:

Optimal tableau: $\lambda \geqslant 1/6$

	x_1	x_2	x_3	x_4	x_5
$8 + \lambda$	1	1			1
$1/3 + (23/12)\lambda$	5/84			1	$-1/12$
$-1/7 + (6/7)\lambda$	$-1/14$		1		$-1/7$
$80 + 10\lambda$	5				10

Note that for all $\lambda > 1/6$, the solution remains optimal. We summarize as follows:

$-\infty < \lambda < -7/4:$ no optimal solution

$-7/4 \leqslant \lambda \leqslant -5/17:$ $x_1 = x_4 = 0$ $x_2 = 42 + 24\lambda$
$x_3 = -5/7 - 17/7\lambda$ $x_5 = -34 - 23\lambda$
$z = 120 + 240\lambda$

$-5/17 \leqslant \lambda \leqslant 1/6:$ $x_1 = x_3 = 0$ $x_2 = 7 + 7\lambda$
$x_4 = 5/12 + 17/12\lambda$ $x_5 = 1 - 6\lambda$
$z = 70 + 70\lambda$

$1/6 \leqslant \lambda < \infty:$ $x_1 = x_5 = 0$ $x_2 = 8 + \lambda$
$x_3 = -1/7 + 6/7\lambda$ $x_4 = 1/3 + 23/12\lambda$
$z = 80 + 10\lambda$

In this section, we have touched upon two types of parameter changes, namely, changes in the objective coefficients and changes in the resource limits. The principal aim in this section was to familiarize the reader with this area of mathematical programming. Changes in the constraint coefficients and the number of constraints and variables are discussed in many linear-programming texts (e.g., Hadley [9]).

4-6 INTEGER LINEAR PROGRAMMING

Sometimes it is necessary to restrict the variables of a linear-programming problem to integer values. For example, for the number of earth-hauling units to be used with a shovel, only integer solutions are sensible. It cannot be assumed that integerization of the optimal (noninteger) solution is the optimal solution to the integer linear-programming problem. For example, consider the problem

Max: $z' = 9x_1 + 10x_2$

Subject to: $x_1 \leqslant 3$
$2x_1 + 5x_2 \leqslant 15$
$x_1, x_2 \geqslant 0$

and its optimal solution $x_1 = 3$, $x_2 = 1.8$, $z = 45$. Truncating to $x_1 = 3$ and $x_2 = 1$ yields $z = 37$. But this is less than the solution to the integer problem, which is $x_1 = x_2 = 2$, yielding $z = 38$. It cannot even be assumed that the integerized solution is feasible. For example, consider the constraints

$-x_1 + x_2 \leqslant 7\frac{1}{2}$
$2x_1 + x_2 \leqslant 18\frac{1}{2}$

and suppose that the optimal solution has yielded $x_1 = 3\frac{1}{2}$ and $x_2 = 11$. Rounding to $x_1 = 3$, $x_2 = 11$ violates the first constraint; rounding to $x_1 = 4$, $x_2 = 11$ is also infeasible (since the second constraint is violated).

In recent years, some success has been achieved in solving integer linear-programming problems. Efficient methods of solution are not generally available. They are, however, a subject of current research.

The essential idea is to "strip" the convex set of the optimal noninteger solutions (as well as other noninteger solutions) at each iteration until an optimal integer solution is achieved. The technique is illustrated (without proof) for a simple example. The references, particularly the work of Gomory [8] and Balinski [3], provide more details.

Example 4-6 Consider the above problem in the standard form, that is,

Max: $z' = 9x_1 + 10x_2$

Subject to: $x_1 + x_3 = 3$
$2x_1 + 5x_2 + x_4 = 15$
$x_i \geqslant 0 \qquad i = 1, 2, \ldots, 4$

Two iterations of the simplex method yield the following optimal tableau:

	x_1	x_2	x_3	x_4
3	1		1	
$1\frac{4}{5}$		1	$-\frac{2}{5}$	$\frac{1}{5}$
$-z' = 45$			5	2

Consider the constraint equation which has yielded the noninteger solution $x_2 = 1\frac{4}{5}$:

$$x_2 - \tfrac{2}{5}x_3 + \tfrac{1}{5}x_4 = \tfrac{4}{5} + 1$$

or

$$-\tfrac{2}{5}x_3 + \tfrac{1}{5}x_4 = \tfrac{4}{5} + (1 - x_2)$$

Since we wish to have a left-hand side with nonnegative fractional coefficients, we add x_3 to both sides to yield

$$\tfrac{3}{5}x_3 + \tfrac{1}{5}x_4 = \tfrac{4}{5} + (1 - x_2 + x_3) = \tfrac{4}{5} + \text{``an integer''}$$

Clearly, the term "an integer" cannot be negative since x_3 and x_4 and, hence, the left-hand side are nonnegative. It follows that

$$\tfrac{3}{5}x_3 + \tfrac{1}{5}x_4 \geqslant \tfrac{4}{5}$$

or

$$3x_3 + x_4 \geqslant 4$$

We have generated a new constraint which we wish to add to the preceding tableau. However, it must first be placed in canonical form. Thus, to $3x_3 + x_4 - x_5 = 4$, $x_5 \geqslant 0$, we add an artificial variable x_6 to yield

$$3x_3 + x_4 - x_5 + x_6 = 4$$

Here we have assumed that x_5 is also integer. Now, however, a phase I routine is required to eliminate x_6. Likewise, this algorithm requires that all variables (real, slack, and artificial) be integer. This will be the case whenever the initial constraints contain only integer coefficients and integer right-hand sides. The constraints can usually be put in this form by multiplying by an appropriate constant.

The tableau becomes:

	x_1	x_2	x_3	x_4	x_5	x_6
3	1		1			
$1\frac{2}{5}$		1	$-\frac{2}{3}$	$\frac{1}{5}$		
4			3	1	-1	1
$-z' = 45$			5	2		
$-w = -4$			-3	-1	1	

Note the new objective function $w = 4 - 3x_3 - x_4 + x_5 (= x_6)$ for the phase I routine.

An iteration yields the tableau:

	x_1	x_2	x_3	x_4	x_5
$1\frac{2}{3}$	1			$-\frac{1}{3}$	$\frac{1}{3}$
$2\frac{1}{3}$		1		$\frac{1}{3}$	$-\frac{2}{15}$
$1\frac{1}{3}$			1	$\frac{1}{3}$	$\frac{1}{3}$
$-z' = \dfrac{115}{3}$				$\frac{1}{3}$	$\frac{5}{3}$

Note that the objective w had become zero so that the appropriate row and the column for x_6 have been eliminated. We note that an optimal noninteger solution has been achieved again. The procedure now is to introduce another constraint. As a rule of thumb, to develop the new constraint choose the constraint equation whose resource limit has the largest fractional part. The fractional parts corresponding to the above three constraints are $\frac{2}{3}$, $\frac{1}{3}$, $\frac{1}{3}$, respectively. We choose $\frac{2}{3}$ and write $-\frac{1}{3}x_4 + \frac{1}{3}x_5 = \frac{2}{3} + 1 - x_1$. To eliminate the negative coefficient on the left, we add x_4 to each side to obtain $\frac{2}{3}x_4 + \frac{1}{3}x_5 = \frac{2}{3} + (1 - x_1 + x_4)$. Hence, we have the constraint $\frac{2}{3}x_4 + \frac{1}{3}x_5 \geqslant \frac{2}{3}$, which will be appended to the last tableau after it is written in standard form. We let x_7 be the excess variable and x_8 the artificial variable in Table 4-9.
Again we have an optimal tableau. This time, however, the optimal solution is integer and the procedure terminates.

Table 4-9 Integer-programming tableaus

	x_1	x_2	x_3	x_4	x_5	x_6	x_7	x_8
$1\frac{2}{3}$	1			$-\frac{1}{3}$	$\frac{1}{3}$			
$2\frac{1}{5}$		1		$\frac{1}{3}$	$-\frac{2}{15}$			
$1\frac{1}{3}$			1	$\frac{1}{3}$	$-\frac{1}{3}$			
2				②	1		-1	1
$-z' = \dfrac{115}{3}$				$\frac{1}{3}$	$\frac{1}{3}$			
$-w = -2$				-2	-1		1	
2	1				$\frac{1}{2}$		$-\frac{1}{6}$	$\frac{1}{6}$
2		1			$-\frac{3}{10}$		$\frac{1}{6}$	$-\frac{1}{6}$
1			1		$-\frac{1}{2}$		$\frac{1}{6}$	$-\frac{1}{6}$
1				1	$\frac{1}{2}$		$-\frac{1}{2}$	$\frac{1}{2}$
$-z' = 38$					$\frac{1}{6}$		$\frac{1}{6}$	$-\frac{1}{6}$
$-w = 0$								1

It is interesting to follow the iterations graphically (Fig. 4-7). The first constraint to be developed was $3x_3 + x_4 \geqslant 4$. This can be written in terms of x_1 and x_2 by using the substitutions $x_3 = 3 - x_1$ and $x_4 = 15 - 2x_1 - 5x_2$ to yield $x_1 + x_2 \leqslant 4$. This constraint removes the shaded triangular region of noninteger solutions (including the previously optimal one) from the convex set (Fig. 4-7b). The next constraint to be developed was $2x_4 + x_5 \geqslant 2$, which is transformed into $3x_1 + 5x_2 \leqslant 16$. This constraint causes the additional triangular strip (also shaded) to be removed (Fig. 4-7c).

This algorithm is particularly suited for the linear-programming problem in which all variables are restricted to be integer. Also important is the

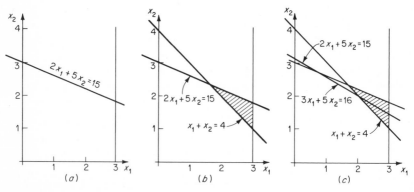

Fig. 4-7 Stripping a convex set.

mixed integer–continuous-variable problem, in which some of the variables are required to be integer while others are allowed to vary continuously. It is beyond the scope of this section to discuss mixed integer–continuous-variable problems, and the reader is referred to Gomory [8] and to Hadley [9].

Many types of problems can be conveniently handled by integer-programming methods. Typically, the "fixed-charge" and "traveling-salesman" (Sec. 7-2) problems and many scheduling and production problems have been formulated as integer-programming problems. Some examples in the next chapter have been formulated so that the variables are restricted to values of 0 or 1.

SUMMARY

The chapter considers aspects of the linear-programming problem in addition to those in Chap. 2.

Transportation problems are linear allocation problems which have mn variables and $m + n$ constraints, where m and n are the numbers of resource origins and destinations, respectively. The units allotted from various origins to destinations are limited only by the total numbers available at the origins and required at the destinations. Transportation problems may be solved using efficient computer routines. In the unbalanced transportation problem, the numbers of required and available units are not equal. A dummy row or column is used to balance the problem.

Assignment problems are a special case of the transportation problem in which the numbers of resource origins and destinations are generally equal and where only one unit is available and required at each origin and destination. These problems are easily solved by subtracting the smallest elements row-wise and column-wise in the cost matrix and making assignments at the intersection of zero elements of the reduced matrix.

Every linear-programming problem (the primal) has a corresponding problem called its dual. If the primal consists of m variables and n constraints, the dual has n variables and m constraints. Duality sometimes offers an important computational advantage because problems with a large number of variables require less computational effort than do problems with many constraints. A problem having many constraints and few variables can conveniently be transformed to its dual for solution.

Occasionally, large problems can be solved by decomposing them into several subproblems. The subproblems are linked together by an additional (hopefully, small) set of constraints. The technique is referred to as decomposition.

The values of parameters in a linear-programming problem may be approximations, or perhaps they may change during the period of interest. In such instances, it is desirable to explore the sensitivity of the optimal solution to changes in the parameters.   Methods for studying the effect of such changes upon the optimal solution are referred to as parametric programming or sensitivity analysis.

Finally, linear-programming problems often require some or all of the variables to be integer-valued—as, for example, assignments of men or pieces of equipment.   Efficient integer linear-programming solution methods are not generally available, but problems can be solved using an algorithm developed by Gomory [8].

PROBLEMS

4-1.   Orders for 15, 20, and 10 steel components have been received from three construction sites (A, B, and C).   These orders are to be filled by steel mills 1, 2, and 3, which have respective availabilities of 35, 30, and 10 components.   The shipping distances in miles from the various mills to each of the construction sites are:

	A	B	C
1	700	800	400
2	100	200	600
3	300	400	700

Assuming an equal shipping cost per mile for all components, how should the sites be supplied so as to minimize total shipping cost?◆

4-2.   Industries I_1, I_2, and I_3 require 2, 3, and 1 ($\times 10^6$) cu ft of water per day, respectively, to be supplied from two reservoirs R_1 and R_2.   Each reservoir can supply up to 3×10^6 cu ft per day.   Given the transportation-cost matrix below, what allocation of water will minimize total transportation cost?   If the solution is not unique, identify the alternative optima.

	I_1	I_2	I_3
R_1	40	30	10
R_2	20	70	50

4-3.   Complete the solution of Example 4-2.

4-4.   Problem 4-2 is to be investigated for the following changes in the conditions of demand and supply:

(a) The maximum capacities of reservoirs R_1 and R_2 are increased to 4 and 5 ($\times 10^6$) cu ft, respectively, and no cost is involved in storing the surplus water after demands have been met.

(b) The amounts of water required by industries I_1, I_2, and I_3 are changed to 3, 4, and 2, respectively, and no penalty is involved for shortage of water at the destinations after all supplies have been exhausted.

In each case, how should the water be allocated in order to minimize the transportation cost?

4-5. Five pumps are available to develop five wells. The efficiency of each pump in producing maximum yield at each well is shown in the table. What assignment will maximize overall efficiency?

Pump	Well 1	2	3	4	5
1	50	30	70	40	50
2	60	40	60	30	60
3	30	60	50	60	30
4	60	80	40	70	80
5	20	50	30	80	60

4-6. A machine shop purchased a drilling machine and two lathes of different capacities. Positioning of the machines among four possible locations on the shop floor is important from the standpoint of materials handling. Given the following cost estimates per unit time of materials handling, determine the optimal locations of the three machines.

Machine	Location 1	2	3	4
Lathe 1	12	9	12	9
Drill	15	Not suitable	13	20
Lathe 2	4	8	10	6

4-7. An engineering firm wishes to assign five of its personnel to the task of designing five projects. Given the following time estimates required by each engineer to design a given project, find the assignments which minimize total time.◆

Engineer	Project 1	2	3	4	5
1	3	10	3	1	8
2	7	9	8	1	7
3	5	7	6	1	4
4	5	3	8	1	4
5	6	4	10	1	6

4-8. Solve the following linear-programming problems with duality, and from the dual solutions find the optimal primal variables. Verify the results graphically if possible.◆

(a) Min: $z = -3x_1 - 6x_2$
Subject to: $4x_1 + 2x_2 \leqslant 4$
$3x_1 - 3x_2 \geqslant -2$
$x_1, x_2 \geqslant 0$

(b) Max: $z' = 4x_1 - 6x_2$
Subject to: $4x_1 - 2x_2 - 3x_3 \leqslant 4$
$2x_1 + 3x_2 + 2x_3 \leqslant 3$
$x_1, x_2, x_3 \geqslant 0$

(c) Max: $z' = 4x_1 + 3x_2$
Subject to: $x_1 \leqslant 5$
$x_2 \leqslant 10$
$2x_1 + 2x_2 \leqslant 11$
$3x_1 + x_2 \leqslant 14$
$x_2 \geqslant -1$
$x_1, x_2 \geqslant 0$

(d) Max: $z' = 1.5x_1 + x_2$
Subject to: $9x_1 + 8x_2 \geqslant 0.25$
$0.05x_1 + 0.1x_2 \leqslant 2$
$0.5x_1 + 15x_2 \leqslant 25$
$7x_1 + 0.5x_2 \geqslant 0.05$
$0.5x_1 + 0.025x_2 \leqslant 3$
$x_1, x_2 \geqslant 0$

4-9. Give the dual of the following problem in a form such that the dual variables are non-negative and no strict equalities appear in the dual constraints.

Max: $z' = 0.9x_1 + 1.2x_2 + 3x_3 + 0.5x_4$
Subject to: $1.2x_1 + 1.6x_2 + 2x_3 + 3.6x_4 = 21$
$1.5x_1 + 8.5x_2 + 40x_3 + x_4 \leqslant 24$
$x_1, x_2 \geqslant 0; x_3, x_4$ unrestricted

4-10. A concrete manufacturer produces two mixes, C_1 and C_2, which he can sell at \$35 and \$38 per cu yd, respectively. Each mix consists of two types of aggregates, Ag 1 and Ag 2. Each aggregate contains two gradations, A and B, in the following proportions:

	Gradation		Cost/cu yd
	A	B	
Ag 1	0.80	0.20	\$25
Ag 2	0.50	0.50	20

The availability of Ag 1 is restricted to 40 cu yd per day. Mix C_1 must not exceed 60% of gradation A, and mix C_2 must have at least 70% of gradation A.

The total daily demand for concrete is 100 cu yd. This demand need not be satisfied, but unfilled orders are lost (i.e., there is no backlog). Production facilities limit the amount of C_1 to 50 cu yd.

For equal production costs, excluding the cost of aggregate, how much of each mix should be produced? Decompose the problem, if possible, and solve.◆

4-11. Solve the following problems:

(a) Min: $z = 3\lambda x_1 + 2\lambda x_2 - (1 - \lambda) x_3 + x_4 + 2x_5 - 4\lambda x_6$

Subject to: $x_1 + 4x_2 - 2x_3 + 3x_5 = 6$

$-2x_2 + 4x_3 + x_4 = 12$

$-3x_2 + 4x_3 + 8x_5 + x_6 = 10$

$x_i \geqslant 0; -\infty < \lambda < \infty$

$i = 1, 2, \ldots, 6$

(b) Max: $z' = 6x_1 + 3x_2 + 5x_3 + 6x_4$

Subject to: $2x_1 + 3x_2 + x_3 + x_4 \leqslant 8 + \lambda$

$x_1 - 2x_2 + 3x_3 + 4x_4 \leqslant 20 - \lambda$

$2x_1 + x_2 - 3x_3 + 2x_4 \leqslant 40 - 2\lambda$

$x_i \geqslant 0; \quad i = 1, 2, \ldots, 4$

$0 < \lambda < \infty$

4-12. Formulate the water-quality management problem, Example 3-2, as an integer-programming problem. Assume that the attainable treatment levels for each plant are either 30%, 60%, or 90% of BOD removal. (See Deininger [6]).

4-13. A structural-clay manufacturer produces products A, B, and C. The production rates, profits, and requirements for clay and kiln space are tabulated below. The available clay per day for all three products is 12,100 lb, and the kiln volume is 4,000 cu ft. Products are manufactured 8 hr per day, placed in the kiln at the end of the day, and removed from the kiln the next morning. The three products thus share total available clay, production time, and kiln space.

	Product		
	A	B	C
Production rate (pieces/hr)	200	100	300
Profit (per piece)	0.18	0.32	0.10
Raw material (lb/piece)	10	14	3
Kiln space (cu ft/piece)	3	4	2

(a) What number of each product should be produced per day?
(b) What premium could the plant pay for additional clay?
(c) What premium could be paid for additional kiln space?
(d) What hourly rate could be paid for more production time?

4-14. Formulate the dual for Prob. 3-8.

4-15. A water-treatment plant with storage capacity of 5×10^6 cu ft provides water to surrounding industries. At the beginning of each month, the plant can sell any quantity of treated water up to its storage capacity. Given the following forecast of treatment costs and sales prices for the next 4 months, determine the policy of the plant as to the quantity of water to be treated (which cannot be sold until the subsequent month) and the quantity to be sold each month.   The treatment plant currently has a supply of 2×10^6 cu ft of treated water.   Solve the problem using the duality theorem.

	Month			
	1	2	3	4
Treatment cost ($/cu ft treated)	27	24	26	28
Sales price ($/cu ft sold)	28	25	27	28

4-16.   Five communities discharge wastes into connecting streams.   Because of the distances between the communities, combined waste-treatment plants are infeasible and each city must provide its own treatment facilities.   The federal government will subsidize the water-treatment program if individual plants cooperate to satisfy specified BOD levels at minimum cost.   Neglecting waste decomposition and given the following data, what levels of treatment for the plants minimize total treatment cost per day?

City j	BOD load, lb/day B_j	Treatment cost, $/lb C_j	Min. streamflow, cfs Q_j	Max. BOD, lb/cu ft B_{mj}
1	1,200	0.18	3.2	0.0012
2	600	0.22	3.6	0.0012
3	2,000	0.15	4.5	0.0010
4	500	0.23	4.8	0.0020
5	1,000	0.20	8.4	0.0010

Maximum treatment at each plant is 90% BOD removal.   Solve by decomposition.

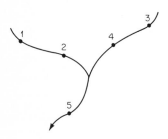

4-17.   Solve the following integer-programming problems:

(a) Max: $z' = 9x_1 + 10x_2$

Subject to: $x_1 \leqslant 3$

$2x_1 + 5x_2 \leqslant 15$

$x_1, x_2 \geqslant 0$

(b) Max: $z' = 4x_1 + 5x_2 + x_3$

Subject to: $3x_1 + 2x_2 \leqslant 10$

$x_1 + 4x_2 \leqslant 11$

$3x_1 + 3x_2 + x_3 \leqslant 13$

$x_1, x_2, x_3 \geqslant 0$

(c) Min: $z = x_1 + 3x_2 + x_3$

Subject to: $x_1 + 2x_2 + 3x_3 \geqslant 7$

$-2x_1 + x_2 + x_3 \leqslant 13$

$x_1 - 2x_2 + 2x_3 \leqslant 5$

$3x_1 + x_2 + 7x_3 \geqslant 14$

$x_1, x_2, x_3 \geqslant 0$

REFERENCES

1. Ackoff, R. L., and M. W. Sasieni: "Fundamentals of Operations Research," John Wiley & Sons, Inc., New York, 1968.
2. Au, T., and T. E. Stelson: "Introduction to Systems Engineering," Addison-Wesley Publishing Company, Inc., Reading, Mass., 1969.
3. Balinski, M. L.: Integer Programming: Methods, Uses, Computation, *Management Sci.*, vol. 12, no. 3, pp. 253–313, 1965.
4. Dantzig, G. B., and P. Wolfe: A Decomposition Principle for Linear Programs, *Rand Rep.* P-1544, The RAND Corporation, Santa Monica, Calif., 1959.
5. Dantzig, G. B., and P. Wolfe: The Decomposition Algorithm for Linear Programs, *Econometrica*, vol. 29, no. 4, October, 1961.
6. Deininger, R. A.: Water Quality Management—The Planning of Economically Optimal Pollution Control Systems, *Proc. 1st Ann. Meeting Am. Water Resources Assoc.*, University of Chicago, pp. 254–282, Dec. 1965.
7. Gass, S. I.: "Linear Programming: Methods and Applications," 2d ed., McGraw-Hill Book Company, New York, 1964.
8. Gomory, R. E.: An Algorithm for Integer Solutions to Linear Programs, in Graves and P. Wolfe, "Recent Advances in Mathematical Programming", McGraw-Hill Book Company, New York, 1963.
9. Hadley, G.: "Linear Programming," Addison-Wesley Publishing Company, Inc., Reading, Mass., 1962.
10. Hadley, G.: "Non-linear and Dynamic Programming," Addison-Wesley Publishing Company, Inc., Reading, Mass., 1964.
11. Hillier, F., and G. Lieberman: "Introduction to Operations Research," Holden-Day, Inc., Publishers, San Francisco, 1967.
12. Pinnell, C., and G. T. Satterly, Jr.: Systems Analysis for Arterial Street Operation, *Proc. ASCE*, vol. 89, no. EM6, pp. 67–96, December, 1963.
13. Prager, W.: Linear Programming and Structural Design II; Limit Design, *Rand Rep.* P-1123, The RAND Corporation, Santa Monica, Calif., 1957.
14. Rubinstein, M. F., and J. Karagozian: Building Design Using Linear Programming, *Proc. ASCE*, vol. 92, no. ST6, pp. 223–245, December, 1966.
15. Sasieni, M., A. Yaspan, and L. Friedman: "Operations Research—Methods and Problems," John Wiley & Sons, Inc., New York, 1960.
16. Simonnard, M.: "Linear Programming," translated by W. S. Jewell, Prentice-Hall, Inc., Englewood Cliffs, N.J., 1966.
17. Williams, A. C.: A Treatment of Transportation Problems by Decomposition, *SIAM J. Appl. Math.*, vol. 10, no. 1, pp. 35–48, 1962.

5
Nonlinear Optimization

The last three chapters treated linear optimization and illustrated the variety of applications. In many instances, nonlinear representations are required to bring out pertinent features of a problem. There are innumerable applications for nonlinear representations, and the subject is a popular research area. Apart from a few older techniques, nonlinear optimization dates from the pioneering work of Kuhn and Tucker in 1951 [21].

The general optimization model cited in Sec. 1-6 can be rewritten

Optimize: $z = f(x_1, x_2, \ldots, x_n)$
Subject to: $g_i(x_1, x_2, \ldots, x_n) \gtreqless 0$ $i = 1, \ldots, m$
   $x_j \geqslant 0$ $j = 1, \ldots, n$

Figure 5-1 shows a typical two-dimensional nonlinear optimization problem. The constraints $g_i(x_1, \ldots, x_n) = 0$ define the feasible region (shaded), and the objective is evaluated for values of x_1 and x_2 to yield contours z_1, z_2, etc.

Although classifications tend to lack permanence in a rapidly developing subject, it is useful to classify nonlinear problems and the techniques for solving them. We suggest two broad categories: *classical optimization techniques* and *search techniques*.

Classical optimization seeks optimal solutions by solving systems of equations. The optimization can be reduced to "root finding." The first four sections of this chapter deal with four classical optimization techniques:

1. Differential calculus
2. Lagrange multipliers
3. Kuhn-Tucker theory
4. Geometric programming

The usefulness of classical techniques depends upon the computational effort required for solving nonlinear systems of equations. However, they are useful for a wide variety of problems, and an understanding is essential

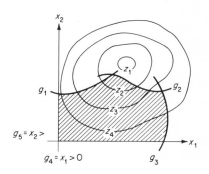

Fig. 5-1 Two-dimensional solution space.

for further development. The newly developed subject of geometric programming appears to have particularly promising implications for engineering design.

Search techniques are iterative in that one starts from an initial solution and seeks improvements until an acceptable tolerance is achieved. While the subject is extensive, in Sec. 5-5 we shall consider only the alternating one-dimensional search and steepest-gradient methods.

Section 5-6 deals with transformations of nonlinear problems into linear ones. The techniques include piecewise linear programming and a transformation for an objective function with step functions, the so-called "production smoothing."

Finally, Sec. 5-7 considers the use of graphical techniques to achieve nonlinear optimizations.

There are many deterrents to deriving solutions from nonlinear models, i.e., to carrying out the optimization. For example:

1. The set of feasible solutions x_1, x_2, ..., x_n may not form a convex set. Recall that our success with linear-programming problems depended upon the presence of a convex set. A similar dependence exists in the nonlinear case.
2. It may be necessary to determine whether maxima and minima are relative or global. In the linear case, the optimum is global. In nonlinear cases, several local optima must frequently be evaluated to identify a global optimum.
3. The objective function may be optimum at points other than on the boundary of the feasible region. Here we lose the considerable advantage of the linear case, in which only extreme points require consideration for optima.

For these reasons, and others, solutions to general nonlinear optimization problems are well beyond our current abilities. Techniques are available for several special classes. One particularly important class of optimization problems, in which the objective function is to be minimized and the feasible solutions are convex, is called *convex programming*. Sometimes the objective function can be rewritten so that it is a sum of functions of a single variable; this is called *separable convex programming* (see [17] and [22]). Linear constraints lead to relatively simple polygonal convex sets. Often the objective is quadratic and the constraints are linear; this is called *quadratic programming* [3].

Recall from calculus that a function of a single variable, $f(x)$, is convex when the second derivative is positive, that is, when $\partial^2 f(x)/\partial x^2 \geqslant 0$; concave when it is negative; and linear when it is zero in the interval of interest. More specifically, a function $f(x_1, x_2, \ldots, x_n)$ is said to be convex over a convex set

X in an n-dimensional space if, for any pair of points, $\mathbf{x}_1 = (x_{11}, x_{21}, \ldots, x_{n1})$ and $\mathbf{x}_2 = (x_{12}, x_{22}, \ldots, x_{n2})$ in X, and all λ, $0 \leqslant \lambda \leqslant 1$,

$$f[\lambda \mathbf{x}_2 + (1 - \lambda)\mathbf{x}_1] \leqslant \lambda f(\mathbf{x}_2) + (1 - \lambda)f(\mathbf{x}_1)$$

that is, if the segment joining the two points lies entirely above or on the graph of $f(x_1, x_2, \ldots, x_n)$. Figure 5-2a illustrates a convex function in one dimension, $n = 1$.

Similarly, a function is said to be concave (Fig. 5-2b) if the $<$ sign in the linear combination is replaced by a $>$ sign, that is, if the corresponding line segment lies below $f(x_1, x_2, \ldots, x_n)$. Clearly, multiplying a convex function by -1 makes it concave.

Further, if feasible solutions to the general optimization model exist, the set of points satisfying

$$
\begin{aligned}
g_i(x_1, \ldots, x_n) &\gtreqless 0 \qquad i = 1, \ldots, m \\
x_j &\geqslant 0 \qquad\quad\ j = 1, \ldots, n
\end{aligned}
$$

form a convex set when:

1. $g_i(x_1, \ldots, x_n)$ is a convex function over the nonnegative orthant of an n-dimensional space if the ith constraint has a $\leqslant$ sign.
2. $g_i(x_1, \ldots, x_n)$ is a concave function over the nonnegative orthant of an n-dimensional space if the ith constraint has a $\geqslant$ sign.
3. $g_i(x_1, \ldots, x_n)$ is linear when the ith constraint is a strict equality. If the inequalities are strict (no equality), the function is called either strictly convex or strictly concave.

Figure 5-3 illustrates a two-dimensional convex programming problem. Most of the available nonlinear optimization techniques depend upon these convex properties because the convex character ensures a global optimum.

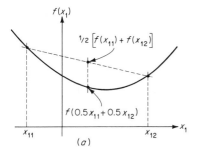 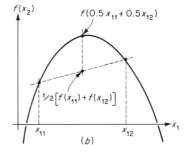

Fig. 5-2 Functions of a single variable. (a) A convex function; (b) a concave function.

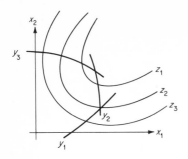

Fig. 5-3 Two-dimensional convex programming.

For functions of two variables, $f(x_1,x_2)$, convexity requires that the following determinant and its pure derivatives be nonnegative:

$$\begin{vmatrix} \dfrac{\partial^2 f(x_1,x_2)}{\partial x_1{}^2} & \dfrac{\partial^2 f(x_1,x_2)}{\partial x_1\,\partial x_2} \\[2ex] \dfrac{\partial^2 f(x_1,x_2)}{\partial x_2\,\partial x_1} & \dfrac{\partial^2 f(x_1,x_2)}{\partial x_2{}^2} \end{vmatrix} \geqslant 0$$

and

$$\frac{\partial^2 f(x_1,x_2)}{\partial x_1{}^2} \geqslant 0 \qquad \text{and} \qquad \frac{\partial^2 f(x_1,x_2)}{\partial x_2{}^2} \geqslant 0$$

If the pure derivatives are nonpositive, $f(x_1,x_2)$ is concave.

For functions of several variables, $f(x_1,\ldots,x_n)$, convexity requires that the $n \times n$ *Hessian matrix* **H** be nonnegative, that is,

$$\mathbf{H} = \begin{bmatrix} f_{x_1 x_1} & f_{x_1 x_2} & \cdots & f_{x_1 x_n} \\ f_{x_2 x_1} & f_{x_2 x_2} & \cdots & f_{x_2 x_n} \\ \cdots\cdots\cdots\cdots\cdots\cdots\cdots\cdots \\ f_{x_n x_1} & f_{x_n x_2} & \cdots & f_{x_n x_n} \end{bmatrix} \geqslant 0$$

5-1 DIFFERENTIAL CALCULUS

The general optimization problem mentioned in the introduction becomes a *classical optimization problem* when (1) all constraints and the objective function are continuous and possess partial derivatives at least through the second order, (2) the constraints are equations whose number does not exceed the number of independent variables, and (3) the nonnegativity restriction on the variables is removed. Classical optimization problems can be solved by differential calculus, but classical techniques are not well adapted to automatic computation.

FUNCTIONS OF A SINGLE VARIABLE

Consider a function of a single variable $z = f(x)$ (Fig. 5-4). The necessary condition for x_0 to be the abscissa of the optimum is that dz/dx vanish at x_0. This corresponds to a horizontal tangent. Figure 5-4 shows seven such points, which are called *stationary* (or *critical*) points. Higher derivatives reveal the character of these points.

If the second derivative at x_0 is positive (negative), the stationary point is at least a local minimum (maximum). If the second derivative vanishes and changes sign about the stationary point, we have a point of inflection. Valleys and ridges correspond to cases where the second derivative vanishes but does not change sign. A global minimum (maximum) is the smallest (largest) of all the local minima (maxima).

An important observation is that if $z = f(x)$ is known to be convex (concave), any point x_0 for which the first derivative is zero is a global optimum. In other words, the condition that the first derivative vanish is both necessary and sufficient for a global minimum (maximum) when the function is convex (concave).

Example 5-1   Refrigerated tank   Find the minimum-cost dimensions for a refrigerated 1,000-cu ft cylindrical tank. The component costs are

Metal ends: $1.00/sq ft
Metal cylinder wall: $0.50/sq ft
Refrigeration (over the useful life): $5.00/sq ft (surface)

Clearly, the objective function is the total cost z,

$$z = 0.50\pi DL + 2(1.0)\frac{\pi D^2}{4} + 5\left[\pi DL + \frac{2\pi D^2}{4}\right] = \pi D(5.5L + 3D)$$

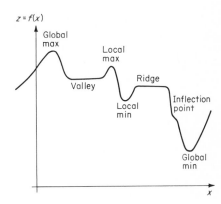

Fig. 5-4   Critical (stationary) points of $z = f(x)$.

where D and L are the diameter and length of the tank, respectively. Also, we have the volume constraint

$$\frac{\pi D^2 L}{4} = 1{,}000$$

Because of the equality constraint, we can eliminate one of the variables in the objective function. Eliminating L, we have

$$z = \frac{22{,}000}{D} + 3\pi D^2$$

We could as well have eliminated D. Setting the derivative of z equal to zero, we find the optimum diameter to be 10.52 ft. From the constraint equation, the corresponding length is 11.5 ft. Note that the second derivative is always positive, so that z is strictly convex and the optimum is global.

LOT-SIZE MODELS

Models which lead to objective functions of the form just encountered are often called *lot-size models*. The name arises from the pioneering work (circa 1915) of Harris in determining optimal sizes of production lots. The lot-size model arises in a remarkable number of seemingly unrelated problems and appears several places in this text, including the geometric-programming section of this chapter. A lot-size model is one in which the objective function is the sum of nonnegative increasing and decreasing terms. The simplest case is

$$\text{Min:} \quad z = \frac{a}{x} + bx \tag{1}$$

The minimizing value of x is obtained by setting the derivative equal to zero:

$$x_0 = \sqrt{\frac{a}{b}} \quad \text{to yield} \quad z_0 = 2\sqrt{ab} \tag{2}$$

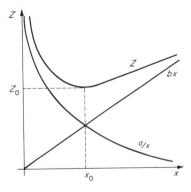

Fig. 5-5 The lot-size model $z = a/x + bx$.

A plot of this objective function and its terms (Fig. 5-5) illustrates that, in this case, the minimum occurs at the abscissa x_0, where the terms a/x and bx are equal. The next example and the problems provide interesting applications.

Example 5-2 A flood-control optimization

A flood-control system is to be designed for a town bordering a river. It will include levees along the riverbank and an upstream reservoir for flow regulation. Assume that it is possible to express both reservoir and levee costs in terms of the channel capacity. For example, suppose that the design flood at the town is to be reduced from a peak flow f to a regulated flow x (Fig. 5-6). It becomes necessary to provide higher levees corresponding to the discharge x and, in addition, to provide storage capacity to impound water having a volume represented by the dashed area in the hydrograph.

Increasing the regulated discharge x would increase the cost of levee protection while decreasing the cost of the reservoir, as shown by Fig. 5-5, where x is the design channel capacity in cubic feet per second, z is the cost of protection, and a and b are positive cost constants. Likewise, decreasing the regulated flow would decrease levee costs and increase the reservoir costs. Thus the lot-size model, Eq. (1), might describe the total cost of flood protection and Eq. (2) gives the minimum cost z_0 corresponding to the optimum channel capacity x_0.

It is important to ask what effect changes in the parameters have upon an optimal solution, i.e., to make a *sensitivity analysis*. For the above model, suppose that we assume "incorrect" values a' and b' for parameters a and b, respectively. Optimization yields the values x' and z' in place of the true values x_0 and z_0. For convenience, set $x' = \alpha x_0$, $\alpha > 0$, and substitute to find

$$\frac{z'}{z_0} = \frac{1 + \alpha^2}{2\alpha} \quad \text{and} \quad \alpha = \sqrt{\frac{b}{b'}\frac{a'}{a}} \tag{3}$$

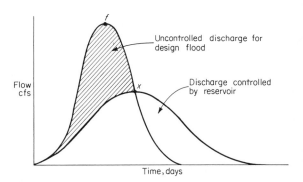

Fig. 5-6 Flood hydrographs.

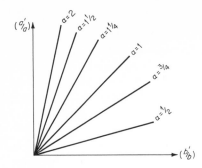

Fig. 5-7   Iso-α lines for a lot-size model.

Note that in this case the parameters do not appear explicitly in z'/z_0. This can be important information because inaccuracies in the parameters could tend to cancel (or aggravate). Table 5-1 gives values of z'/z_0 for several values of α, and Fig. 5-7 plots the iso-α lines of a'/a vs. b'/b. Thus, for example, points on the $\alpha = 1$ line define pairs of values of a'/a and b'/b for which the system operates optimally even with inaccurate parameter information.

FUNCTIONS OF SEVERAL VARIABLES

For unconstrained functions of several variables, $f(x_1, \ldots, x_n)$, a necessary condition for $x_{10}, x_{20}, \ldots, x_{n0}$ to be an optimum is

$$\frac{\partial f}{\partial x_j} = 0 \qquad \text{for } j = 1, 2, \ldots, n \text{ at } \mathbf{x}_0 = [x_{10}, x_{10}, \ldots .x_{n0}]$$

As in the case of a single variable, the solutions to these equations yield the stationary points. The Hessian matrix (of second partial derivatives) determines the character of these solutions. If the Hessian matrix is positive (negative) definite, that is, if $\mathbf{H} > 0$ ($\mathbf{H} < 0$), and if the pure derivatives are positive (negative), the optimum is at least a local minimum (maximum). If the Hessian matrix vanishes, perturbations about the stationary point can be used to determine its nature. Analytic considerations appear in Hadley [17].

The global optimum is selected from among the local optima. If the function is known to be strictly convex or concave, a sufficient condition is established and the selection process is not needed (a local optimum is global).

Table 5-1 z'/z_0 for several values of α

α	0.50	0.75	1.00	1.25	1.50	2.00
z'/z_0	1.25	1.04	1.00	1.02	1.08	1.25

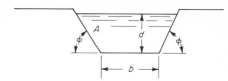

Fig. 5-8 Canal of trapezoidal section.

Example 5-3 Canal design Consider a trapezoidal canal whose cross-sectional area A is to be 100 sq ft (Fig. 5-8). The mean flow velocity increases with hydraulic radius A/p, where p is the wetted perimeter. The discharge is maximum when the mean velocity is maximum. Therefore, the design optimization reduces to minimizing the wetted perimeter p.

For the trapezoid,

$$p = b + 2d\csc\phi$$

and

$$A = db + d^2\cot\phi$$

These two equations enable a reduction in the number of variables. It is convenient to eliminate b, to yield

$$p = \frac{A}{d} - d\cot\phi + 2d\csc\phi$$

Setting the derivatives $\partial p/\partial d$ and $\partial p/\partial\phi$ equal to zero gives

$$\frac{\partial p}{\partial d} = \frac{-A}{d^2} - \cot\phi + 2\csc\phi = 0$$

$$\frac{\partial p}{\partial\phi} = d\csc^2\phi - 2d\csc\phi\cot\phi = 0$$

A solution to the last equation is $\phi_0 = \pi/3 = 60°$. Substituting into the preceding equation gives $d = 7.58$ ft and, subsequently, $b = 8.82$ ft.

To check the character of the stationary point, we find the second derivatives

$$\frac{\partial^2 p}{\partial d^2} = \frac{2A}{d^3} = \frac{200}{d^3}$$

After simplification,

$$\frac{\partial^2 p}{\partial\phi^2} = \frac{2d}{\sin^3\phi}(\cos^2\phi - \cos\phi + 1)$$

and

$$\frac{\partial^2 p}{\partial d\,\partial\phi} = \csc^2\phi - 2\csc\phi\cot\phi$$

The Hessian matrix is

$$\mathbf{H} = \begin{bmatrix} \dfrac{\partial^2 p}{\partial d^2} & \dfrac{\partial^2 p}{\partial d\,\partial\phi} \\[2ex] \dfrac{\partial^2 p}{\partial\phi\,\partial d} & \dfrac{\partial^2 p}{\partial\phi^2} \end{bmatrix} = \begin{bmatrix} \dfrac{200}{7.58^3} & 0 \\[2ex] 0 & \dfrac{2(7.58)}{0.866^3}(0.5^2 - 0.5 + 1) \end{bmatrix}$$

$$= \left[\dfrac{200}{7.58^3}\right]\left[\dfrac{2(7.58)}{0.866^3}(0.5^2 - 0.5 + 1)\right] > 0$$

Since the pure derivatives and the Hessian matrix are positive, we have a global minimum.

5-2 LAGRANGE MULTIPLIER

In the general classical optimization problem, there may be several equality constraints $g_i(x_1, x_2, \ldots, x_n)$ which are nonlinear (or with variables interspersed), so that we cannot readily solve for the variables explicitly and substitute them into the objective function. The Lagrange multiplier technique is useful for such problems. It proceeds as follows: Multiply each of the m constraint equations by $\lambda_1, \ldots, \lambda_m$, respectively, and add them to the objective function to obtain

$$L = z(x_1, \ldots, x_n) + \sum_{i=1}^{m} \lambda_i g_i(x_1, \ldots, x_n)$$

In this form, the objective function is often called the *Lagrangian* and is denoted by L. If we regard L as an objective function in $m + n$ variables and proceed by setting the $m + n$ derivatives equal to zero, we obtain

$$\frac{\partial L}{\partial x_j} = \frac{\partial z}{\partial x_j} + \sum_{i=1}^{m} \lambda_i \frac{\partial g_i}{\partial x_j} = 0 \qquad j = 1, \ldots, n$$

and

$$\frac{\partial L}{\partial \lambda_i} = g_i = 0 \qquad i = 1, \ldots, m$$

Solving these equations simultaneously gives the desired solution. A little reflection shows that this is exactly the solution that would have been obtained if we had solved the constraints explicitly for some of the variables in terms of others, used them to eliminate those variables from $z(x_1, \ldots, x_n)$, and then used the differential calculus technique directly, as we did in the last section.

Example 5-4 Refrigerated tank (continued) Consider the refrigerated-tank example again. The Lagrangian is

$$L = \pi D(5.5L + 3D) + \lambda \left[\frac{\pi D^2 L}{4} - 1{,}000 \right]$$

Differentiation yields

$$\frac{\partial L}{\partial D} = 5.5\pi L + 6\pi D + \frac{\pi DL}{2}\lambda = 0$$

$$\frac{\partial L}{\partial L} = 5.5\pi D + \frac{\pi D^2}{4}\lambda = 0$$

$$\frac{\partial L}{\partial \lambda} = \frac{\pi D^2 L}{4} - 1{,}000 = 0$$

Solving these simultaneously, we find the same answers as before and, in addition, $\lambda = -2.09$. The multiplier λ is interpreted as the increased cost which would result from a unit increase in the volume of the tank—a so-called "marginal cost."

Consider a structural application [15].

Example 5-5 Sizing of a steel beam The web thickness t, flange width b, and thickness f of a steel beam (Fig. 5-9) are to be determined so that the beam weight W is a minimum for a given loading and maximum allowable beam depth d. Assuming for simplicity that flexural stress will govern, we write

Min: $W = [2bf + (d - 2f)t]c$

Subject to: $g_1 = I - \frac{bf}{2}\left[(d-f)^2 + \frac{f^2}{3}\right] - (d - 2f)^3 \frac{t}{12} = 0$

required moment of inertia

$$g_2 = \frac{b}{f} - \frac{6{,}000}{\sqrt{F_y}}$$

AISC maximum allowable flange width [1]

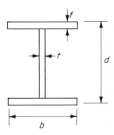

Fig. 5-9 Beam section.

where c is a density coefficient, F_y the yield stress, and I the moment of inertia of the steel beam.   Using the Lagrange multiplier technique,

$$\frac{\partial W}{\partial b} + \lambda_1 \frac{\partial g_1}{\partial b} + \lambda_2 \frac{\partial g_2}{\partial b} = 0$$

$$\frac{\partial W}{\partial f} + \lambda_1 \frac{\partial g_1}{\partial f} + \lambda_2 \frac{\partial g_2}{\partial f} = 0$$

$$\frac{\partial W}{\partial t} + \lambda_1 \frac{\partial g_1}{\partial t} + \lambda_2 \frac{\partial g_2}{\partial t} = 0$$

Substitution yields

$$2cf - \lambda_1 \left[\frac{f}{2}(d-f)^2 + \frac{f^3}{6} \right] + \frac{\lambda_2}{f} = 0$$

$$2c(b-t) + \lambda_1 \left[b\left(2df - \frac{d^2}{2} - 2f^2 \right) + t\left(2f^2 - 2df + \frac{d^2}{2} \right) \right] - \lambda_2 \frac{b}{f^2} = 0$$

$$c(d-2f) + \lambda_1 [-\tfrac{1}{12}(d-2f)^3] = 0$$

These three equations and the two constraint equations can be solved for λ_1 and λ_2 and the design parameters b, f, and t.   That this is not a trivial computation illustrates a practical limitation on the use of the Lagrange multiplier technique.   The possibility of many stationary points also limits the usefulness of the technique.

The Lagrange multiplier technique can be generalized to handle non-negativity and inequality constraints, but the accompanying computational cost can be discouraging.   A situation occasionally arises in which an inequality constraint "binds."   In this case, the inequality can be replaced by an equality (see Sec. 10-2).

Incidentally, the standard linear-programming problem can be solved using Lagrange multiplier techniques since the objective and constraint functions are differentiable everywhere.   However, the technique is impractical because it does not indicate which of the feasible solutions are optimal and it is necessary to enumerate at each vertex.

NEWTON-RAPHSON APPROXIMATION

We have mentioned the frequency with which classical optimization techniques require the simultaneous solution of nonlinear systems of equations. A number of numerical approximation techniques are available, one of which is the *Newton-Raphson approximation*.   First, we illustrate the technique using a single nonlinear equation, $y = f(x)$.

To obtain the positive root r (Fig. 5-10), we arbitrarily guess the root, say x_0, and draw the tangent to the curve at the point (x_0, y_0).   The tangent intersects the x axis at x_1.   This abscissa, x_1, replaces x_0 as an improved

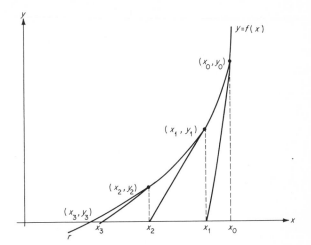

Fig. 5-10 Newton-Raphson approximation technique.

approximation to the root. The procedure is repeated using the points (x_1, y_1), and so on, until a satisfactory approximation is achieved.

The equation of the tangent to the curve $y = f(x)$ at (x_0, y_0) is written as $f'(x) = (y - y_0)(x - x_0)^{-1}$. The second approximation, x_1, is the x intercept of this tangent. Substituting $y = 0$, $y_0 = f(x_0)$, gives

$$f'(x_0) = -\frac{f(x_0)}{x_1 - x_0}$$

or

$$x_1 = x_0 - \frac{f(x_0)}{f'(x_0)}$$

More generally,

$$x_{n+1} = x_n - \frac{f(x_n)}{f'(x_n)}$$

The last expression is called the Newton-Raphson formula for the $(n + 2)$nd approximation.

When x_{n+1} is close to r, the formula can be interpreted as the Taylor expansion (to first-order terms) of $f(x)$ about x_n. Specifically,

$$f(x) = f(x_n) + f'(x_n)(x - x_n)$$

For $x = x_{n+1} \sim r, f(x_{n+1}) \sim f(r) = 0$, and the last expression yields the Newton-Raphson formula. In optimization, one usually seeks the roots of the first derivative of the objective function, $z(x)$. To use the Newton-Raphson approximation, one simply replaces $f(x_n)$ by $z'(x_n)$.

For example, let $z(x) = x^3 - 3x + 10$. Then $f(x) = z'(x) = 3x^2 - 3$ and $f'(x) = 6x$, and the Newton-Raphson formula becomes

$$x_{n+1} = x_n - \frac{3x_n^2 - 3}{6x_n}$$

This formula is used repetitively until a suitable approximation to $z'(r) = 0$ is achieved.

For functions of several variables, the procedure is similar. For example, let $f(x,y) = 0$ and $g(x,y) = 0$ be two nonlinear simultaneous equations. Using (x_n,y_n) as the point of expansion, we write, to first order,

$$f(x,y) = f(x_n,y_n) + \frac{\partial f}{\partial x}\bigg|_n (x - x_n) + \frac{\partial f}{\partial y}\bigg|_n (y - y_n)$$

$$g(x,y) = g(x_n,y_n) + \frac{\partial g}{\partial x}\bigg|_n (x - x_n) + \frac{\partial g}{\partial y}\bigg|_n (y - y_n)$$

where the subscripted derivatives indicate evaluation at (x_n,y_n). Let $x = x_{n+1}$ and $y = y_{n+1}$, and further, suppose that these are close to the roots $x = r$, $y = s$. It follows that $f(x_{n+1},y_{n+1}) \sim g(x_{n+1},y_{n+1}) \sim 0$. Solving the above equations simultaneously yields

$$x_{n+1} = x_n - \frac{f(x_n,y_n)\dfrac{\partial g}{\partial y}\bigg|_n - g(x_n,y_n)\dfrac{\partial f}{\partial y}\bigg|_n}{\dfrac{\partial f}{\partial x}\bigg|_n \dfrac{\partial g}{\partial y}\bigg|_n - \dfrac{\partial f}{\partial y}\bigg|_n \dfrac{\partial g}{\partial x}\bigg|_n}$$

and

$$y_{n+1} = y_n - \frac{g(x_n,y_n)\dfrac{\partial f}{\partial x}\bigg|_n - f(x_n,y_n)\dfrac{\partial g}{\partial x}\bigg|_n}{\dfrac{\partial f}{\partial x}\bigg|_n \dfrac{\partial g}{\partial y}\bigg|_n - \dfrac{\partial f}{\partial y}\bigg|_n \dfrac{\partial g}{\partial x}\bigg|_n}$$

which are the two-variable Newton-Raphson formulas.

As an example of the above formulas, consider

$$f(x,y) = x^2 - xy - 5 = 0$$

$$g(x,y) = x^2 + x - \frac{6x}{y} = 0$$

Here

$$\frac{\partial f}{\partial x} = 2x - y \qquad \frac{\partial f}{\partial y} = -x$$

and

$$\frac{\partial g}{\partial x} = 2x + 1 - \frac{6}{y} \qquad \frac{\partial g}{\partial y} = \frac{6x}{y^2}$$

The arbitrary selection $x_0 = 3$, $y_0 = 1$ begins the process. We have

$$f(3,1) = 1 \qquad g(3,1) = 6$$

and

$$\left.\frac{\partial f}{\partial x}\right|_0 = 5 \qquad \left.\frac{\partial f}{\partial y}\right|_0 = -3 \qquad \left.\frac{\partial g}{\partial x}\right|_0 = 1 \qquad \left.\frac{\partial g}{\partial y}\right|_0 = 18$$

Substitution into the Newton-Raphson formulas yields

$$x_1 = 3 \qquad \text{and} \qquad y_1 = 4/3$$

Another iteration yields $x_2 = 3.369$, $y_2 = 1.907$, and so on.

It is useful to note that the Newton-Raphson formulas for $f(x,y)$ and $g(x,y)$ can be written in the matrix form:

$$\begin{bmatrix} f_x & f_y \\ g_x & g_y \end{bmatrix} \begin{bmatrix} x_{n+1} - x_n \\ y_{n+1} - y_n \end{bmatrix} = \begin{bmatrix} -f(x_n, y_n) \\ -g(x_n, y_n) \end{bmatrix}$$

where the x and y subscripts denote partial derivatives. The generalization of this method to functions of several variables $x, y, \ldots, z$ follows easily:

$$\begin{bmatrix} f_x & f_y & \cdots & f_z \\ g_x & g_y & \cdots & g_z \\ \multicolumn{4}{c}{\cdots\cdots\cdots\cdots\cdots} \\ h_x & h_y & \cdots & h_z \end{bmatrix} \begin{bmatrix} x_{n+1} - x_n \\ y_{n+1} - y_n \\ \vdots \\ z_{n+1} - z_n \end{bmatrix} = \begin{bmatrix} -f(x_n, \ldots, z_n) \\ -g(x_n, \ldots, z_n) \\ \vdots \\ -h(x_n, \ldots, z_n) \end{bmatrix}$$

In the optimization problem, the objective functions are replaced by their derivatives and the left matrix becomes the Hessian matrix.

Figure 5-11 shows two instances in which the Newton-Raphson technique does not converge. The first shows that if the slope $f'(x)$ is close to zero, the next trial value will approach infinity. The second shows an infinite looping between two trials x_1 and x_2. Even if convergence is attained, the

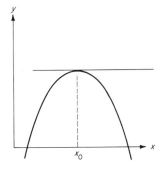
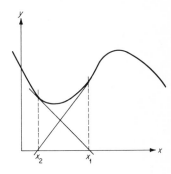

Fig. 5-11 Sources of divergence in the Newton-Raphson method.

root may correspond only to a local optimum, depending upon the initial choice of x_0.   Notwithstanding, the technique is widely useful.

5-3 KUHN-TUCKER OPTIMALITY CONDITIONS

The extension of the Lagrange multiplier technique to nonnegativity conditions and inequality constraints forms the basis for considering general nonlinear optimization problems.   These extensions are the *Kuhn-Tucker conditions*, named after the original investigators [21].   Although they often lead to computational impracticalities, the Kuhn-Tucker conditions provide clues to the optimal solution and enable one to check the optimality (or nonoptimality) of proposed solutions.

The purpose of this section is to acquaint the reader with Kuhn-Tucker theory for the reasons just cited and to develop concepts needed in the next section.   The proof of the Kuhn-Tucker conditions is beyond our scope, and our statement of the conditions is less than rigorous.   A brief, readable account of the subject appears in Hillier and Lieberman [18].   The discussion here is similar to theirs.

Recall that a necessary condition for a local optimum is that the first derivative vanish.   If the function is convex or concave, a vanishing first derivative is also a sufficient condition for a global optimum.

Suppose we now require the variables to satisfy nonnegativity conditions. The above necessary condition must be modified to allow for the possibility of optima occurring at boundaries, i.e., that one or more of the variables may take the value zero, as in Fig. 5-12.   A local minimum exists at $x = 0$ if the first derivative with respect to that variable is nonnegative; similarly, a local maximum exists if the derivative is nonpositive.

The required modifications are not so easy, however, if the optimization is subject to constraints.   The Kuhn-Tucker conditions extend the necessary conditions for an optimum to situations in which there are inequality constraints, i.e., to the *generalized Lagrange multiplier problem*.

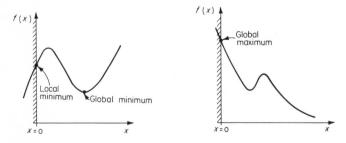

Fig. 5-12   Optima with nonnegativity conditions.

Specifically, let $z = f(x_1, x_2, \ldots, x_n)$ be a differentiable function of several variables $x_1, \ldots, x_n$ whose minimum is sought. Also, let the constraints $g_i(x_1, \ldots, x_n) \leqslant b_i$, $i = 1, \ldots, m$, be differentiable functions, and let x_i be restricted to nonnegative values. The Kuhn-Tucker theorem asserts that an optimal solution $x_1^*, \ldots, x_n^*$ to this problem, with nonnegativity conditions, will exist only if there exist numbers $\lambda_1, \ldots, \lambda_m$ such that all the following (Kuhn-Tucker) conditions are satisfied:

1. If $x_j^* > 0$, then $\dfrac{\partial f}{\partial x_j} + \sum\limits_{i=1}^{m} \lambda_i \dfrac{\partial g_i}{\partial x_j}\bigg|_{x_j^*} = 0; j = 1, \ldots, n.$

2. If $x_j^* = 0$, then $\dfrac{\partial f}{\partial x_j} + \sum\limits_{i=1}^{m} \lambda_i \dfrac{\partial g_i}{\partial x_j}\bigg|_{x_j^*} \geqslant 0; j = 1, \ldots, n.$

3. If $\lambda_i > 0$, then $g_i(x_1^*, \ldots, x_n^*) = b_i$; $i = 1, 2, \ldots, m.$
4. If $\lambda_i = 0$, then $g_i(x_1^*, \ldots, x_n^*) \leqslant b_i$; $i = 1, 2, \ldots, m.$
5. $x_j^* \geqslant 0; j = 1, \ldots, n.$
6. $\lambda_i \geqslant 0; i = 1, \ldots, m.$

where $|_{x_j^*}$ implies evaluation at the optimal solution.

Condition 1 expresses the necessary condition for an optimum provided that the stationary point is not at the boundary. Condition 2 supplements the first condition for the case where the optimum may be at the boundary. Condition 3 suggests that the inequality constraints introduced into the Lagrangian are binding; i.e., it suggests equality. Condition 4 indicates that constraints which do not bind have associated vanishing Lagrange multipliers which effectively remove them from the Lagrangian. Conditions 5 and 6 express the nonnegativity of the decision variables and of the Lagrange multipliers.

If the objective function and the feasible region are convex, the Kuhn-Tucker conditions are both necessary and sufficient for a global optimum. If the objective is to maximize, then conditions 1 to 6 hold, providing $f(x_1, \ldots, x_n)$ is replaced by its negative. A sufficient condition for a global optimum is that the objective be concave while the feasibility region remains convex. Consider two examples illustrating the Kuhn-Tucker conditions.

Example 5-6   Kuhn-Tucker conditions

Min: $z = f(x_1, x_2) = 6x_1{}^2 - 3x_2 - 4x_1 x_2 + 4x_2{}^2$

Subject to: $g_1(x_1, x_2) = e^{x_1} + \tfrac{1}{2}x_1 x_2 + \tfrac{1}{2}x_2{}^2 \leqslant 5$

$x_1, x_2 \geqslant 0$

We determine whether $f(x_1,x_2)$ is convex by calculating the derivatives:

$$\frac{\partial f}{\partial x_1} = 12x_1 - 4x_2 \qquad \frac{\partial^2 f}{\partial x_1^2} = 12 > 0 \qquad \frac{\partial^2 f}{\partial x_1 \, \partial x_2} = -4$$

$$\frac{\partial f}{\partial x_2} = -3 - 4x_1 + 8x_2 \qquad \frac{\partial^2 f}{\partial x_2^2} = 8 > 0$$

The Hessian matrix is

$$\mathbf{H} = \begin{bmatrix} 12 & -4 \\ -4 & 8 \end{bmatrix}$$

whose determinant has the value $96 - 16 = 80 > 0$. Since the determinant is positive and since the pure second derivatives are also positive, $f(x_1,x_2)$ is convex.

Now we seek the character of $g_1(x_1,x_2)$. The derivatives are

$$\frac{\partial g_1}{\partial x_1} = e^{x_1} + \tfrac{1}{2}x_2 \qquad \frac{\partial^2 g_1}{\partial x_1^2} = e^{x_1} \qquad \frac{\partial^2 g_1}{\partial x_1 \, \partial x_2} = \tfrac{1}{2}$$

$$\frac{\partial g_1}{\partial x_2} = \tfrac{1}{2}x_1 + x_2 \qquad \frac{\partial^2 g_1}{\partial x_2^2} = 1$$

and the Hessian matrix is

$$\mathbf{H} = \begin{bmatrix} e^{x_1} & 1/2 \\ 1/2 & 1 \end{bmatrix}$$

whose determinant is also positive. Again, since the pure derivatives are positive, it follows that $g_1(x_1,x_2)$, and hence the feasibility region, is convex.

Now we check to see if the Kuhn-Tucker conditions are satisfied, that is:

1. (a) If $x_1 > 0$, $12x_1 - 4x_2 + \lambda_1(e^{x_1} + \tfrac{1}{2}x_2) = 0$.
   (b) If $x_2 > 0$, $-3 - 4x_1 + 8x_2 + \lambda_1(\tfrac{1}{2}x_1 + x_2) = 0$.
2. (a) If $x_1 = 0$, $12x_1 - 4x_2 + \lambda_1(e^{x_1} + \tfrac{1}{2}x_2) \geqslant 0$.
   (b) If $x_2 = 0$, $-3 - 4x_1 + 8x_2 + \lambda(\tfrac{1}{2}x_1 + x_2) \geqslant 0$.
3. (a) If $\lambda_1 > 0$, $e^{x_1} + \tfrac{1}{2}x_1\,x_2 + \tfrac{1}{2}x_2^2 = 5$.
4. (a) If $\lambda_1 = 0$, $e^{x_1} + \tfrac{1}{2}x_1\,x_2 + \tfrac{1}{2}x_2^2 \leqslant 5$.
5. (a) $x_1 \geqslant 0$.
   (b) $x_2 \geqslant 0$.
6. (a) $\lambda_1 \geqslant 0$.

If values of x_1, x_2, and λ_1 can be found which satisfy these conditions, they constitute the optimal solution. Now we seek the conditions which apply. First, assume $\lambda_1 = 0$ (condition 4). Then $12x_1 - 4x_2 = -3 - 4x_1 + 8x_2 = 0$

(from conditions 1a and b). Solving simultaneously, $x_1 = 3/20$ and $x_2 = 9/20$. Do these constitute an optimal solution? Substituting, we find that condition 4 is satisfied. Since the determinants of the Hessian matrices for the objective function and constraints are nonnegative and the Kuhn-Tucker conditions are satisfied, the solution is a global minimum.

Example 5-7 Kuhn-Tucker conditions (continued) As a second illustration, consider

$$\text{Min:} \quad z = f(x_1, x_2) = -x_1 - 2x_2 + \frac{x_1^2}{2} + \frac{x_2^2}{2}$$

$$\text{Subject to:} \quad 2x_1 + 3x_2 \leqslant 6$$
$$x_1 + 4x_2 \leqslant 5$$
$$x_1, x_2 \geqslant 0$$

The objective function is convex since

$$\frac{\partial^2 f}{\partial x_1^2} = 1 > 0 \qquad \frac{\partial^2 f}{\partial x_2^2} = 1 > 0 \qquad \frac{\partial^2 f}{\partial x_1 \partial x_2} = 0$$

and

$$\mathbf{H} = \begin{vmatrix} 1 & 0 \\ 0 & 1 \end{vmatrix} = 1 > 0$$

The constraints are linear and thus constitute a convex set. The Kuhn-Tucker conditions (below) become both necessary and sufficient for a global minimum.

1. (a) If $x_1 > 0$, $-1 + x_1 + 2\lambda_1 + \lambda_2 = 0$.
   (b) If $x_2 > 0$, $-2 + x_2 + 3\lambda_1 + 4\lambda_2 = 0$.
2. (a) If $x_1 = 0$, $-1 + x_1 + 2\lambda_1 + \lambda_2 \geqslant 0$.
   (b) If $x_2 = 0$, $-2 + x_2 + 3\lambda_1 + 4\lambda_2 \geqslant 0$.
3. (a) If $\lambda_1 > 0$, $2x_1 + 3x_2 = 6$.
   (b) If $\lambda_2 > 0$, $x_1 + 4x_2 = 5$.
4. (a) If $\lambda_1 = 0$, $2x_1 + 3x_2 \leqslant 6$.
   (b) If $\lambda_2 = 0$, $x_1 + 4x_2 \leqslant 5$.
5. (a,b) $x_1, x_2 \geqslant 0$.
6. (a,b) $\lambda_1, \lambda_2 \geqslant 0$.

If $\lambda_1 = 0$ and $\lambda_2 = 0$, it follows from conditions 1a and b that $x_1 = 1$ and $x_2 = 2$. These values violate conditions 4a and b and, thus, cannot be permitted. If $\lambda_1 > 0$ and $\lambda_2 > 0$, then (from conditions 3a and b) $x_1 = 9/5$ and $x_2 = 4/5$. From conditions 1a and b, for these values of x_1 and x_2, we obtain $\lambda_1 = 22/25$, $\lambda_2 = -24/25$, and thus $\lambda_2 < 0$, which violates condition 3b. Next, we consider $\lambda_1 = 0$ and $\lambda_2 > 0$.   Solving conditions $1a$ and b and $3b$, we obtain $x_2 = 18/17$, $x_1 = 13/17$, and $\lambda_2 = 4/17$.   A check of condition $4a$ shows that the solution is feasible.   Therefore, conditions $3a$, $2a$, $2b$, and $4b$ do not arise and the solution at hand is optimal.

5-4 GEOMETRIC PROGRAMMING

Geometric programming evolved in the 1960s.   Largely developed by Duffin, Peterson, and Zener ([8] and [9]), it differs from other optimization techniques in the emphasis it places upon the relative magnitudes of the terms of the objective function rather than the variables.   Instead of finding optimal values of the variables directly, geometric programming first finds the optimal way to distribute total cost among the various terms in the objective function. This quality makes it an important technique for engineering design.   It indicates how resources should be apportioned among the components contributing to the design objective.   Additional advantages, compared with the calculus and Lagrange multiplier methods, are that the resulting simultaneous equations are often easier to obtain and that the method provides an important insight into the effect of changes in the values of variables on the value of the objective function.

In this section we provide an introduction to geometric programming patterned after Wilde and Beightler [31].   We introduce geometric programming from two points of view.   The first view stems from the calculus techniques of the earlier sections of this chapter.   The second view, used by Duffin and Peterson, stems from the so-called *geometric inequality*.

CALCULUS VIEWPOINT

Let $y_j(\mathbf{x})$ denote the product function

$$y_j(\mathbf{x}) = \prod_{i=1}^{n} x_i^{a_{ij}} \qquad j = 1, \ldots, m \tag{4}$$

where $\mathbf{x}$ designates the vector $[x_1, \ldots, x_n]$ and the exponents a_{ij} are real constants.   Now consider an objective function of the form

$$\text{Min:} \quad z = \sum_{j=1}^{m} c_j y_j(\mathbf{x}) \tag{5}$$

where the coefficients c_j are, for the time being, positive constants.   Such polynomials as the right side of Eq. (5) are called *posynomials* because of the positive coefficients and the real exponents.

For example, the lot-size model defined by Eq. (1) has one independent variable, that is, $n = 1$, two terms in the objective function, that is, $m = 2$, and considered respectively, $a_{11} = -1$, $a_{12} = 1$, $c_1 = a$, and $c_2 = b$.

A necessary condition for z to be a minimum is that its first derivatives vanish. That is,

$$\frac{\partial z}{\partial x_i} = \sum_{j=1}^{m} c_j a_{ij} x_i^{-1} y_j(\mathbf{x}) = 0 \qquad i = 1, \ldots, n \tag{6}$$

where the factor $a_{ij} x_i^{-1}$ arises from the differentiation of $y_j(\mathbf{x})$ with respect to x_i. Customarily, one attempts to solve these n equations for the set $x_{10}, \ldots, x_{n0}$ of optimal solutions. Again, recall that this is only a necessary condition and that further tests are required to establish the optimal character of the solutions. Also, the minimum may not be global. We return to these matters later.

Geometric programming proceeds by identifying weights ω_j, defined by

$$\omega_j = \frac{c_j y_j(\mathbf{x}_0)}{z_0} \qquad j = 1, \ldots, m \tag{7}$$

where the zero subscript denotes values corresponding to optima. That is, *the weights describe the fraction of the total resource that should be assigned to the corresponding terms of the design objective to achieve an optimum design.*

We have the normality condition[1]

$$\sum_{j=1}^{m} \omega_j = 1 \tag{8}$$

Also, it follows from Eq. (6), after replacing $\mathbf{x}$ by $\mathbf{x}_0$, multiplying by x_{i0}/z_0, and using Eq. (7), that

$$\sum_{j=1}^{m} a_{ij} \omega_j = 0 \qquad i = 1, \ldots, n \tag{9}$$

a so-called orthogonality condition.[1] For example, using Eqs. (8) and (9) for the lot-size model of Eq. (1), we have the set

$$\omega_1 + \omega_2 = 1$$
$$-\omega_1 + \omega_2 = 0$$

from which $\omega_1 = \omega_2 = 1/2$.

Now, using Eqs. (7) and (8),

$$z_0 = \prod_j (z_0)^{\omega_j} = \prod_j \left[\frac{c_j y_j(\mathbf{x}_0)}{\omega_j} \right]^{\omega_j} = \prod_j \left[\frac{c_j}{\omega_j} \right]^{\omega_j} \prod_j [y_j(\mathbf{x}_0)]^{\omega_j}$$

and, since the last product

$$\prod_j [y_j(\mathbf{x}_0)]^{\omega_j} = \prod_j \prod_i (x_{i0})^{a_{ij} \omega_j} = \prod_i (x_{i0})^{\sum a_{ij} \omega_j} = \prod_i (x_{i0})^0 = 1$$

[1] Vectors are said to be normal if their sum is unity and orthogonal if their product is zero.

where the summation is over j, we conclude

$$z_0 = \prod_j \left[\frac{c_j}{\omega_j}\right]^{\omega_j} \tag{10}$$

For the lot-size model, we conclude, as in Sec. 5-1, that

$$z_0 = \left[\frac{c_1}{\omega_1}\right]^{\omega_1} \left[\frac{c_2}{\omega_2}\right]^{\omega_2} = \left[\frac{a}{1/2}\right]^{1/2} \left[\frac{b}{1/2}\right]^{1/2} = 2(ab)^{1/2}$$

Note that we have determined z_0 prior to determining x_0.

We restate these results in the context of the flood-control optimization of Example 5-2. Since $\omega_1 = \omega_2 = 1/2$, we conclude that for optimality, *the cost of the reservoir is equal to the levee cost and the minimum flood protection cost is $2\sqrt{ab}$.* Note that a design rule has emerged before we have evaluated the optimal channel capacity.

The lot-size model illustrates geometric programming at its best. More general problems cannot always be analyzed with comparable elegance. The reason is that the lot-size model possesses zero *degrees of difficulty*. The number of degrees of difficulty is defined as the number of terms in the objective function less the number of variables less 1, that is, $m - n - 1$. This measure arises from Eqs. (8) and (9) since they are to be solved simultaneously for the weights. There are a total of $n + 1$ equations (orthogonality and normality conditions) for the m weights. Thus, if the equations are independent, a unique solution exists when the numbers of weights and equations are equal. This does not mean that geometric programming is effective only for problems with zero degrees of difficulty. When the number of degrees of difficulty is small, useful results are usually attainable. We shall return to this matter after considering geometric programming from the point of view of a geometric inequality.

GEOMETRIC INEQUALITY: PRIMAL-DUAL RELATIONS

The general geometric inequality can be written

$$u_1 + u_2 + \cdots + u_n \geqslant \left[\frac{u_1}{\omega_1}\right]^{\omega_1} \left[\frac{u_2}{\omega_2}\right]^{\omega_2} \cdots \left[\frac{u_n}{\omega_n}\right]^{\omega_n}$$

or, similarly,

$$\omega_1 v_1 + \omega_2 v_2 + \cdots + \omega_n v_n \geqslant v_1^{\omega_1} v_2^{\omega_2} \cdots v_n^{\omega_n} \tag{11}$$

where $u_1 = \omega_1 v_1, \ldots, u_n = \omega_n v_n$ are nonnegative and the positive weights $\omega_1, \omega_2, \ldots, \omega_n$ satisfy the normality condition [Eq. (8)]. Also, the equality sign holds if, and only if, $u_1/\omega_1 = u_2/\omega_2 = \cdots = u_n/\omega_n$. This inequality is fundamental to geometric programming. A proof is beyond our scope but references are easily available (e.g., Chap. IV of Duffin et al. [9]).

Using the geometric inequality for the objective function of Eq. (5), we can write

$$c_1 y_1 + \cdots + c_n y_n \geqslant \left[\frac{c_1 y_1}{\omega_1}\right]^{\omega_1} \cdots \left[\frac{c_n y_n}{\omega_n}\right]^{\omega_n}$$

where $y_1 = y_1(\mathbf{x})$, etc.   The left side is called the *primal* function, and the right side, the *predual*.   Recalling Eqs. (4), the right side of the last inequality can be written

$$\left[\frac{c_1}{\omega_1}\right]^{\omega_1} \cdots \left[\frac{c_n}{\omega_n}\right]^{\omega_n} x_1^{\Sigma a_{1j}\omega_j} x_2^{\Sigma a_{2j}\omega_j} \cdots x_n^{\Sigma a_{nj}\omega_j}$$

where $j = 1, \ldots, m$ and the summations are over the index j.

If the weights are chosen so that the exponents vanish, then we have, again, the Eqs. (9).   The inequality becomes simply

$$c_1 y_1 + \cdots + c_n y_n \geqslant \left[\frac{c_1}{\omega_1}\right]^{\omega_1} \cdots \left[\frac{c_n}{\omega_n}\right]^{\omega_n} \tag{12}$$

and the right side is called the *dual* function, $d(\omega_1, \ldots, \omega_n)$.

A basic result is that *the maximum of the dual function equals the minimum of the primal function*.   This theorem, whose proof is beyond our scope, enables us to accomplish the optimization by minimizing the primal *or* by maximizing the dual, whichever is easier.   Also, the maximization of the dual function subject to the orthogonality and normality conditions is a *sufficient* condition for z, the primal function, to be a global minimum.   An easy-to-follow derivation using the Lagrange multiplier technique is given on p. 105 *et seq.* of [31].

For example, for the lot-size model, the geometric inequality gives a lower bound of $(2a/x)^{1/2}(2bx)^{1/2} = 2\sqrt{ab}$ for the primal since no dual value can exceed a primal value.   However, note that for $x = \sqrt{a/b}$, the primal function $a/x + bx$ also takes the value $2\sqrt{ab}$.   Therefore, $2\sqrt{ab}$ is the greatest lower bound (because, again, no value of the dual function can exceed a value of the primal function).   A moment's reflection shows that the greatest lower bound of $2\sqrt{ab}$ is simultaneously the maximum of the dual and the minimum of the primal.

Consider again the "degrees of difficulty."   For zero degrees of difficulty, i.e., when the number of terms in the objective function exceeds the number of variables by unity, Eqs. (8) and (9) have a unique solution for the weights. These weights correspond to the optimal solution.   Using these weights, the dual function can be evaluated, and in view of the equality of primal and dual at the optimum, the value of z_0 is at hand.   To obtain the values of $x_{10}, \ldots, x_{n0}$ corresponding to the optimum, one uses Eqs. (7).

Suppose that in the flood-control optimization of Example 5-2, replacement and maintenance of levees incur additional costs, which are approximated by the square of the channel capacity. The total flood-protection cost z is then

$$z = \frac{c_1}{x} + c_2 x + c_3 x^2$$

where $c_1 = a$, $c_2 = b$, and c_3 is a positive constant. Now $m = 3$ and $n = 1$, so that there is one $(3 - 1 - 1)$ degree of difficulty.

The orthogonality and normality conditions [Eqs. (8) and (9)] yield

$$\omega_1 + \omega_2 + \omega_3 = 1$$
$$-\omega_1 + \omega_2 + 2\omega_3 = 0$$

While we cannot solve for each of the weights, any two of them can be expressed in terms of the third. For example,

$$\omega_2 = 2 - 3\omega_1 \quad \text{and} \quad \omega_3 = 2\omega_1 - 1 \tag{13}$$

The dual function, $d(\omega_1)$, is written

$$d(\omega_1) = \left[\frac{c_1}{\omega_1}\right]^{\omega_1} \left[\frac{c_2}{2 - 3\omega_1}\right]^{2-3\omega_1} \left[\frac{c_3}{2\omega_1 - 1}\right]^{2\omega_1 - 1} \tag{14}$$

According to the basic result cited earlier, the maximum of the dual with respect to the variable $\omega_1 (\geq 0)$ is the optimal solution. Since the logarithm is an increasing function, maximizing $\ln d(\omega_1)$ yields the same result as maximizing $d(\omega_1)$. Thus

$$\ln d(\omega_1) = -\omega_1 \ln \frac{\omega_1}{c_1} - (2 - 3\omega_1)\ln \frac{2 - 3\omega_1}{c_2} - (2\omega_1 - 1)\ln \frac{2\omega_1 - 1}{c_3}$$

and equating the derivative to zero yields

$$-\ln \frac{\omega_1}{c_1} - 1 + 3\ln \frac{2 - 3\omega_1}{c_2} + 3 - 2\ln \frac{2\omega_1 - 1}{c_3} - 2 = 0$$

or

$$= \ln \frac{(2 - 3\omega_1)^3}{(2\omega_1 - 1)^2 \omega_1} - \ln \frac{c_2^{\,3}}{c_3^{\,2} c_1} = 0$$

Notice that the sum of the nonlogarithmic terms is zero. The maximizing value of ω_1, ω_{10}, satisfies

$$\frac{(2 - 3\omega_{10})^3}{(2\omega_{10} - 1)^2 \omega_{10}} = \frac{c_2^{\,3}}{c_3^{\,2} c_1}$$

Once ω_{10} is obtained, Eq. (14) can be used to determine the optimum value of the dual function and therefore z_0. Note that the weights may no longer be independent of the objective coefficients when there are nonzero degrees of difficulty. Even before the maximization was performed, Eqs. (13) yielded interesting design information. For example, the equation for ω_2 implies that $\omega_1 \leqslant 2/3$ and $\geqslant 1/3$ if ω_2 can take all values in the unit interval. Under similar conditions, the equation for ω_3 implies that $\omega_1 \leqslant 1$ and $\geqslant 1/2$. Since $1/2$ is greater than $1/3$, ω_2 cannot achieve the full range. In fact, ω_2 cannot exceed $1/2$. Since $2/3$ is smaller than unity, we have that $\omega_3 \leqslant 1/3$. Summarizing,

$$1/2 \leqslant \omega_1 \leqslant 2/3 \qquad 0 \leqslant \omega_2 \leqslant 1/2 \qquad 0 \leqslant \omega_3 \leqslant 1/3$$

Many an experienced designer could probably effect significant design improvements even with these rudimentary results. The optimal design will have the character that no matter what the values of the cost coefficients c_1, c_2, and c_3, the reservoir cost is never less than one-half nor greater than two-thirds of the total cost.

Note that any assignment of weights, consistent with the preceding expressions, can be used to evaluate the dual function to provide a lower bound on the minimum cost of the design. The corresponding values of the x's can be substituted in the primal function to obtain an upper bound on the optimum cost. We shall illustrate this point later.

INEQUALITY CONSTRAINTS

Most engineering optimization problems are subject to constraints. In addition to the posynomial objective [Eqs. (4) and (5)], consider l posynomial constraints $g_k(\mathbf{x})$ given by

$$g_k(\mathbf{x}) = \sum_{j=1}^{m_k} c_{kj} y_{kj}(\mathbf{x}) \lessgtr 1 \qquad k = 1, \ldots, l \tag{15}$$

where $c_{kj} > 0$ and $y_{kj}(\mathbf{x}) = \prod_{i=1}^{n} x_i^{a_{kij}}$. As before, we introduce weights ω_j given by Eq. (7) and constraint weights ω_{kj} defined by

$$\omega_{kj} = c_{kj} y_{kj}(\mathbf{x}) = c_{kj} \prod_{i=1}^{n} x_i^{a_{kij}} \tag{16}$$

Two preliminary considerations will simplify our description of how to deal with geometric programming under constraints. First, we introduce a *signum function* σ_k for the kth constraint such that it takes on the value $+1$ or -1 depending on whether $g_k(\mathbf{x}) \leqslant 1$ or >1, respectively. Specifically, we can write the kth constraint $1 - g_k(\mathbf{x})$, and this function may be less than or greater than zero according as it is a "greater than" or "less than" constraint. Using the signum function, we can summarize both cases as

$$\sigma_k[1 - g_k(\mathbf{x})] \geqslant 0 \qquad \text{all } k \tag{17}$$

A second preliminary concerns an exponential transformation which aids our discussion. Imagine replacing x_i by $\exp(u_i)$, for all i in constraint Eqs. (7) and (16). Note that u_i can take any real value without x_i becoming negative. Taking natural logarithms of Eqs. (7) and (16), the original problem [defined by Eqs. (5) and (17)] can be transformed into one of minimizing $\ln z$ subject to normality condition (8), inequality constraints (17), and the new set of Eqs. (7) and (16). The resulting expressions and the accompanying proofs are cumbersome but not difficult. In the remainder of this section we describe the main ideas without proof and with minor symbolic detail. The application-oriented reader may find the treatment adequate to his purpose, while the reader interested in mathematical details may find it a useful overview to Chap. 4, Secs. 4 to 11, of Wilde and Beightler [31].

To solve the constrained problem, one formulates the Lagrangian of the transformed primal problem and utilizes the Kuhn-Tucker conditions. As mentioned, after employing the exponential transformation and taking logarithms, one has $\ln z$ as the objective function subject to equality constraints involving the objective and constraint weights and the new variables u_i. The constraints corresponding to inequality (17), using expressions (15) and (16), are written

$$\sigma_k \left[1 - \sum_{j=1}^{m_k} \omega_{kj} \right] \geqslant 0 \qquad \text{all } k \tag{18}$$

To form the Lagrangian for $\ln z$, these inequality constraints (18) require Lagrange multipliers which vanish when the constraint is slack (see Sec. 5-3 and [31]). (This restriction can be ignored if the constraint is an equality.) Having formed the Lagrangian, we apply the Kuhn-Tucker conditions. Finally, the result given by Wilde and Beightler [31] is the dual problem corresponding to the original primal problem:

$$\text{Max:} \quad d(\boldsymbol{\mu}) = \prod_{k=0}^{l} \prod_{j=1}^{m_k} \left[\frac{c_{kj}}{\mu_{kj}} \sum_{t=1}^{m_k} \mu_{kt} \right]^{\sigma_k \mu_{kj}} \tag{19}$$

$$\text{Subject to:} \quad \sum_{j=1}^{m_0} \mu_{0j} = 1 \qquad \text{normality condition} \tag{20}$$

$$\sum_{k=0}^{l} \sum_{j=1}^{m_k} \sigma_k a_{kij} \mu_{kj} = 0 \qquad \begin{array}{l} \text{orthogonality condition} \\ \text{for } i = 1, \ldots, n \end{array} \tag{21}$$

$$\sum_{j=1}^{m_k} \mu_{kj} \geqslant 0 \qquad \text{nonnegativity condition} \tag{22}$$

where μ is the set of dual variables and the subscript $k = 0$ (with the convention that $\sigma_0 = 1$) denotes the objective function while the higher values of k identify the constraints. As before, the dual variables μ_{0j} (one of each term of the objective function) are identical to the objective weights ω_j given by Eq. (7), whereas the dual variables μ_{kj} and the constraint weights ω_{kj} are related by

$$\omega_{kj} = \frac{\mu_{kj}}{\sum\limits_{j=1}^{m_k} \mu_{kj}} \tag{23}$$

We have now cast our original constrained problem into an equivalent problem with linear constraints which can be treated in the same manner as the unconstrained case.

There are $n + 1$ linear equations and the total number of terms in both objective and constraint functions is $m = \sum\limits_{k=0}^{l} m_k$. As in the unconstrained case, if the equations are linearly independent, the degree of difficulty is $m - n - 1$. For zero degree of difficulty, the solution is unique. Once the optimum values of μ_{kj} are obtained, evaluating Eq. (19) yields the maximum of the dual, which is also the minimum of the primal, that is, $d(\mu_0) = z_0$. Having the optimum value of the objective, the next step is to determine the value of the design variables x_i. This is achieved by solving simultaneously the equations

$$c_{0j} \prod_{i=1}^{n} x_i^{a_{0ij}} = \mu_{0j} z_0 \qquad \text{for } j = 1, 2, \ldots, m_0 \tag{24}$$

$$c_{kj} \prod_{i=1}^{n} x_i^{a_{kij}} = \frac{\mu_{kj}}{\sum\limits_{j=1}^{m_k} \mu_{kj}} \qquad \begin{array}{l} \text{for } j = 1, 2, \ldots, m_k \\ k = 1, 2, \ldots, l \end{array} \tag{25}$$

Unfortunately, we cannot immediately conclude that maximization of the dual function (19) will yield the desired optima as in the unconstrained case unless there are zero degrees of difficulty. Otherwise, we need to distinguish two cases.

LESS-THAN INEQUALITIES

First, if the $\sigma_k = 1$ for all k, the Lagrangian is a strictly convex function of the u_i. This follows because the objective and constraint posynomials are convex. The local minimum (or dual maximum) satisfying the normality and orthogonality conditions in this case must also be global. The following two examples help clarify these ideas.

Example 5-8 A less-than inequality: zero degrees of difficulty

Min: $z = 2x_1 x_2^2 x_3^{-1} + 4x_1^{-1} x_2^{-3} x_4$

Subject to: $3x_1^{-1} x_3 x_4^{-2} + 4x_4 x_3 \leqslant 1$

$5x_1 x_2 \leqslant 1$

$x_i \geqslant 0 \qquad i = 1, 2, 3, 4$

The dual function [using Eq. (19)] is written

$$\text{Max:} \quad d(\boldsymbol{\mu}) = \left[\frac{2(\mu_{01} + \mu_{02})}{\mu_{01}} \right]^{\mu_{01}} \left[\frac{4(\mu_{01} + \mu_{02})}{\mu_{02}} \right]^{\mu_{02}}$$

$$\left[\frac{3(\mu_{11} + \mu_{12})}{\mu_{11}} \right]^{\mu_{11}} \left[\frac{4(\mu_{11} + \mu_{12})}{\mu_{12}} \right]^{\mu_{12}} \left[\frac{5\mu_{21}}{\mu_{21}} \right]^{\mu_{21}}$$

The maximization is subject to the constraints (20) to (22):

$\mu_{01} + \mu_{02} = 1$	normality condition
$\mu_{01} - \mu_{02} - \mu_{11} + \mu_{21} = 0$	orthogonality condition for variable x_1
$2\mu_{01} - 3\mu_{02} + \mu_{21} = 0$	orthogonality condition for variable x_2
$-\mu_{01} + \mu_{11} + \mu_{12} = 0$	orthogonality condition for variable x_3
$\mu_{02} - 2\mu_{11} + \mu_{12} = 0$	orthogonality condition for variable x_4
$\mu_{11} + \mu_{12} \geqslant 0$	nonnegativity condition
$\mu_{kj} \geqslant 0$	for $k = 0, 1, 2; j = 1, 2$

The degree of difficulty in this example is $5 - 4 - 1 = 0$, and the set of five linear equations have the unique solution $\mu_{01} = \frac{5}{9}$, $\mu_{02} = \frac{4}{9}$, $\mu_{11} = \frac{1}{3}$, $\mu_{12} = \mu_{21} = \frac{2}{9}$. The optimum value of the objective is given by

$$z_0 = d_0 = \left[\frac{2 \times 9}{5} \right]^{5/9} \left[\frac{4 \times 9}{4} \right]^{4/9} \left[\frac{3 \times 5/9}{1/3} \right]^{1/3} \left[\frac{4 \times 5/9}{2/9} \right]^{2/9} (5)^{2/9} = 22.6$$

The design variables can be obtained from Eqs. (24) and (25):

$2x_1 x_2^2 x_3^{-1} = \frac{5}{9}(22.6) = 12.55$

$4x_1^{-1} x_2^{-3} x_4 = \frac{4}{9}(22.6) = 10.04$

$3x_1^{-1} x_3 x_4^{-2} = \dfrac{1/3}{5/9} = \frac{3}{5}$

$5x_1 x_2 = \dfrac{2/9}{2/9} = 1$

Thus $x_1 = 0.111$, $x_2 = 1.79$, $x_3 = 0.057$, $x_4 = 1.6$. Since the degree of difficulty is zero, the solution is unique and, hence, global.

In the next example we add an additional term to the objective function just considered.

Example 5-9   A less-than inequality: one degree of difficulty

$$\text{Min:}\quad z = 2x_1 x_2^2 x_3^{-1} + 4x_1^{-1} x_2^{-3} x_4 + 5x_1 x_3$$

$$\text{Subject to:}\quad 3x_1^{-1} x_3 x_4^{-2} + 4x_4 x_3 \leqslant 1$$
$$5x_1 x_2 \leqslant 1$$
$$x_i \geqslant 0 \qquad i = 1, 2, 3, 4$$

Note that we have added the term $5x_1 x_3$ to the previous objective function, with the result that the problem now has one degree of difficulty.

The dual problem is written

$$\text{Max:}\quad d(\mathbf{\mu}) = \left[\frac{2}{\mu_{01}}\right]^{\mu_{01}} \left[\frac{4}{\mu_{02}}\right]^{\mu_{02}} \left[\frac{5}{\mu_{03}}\right]^{\mu_{03}} \left[\frac{3(\mu_{11} + \mu_{12})}{\mu_{11}}\right]^{\mu_{11}}$$

$$\left[\frac{4(\mu_{11} + \mu_{12})}{\mu_{12}}\right]^{\mu_{12}} (5)^{\mu_{21}}$$

Subject to:
$$\mu_{01} + \mu_{02} + \mu_{03} = 1 \qquad\qquad \text{normality condition}$$
$$\mu_{01} - \mu_{02} + \mu_{03} - \mu_{11} + \mu_{21} = 0 \qquad \text{orth. cond. for var. } x_1$$
$$2\mu_{01} - 3\mu_{02} + \mu_{21} = 0 \qquad\qquad \text{orth. cond. for var. } x_2$$
$$-\mu_{01} + \mu_{03} + \mu_{11} + \mu_{12} = 0 \qquad\quad \text{orth. cond. for var. } x_3$$
$$\mu_{02} - 2\mu_{11} + \mu_{12} = 0 \qquad\qquad \text{orth. cond. for var. } x_4$$
$$\mu_{11} + \mu_{12} \geqslant 0 \qquad\qquad\qquad \text{nonnegativity cond.}$$
$$\mu_{kj} \geqslant 0 \qquad\qquad\qquad\qquad \text{for } k = 0, 1, 2;$$
$$j = 1, 2, 3$$

In order to obtain bounds on z_0, assume the added term $5x_1 x_3$ has no effect on the total cost, that is, $\mu_{03} = 0$. The solution from Example 5-8 is $\mu_{01} = \frac{5}{9}, \mu_{02} = \frac{4}{9}, \mu_{11} = \frac{1}{3}, \mu_{12} = \mu_{21} = \frac{2}{9}$. Substituting these values in the dual objective, we obtain a lower bound on z_0, $d(\frac{5}{9}, \frac{4}{9}, 0, \frac{1}{3}, \frac{2}{9}, \frac{2}{6}) = 22.6$. Evaluating the variables results in values identical to those obtained in Example 8, that is, $x_1 = 0.111$, $x_2 = 1.79$, $x_3 = 0.057$, and $x_4 = 1.6$. Substituting these values in the primal objective, including the effect of the third term, we obtain the upper bound on z_0 to be 22.61. Thus

$$22.6 \leqslant z_0 \leqslant 22.61$$

In this instance, we conclude that the added term, $5x_1 x_3$, has negligible effect upon the total (optimal) cost and that its inclusion in the design problem is not particularly useful.

It is important to note that since all the constraints have the form $g_k(\mathbf{x}) \leqslant 1$, a local minimum satisfying the normality and orthogonality conditions is also the global minimum and that

$$d(\mathbf{\mu}) \leqslant z_0 = d_0 \leqslant z(\mathbf{x}) \tag{26}$$

This result is established by Duffin et al. [9]. As illustrated, it can be used to obtain quick estimates of the optimal value of the objective function when the number of degrees of difficulty exceeds zero. The estimate is obtained by arbitrarily assigning zero values to as many dual variables as there are degrees of difficulty and solving the resulting zero-degree problem for the remaining dual variables. These dual variables, when substituted into the dual function, give a lower bound on the true optimum. The corresponding design variables x_i can be used to construct an upper bound by substituting their values into the objective function. If the gap between the lower and upper bounds is large, one concludes that the neglected terms in fact play an important part in the overall cost picture; the choice of zero dual variables has not been a good one. The procedure is repeated with another set of dual variables set equal to zero until an acceptable difference is achieved.

MIXED INEQUALITIES

Now consider the case $\sigma_k = -1$ for at least some k. The convexity of the Lagrangian is no longer certain. In this case, all stationary points must be located and evaluated for the desired minimum. Unfortunately, a useful feature of the previous geometric-programming formulation is lost since Eq. (26) can no longer be used for obtaining quick estimates of the bounds. Instead, normality and orthogonality conditions are used to eliminate $n + 1$ variables from the dual, $d(\mu)$. The partial derivatives of the logarithm of this function, $\ln d(\mu)$, with respect to the remaining dual variables can be set equal to zero and solved simultaneously. These resulting nonlinear equations (as many as there are degrees of difficulty) yield the best values of the dual variables. This approach is occasionally impractical due to the computations required. However, if the set of nonlinear equations can be solved, geometric programming provides an elegant approach. Consider an example having mixed inequalities.

Example 5-10   Mixed inequalities: one degree of difficulty

Min: $z = 2x_1 x_2^2 x_3^{-1} + 4x_1^{-1} x_2^{-3} x_4 + 5x_1 x_3$

Subject to: $3x_1 x_3^{-1} x_4^2 + 4x_4^{-1} x_3^{-1} \geqslant 1$
$5x_1 x_2 \leqslant 1$
$x_i \geqslant 0 \qquad i = 1, 2, 3, 4$

The example is the same as Example 5-9 except that the inequality of the first constraint has been reversed. The signum functions for the first and second constraints are $\sigma_1 = -1$ and $\sigma_2 = 1$, respectively. There are six terms and four variables, giving one degree of difficulty. The normality and orthogonality conditions are

$$\mu_{01} + \mu_{02} + \mu_{03} = 1 \qquad\qquad \text{normality}$$
$$\mu_{01} - \mu_{02} + \mu_{03} - \mu_{11} + \mu_{21} = 0 \qquad \text{orthogonality, for } x_1$$
$$2\mu_{01} - 3\mu_{02} + \mu_{21} = 0 \qquad\qquad \text{orthogonality, for } x_2$$
$$-\mu_{01} + \mu_{03} + \mu_{11} + \mu_{12} = 0 \qquad \text{orthogonality, for } x_3$$
$$\mu_{02} - 2\mu_{11} + \mu_{12} = 0 \qquad\qquad \text{orthogonality, for } x_4$$
$$\mu_{11} + \mu_{12} \geqslant 0$$
$$\mu_{kj} \geqslant 0 \qquad\qquad\qquad k = 0,1,2; j = 1,2,3$$

The solution, in terms of μ_{03}, is

$$\mu_{01} = \tfrac{5}{9} + \tfrac{2}{9}\mu_{03} \qquad \mu_{02} = \tfrac{4}{9} - \tfrac{11}{9}\mu_{03} \qquad \mu_{11} = \tfrac{1}{3} - \tfrac{2}{3}\mu_3$$

$$\mu_{12} = \tfrac{2}{9} - \tfrac{1}{9}\mu_{03} \qquad \mu_{21} = \tfrac{2}{9} - \tfrac{37}{9}\mu_{03}$$

and the dual function in terms of μ_{03} is

$$d(\mu_{03}) = \left[\frac{2}{\tfrac{5}{9} + \tfrac{2}{9}\mu_{03}}\right]^{\tfrac{5}{9}+\tfrac{2}{9}\mu_{03}} \left[\frac{4}{\tfrac{4}{9} - \tfrac{11}{9}\mu_{03}}\right]^{\tfrac{4}{9}-\tfrac{11}{9}\mu_{03}} \left[\frac{5}{\mu_{03}}\right]^{\mu_{03}}$$
$$\left[\frac{3(\tfrac{5}{9} - \tfrac{7}{9}\mu_{03})}{\tfrac{1}{3} - \tfrac{2}{3}\mu_{03}}\right]^{-(\tfrac{1}{3}-\tfrac{2}{3}\mu_{03})} \left[\frac{4(\tfrac{5}{9} - \tfrac{7}{9}\mu_{03})}{\tfrac{2}{9} - \tfrac{1}{9}\mu_{03}}\right]^{-(\tfrac{2}{9}-\tfrac{1}{9}\mu_{03})} \left[\frac{2}{5}\right]^{\tfrac{2}{9}-\tfrac{37}{9}\mu_{03}}$$

To simplify the computations, we differentiate $\ln d(\mu_{03})$ rather than $d(\mu_{03})$ and set its derivative to zero. Once the dual variables are known, the procedure of previous examples is used for the solution.

NEGATIVE COEFFICIENTS

Our consideration thus far has been restricted to posynomials, i.e., positive coefficients in all terms of the constraint and objective functions. Clearly, it is of importance for applications that we be able to include problems with negative coefficients. Our strategy, again, is to cast the problem into a form which enables us to use the methods just described.

Imagine that the kth constraint has terms with positive and negative coefficients. We write

$$g_k(\mathbf{x}) = P_k(\mathbf{x}) - N_k(\mathbf{x}) \qquad k = 1, \ldots, l$$

where $P_k(\mathbf{x})$ and $N_k(\mathbf{x})$ are posynomial aggregations of the terms with positive and negative coefficients, respectively. Therefore, we write inequation (17) as

$$\sigma_k[1 - P_k(x) + N_k(x)] \geqslant 0 \qquad \text{all } k \tag{27}$$

We now indicate a clever device by which we split the last expression into two constraints, introduce an additional variable, and reduce the problem to the case considered earlier. Rearranging inequation (27), we obtain

$$\sigma_k[1 + N_k(\mathbf{x})] \geqslant \sigma_k P_k(\mathbf{x}) \qquad \text{all } k \tag{28}$$

Let v_k be a nonnegative variable defined by

$$v_k = 1 + N_k(\mathbf{x}) \qquad k = 1, 2, \ldots, l \tag{29}$$

such that the inequality constraints (28) can be replaced by the following two inequations:

$$\sigma_k[1 - v_k^{-1} P_k(\mathbf{x})] \geqslant 0 \tag{30}$$

and

$$-\sigma_k[1 - v_k^{-1} - v_k^{-1} N_k(\mathbf{x})] \geqslant 0 \tag{31}$$

Note that adding inequations (30) and (31) simply yields the original constraint (27) since $v_k \geqslant 0$. Note, also, that the two new constraints bind whenever the original constraint binds. Using this technique, all constraints which have negative coefficients can be replaced by two posynomial constraints which introduce both an additional term (v_k^{-1}) and an additional variable (v_k) and, hence, *leave the number of degrees of difficulty unchanged*.

Again, omitting the derivation (see [31]) we cite the dual problem for this case:

$$\text{Max:} \quad d(\boldsymbol{\mu}) = \prod_{k=0}^{l} \prod_{j=1}^{m_k} \left[\frac{c_{kj}}{\mu_{kj}} \sigma_k \sum_{t=1}^{mk} \sigma_{kt} \mu_{kt} \right]^{\sigma_{kj}\mu_{kj}} \tag{32}$$

$$\text{Subject to:} \quad \sum_{j=1}^{m_0} \mu_{0j} = 1 \qquad \qquad \text{normality condition}$$

$$\sum_{k=0}^{l} \sum_{j=1}^{m_k} \sigma_{kj} a_{kij} \mu_{kj} = 0 \qquad \begin{array}{l} \text{orthogonality condition} \\ \text{for } i = 1, \ldots, m \end{array}$$

$$\sigma_k \sum_{j=1}^{m_k} \sigma_{kj} \mu_{kj} \geqslant 0 \qquad \begin{array}{l} \text{nonnegativity condition} \\ \text{for } k = 1, \ldots, l \end{array}$$

$$\mu_{kj} \geqslant 0$$

where $\sigma_{kj}(=\pm 1)$ is the signum function for each term of the constraint functions. A comparison of these results with Eqs. (19) to (22) indicates that the dual function, orthogonality conditions, and nonnegativity restrictions of the constrained posynomial problem are slightly modified for the case when the constraints are generalized polynomials (i.e., when they contain negative coefficients).

Negative coefficients can arise not only in the constraints but in the objective function as well. Such terms can be interpreted as negative costs (revenue). The procedure is much the same as for the negative constraint coefficients. Let V represent

$$z = V = P(\mathbf{x}) - N(\mathbf{x}) \geqslant P(\mathbf{x}_0) - N(\mathbf{x}_0) > 0$$

where $P(\mathbf{x})$ and $N(\mathbf{x})$ represent the aggregated terms of the objective function. Note that we have assumed $z_0 > 0$. This is convenient for the analytic development, but it is not required, as will be shown shortly. The above expression can be written

$$1 - V^{-1} P(\mathbf{x}) + V^{-1} N(\mathbf{x}) \geqslant 0$$

This is precisely the form in inequation (27), with $\sigma_k = 1$. Hence, we can also replace this expression by two posynomial constraints

$$1 - v^{-1} V^{-1} P(\mathbf{x}) \geqslant 0$$
$$-[1 - v^{-1} - v^{-1} V^{-1} N(\mathbf{x})] \geqslant 0$$

where $v = 1 + V^{-1} N(\mathbf{x})$ for the same reasons as before. Thus, the "original" objective function is replaced by the "new" objective function, $z = V$, subject to the last two posynomial constraints (in addition to the original set of constraints). Again, the appropriate dual problem is

$$\text{Max}: \; d(\mu) = \sigma \left[\prod_{k=0}^{l} \prod_{j=1}^{m_k} \left(\frac{c_{kj} \mu_{k0}}{\mu_{kj}} \right)^{\sigma_{kj} \mu_{kj}} \right]^{\sigma}$$

Subject to: $\displaystyle\sum_{j=1}^{m_0} \sigma_{0j} \mu_{0j} = \sigma(=\pm 1)$ generalized normality condition

$\displaystyle\sum_{k=0}^{l} \sum_{j=1}^{m_k} \sigma_{kj} a_{kij} \mu_{kj} = 0$ generalized orthogonality conditions for $i = 1, \ldots, m$

$\mu_{k0} = \sigma_k \displaystyle\sum_{j=1}^{m_k} \sigma_{kj} \mu_{kj} \geqslant 0$ generalized nonnegativity condition for $k = 1, \ldots, l$

$\mu_{kj} \geqslant 0$

with $\sigma = 1$ for the case (assumed) that $V > 0$ and $\sigma = -1$ for $V < 0$ (profitable operation) and where $\sigma_{0j}(=\pm 1)$ is the signum function for each term of the objective function. Once the dual variables are known, the corresponding primal variables are found from the following equations:

$$c_{0j} \prod_{i=1}^{n} x_i^{a_{0ij}} = \sigma \mu_{0j} z_0 \qquad\qquad \text{for } j = 1, 2, \ldots, m_0 \qquad\qquad (33)$$

and

$$c_{kj} \prod_{i=1}^{n} x_i^{a_{kij}} = -\frac{\mu_{kj}}{\sigma_k \displaystyle\sum_{j=1}^{m_k} \sigma_{kj} \mu_{kj}} \qquad\qquad \begin{array}{l} \text{for } j = 1, 2, \ldots, m_k \\ k = 1, 2, \ldots, l \end{array} \qquad (34)$$

We conclude that geometric programming is applicable to optimization problems with generalized polynomial objective and constraint functions. When negative signs are present, the solution obtained by geometric programming can only be assumed to be a stationary point. To determine the nature of the stationary point, one can use the methods described in Sec. 5-1. We illustrate with an example.

Example 5-11   Negative coefficients: zero degrees of difficulty

Max: $-4x_1{}^2 x_4 + 5x_2{}^{-1} x_3{}^2$

Subject to: $-2x_2{}^{-2} x_3{}^{-1} + 3x_1{}^{-1} x_2{}^{-1} \leqslant 1$

$7x_1{}^{-1} x_4{}^{-1} \leqslant 1$

The primal problem in the usual form is

Min: $z = 4x_1{}^2 x_4 - 5x_2{}^{-1} x_3{}^2$

subject to the same constraints.

Note that there are zero degrees of difficulty and that the dual problem can be written

$$
\text{Max:}\quad d(\mu) = \sigma \left\{ \left(\frac{4}{\mu_{01}} \right)^{\mu_{01}} \left(\frac{5}{\mu_{02}} \right)^{-\mu_{02}} \left[\frac{2(-\mu_{11} + \mu_{12})}{\mu_{11}} \right]^{-\mu_{11}} \right.
$$
$$
\left. \left[\frac{3(-\mu_{11} + \mu_{12})}{\mu_{12}} \right]^{\mu_{12}} \left[\frac{7(\mu_{21})}{\mu_{21}} \right]^{\mu_{21}} \right\}^{\sigma}
$$

Subject to: $\mu_{01} - \mu_{02} = \sigma$ normality conditions

$2\mu_{01} - \mu_{12} - \mu_{21} = 0$ orthogonality condition for x_1

$\mu_{02} + 2\mu_{11} - \mu_{12} = 0$ orthogonality condition for x_2

$-2\mu_{02} + \mu_{11} = 0$ orthogonality condition for x_3

$\mu_{01} - \mu_{21} = 0$ orthogonality condition for x_4

$+ (-\mu_{11} + \mu_{12}) > 0$

The solution is $\sigma = +1$, $\mu_{01} = \mu_{12} = \mu_{21} = \frac{5}{4}$, $\mu_{02} = \frac{1}{4}$, and $\mu_{11} = \frac{1}{2}$. The value of z at optimum, z_0, is

$$z_0 = d(\tfrac{5}{4}, \tfrac{1}{4}, \tfrac{1}{2}, \tfrac{5}{4}, \tfrac{5}{4}) = 27.74$$

The primal variables are obtained from

$4x_1{}^2 x_4 \quad = \mu_{01} \sigma z_0 = \frac{5}{4}(1)(27.74) = 34.7$

$5x_2{}^{-1} x_3{}^2 = \mu_{02} \sigma z_0 = \frac{1}{4}(1)(27.74) = 6.96$

$2x_2{}^{-2} x_3{}^{-1} = \dfrac{\mu_{11}}{\sigma_1(-\mu_{11} + \mu_{12})} = \dfrac{1/2}{+1(+3/4)} = \dfrac{2}{3}$

$3x_1{}^{-1} x_2{}^{-1} = \dfrac{\mu_{12}}{\sigma_1(-\mu_{11} + \mu_{12})} = \dfrac{5/4}{+1(+3/4)} = \dfrac{5}{3}$

$$7x_1^{-1}x_4^{-1} = \frac{\mu_{21}}{\sigma_2(\mu_{21})} = \frac{5/4}{+1(5/4)} = 1$$

The solution is $x_1 = 1.24$, $x_2 = 1.45$, $x_3 = 1.43$, and $x_4 = 5.64$.

Since there are zero degrees of difficulty, the solution corresponds to the unique stationary point. This point is a minimum if the Hessian matrix for the primal objective is positive definite.

Example 5-12 Cofferdam design This example is due to F. Neghabat [26], who used geometric programming to design cellular cofferdams. The cofferdam height is one design variable since increasing height decreases the flood-risk cost at the expense of increased construction cost. The design problem is to minimize the sum of construction and flood-risk costs.

Figure 5-13 shows elevation and plan views of a cellular cofferdam on bedrock with no overburden or berm. Construction cost includes the material and labor associated with sheetpiling and granular fill. Flood-damage costs include the removal of water and debris and of repairing flood damage to the cofferdam and permanent structure under construction.

For simplicity, assume that the flood cost, c_f, is a constant expressed in dollars per flood. Using streamflow records, one can plot a flood frequency curve. As an approximation, the *expected* cost of flooding, based on the flood frequency curve, during the required life of the cofferdam can be represented by

$$\frac{c_f}{ah - b} \qquad h > \frac{b}{a}$$

where h is the flood height required to top the cofferdam and a and b are constants obtained from the flood frequency curve which corresponds to the life of the cofferdam.

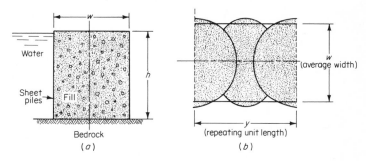

Fig. 5-13 Elevation and plan views of a circular cellular cofferdam.

If the "in-place" costs of sheetpiling and fill are c_s dollars per sq yd and c_e dollars per cu yd, respectively, then the total construction cost is

$$c_s s + c_e v$$

where s and v are the total surface area of sheet piles and total volume of fill, respectively.

The design of a cofferdam is often formulated for a rectangular cell (Fig. 5-13) of length y and width w, rather than for the actual cell of varying width. Then the area and perimeter of one cycle become wy and $2w + 2y$, respectively.

Since the cell cycle length is y, the number of cells in a total length L of cofferdam is L/y. Thus,

$$s = h(2w + 2y)\frac{L}{y} = 2Lhwy^{-1} + 2Lh$$

and

$$v = h(wy)\frac{L}{y} = Lhw$$

Therefore, the construction cost is

$$2Lc_s hwy^{-1} + 2Lc_s h + Lc_e hw \tag{35}$$

Typical failure modes for a cellular cofferdam are:

1. Failure along the center of the cell due to *vertical shear* caused by the horizontal water force (Fig. 5-14a).
2. *Vertical slipping* of sheet piles on the river side, allowing part of the fill to flow from the bottom of the cell (Fig. 5-14b).
3. Failure in *interlock tension* between adjacent piles near the bottom of the cell due to the soil pressure within the cell

To simplify the illustration, we consider only the last two failure modes. Without writing the complete equations for these modes (see [2] or [26]), we simply state

$$k_1 hw^{-1} \leqslant 1 \qquad \text{slipping constraint}$$

and

$$k_2 hy \leqslant 1 \qquad \text{interlock-tension constraint}$$

where h, y, and w are dimensions shown in Fig. 5-13, k_1 is a constant dependent upon the coefficient of friction between piling and fill, and k_2 is a constant dependent upon the allowable interlock tension of the sheet pile and the unit weights of water and soil (Fig. 5-13a).

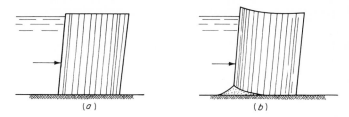

Fig. 5-14 Some cofferdam failure modes. (*a*) Vertical shear; (*b*) slipping.

The design problem may now be stated as

Min: $z = 2Lc_s hwy^{-1} + 2Lc_s h + Lc_e hw + c_f(ah - b)^{-1}$

Subject to: $k_1 hw^{-1} \leqslant 1$
$k_2 hy \leqslant 1$
$h, w, y > 0$

where z is the total expected cost of the cofferdam.

Although the constraints are properly represented for geometric-programming purposes, the last term is inconvenient in an otherwise satisfactory objective function. We set a new variable, x, equal to $ah - b$ and introduce a constraint

$$x \leqslant ah - b$$

which we write in the usual form:

$$\frac{1}{a} xh^{-1} + \frac{b}{a} h^{-1} \leqslant 1$$

Thus we have the final form

Min: $z = 2c_s Lwhy^{-1} + 2c_s Lh + c_e Lhw + c_f x^{-1}$

Subject to: $\dfrac{1}{a} xh^{-1} + \dfrac{b}{a} h^{-1} \leqslant 1$

$k_1 hw^{-1} \leqslant 1$
$k_2 hy \leqslant 1$
$x, h, w, y \geqslant 0$

Since there are eight terms and four variables, the problem has three degrees of difficulty. Also, since the signum functions are positive, we know that the solution is global.   The dual problem is written

$$\text{Max:}\quad d(\mu) = \left(\frac{2c_s L}{\mu_{01}}\right)^{\mu_{01}} \left(\frac{2c_s L}{\mu_{02}}\right)^{\mu_{02}} \left(\frac{c_e L}{\mu_{03}}\right)^{\mu_{03}} \left(\frac{c_f}{\mu_{04}}\right)^{\mu_{04}}$$

$$\left[\frac{(1/a)(\mu_{11}+\mu_{12})}{\mu_{11}}\right]^{\mu_{11}} \left[\frac{(b/a)(\mu_{11}+\mu_{12})}{\mu_{12}}\right]^{\mu_{12}} k_1{}^{\mu_{21}} k_2{}^{\mu_{31}}$$

Subject to: $\mu_{01} + \mu_{02} + \mu_{03} + \mu_{04} = 1$ normality cond.

$\mu_{01} + \mu_{02} + \mu_{03} - \mu_{11} - \mu_{12} + \mu_{21} + \mu_{31} = 0$ orth. cond. for h

$\mu_{01} + \mu_{03} - \mu_{21} = 0$ orth. cond. for w

$-\mu_{01} + \mu_{31} = 0$ orth. cond for y

$-\mu_{04} + \mu_{11} = 0$ orth. cond. for x

$\mu_{ij} \geqslant 0$ all i,j

We express the solution in terms of μ_{02}, μ_{03}, and μ_{12} as

$$\mu_{01} = \mu_{31} = \tfrac{1}{4} - \tfrac{1}{2}\mu_{02} - \tfrac{3}{4}\mu_{03} + \tfrac{1}{4}\mu_{12}$$
$$\mu_{11} = \mu_{04} = \tfrac{3}{4} - \tfrac{1}{2}\mu_{02} - \tfrac{1}{4}\mu_{03} - \tfrac{1}{4}\mu_{12}$$
$$\mu_{21} = \tfrac{1}{4} - \tfrac{1}{2}\mu_{02} + \tfrac{1}{4}\mu_{03} + \tfrac{1}{4}\mu_{12}$$

These are substituted into the dual function, so that it is now a function of the three variables μ_{02}, μ_{03}, and μ_{12}.   For the maximization, we set the partial derivatives of the logarithm of the dual to zero.   Simplification yields the simultaneous equations

$$\left(\frac{2c_s}{c_e}\right)^2 \frac{k_2}{k_1} \mu_{03}{}^2 \mu_{02}{}^{-1} - \tfrac{1}{4}\mu_{12} + \tfrac{3}{4}\mu_{03} + \tfrac{1}{2}\mu_{02} \qquad = \tfrac{1}{4}$$

$$\sqrt{\frac{c_e c_f k_1}{4c_s{}^2 Lb}}\, \mu_{02}\, \mu_{12}{}^{1/2}\, \mu_{03}{}^{-1/2} + \tfrac{1}{4}\mu_{03} + \tfrac{1}{4}\mu_{12} + \tfrac{1}{2}\mu_{02} = \tfrac{3}{4}$$

$$\frac{2c_s a}{c_e bk_1} \mu_{03}\, \mu_{12}\, \mu_{02}{}^{-1} + \tfrac{1}{4}\mu_{03} - \tfrac{3}{4}\mu_{12} + \tfrac{1}{2}\mu_{02} \qquad = \tfrac{3}{4}$$

Unfortunately, explicit solutions for μ_{02}, μ_{03}, and μ_{12} appear hopeless.   However, when numerical values for the coefficients are available, these equations are easily solved by computer and often simply by hand.   Once the dual variables are known, the dual function can be evaluated to yield the minimum total expected cost, z_0.   The design variables are obtained from solutions of

$$2c_s L(why^{-1}) = \mu_{01} z_0$$

$$2c_s L(h) \quad = \mu_{02} z_0$$

$$c_e L(wh) \quad = \mu_{03} z_0$$

$$c_f(x^{-1}) \quad = \mu_{04} z_0$$

$$\frac{1}{a}(xh^{-1}) \quad = \frac{\mu_{11}}{\mu_{11} + \mu_{12}}$$

$$\frac{b}{a}(h^{-1}) \quad = \frac{\mu_{12}}{\mu_{11} + \mu_{12}}$$

$$k_1(hw^{-1}) \quad = 1$$

$$k_2(yh) \quad = 1$$

The dual multipliers yield important design information. The sum $\mu_{01} + \mu_{02}$ is the fraction of the total cost which should be allocated to sheet-piling for an optimal design. Similarly, μ_{03} is the fraction of z_0 to be allocated to the fill and its placement, and so on.

5-5 SEARCH TECHNIQUES

Various search techniques are available when analysis is impractical. Search techniques evaluate the objective function for a variety of values of the variables. Successive trials, guided by results of previous ones, try to improve the value of the objective function until an optimum, or near optimum, is reached. Search techniques deal with equality constraints by including them in the objective function. Inequality constraints are satisfied at each trial. As with classical techniques, computational effort is often substantially reduced when the objective and constraint functions have the necessary convexity properties so that a local optimum is also global. When the function has several peaks or valleys within the feasible region, the search must be repeated from various starting points to ensure locating the global optimum. Search techniques are classified by the selection rules for trial values. The techniques to be described are only a sample of the many available.

The simplest technique is an *alternating one-dimensional* or *sectioning* search [30]. Here all variables except one are held constant while the remaining one varies until a minimum (or maximum) of the objective function is obtained. The remaining variables are treated in the same manner, one at a time. The cycle is repeated until a desired level of convergence in the value of the objective function has been achieved. The optimization at each trial is performed with appropriate techniques, e.g., numerical, graphical, or analytical techniques.

Example 5-13   An alternating one-dimensional search   We illustrate sectioning search for the two-dimensional problem,

$$\text{Min:}\quad z = x_1{}^2 + 2x_2{}^2 - 4x_1 - 2x_1 x_2$$
$$\text{Subject to:}\quad 2x_1 + x_2 \leqslant 6$$
$$x_1, x_2 \geqslant 0$$

The tabulation in Fig. 5-15 illustrates an alternating one-dimensional search for this problem.   We first observe variations in z along an arbitrarily selected line, $x_1 = 2$, for the trial values $x_2 = 2, 0, 1$.   Since the smallest of the test values of z is obtained at $x_2 = 1$, we next explore variations of z along the line $x_2 = 1$ (trials 3, 4, 5), etc., until the desired degree of convergence to z_{min} is obtained.   The computations can often be reduced by a fortuitous initial selection.   Figure 5-16 shows contours of the objective function.

The alternating one-dimensional search is disadvantageous because it depends significantly upon the character of the contours.   In some instances, convergence is inefficient, as shown in Fig. 5-17a.   For problems of higher dimensionality, convergence can be extremely slow.   At times, as when the search encounters a ridge (Fig. 5-17b), the method fails completely.   No further variation in either x_1 or x_2 will improve the current solution since there is no provision for diagonal movement.

More efficient techniques have been developed—as, for example, the *steepest-gradient technique* and the *contour-tangent technique*.   The steepest-gradient technique computes the slope of the objective surface at

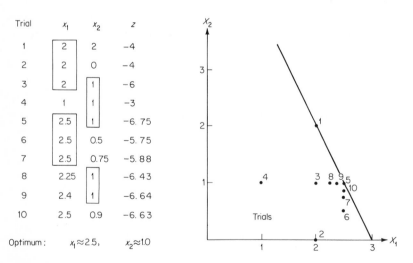

Fig. 5-15   One-dimensional search.

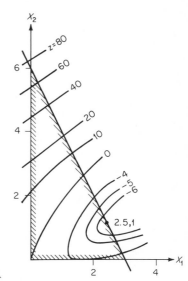

Fig. 5-16   Objective and constraint functions.

each trial point and adjusts the values of all variables simultaneously, so that the next trial point lies in the direction of steepest gradient.   The contour-tangent method eliminates a portion of the feasible region at each step by locating the tangent line to a contour of the objective surface and seeking a point in a higher (or lower) contour area.   For multidimensional problems, the rapidity of convergence of both techniques is strongly dependent upon the scale factors selected for variables which are not expressed in similar units and upon the unimodality of the objective surface.

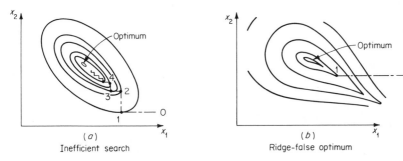

Fig 5-16   Disadvantages of alternating one dimensional search.   (*a*) Inefficient search; (*b*) ridge-false optimum.

Example 5-14 A steepest-gradient search Consider a two-dimensional unconstrained steepest-gradient search. Given a trial point, say x_1, y_1 (Fig. 5-18), the direction of the steepest slope at the point is given in terms of the partial derivatives $\partial z/\partial x_1$ and $\partial z/\partial y_1$ as

$$\frac{\Delta x_1}{\Delta y_1} = \frac{(\partial z/\partial x)_1}{(\partial z/\partial y)_1}$$

While this relationship indicates the direction in which to move, it does not indicate the best distance to the next trial point. However, the new coordinate values of x and y may be defined as

$$x_2 = x_1 - v\left(\frac{\partial z}{\partial x}\right)_1$$

$$y_2 = y_1 - v\left(\frac{\partial z}{\partial y}\right)_1 \tag{36}$$

where v is a distance-proportionality factor. The objective at the ith trial is

$$z_{i+1} = z\left\{\left[x_i - v\left(\frac{\partial z}{\partial x}\right)_i\right], \left[y_i - v\left(\frac{\partial z}{\partial y}\right)_i\right]\right\} \tag{37}$$

Since we desire a value of v where z is minimum, v may be obtained from

$$\frac{dz}{dv} = 0 \tag{38}$$

Having v, values of x and y are given by Eqs. (36) to begin the next iteration.

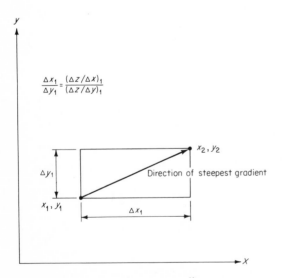

Fig. 5-18   Direction of steepest gradient.

To illustrate the technique, we choose the arbitrary starting values of $x_1 = 1$, $y_1 = 1$ for the objective function of the previous example, that is,

Min: $z = x^2 + 2y^2 - 4x - 2xy$

The partial derivatives are

$$\frac{\partial z}{\partial x} = 2x - 4 - 2y \qquad \frac{\partial z}{\partial y} = 4y - 2x$$

By Eq. (37),

$$z = \left[x_1 - v\left(\frac{\partial z}{\partial x}\right)_1\right]^2 + 2\left[y_1 - v\left(\frac{\partial z}{\partial y}\right)_1\right]^2 - 4\left[x_1 - v\left(\frac{\partial z}{\partial x}\right)_1\right]$$

$$-2\left[x_1 - v\left(\frac{\partial z}{\partial x}\right)_1\right]\left[y_1 - v\left(\frac{\partial z}{\partial y}\right)_1\right]$$

$$= [1 - v(2x - 4 - 2y)_1]^2 + 2[1 - v(4y - 2x)_1]^2$$
$$-4[1 - v(2x - 4 - 2y)_1]$$
$$-2[1 - v(2x - 4 - 2y)_1][1 - v(4y - 2x)_1]$$
$$= -3 - 20v + 40v^2$$

By Eq. (38),

$$\frac{\partial z}{\partial v} = -20 + 80v = 0$$

and $v = 1/4$. Since $\partial^2 z / \partial v^2$ is positive, this value of v indeed tends to minimize the objective. By Eqs. (36),

$$x_2 = 1 - 1/4(-4) = 2$$
$$y_2 = 1 - 1/4(2) = 1/2$$

which constitute a starting point for the second iteration, and so on. The reader may wish to carry through one or two more iterations to observe the convergence. When the objective function varies inversely with some of the variables or when the variables contain exponential or trigonometric functions, Eq. (38) is almost always a transcendental equation and machine computation is needed.

Equality constraints can, again, usually be incorporated into the objective, but inequality constraints are considerably more complex to handle in both the gradient and the contour methods. Details of these and other search methods are given in texts on optimization ([6], [17], [30], [31]).

5-6 REDUCTIONS TO LINEAR FORM

The remarkable efficiency with which linear-programming problems can be solved suggests trying to transform nonlinear problems into linear ones. Attractive as the suggestion is, not many transformations have been found. In this section we illustrate a few such transformations.

PIECEWISE LINEAR PROGRAMMING

One transformation technique used to obtain approximate solutions to non-linear problems is the *cutting-plane method* [20]. The technique depends on the piecewise linearization of nonlinear terms through first-order Taylor series expansions.

Consider the nonlinear problem,

$$\text{Min:} \quad z(\mathbf{x}) \tag{39'}$$

$$\text{Subject to:} \quad g_j(\mathbf{x}) \lessgtr 0 \qquad j = 1, \ldots, m$$

$$L_i \leqslant x_i \leqslant U_i \qquad i = 1, \ldots, n \tag{40'}$$

where $\mathbf{x}$ is the n-dimensional decision vector (variables) and L_i and U_i are the lower and upper limits of the design variable. The generalized expressions for the Taylor series linearization of the nonlinear objective function and constraints, expressions (39') and (40'), are[2]

$$\text{Min:} \quad z(\mathbf{x}^0) + \sum_{i=1}^{n} \frac{\partial z}{\partial x_i}\bigg|_0 (x_i - x_i^0) \tag{39}$$

$$\text{Subject to:} \quad \sum_{i=1}^{n} \frac{\partial g_j}{\partial x_i}\bigg|_0 (x_i - x_i^0) \lessgtr 0 \qquad j = 1, \ldots, m \tag{40}$$

$$L_i \leqslant x_i \leqslant U_i \qquad i = 1, \ldots, n \tag{41}$$

where x_i^0 is an approximation of the optimal decision variable x_i^* and $|_0$ indicates evaluation at the approximate solution point x_i^0.

Optimization is obtained after several linear-programming cycles, each of which includes a linearization, expressions (39) and (40), of the objective and/or constraints. The following steps are indicated for solution:

1. As in conventional design, assume values of the design variables x_i^0, $i = 1, \ldots, n$, which, in general, satisfy inequations (40').

---

[2] In this section a superscript asterisk on x is used to indicate optimality rather than the subscripted zero used in the preceding sections. The zero superscript in this section stands for "zero[th]" iteration.

2. Solve the linear-programming problem, (39) to (41), using the assumed values to determine a new set of variables $(x_i{}^1)$. The solution, $(\mathbf{x}^1)$, will satisfy these equations but may not satisfy, in general, inequations (40′).
3. If any of the $(x_i{}^1)$ violate the constraints (40′), uniformly adjust the variables until all violations are eliminated.
4. Repeat steps 2 and 3 until the desired accuracy is achieved. The approximate "optimal" solution is obtained when successive designs approach a constant value of the objective function.

Unfortunately, the technique is not always efficient, and like many approximation techniques, it is used with caution.

Moses [25] applies the technique to problems of sizing structural members. The following illustration is a simplification.

Example 5-15   Sizing structural members   A three-member hinge-connected wall bracket is subjected to a load P (Fig. 5-19). If the allowable stresses in the bracket members are T_i kips per sq in. in tension and C_i kips per sq in. in compression, determine the cross-sectional areas which minimize total weight (volume).

The total volume of the three members is

$$V = \frac{L}{\cos 30} A_1 + LA_2 + \frac{L}{\cos 60} A_3 \tag{42′}$$

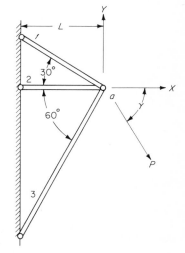

Fig. 5-19   Wall bracket.

where A_1, A_2, and A_3 are the unknown cross-sectional areas of the members. Necessary equilibrium equations at joint a are

$$P_x = \sigma_1 A_1 \cos 30 + \sigma_2 A_2 + \sigma_3 A_3 \cos 60 \qquad (43a')$$

$$P_y = -\sigma_1 A_1 \sin 30 + \sigma_3 A_3 \sin 60 \qquad (43b')$$

where P_j is the jth component of the load and σ_k is the stress (psi) in the kth member.

The displacement equations at joint a are

$$\frac{L}{\cos 30} \frac{\sigma_1}{E_1} = Y_x \cos 30 - Y_y \sin 30$$

$$\frac{\sigma_2}{E_2} L = Y_x \qquad (44')$$

$$\frac{L}{\cos 60} \frac{\sigma_3}{E_3} = Y_x \cos 60 + Y_y \sin 60$$

where Y_j is the displacement in the jth direction and E_i is the Young's modulus. Assuming $E_1 = E_2 = E_3$, simultaneous solution of Eqs. (44') yields the single compatibility equation in the stress variables,

$$\sigma_1 - \sigma_2 + \sigma_3 = 0 \qquad (44)$$

The problem becomes

$$\text{Min:}\quad V = \frac{L}{\cos 30} A_1 + L A_2 + \frac{L}{\cos 60} A_3 \qquad (42)$$

$$\begin{aligned}
\text{Subject to:}\quad & \sigma_1 A_1 \cos 30 + \sigma_2 A_2 + \sigma_3 A_3 \cos 60 = P \cos \gamma \\
& -\sigma_1 A_1 \sin 30 + \sigma_3 A_3 \sin 60 = P \sin \gamma \qquad (43)
\end{aligned}$$

$$\sigma_1 - \sigma_2 + \sigma_3 = 0 \qquad (44)$$

$$C_i \leqslant \sigma_i \leqslant T_i \qquad i = 1, 2, 3 \qquad (45)$$

Equations (43) are nonlinear because they contain products of variables. A Taylor series expansion of these equations about the decision variables A_i^0 and σ_i yields

$$\begin{aligned}
& \sigma_1^0 (A_1 - A_1^0)\cos 30 + \sigma_2^0(A_2 - A_2^0) + \sigma_3^0 (A_3 - A_3^0)\cos 60 \\
& \quad + A_1^0 (\sigma_1 - \sigma_1^0)\cos 30 + A_2(\sigma_2 - \sigma_2^0) + A_3 (\sigma_3 - \sigma_3^0)\cos 60 = 0 \\
& -\sigma_1 (A_1 - A_1^0)\sin 30 + \sigma_3^0 (A_3 - A_3^0)\sin 60 - A_1^0 (\sigma_1 - \sigma_1^0)\sin 30 \qquad (46) \\
& \quad + A_3^0 (\sigma_3 - \sigma_3^0)\sin 60 = 0
\end{aligned}$$

The linear-programming problem is to determine the area A_k and stresses σ_k which minimize Eq. (42) subject to linear constraints (44) to (46). The solution proceeds by assuming values for the design variables A_k^0. Equations (44) and (46) are used to determine the stress variables σ_k^0. If constraints (45) are violated, the design variables A_k are modified and the linear-programming routine is performed to obtain a better approximation.

To illustrate the initial steps for the wall bracket (Fig. 5-19), assume that $P = 7.37K$, $\gamma = 61.4^0$, $L = 2$ ft, $T_i = 10$ kips per sq in., and $C_i = -10$ kips per sq in. Using Eqs. (43) and (44), an initial trial design, $A_1 = A_2 = A_3 = 0.5$ sq in., gives

$$\sigma_k{}^0 = \begin{bmatrix} 10.79 \\ 2.09 \\ -8.71 \end{bmatrix}$$

Since $\sigma_1{}^0$ violates the stress limit of 10 kips per sq in., each area is increased by the ratio $10.79:10$ to yield $A_1{}^0 = A_2{}^0 = A_3{}^0 = 0.54$ sq in. Accordingly, the stresses are

$$\sigma_k{}^0 = \begin{bmatrix} 10.00 \\ 1.95 \\ -8.10 \end{bmatrix}$$

These values constitute the initial trial design. From Eq. (42), the total volume V is 53.9 cu in. The rate of convergence of the solution after successive linear-programming iterations is an indicator of the solution accuracy. The method is also applicable for two or more simultaneous or nonsimultaneous loads. Unfortunately, convergence cannot be guaranteed without additional measures. More recent work is available.

Example 5-16 Cover-plated steel beam The following problem, by Douty [7], also illustrates an application of piecewise linear programming.

A two-span continuous wide-flange beam having unequal spans is to be strengthened with cover plates at the interior support (Fig. 5-20). Determine all cross-sectional dimensions of the beam and cover plates, as well as the cover-plate length and position which will minimize the weight of the structure. Use a uniform load, w lb per in., and assume full lateral support

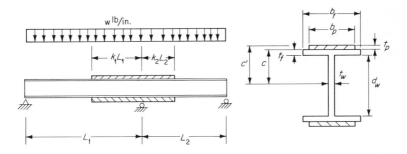

Fig. 5-20 Two-span continuous beam.

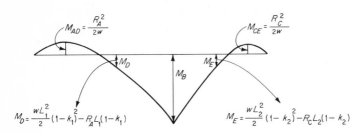

$$M_D = \frac{wL_1^2}{2}(1-k_1)^2 - R_A L_1(1-k_1) \qquad\qquad M_E = \frac{wL_2^2}{2}(1-k_2)^2 - R_C L_2(1-k_2)$$

Fig. 5-21   Moment diagram.

for the top flange. AISC design specifications [1] are to be followed, except, for simplicity, omit shear stress and deflection constraints. The allowable bending stress F_b and specified yield point of the steel F_y, both in pounds per square inch, and L_1 and L_2 are assumed to be given.

An indeterminate analysis by moment distribution yields the maximum moments shown in Fig. 5-21.

Solution

Min: Weight $= z = [(2t_f b_f + d_w t_w)(L_1 + L_2)$

$$+ (2t_p b_p)(k_1 L_1 + k_2 L_2)] \frac{490 \text{ lb/cu ft}}{1{,}728 \text{ cu in./ cu ft}}$$

where all dimensions are in inches and weight is in pounds.

    Subject to:

1.   Moment constraints (actual bending stress $Mc/I \leqslant$ allowable bending stress F_b):

    For $M_{AD'}$

$$\frac{M_{AD}\, c}{I} = \frac{\dfrac{R_A^2}{2w}\left(\dfrac{d_w}{2} + t_f\right)}{P} \leqslant F_b$$

    For $M_{CE'}$

$$\frac{M_{CE}\, c}{I} = \frac{\dfrac{R_C^2}{2w}\left(\dfrac{d_w}{2} + t_f\right)}{P} \leqslant F_b$$

For $M_{D'}$

$$\frac{M_D c}{I} = \frac{\left[\dfrac{wL_1^2}{2}(1-k_1)^2 - R_A L_1(1-k_1)\right]\left(\dfrac{d_w}{2}+t_f\right)}{P} \leqslant F_b$$

For $M_{E'}$

$$\frac{M_E c}{I} = \frac{\left[\dfrac{wL_2^2}{2}(1-k_1)^2 - R_c L_2(1-k_2)\right]\left(\dfrac{d_w}{2}+t_f\right)}{P} \leqslant F_b$$

For $M_{B'}$

$$\frac{M_B c'}{I'} = \frac{M_B\left(\dfrac{d_w}{2}+t_f+t_p\right)}{P+2b_p t_p\left(\dfrac{d_w+t_p}{2}+t_f\right)^2} \leqslant F_b$$

where I' and I are the moments of inertia of the beam's cross section with and without the cover plate, respectively, and

$$P = \frac{t_w d_w^3}{12} + 2b_f t_f\left(\frac{d_w+t_f}{2}\right)^2$$

2. Web constraint (Sec. 1.10.2 of AISC manual [1]):

$$d_w \leqslant \frac{14 \times 10^6}{Fy(Fy+16{,}500)} t_w$$

3. Minimum-fillet-weld constraint (Sec. 1.17.4 of AISC):

$t_f \geqslant 5/16$

$t_p \geqslant 5/16$

$t_w \geqslant 5/16$

4. Flange-width constraint (Sec. 1.5.1.4 of AISC):

$$b_f \leqslant \frac{6{,}000}{\sqrt{F_y}} t_f$$

Notice that the objective-function and constraint equations are all nonlinear.
    The linear terms of the Taylor series for the nonlinear objective expanded around the point $(b_f^0, b_p^0, k_1^0, k_2^0, t_f^0, t_p^0)$ are

$$\begin{aligned}
z = {}& 2t_f^0(L_1+L_2)b_f + 2b_f^0(L_1+L_2)t_f + 2t_p^0(k_1^0 L_1 + k_2^0 L_2)b_p \\
& + 2b_p^0(k_1^0 L_1 + k_2^0 L_2)t_p + t_w^0(L_1+L_2)d_w + d_w^0(L_1+L_2)t_w \\
& + 2L_1 b_p^0 t_p^0 k_1 + 2L_2 b_p^0 t_p^0 k_2^0
\end{aligned}$$

A similar Taylor series linearization exists for each of the nonlinear constraints. The approximating linear-programming problem can be solved by the procedures of the preceding example.

A LOGARITHMIC TRANSFORMATION

As a simple example, imagine a structural system to be composed of n independent and serially connected subsystems. If $y_1, y_2, \ldots, y_n$ denote the reliabilities[3] of the subsystems, how should they be chosen to maximize the overall system reliability z, given by

$$z = \prod_{i=1}^{n} y_i$$

In practical situations, the maximization is subject to constraints. An obvious constraint is

$$0 \leqslant y_i \leqslant 1 \qquad i = 1, \ldots, n$$

since reliability, in effect, is a probability. Certain minimum levels of reliability (safety) are expressed by lower bounds, and since reliability necessarily entails a cost, there are upper bounds as well. These ideas are expressed by constraints of the form

$$\alpha_i \leqslant y_i \leqslant \beta_i \qquad y_i y_j \leqslant \gamma \qquad\qquad i, j = 1, \ldots, n$$

where α, β, and γ are constants.

Taking logarithms of the objective function and constraints transforms this nonlinear (geometric) programming problem into a linear one.

A variant of this transformation arises in problems in which the objective function is a product of variables while the constraints are linear functions of the variables. Since the logarithm is a strictly increasing function, it is entirely proper to maximize the logarithm of the (product) objective which has become a linear function of the logarithms of the variables.

A further illustration of the logarithmic transformation is provided in Example 11-2, where the objective function consists of variable exponents.

An example by Galler and Gotaas [16] on the problem of biological filter design combines several of the preceding techniques. In seeking the radius and depth of a biological filter to minimize construction and operating costs, the objective function and one of the constraints were found to contain nonlinear terms. A logarithmic transformation was used to linearize the constraint and most of the nonlinear terms in the objective function. Piecewise linear programming was employed on the resulting partially nonlinear objective function, and the computations were further reduced by the dual method (Sec. 4-3).

---

[3] The reliability of an element (system, etc.) is the probability that the element will perform according to specifications for a specified time; see Sec. 11-1.

OBJECTIVES WITH STEP FUNCTIONS

Suppose that an objective function contains terms of the form

$$(a - x)\, \mathcal{U}(a - x)$$

where x is the nonnegative decision variable, a is a constant, and the step function $\mathcal{U}(a - x)$ is defined as

$$\mathcal{U}(a - x) = \begin{cases} 0 & a < x \\ 1 & a \geqslant x \end{cases}$$

The following transformation enables one to eliminate this type of non-linearity: Let

$$a - x = u - v \qquad \begin{cases} u = 0 \text{ if } a < x \\ v = 0 \text{ if } a \geqslant x \end{cases} \qquad u, v \geqslant 0$$

Next replace $(a - x)\, \mathcal{U}(a - x)$ in the objective function by the new decision variable u and add

$$u - v + x = a$$

to the constraint set. The conversion to a linear form is complete.

Example 5-17 Production smoothing Production managers strive to take advantage of the economies to be achieved by "smoothing" production in order to minimize costs of tooling up (or down) while satisfying production quotas.

Denote the production quota (demand) for the ith period to be r_i and the (to be determined) amount to be produced in the ith period by x_i, $i = 1$, $\ldots$, n. The items cost c dollars per unit and are sold at a price of p dollars per unit.

The plant is currently geared to a production level of x_0 units. Each unit increase in production level will cost a dollars per unit, and each unit decrease will cost b dollars per unit. Management seeks a production schedule which maximizes profits.

The profit function for the ith period is

$$z_i = p[r_i - (r_i - x_i)\, \mathcal{U}(r_i - x_i)] = cx_i - a(x_i - x_{i-1})\, \mathcal{U}(x_i - x_{i-1})$$
$$- b(x_{i-1} - x_i)\, \mathcal{U}(x_{i-1} - x_i)$$

Using the transformations

$$r_i - x_i = u_i - v_i \qquad \begin{cases} u_i = 0 \text{ if } r_i \leqslant x_i \\ v_i = 0 \text{ if } r_i > x_i \end{cases}$$

and

$$x_i - x_{i-1} = w_i - z_i \qquad \begin{cases} z_i = 0 \text{ if } x_i \geqslant x_{i-1} \\ w_i = 0 \text{ if } x_{i-1} \geqslant x_i \end{cases}$$

the profit function for n periods becomes

$$\text{Max:} \quad z' = \sum_{i=1}^{n} [p(r_i - u_i) - cx_i - aw_i - bz_i]$$

Subject to: "The original constraint set"
and

$$u_i - v_i + x_i = r_i$$
$$x_i - w_i + z_i - x_{i-1} = 0 \qquad i = 1, \ldots, n$$

This transformation has a particularly important application in fitting curves with a minimum-absolute-deviation criterion (see Prob. 5-16 and Appendix 1).

5-7 GRAPHICAL OPTIMIZATION

Problems frequently do not yield conveniently or economically to mathematical solution.   Although graphical techniques have long been used to differentiate, integrate, and obtain powers and roots of numbers ([24] and [32]), their application to nonlinear optimization has received scant attention.   Graphical optimization consists of processing data and plotting them in such a manner that optima can be obtained by inspection.   The particular graphical feature which reveals optimal values depends upon the nature of the problem and upon how the data are processed and plotted.   It may be the minimum point on a curve, the point of minimum slope, a point of tangency, the intersections of two or more curves, and so on.

Although graphical methods frequently involve frustration and uncertainty, at times they work with admirable ease.   Unfortunately, their use for higher-dimensional problems often depends upon discreet and sometimes subtle observations regarding the raw data and upon a judicious or lucky choice of the hierarchical sequence in which data are manipulated.   Graphical solutions usually involve combinations of basic operations.   The first step is to arrange these operations in logical sequence.   During solution, the problem must be continually studied with a view to obtaining additional simplifications.

We shall illustrate techniques with a few examples.   First, let us consider an objective function with discontinuous cost.

Example 5-18   Location of a mobile plant   An asphalt-paving contractor will build a 32-mile section of bituminous shoulders for a highway. He has offers to lease sites for his mobile mix plant from five property owners

Table 5-2 Data for mix-plant location

	Site No.				
	1	2	3	4	5
Lease price, $/working day	25	30	45	35	25
Transportation of bitumen and aggregate from nearby rail headings and aggregate sources to mix plant; cost per ton of hot mix produced	$0.30	0.25	0.15	0.10	0.25

along the route.   From the data (Table 5-2), he seeks to determine which sites to use and the distance to pave in each direction from each site to minimize total paving cost.

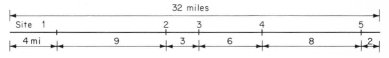

Hot-mix requirement:	2,200 tons/mile
Production rate:	900 tons/working day
Transportation cost, mix plant to shoulder:	$0.02/ton-mile
Estimated total cost of each plant relocation, including labor, lost time, etc.:	$400

A simple graphical solution is apparent when paving cost per mile from each available plant site (all costs exclusive of the $400 moving cost) is plotted against distance along the route (Fig. 5-22).   From inspection of the graph,

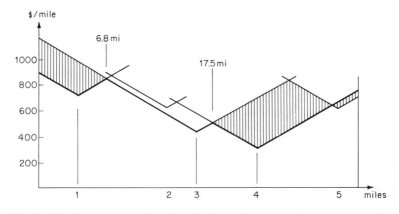

Fig. 5-22 Paving cost as a function of distance from plant sites.

site 2 should not be occupied because paving of any portion can be performed more cheaply from site 3.   Further, if the area within any crosshatched segment (area = $/mile × mile = cost difference for paving that segment from adjacent plant sites) is less than the moving cost of $400, it is then cheaper not to occupy the corresponding site.   This occurs at site 5, where the cross-hatched area equals $115.   Hence, only sites 1, 3, and 4 should be occupied. The optimum paving distances from each of these sites are tabulated below:

Site	Optimum paving distance, miles
1	0–6.8
3	6.8–17.5
4	17.5–32

Total cost equals the area under the heavy line on the graph ($19,250) plus $1,200 for the three plant relocations.

Example 5-19   Pump operation   A municipal water-pumping station has three turbine-driven pumps (A, B, and C), whose operating-cost characteristics appear in Fig. 5-23.   A discharge of 5,000 gpm is required at minimum cost.

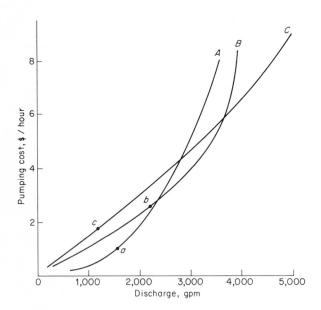

Fig. 5-23   Discharge-cost characteristics of three pumps.

Note that the problem is one of locating points *a*, *b*, and *c* in Fig. 5-23 so that the sum of their abscissas is 5,000 gpm *and* the sum of their ordinates is a minimum. Since the pumping costs are continuously increasing at a non-decreasing rate (convex functions), this can be accomplished graphically by locating points on the curves where the *slopes are equal* and for which the sum of abscissas is 5,000 gpm. This can be quickly done in several trials with a pair of draftsman's triangles. The answer obtained, however, is the minimal-cost solution only when all three pumps are used. Minimum-cost combinations for any pair of pumps, as well as costs for using single pumps, when possible, should also be investigated. In many problems, some of the combinations can be eliminated by inspection. The reader may verify from Fig. 5-23 the results in Table 5-3.

A policy which reduces graphical work is to first evaluate those curves having tangents from the origin which make smaller angles with the *x* axis and then to proceed to successively larger numbers of curves having steeper tangents. By this method, the graphical testing can be stopped when total

Table 5-3 Results of graphical solution

Pump combination	Discharge, gpm^2	Cost per hr
C only	5,000	$9.00
A	1,900	1.60
B	3,100	4.10
		$5.70
A	1,600	1.00
B	2,200	2.30
C	1,200	1.70
	5,000	$5.00
A	1,800	1.40
C	3,200	5.00
	5,000	$6.40
B	2,500	3.00
C	2,500	3.80
	5,000	$6.80

Hence the optimal solution is

Pump A: 1,600 gpm
Pump B: 2,200 gpm
Pump C: 1,200 gpm

cost exceeds a minimum; e.g., pump combinations AC and BC would have been eliminated by the combination ABC.

Numerous variants of this problem can be solved as long as the data can be represented by two-dimensional graphs (see Sec. 10-2). To illustrate the basis for this graphical procedure, suppose that $y_A = y_A(x_A)$, $y_B = y_B(x_B)$, and $y_C = y_C(x_C)$ are the equations which describe the curves in Fig. 5-23, that is, y_A is the pumping cost per hour, x_A is the discharge for pump A, and so on. We form the following optimization problem:

Min: $y_A(x_A) + y_B(x_B) + y_C(x_C)$

such that

$$x_A + x_B + x_C = 5,000 \text{ gpm}$$

Assuming that the cost functions are differentiable, we form the Lagrangian and obtain the simultaneous equations $y_A'(x_A) + \lambda = y_B'(x_B) + \lambda = y_C'(x_C) + \lambda = x_A + x_B + x_C - 5,000 = 0$, or $-\lambda = y_A'(x_A) = y_B'(x_B) = y_C'(x_C)$. This explains why we located points of equal slope. The convexity properties simply assured us of a global optimum. Also, it is interesting to note that λ represents the added hourly cost of increasing the total discharge—a factor to be considered, say, in deciding upon the acquisition of a fourth pump.

Let us consider a graphical example requiring operations which can be performed with an analog computer.

Example 5-20   Pumped-storage hydroelectric design   In pumped-storage hydroelectric projects, reservoirs are maintained at two elevations. Reversible pump-turbines use electrical energy to pump water from the lower to the upper reservoir during nightly periods of low power demand and then generate power with the same water during daytime periods of peak demand.

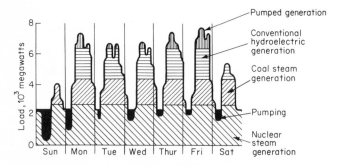

Fig. 5-24   Average weekly power demand with pumped generation.

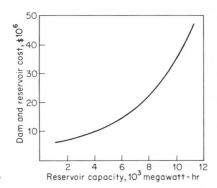

Fig. 5-25 Dam and reservoir cost.

Although pumped generation reduces efficiency (more energy is required for pumping than is generated), it provides a means to satisfy otherwise excessive demands. Pumping in off-peak hours also allows base-load steam electric stations to operate at efficient levels for longer periods.

Assume that an electrical utility plans to add pumped storage to its existing steam and hydroelectric generators. We want to determine the optimum capacity of the upper reservoir, the pump-generator capacity, and the operating levels for the various types of generating units. The mean weekly power demand is shown in Fig. 5-24 [28]. For operational reasons, fixed generating levels, indicated by the horizontal lines, are to be used, and the optimal levels are sought. For convenience, construction cost for the dam and reservoir (Fig. 5-25) is expressed as a function of megawatt-hours of storage capacity (rather than acre-feet). The construction cost of the generator installation—including generators, penstocks, powerhouse, and transformer station—is estimated at $1,000 per kilowatt capacity.

The generating equipment includes nuclear, coal, and conventional hydroelectric plants and the proposed pumped-storage hydroelectric plant. Operating costs for the nuclear and coal plants are shown in Fig. 5-26. Operating costs for the hydroelectric plants are assumed constant and independent of operating levels. However, water availability limits the energy from conventional hydroelectric generation to a maximum level, in megawatt-hours per week. Pumped storage will use 1.4 megawatt-hr for each megawatt-hour returned to the system, due to transmission-line losses and pump-generator efficiencies.

Assume, for simplicity of preliminary design, that we satisfy the weekly demand (Fig. 5-24), neglecting demand growth rate, monthly hydrologic and demand variations, the cost of energy from neighboring utilities when demand exceeds available supply, etc. Assume an economic life of N years for the pumped-storage plant, with zero salvage value and zero interest rate.

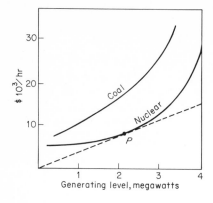

Fig. 5-26   Operating costs for steam electric generation.

The problem can be formulated as

Min: $z = \sum_{i=1}^{n} \int_{t=0}^{7} c_j\, dt$ weekly generating cost

Subject to: $\int_{t=0}^{7} q_h\, dt \leqslant E_h$ weekly energy from conventional hydro. generation   (47)

$\sum_{i=1}^{n} q_i = D$ over all t instantaneous demand   (48)

$q_i \leqslant m_i$ over all t,   max. output for each type of generation   (49)

$\int_{t=0}^{7} q_p\, dt + 1.4 \int_{t=0}^{7} p_p\, dt$ pumping-generating factor   (50)

where $c_i(t)$ = cost per unit time at time t for generation type i
  $D(t)$ = total demand at time t, mw
  E_h = weekly energy available from conventional hydroelectric generation, megawatt-hr
  m_i = output capacity from generating type i, mw
  n = number of generation equipment types (=4)
  $q_i(t)$ = output from generating type i at time t, mw
  $q_h(t)$ = output from conventional hydroelectric generation at time t, mw
  $q_p(t)$ = output from pumped-storage generation at time t, mw
  $p_p(t)$ = pumping power at time t, mw
  t = time, days
  z = weekly generating cost

Because the objective function and two of the constraints contain integrals of functions for which only the data of Fig. 5-24 are available, we consider a graphic-analog solution.

The computational sequence evolves from a search for operations which can be performed on the initial data to obtain a graphical representation that permits convenient testing for optimality. Computational efficiency depends upon judicious selection of successive transformations in the units of measure on the coordinate axes. Figure 5-27 illustrates one suitable sequence. The graphs are designated by letters, and arrows indicate the sequence of operations. The relative graph sizes have no significance. An analog computer may be used for the integration, multiplication, etc.

Graph a is Fig. 5-24 rotated 90°. Graph b is obtained by summing the time at each watt-output level in a. The function shown in graph b is differentiated to obtain graph c and integrated to obtain graph d. Graphs c and e (from Fig. 5-26) have logarithmic ordinate scales, so their absolute ordinate values can be added to obtain the logarithm of their product in graph f. This graphical operation corresponds to the logarithmic transformation in Sec. 5-6 (minimizing the logarithm of the function will minimize the function). The total area under the curve of graph c, before taking the logarithm, is 168 hr (7 days).

Nuclear generation starts at zero load, and its cost variation with load level is represented in graph f. The load level at which to start coal generation is a variable to be determined. We must, therefore, generate a family of curves in graph g in the same manner as the single curve was generated in graph f, except that the zero abscissa value in graph e is placed at various starting points along the abscissa of graph c before adding the ordinate values of these two graphs. Analog computation simplifies this step and makes the logarithmic plots unnecessary.

We seek to minimize the sum of four costs:

1. Weekly nuclear generating cost
2. Weekly coal generating cost
3. The construction cost of the dam and reservoir expressed as equivalent weekly operating cost over the life of the structure
4. A similarly distributed construction cost for the pumping-generating facility

Observe that areas in graphs f and g involve units of dollars (the product of ordinate and abscissa units). In graph h we seek the operating ranges of pumped-storage (a), conventional hydroelectric (b), coal (c), and nuclear (d) generation which minimize the sum of costs 1 to 4 while satisfying constraints (47) to (50). We can accomplish this by the following steps:

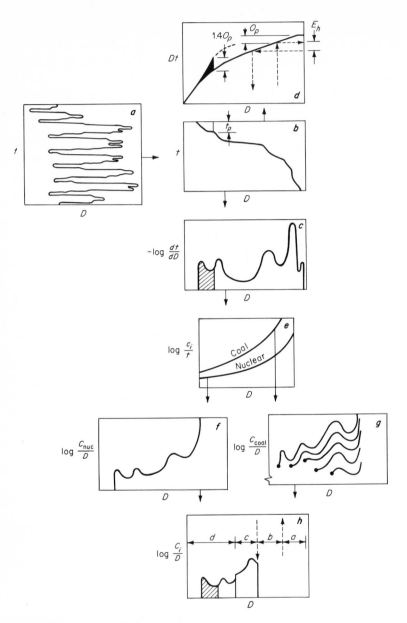

Fig. 5-27 Graphic solution sequence.

1. Choose a trial pumped-storage generating capacity (*a*) in graph *h*.
2. Determine the hydroelectric generating range (*b*) by projecting vertically to graph *d* and marking the hydroelectric generating capacity E_h on the ordinate scale. This step, shown by the dotted lines with arrows in graphs *h* and *d*, satisfies constraint (47).
3   Determine the nuclear and coal generating ranges, (*c*) and (*d*), by test-fitting various curves of the family from graph *g* with the curve from graph *f* until a minimum total area under the two curves is obtained. This can be accomplished by inspection. If inspection is difficult, one can use an overlay to permit visual comparison between the area added and the area deducted as family *g* is moved a small increment parallel to the abscissa on graph *h*.

Constraint (48) is satisfied automatically in the graphical process and constraint (49) must be obeyed in steps 1 and 3.

4. Next, determine the cost of energy consumed in pumping. Observe that pumping would be accomplished at minimum cost if all pumping could be done at the power level having the lowest unit generating cost, i.e., at the point of tangency *P* on the nuclear cost curve in Fig. 5-26. Since all pumping cannot be accomplished at a single power level, we minimize costs by pumping during periods when the load is less than level *P*, to bring the resulting output closer to this optimum operating level. We accomplish this in graph *d* by measuring the weekly pumped-storage generation energy O_p, multiplying it by 1.4 to obtain the weekly energy consumed in pumping, and extending the continuous base load (168 hr per week) until an additional output equal to $1.4O_p$ is obtained, as labeled. This satisfies constraint (50). The pumping energy is then translated to additional graphs as shown. Shaded areas show additions, and crosshatched areas show deductions. The logarithm of the time t_p in graph *b* replaces, and is equal to, the crosshatched area in graph *c*. The adjusted cost due to pumping in graph *h* amounts to the removal of the crosshatched area and the addition of a discontinuous cost obtained by adding log t_p to its corresponding ordinate value on the nuclear curve in graph *e*.
5. Compute the weekly operating equivalent of construction cost for the pump-generator installation, based on the trial pumped-storage generating capacity selected in step 1.
6. Determine the required reservoir size for the trial generating capacity chosen in step 1. To do this, we tabulate storage in the reservoir, starting with zero storage at the time of maximum drawdown after the Friday demand peak, and observe the maximum storage required during one week. This step is identical to the mass-diagram analysis used by

hydrologists to determine reservoir capacity. The required data are obtained from the pumping and generating areas in Fig. 5-24, for which operating levels are obtained from the results of graph *h*. Having the required reservoir capacity, the construction cost is obtained from Fig. 5-25, and the equivalent weekly operating cost is computed.

7. Add the total-cost area in graph *b* (obtained from steps 3 and 4) to the equivalent weekly operating costs obtained in steps 5 and 6 to obtain total weekly cost.

8. Repeat steps 1 to 7 for different trial values of pumped-storage generating capacity to determine a minimum-cost value.

This is an inventory problem with stochastic supply and demand (see Sec. 10-1). It is apparent that a low unit cost for the storage facility (dam and reservoir) would favor large storage capacity and low pump capacity, and vice versa. In most pumped-storage projects, storage based upon at least a weekly cycle is found economical in order to take advantage of long pumping periods made available by low electrical demand on weekends. Numerous other starting assumptions could have been made. For example, a fifth constraint that pumping power cannot exceed generating power makes the computation only slightly longer.

The example illustrates a process of graphical reasoning and demonstrates the versatility of graphic-analog methods for highly nonlinear optimization problems. Problems 5-32 and 5-33 provide exercises with simpler graphical solutions.

REDUCTION OF VARIABLES

In many design problems, the less we understand the underlying phenomena, the more variables we require to explain them. Complexity and simplicity often are characteristics not so much of a problem as of our state of knowledge when we seek its solution. In addition to excluding irrelevant variables (Sec. 1-6) and identifying variables to which the objective function is only slightly sensitive (Secs. 4-5, 5-1, and 10-1), one can sometimes recognize design variables which can be separated from the total problem. The resulting subproblems lead to proper suboptimizations. Consider an example.

Example 5-21   Cantilever retaining-wall design A cantilever retaining wall is to be designed for minimum cost. Normal practice consists of choosing a trial base length and a trial stem location on the base and then adjusting these two variables by successive trials until a near-optimal solution is obtained. Let us consider a direct optimization, given the required properties of concrete, steel, and soil, the wall height, and the estimated in-place unit costs of concrete and steel.

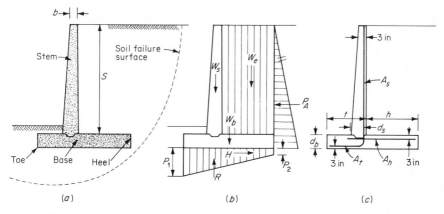

Fig. 5-28 Cantilever retaining wall. (*a*) Fixed dimensions; (*b*) forces; (*c*) design variables.

The wall is designed as three reinforced-concrete cantilever beams: the stem, toe, and heel (Fig. 5-28). The potential failure modes include:

Soil failure:
1. Shear failure in the soil surrounding the wall (Fig. 5-28*a*)
2. Sliding of wall on its base
3. Overturning of wall about its toe
4. Failure of soil in bearing beneath the toe

Structural failure of one of the three cantilever beams:
5. Inadequate beam depth for shear
6. Inadequate beam depth for bending
7. Tensile failure of reinforcing steel
8. Failure in bond between steel and concrete
9. Insufficient steel anchorage

We seek values of t, h, d_s, and d_b (Fig. 5-28*c*) and A_s, A_t, and A_h which minimize cost. A_s, A_t, and A_h are steel areas per linear foot of wall at the base of the stem, toe, and heel, respectively. There are thus seven design variables and nine failure modes (constraints). We try to identify the non-critical variables.

First, the cost of the stem is observed to be independent of its position on the base since the required stem concrete and steel (a function of bending and/or shear) are independent of stem position. Therefore, the stem design, with variables d_s and A_s, can be uncoupled as a separate problem—in this case, one not requiring optimization.

For the base, failure modes 8 and 9 might be safely neglected.   Mode 8 dictates the diameters of reinforcing steel but not its total weight, and the total cost is relatively insensitive to the anchorage length dictated by mode 9. Further, because safety with respect to mode 1 is usually not significantly affected by the length of base or position of stem, mode 1 can be uncoupled as a separate problem.

The problem is now reduced to minimizing the base cost as a function of base length and stem location, subject to constraints imposed by failure modes 2 to 7.   If we ignore mode 6, based on the experience that shear rather than bending controls the thickness of short, heavily loaded beams, we have five variables and six constraints, since mode 7 applies to both the toe and the heel.   The five design variables are A_t, A_h, t, h, and d_b.

A typical objective function and constraints are

Min: $z = C_c\, d_b(t + h) + C_s(hA_h + tA_t)$

Subject to:

$$R \tan \frac{\phi}{P_A} \geqslant 1.5 \text{ (safety factor)} \qquad\qquad \text{sliding}$$

$$\frac{W_s\, D_s + W_b\, D_b + W_e\, D_e}{P_A D_A} \geqslant 1.5 \qquad\qquad \text{overturning}$$

$$P \left\{ \frac{2}{t+h}(W_s + W_b + W_e) - \frac{6}{(t+h)^2}\left[W_s\left(D_s - \frac{t+h}{3}\right) + W_b\left(D_b - \frac{t+h}{3}\right) \right. \right.$$
$$\left. \left. + W_e\left(D_e - \frac{t+h}{3}\right) \right] + P_A D_A \right\}^{-1} \geqslant 1.5 \quad \text{bearing at toe}$$

$$d \geqslant \frac{V}{bjv} \qquad\qquad\qquad\qquad \text{shear}$$

$$A_t = \frac{M_t}{f_s jd} \qquad\qquad\qquad\qquad \text{tensile failure, toe}$$

$$A_h = \frac{M_h}{f_s jd} \qquad\qquad\qquad\qquad \text{tensile failure, heel}$$

where C_c, C_s = costs per unit volume of concrete and steel, respectively
c = required steel coverage

P_A, R, and W_i = forces/lin ft of wall (Fig. 5-28b)

D_i = corresponding moment arms about the toe

P = allowable soil bearing pressure

Figure 5-29 shows the load, shear, and moments for the base.   The first three constraints are obtained from soil statics, and the last three use the

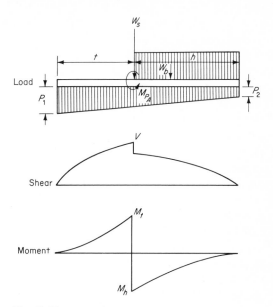

Fig. 5-29   Load, shear, and moments on the base.

standard notation for elastic analysis of reinforced concrete [4, pp. 345–351]. An analogous optimization for a conical shell footing can be found in [27].

Solutions to Probs. 5-31 and 5-32 depend upon similar reductions in the numbers of variables.

SUMMARY

Nonlinear optimization problems are characterized by objective and/or constraint functions which are nonlinear.   The subject is still being actively developed.   It can be organized into two broad categories: classical optimization and search techniques.

Classical techniques solve systems of equations.   Search techniques are iterative; i.e., successive improvements are sought to an initial solution.

The consideration of classical optimization techniques began with differential calculus (Sec. 5-1).   The extension to optimization subject to differentiable equality constraints, the Lagrange multiplier, was treated in Sec. 5-2.

The fundamental work of Kuhn and Tucker was described in Sec. 5-3. The Kuhn-Tucker conditions extend the Lagrange multiplier technique to problems with inequality constraints.   In addition, they provide necessary and sufficient conditions for global optima.

Unfortunately, classical optimization techniques usually require the simultaneous solution of nonlinear equations, which is sometimes impractical. Approximation techniques, such as the Newton-Raphson method, are frequently used to obtain solutions.

Geometric programming possesses distinctive features which have special promise for design. The emphasis is upon the relative magnitudes of the terms of the objective function rather than upon the variables. This technique suggests how resources should be apportioned among the components contributing to the design objective. Section 5-4 developed geometric programming from the calculus and inequality points of view.

Search techniques were briefly illustrated in Sec. 5-5. An enormous literature has developed, and the techniques are often of a heuristic or ad hoc variety. The techniques of alternating one-dimensional search, steepest gradient, and contour tangents were mentioned.

The unusual success with which linear-programming problems can be solved has motivated many to seek means for reducing nonlinear problems to linear ones. One approach is to replace an arc by a series of chords, i.e., a segmented linearization. This is called piecewise linear programming, and was considered in Sec. 5-6. Another approach is to seek transformations which will reduce a nonlinear problem to a linear one. One uses a logarithmic transformation for functions of products of decision variables, and a second transformation (Sec. 5-6) is valuable in "smoothing" problems where the objective contains step functions.

The application of graphical techniques to nonlinear optimization was the subject of Sec. 5-7.

PROBLEMS

5-1. Min: $z = 8x_1 + \dfrac{814}{x_1 x_2}$

Subject to: $5x_2 + \dfrac{2}{x_1 x_2} \leqslant 1$

$x_1, x_2 \geqslant 0$ ◆

5-2. Min: $z = \dfrac{4}{x_1{}^2} + x_2{}^2 x_3$

Subject to: $\dfrac{3x_1{}^2}{x_2{}^2} - 3/2\, x_2 x_3{}^2 \leqslant 4$

$x_1, x_2, x_3 \geqslant 0$

5-3. Prove the arithmetic-mean–geometric-mean inequality for n numbers, that is,

$$\frac{1}{n} \sum_{i=1}^{n} a_i \geqslant \sqrt[n]{\prod_{i=1}^{n} a_i}$$

5-4. Solve using the Lagrange multiplier:

Min: $z = 4x_1^2 + 3x_2^2 - 5x_1x_2 - 8x_1$

Subject to: $x_1 + x_2 = 4$

5-5. Obtain an approximate solution for x and y by two iterations of the Newton-Raphson method. Start from the point $x_0 = 3$, $y_0 = 1$.

$$f(x,y) = x^2 + xy - 5 = 0$$

$$g(x,y) = x^2 + x - \frac{6x}{y} = 0$$

5-6. Determine x_1^* and x_2^* which maximize the following equation:

$$z = 100x_1 + 4 \times \frac{10^3}{x_1x_2} + 50x_2 \quad \blacklozenge$$

subject to the constraints

$x_1 - 2x_1x_2 + x_2 \leqslant 0$

$x_1, x_2 \geqslant 0$

5-7. Min: $z = x_1^2 + x_2^2$

Subject to: $x_1 + 2x_2 \geqslant 6$

$x_1 + x_2 \geqslant 3$

$x_1, x_2 \geqslant 0$

Show that the Kuhn-Tucker conditions are satisfied at the stationary point.

5-8. Apply the Kuhn-Tucker theory to the generalized transportation problem of Sec. 4-1. Solve Prob. 4-1 using Kuhn-Tucker theory.

5-9. Max: $z = x_1(2 + x_1) + x_2(1 + x_1 + 2x_2)$

Subject to: $x_1 + 4x_2 \leqslant 8$

$3x_1 + 2x_2 \leqslant 6 \quad \blacklozenge$

5-10. Consider the nonlinear programming problem:

Max: $2x_1 + 3x_2 - x_1^3 - 2x_2^2$

Subject to: $x_1 + 3x_2 \leqslant 6$

$5x_1 + 2x_2 \leqslant 10$

$x_1, x_2 \geqslant 0$

(a) Determine the convexity or concavity of the objective function and the constraints.

(b) Derive the optimal solution from the Kuhn-Tucker conditions.

5-11. The total cost associated with the manufacture and storage of a certain product is given by

$$C_T = \frac{Q}{2} C_s + \frac{D}{Q} C_f$$

where Q = quantity of product manufactured in any given run

C_s = unit cost of storage per year

D = annual demand for product

C_f = fixed cost per run

By inspection, determine the optimal run size Q which minimizes total cost. This problem has been adapted from [31].

5-12. A vertical cylindrical tank has top and bottom surfaces which cost twice as much per square foot as the sides. Find the best diameter-to-height ratio for any given volume.

5-13. 400 cu yd of material is to be shipped across a river in an open rectangular box of dimensions x_1, x_2, and x_3. The sides and bottom of the box cost $10 per sq yd, and the ends $20 per sq yd. Two runners, each the length of the box, are required for the box to slide, and these cost $2.50 per yd. Each round trip costs $0.20 in transportation charges. Find the box dimensions which minimize total cost. If material costs (including the cost of runners) were to double, by what factor would total transportation cost be affected? This problem has been adapted from [9].

5-14. In the design of a heat exchanger, the following variables are to be chosen:

N = no. of tubes in condenser
L = tube length
D_i = inside tube diameter
D_o = outside tube diameter

The cost may be written

$$C = \frac{a_1}{N^{7/6} D_o L^{4/3}} + \frac{a_2 D_i^{0.8}}{N^{0.2} L} + \frac{a_3 L}{D_i^{4.8} N^{1.8}} + a_4 N D_o L$$

where the first two terms represent the cost of steam, the third term is the cost of pumping, and the fourth term represents the fixed charges associated with the condenser. There are two restrictions:

$D_o \geqslant D_{min}$ Tube diameter cannot be too small.

$D_o - D_i = 2t$ Outer diameter exceeds inner diameter by twice the wall thickness.

a_1, a_2, a_3, a_4, t, and D_{min} are known constants.

(a) Consider the problem in the context of geometric programming. What is the dual problem? Discuss procedures for the solution of the dual problem.

(b) How can the variables N, L, D_i, and D_o be obtained from the solution of the dual problem?

(See the paper by M. Avriel and D. J. Wilde in *Industrial and Engineering Chemistry, Process Design and Development*, vol. 6, p. 256, April, 1967, for a discussion of parts of this problem.)

5-15. Using gradient methods, find the minimum of the following functions:

(a) $z = x_1^2 + x_1(1 + x_2) + 2x_2^2$
(b) $z = (x_1 - x_2)^2 + 2(x_2 - 1)^2$

In each case, begin from the starting point $x_1 = [2, -1]$.

5-16. For given data, it is instructive to compare curves which have been fitted by least-square and absolute-deviation criteria (see Appendix 1). To illustrate how data can be simulated for a straight line, select two digits from the random-number table in Appendix 4—say 3 and 7. The true equation is taken as $y = 3x + 7$. To generate data corresponding to the seven fixed points $x = -3, -2, -1, 0, 1, 2, 3$, we observe that corresponding true values of y are $-2, 1, 4, 7, 10, 13, 16$.

· Next, select 7 two-digit random numbers—say 36, 24, 96, 23, 12, 05, and 91—and read them as 3.6%, 2.4%, 9.6%, −2.3%, 1.2%, −0.5%, and −9.1%. These percentages correspond to perturbations of the true values; a negative value is assumed if the second digit is odd. The resulting simulated values of y (rounded to two decimal places) are given in the table:

x	y true	y simulated
−3	−2	−1.93
−2	1	1.02
−1	4	4.38
0	7	6.86
1	10	11.20
2	13	12.94
3	16	14.54

Calculate the least-square and minimum-absolute-deviation lines and plot them together with the true line $y = 3x + 7$.

5-17. The techniques in Appendix 1 for least squares and minimum absolute deviation also apply to polynomials. Consider the quadratic $y = a_0 + a_1 x + a_2 x^2$ and the n measurements $(x_1, y_1), \ldots, (x_n, y_n)$. The square and absolute deviations are, respectively,

$$E_s = \sum_{i=1}^{n} [y_i - (a_0 + a_1 x_i + a_2 x_i^2)]^2$$

$$E_{ad} = \sum_{i=1}^{n} \{[y_i - (a_0 + a_1 x_i + a_2 x_i^2)]\mho[y_i - (a_0 + a_1 x_i + a_2 x_i^2)]$$

$$+ [(a_0 + a_1 x_i + a_2 x_i^2) - y_i]\mho[(a_0 + a_1 x_i + a_2 x_i^2) - y_i]\}$$

Since the deviations are linear functions of the parameters a_0, a_1, and a_2, the curve-fitting techniques in Appendix 1 also apply here.

For the parabola $a_0 = 1$, $a_1 = 2$, and $a_2 = 3$, simulate data and calculate the two curves as in Prob. 5-16.

5-18. Subway systems are usually self-ventilating, since trains move significant slugs of air. It is desirable to reduce wind velocities across station platforms by diverting air through vertical vent shafts near the stations [5].

Excavation of vent shafts may cause settlement of adjacent buildings, due either to lowering the water table or to "loosing ground" into the excavation. A method which reduces this danger is to dig narrow trenches for the walls of the vent, simultaneously fill the trenches with a slurry, and eventually displace the slurry with concrete. When the concrete walls harden, the soil within them is excavated to form the vent.

Assume that a vertical vent is required which will have a cross-sectional area of 600 sq ft. The vent cross section is to be polygonal, with sides of equal length. Determine the optimum number of sides, given the following cost data:

Trench excavation: $35 per ft of trench perimeter, plus $3,000 per side
Concrete: $200 per ft of trench perimeter plus $20nL^2$, where L is the length (ft) of one side and n is the number of sides.

Assume that the costs of the bentonite slurry and the excavation within the concrete walls are fixed, independent of the number of sides.

5-19. Figure 5-30 shows an underwater reservoir for offshore oil operations [13]. It consists of a bottomless conical steel tank with a vertical shaft which supports a mooring dolphin. Anchor piles prevent movement in heavy seas. The reservoir is initially full of seawater. Oil pumped into the shaft displaces the water through ports at the base of the cone. When a tanker is filled from the reservoir, water reenters the same ports. The reservoir can be floated with compressed air and towed to a new site. The steel weight is less than required for a tank on land because pressures are approximately equal on both sides of the shell.

Assume that the reservoir will rest in 180 ft of water and that preliminary studies suggest a capacity of 1,405,000 cu ft (within the dotted cone in Fig. 5-30). Determine the optimum dimensions for the cone height H and base diameter D (in feet) from the following cost estimates:

Cost of mooring cylinder: $4,000 (200 - H)$
Cost of cone: $8S$, where S is surface area of cone (within dotted line), sq ft

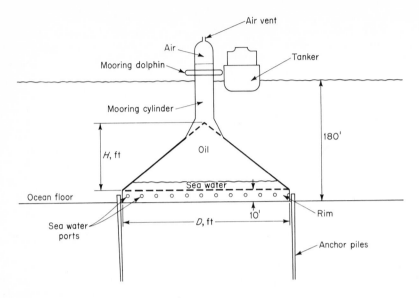

Fig. 5-30   Submarine oil reservoir.

Cost of rim: $1,800D
Cost of anchor piles: $200,000 + $3 × 10⁷/D

The cone height cannot exceed 150 ft.

5-20.   Outline a solution for optimal backstay length t and strut length s of the aerial cableway tower shown in Fig. 5-31, having horizontal cable tension P, required height h,

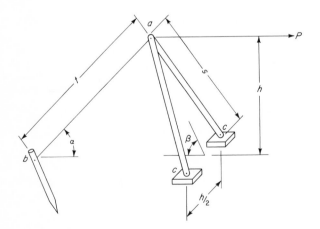

Fig. 5-31   Cableway tower.

and base width $h/2$. The costs are:

$$c_s = k_1 sS \qquad \text{struts}$$
$$c_f = k_2 F_v + k_3 F_h \qquad \text{strut footings}$$
$$c_t = k_4 tT \qquad \text{backstay cable}$$
$$c_a = k_5 A_v + k_6 A_h \qquad \text{backstay anchor}$$

where $k_1, k_2, \ldots, k_6$ = cost coefficients
$\qquad\qquad\qquad T$ = backstay tension
$\qquad\qquad\qquad S$ = strut compression
$\qquad\qquad\qquad F_v, F_h$ = total vertical and horizontal force components on footings
$\qquad\qquad\qquad A_v, A_h$ = vertical and horizontal force components on backstay anchor

5-21.   The optimum tower height H and number and inclinations θ_i of support cables are to be determined for the 1,000-ft main span of a cable-stayed girder span bridge [11].   We can determine local optima for various numbers of cables until a global optimum is identified. Determine the local optimum for a bridge having cables at a single inclination θ, based on the following cost estimates, in dollars:

$$C_t = 4{,}000{,}000 + \frac{200H^{1.5}}{L} \qquad \text{cost of tower}$$

$$C_c = 6{,}000 + 0.07LT \qquad \text{cost per cable support}$$
$$C_d = 10{,}000 + 0.15SM + 0.08C \qquad \text{cost per span of deck and girder}$$

where L = length of cable, ft
$\qquad\quad T$ = cable tension, kips
$\qquad\quad S$ = span length between adjacent supports, ft
$\qquad\quad M$ = maximum moment at center of span, ft-lb
$\qquad\quad C$ = compression in span due to horizontal components of cable forces, lb

Assume weightless cables, total dead and live load of 6,000 lb per 1 in ft of span, and hinge connections at the points of support by cables and towers.

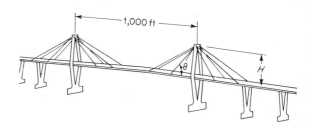

Fig. 5-32   Cable-stayed girder span bridge.

5-22.   Several pumping stations are to be designed for a regional sewage-collector system. The machinery will be housed in 45-ft-diameter vertical concrete cylinders extending below grade.   A single slip form will be used to pour the cylinders at all stations.   At a particular station, the cylinder is to be 40 ft deep and the expected high groundwater level is at grade. Determine the optimum diameter D and thickness T of a base slab to prevent flotation of the structure due to buoyancy, given the following data:

Weight of cylinder, superstructure, and installed machinery: 1,400 kips
Density of concrete in base: 150 lb/cu ft

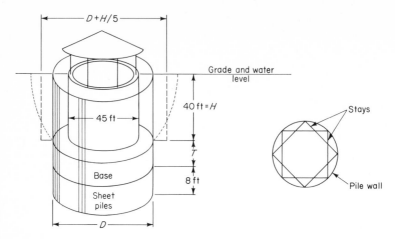

Fig. 5-33 Pumping station.

Submerged weight of soil: $W_s = 70$ lb/cu ft
Cost of concrete in base: \$35/cu yd
Cost of excavation: \$2/cu yd
Cost of steel sheet-pile walls: \$7/sq ft
Assume all other costs fixed, i.e., dewatering the site, backfilling, etc.

The construction sequence will consist of driving a circular sheet-pile wall, dewatering the site with wellpoints, excavating, pouring base slab, slip-forming the concrete cylinder, backfilling, and removing the sheet piles. The sheet-pile wall will be braced internally with turnbuckle stays. Plastic film between the sheet piles and base will permit removal of piling after the base hardens.

Assume that the theoretical shear-failure surface in the soil caused by flotation of the structure (dotted) is approximated by a cylindrical failure surface of diameter $D + H/5$ (dashed). The shear strength s (psf) on this surface is

$$s = 0.4hw_s \tan 25°$$

where h is the depth below grade (ft), 0.4 is the horizontal earth pressure coefficient, and 25° is the internal friction angle. The coefficient of friction between concrete and soil is 0.25.

5-23. Trash heaps, after suitable landscaping, have been proposed as ski slopes with parking areas at the top.

Determine the optimal height, length, and width of a "sanitary land hill," given the following data:

Costs

Cost of land:	$c_1 = \$4,000$/acre ($=43,560$ sq ft)
Cost of construction/cu yd:	$c_c = \$0.50$

Net annual incomes
From skiing:
   For hills (over 100 ft high): $p_s = \$(H - 100)(400)$ $H \geqslant 100$
where H is total height of fill.
From parking:
$p_p = \$0.15$/sq ft of top area on hill

The hill must be in the shape of a truncated rectangular pyramid with 2:1 side slopes. Assume infinite life, zero salvage, and 4% required interest rate.

5-24. A chemical manufacturer needs a 400,000 cu ft underground liquid-propane cylindrical storage tank, which will require refrigeration. Given the following data, formulate the objective function and indicate a solution method to determine the optimal diameter D and height H of the tank and depth d of earth cover (Fig. 5-34).

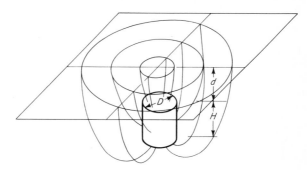

Fig. 5-34 Heat-flow net.

Thermal data

Liquid propane temperature: $t = -44°F$
Average annual ground surface temperature: $t_1 = 60°F$
Average thermal conductivity of frozen and unfrozen soil surrounding tank with steady-state heat loss:
$\lambda = (1.4 \text{ Btu/hr})/\text{sq ft}/(°F/ft)\,(=1.4 \text{ Btu/hr-ft-}°F)$
Heat loss from tank is approximated by [23]:

$$q \simeq \frac{8\pi hR\lambda(t_1 - t_0)}{2h + R}$$

where q = heat loss, Btu/hr
h = depth from ground surface to center of tank, ft
R = radius of sphere having volume equal to tank, ft

Costs

Excavation: $8/cu yd (includes cost of freezing to support sides of excavation)
Tank floor: $1/sq ft
Walls: $0.10/sq ft/100 lb/lin in. maximum hoop compression in tank (lateral earth pressure = $60x$ psf, where x is depth below ground, ft)
Roof: $3/sq ft plus $0.20/sq ft for each foot of soil overburden
Refrigeration: installation—$0.008/Btu hr capacity
operation—$1/100,000 Btu
Assume 40-year operating life, zero maintenance, zero salvage, 9% interest on investment.

5-25. (a) A community is to develop a public water system supplied from m noninteracting wells. It must decide how much water to pump from each well to meet the community's need. The daily pumping cost at each well consists of a fixed cost a and a variable cost b, proportional to the quantity of water pumped, $c_p = a + bQ$, where a and b are constants. The cost required to overcome friction losses in the line is cQ^2, where c is a proportionality constant depending on pipe size and length and terrain.   The total cost per day of operating a well is, therefore, $a + bQ + cQ^2$.   The maximum amount of water pumped from each well cannot exceed the limit L_i ($i = 1, \ldots, m$).   Furthermore, the total volume of water supplied by all wells must meet the community's requirement R.

Formulate an optimization model and set up the necessary conditions required for an optimum solution.

(*b*) Repeat part *a* for the case when the *k*th and *j*th wells are required to deliver at least $d\%$ of the total demand.

5-26.   An irrigation farming cooperative has three pumps (A, B, and C), whose discharge-cost characteristics are shown in Fig. 5-35.   The pumps are on high ground, and connecting ditches allow each field in the cooperative to be supplied from any of the three pumps.

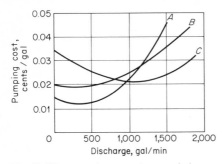

Fig. 5-35   Pumping cost characteristics.

Water requests for a 12-hr period include 900 gpm at field *a*, 1,300 gpm at field *b*, and 1,700 gpm at field *c* (Fig. 5-36).   Seepage and evaporation losses account for the ratio of water delivered to water pumped, shown beside each of the connecting ditches.

Formulate a solution for the delivery rates from each pump to each field which minimize total pumping cost.

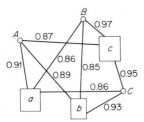

Fig. 5-36   Ditch losses.

Note: One example of a more complex nonlinear network problem is the optimal delivery of electrical power from several generating stations, with power loss a function of transmission distance.   Another is the optimal delivery of water to a municipal water system from several pumping stations where hydrostatic head losses are a function of flow distances and flow rates.

5-27.   Solid materials such as coal, pulpwood chips, and mineral ore concentrates can be transported in pipelines by suspension in fluids such as water or crude oil [10].   Given the following data, formulate the problem and indicate an appropriate solution method to determine the pipe diameter and slurry concentration which minimize total cost.

Length of pipeline: $L = 60$ miles
Change in elevation: $h = -300$ ft
Required capacity: 10 tons of coal/hr
Specific gravity of coal: $G = 1.3$
Installed cost of pipe ($/ft), including right of way: $c_1 = 1 + 0.03 D^{5/2}$, where D is the inside diameter of pipe, in.
Installed cost of pumping stations: $c_p = $250/hp$ of pump capacity
Installed cost of systems for injecting coal at beginning of line and separating it at end of line: $c_{is} = $50/ton$ capacity/day
Cost of water treatment at outfall: $c_t = $100/million gal.$ (Water may be obtained at the source at no cost.)
Electrical energy cost: $c_e = 0.01/kilowatt-hr$
Efficiency of electrical motor-pump combination: $E = 0.60$
Required horsepower delivered by pumps:

$$\cdot HP = \frac{W_w + W_c}{550}(h + H)$$

where W_w and W_c are weights of water and coal delivered per second and H is total head loss (ft) due to friction losses.

The head loss is estimated to be

$$H = 4,800 \frac{V^2}{D}(1 + 1.4c)$$

where V is flow velocity (ft/sec) and c is coal concentration (percentage of total weight). Assume the operation is continuous, 7 days per week. The overhead and maintenance costs are (assumed) independent of pipe size and slurry concentration. All components have a 30-year economic life, with zero salvage. Required interest rate is 10%.

5-28. Assume that coal in the previous problem is to be pumped from two sources to a common discharge point. The required capacities are 9 tons of coal per hr from source 1 and 6 tons per hr from source 2. The pipe lengths and elevations are shown in Fig. 5-37. Using necessary data from Prob. 5-27, formulate the problem and indicate an appropriate solution method for obtaining pipe sizes and slurry concentrations in the three pipe branches which minimize total cost.

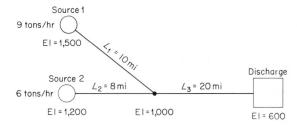

Fig. 5-37 Three-line network.

5-29. A penstock of diameter $d = 3$ ft and length $L = 2,000$ ft will deliver water from a reservoir of constant elevation $H = 250$ ft to a turbine. A surge tower of diameter D will prevent excessive pressure rise in the penstock when the valve must be closed quickly during an emergency. Neglecting the effect of acceleration of water in the surge tower, a momentum balance on water in the pipe yields

$$g(H - h) - \tfrac{1}{2}f\frac{L}{d}v^2 = L\frac{dv}{dt}$$

where h = height of water in surge tower, ft
  f = Moody friction factor ($=0.025$)
  v = water velocity in pipe, ft/sec
  g = acceleration due to gravity ($=32.2$ ft/sec^2)
  t = time, sec
Continuity requires that

$$\frac{\pi d^2}{4} v = \frac{\pi D^2}{4}\frac{dh}{dt} + Q$$

where Q, the flow in cubic feet per minute through the valve during shutoff, is approximated by

$$Q = k\left(1 - \frac{t}{t_c}\right)(h - h_d)^{1/2}$$

where k = a constant ($=18$ ft$^{2.5}$/sec)
  t_c = the shutoff period ($=8$ sec)
  h_d = the downstream head, ft

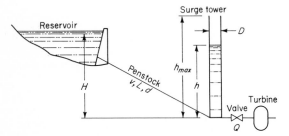

Fig. 5-38   Penstock and surge tower.

Assuming $h = 220$ ft during open-valve steady-state operation and $h_d = 0$, formulate the solution for the optimum diameter D of surge tower and height h_{max} if total cost is given by

$$1,100h_{max} + 90Dh_{max}$$

(The first term represents the cost of penstock, and the second the cost of surge tower.)

5-30. For a given height of circular cellular cofferdam, the in-place costs of steel and granular fill are estimated at $25.5 per lin ft of sheet-pile wall and $0.85 per sq ft of cell surface area, respectively. A design study for the various failure modes provides the following constraint:

$$B^2 \geqslant 38.3L$$

where L is center-to-center distance between two adjacent cells. If $90°$ T sections are used at all joints between cells, determine the optimum values of R, r, and θ.

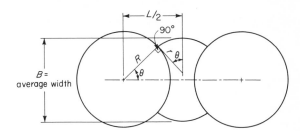

Fig. 5-39   Cellular cofferdam.

5-31.   A major cost in cantilever retaining-wall construction is for the erection of formwork and reinforcing steel.   The cost might be reduced by precasting the wall stem.   A proposed wall (Fig. 5-40) consists of base slab A, precast stem B, and noncorroding tie rods C, which bolt to yokes cast into the stem and base.   Construction involves pouring the base, bolting tie rods to the base yokes, tilting the precast stem sections into position, and bolting the tie rods to them.   Mastic is poured into the base slot before placing the stem and into tongue-and-groove joints between adjacent stem sections.

Assume a stem height H and horizontal pressure wy, where y is the depth below the top of stem and w is a constant.   Assume that the component costs are functions of the quantities of steel and concrete and can be expressed as

$$C_b = k_1 bV \qquad \text{base}^4$$
$$C_s = k_2 m^{1.3} \qquad \text{stem}$$

where C_b and C_s = costs/lin ft of wall for base and stem, respectively

$\qquad\qquad k_i$ = constants
$\qquad\qquad b$ = base width
$\qquad\qquad m$ = maximum moment in stem
$\qquad\qquad V$ = critical shear in base directly under stem

---

⁴ Assume that toe and heel are of same thickness and that shear, not bending, governs base thickness.

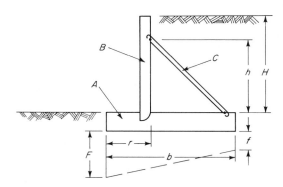

Fig. 5-40   Cantilever retaining wall with precast stem and ties.

The cost of ties is quite insensitive to wall geometry and may be omitted from the optimization.

The constraints are

$F \leqslant 2,000$ psf   allowable bearing pressure at toe

$f \geqslant 0$ psf   stability against overturning[5]

$r \geqslant 1.5$ ft   toe support for base of stem

where F and f are bearing pressures at the toe and heel of the base, respectively, assuming a straight-line pressure distribution, and r is the toe length measured from the back of the stem.

Formulate the objective function and constraints for minimum cost in terms of the dimensions h, r, and b (Fig. 5-36) and suggest a solution method.

5-32. A petroleum company pays $0.08 per barrel per 1,000 miles for transporting crudes by ocean tanker to its refineries. Deliveries average 800,000 barrels (4,500,000 cu ft) per week from an average distance of 3,000 miles.

It is proposed to investigate the economy of underwater shipping containers made of plastic, to be towed by submarines. The following advantages are anticipated:

1. Reduction of delays and shipping losses caused by storms at the ocean surface.
2. Reduction in hydraulic drag. Total displacement volume of the plastic-container–submarine combination per barrel capacity is less than for steel ships designed to resist surface wave and wind forces.
3. When returned empty, the plastic containers are collapsed so that their hydraulic drag is further reduced.
4. The towing submarines need not stand idle while containers are being filled or emptied. The containers serve as temporary offshore storage reservoirs, which are cheaper than onshore steel tanks.
5. A submarine towing containers can travel on the surface in congested port areas, in shallow canals, or on open sea on calm days. It could, if needed, travel under ice flows in arctic areas.

The container (Fig. 5-41) is a cylindrical plastic bag surrounded by elastic webbing, which collapses the bag when not filled. A small metal keel provides rigidity for maneuvering and serves as a mounting rail for ballast to sink the container and its contents below the surface. A parabolic metal cone containing a towing hook is built into the fabric at both ends of the cylindrical bag. Several containers can be towed in tandem. Air for maintaining proper buoyancy of each container is provided through air lines from a small reservoir and return pump in the submarine.

Given the data below, determine if surface shipping should be replaced with underwater shipping. If underwater shipping is proposed, determine the following:

(*a*) How many submarine tugs should be used?

[5] Neglect additional constraints, such as sliding on base and deep shear failure.

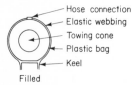

Filled

Empty   **Fig. 5-41**   Proposed plastic container.

(b) How many containers enroute should be used (not counting those being filled or emptied at terminals)?

(c) What should be the length and diameter of the containers?

(d) How many containers should be towed by each submarine?

(e) What are the optimal towing speeds for full and empty containers?

Assume that submarines always tow the same number of containers and that operating speeds are adjusted to develop the same tow tension for empty containers as for full containers.

Submarine tugs

1. Assume 20% nonrunning (in-port) time.
2. Total fixed annual costs for crew, maintenance, etc., are $100,000.
3. Additional costs, which vary with tow tension (fuel, extra maintenance, etc.), are shown in Fig. 5-42. Assume that developable tow tension is independent of submarine speed (independent of submarine drag). This assumption is reasonable if the displacement of the towed containers is several times the displacement of the submarine.

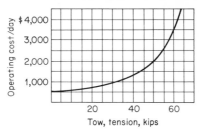

Fig. 5-42 Submarine towing cost.

Containers

1. Hydraulic drag, in kips:
$$D = 4 \times 10^{-5} V^2 d^2 L^{1/3}$$
where V is velocity in miles per hour, L is length in feet, and d is diameter of cylinder in feet.

2. Effective diameter of collapsed empty container is one-fourth the diameter of full container.

3. Total annual costs for construction, maintenance, etc., are shown in Fig. 5-43. The

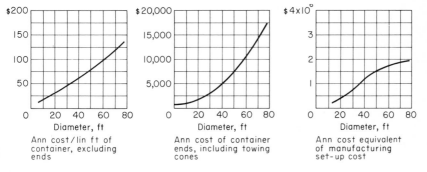

Fig. 5-43 Annual costs of a plastic container as a function of its diameter d.

third graph in this figure shows the setup cost to manufacture containers expressed as an annual cost.

4. Berthing facilities restrict the maximum container size to 80 ft diameter by 1,000 ft long.

5-33. Figure 5-44 shows the foundation profile and required roadway profile for a major highway bridge which will cross a bay.   Figures 5-45 and 5-46 show the estimated costs for roadway on approach fill and roadway on bridge superstructure.   In Fig. 5-47, the

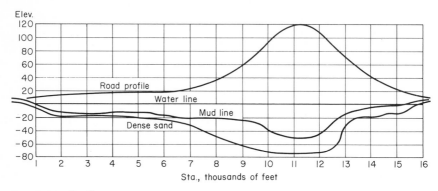

Fig. 5-44   Profile.

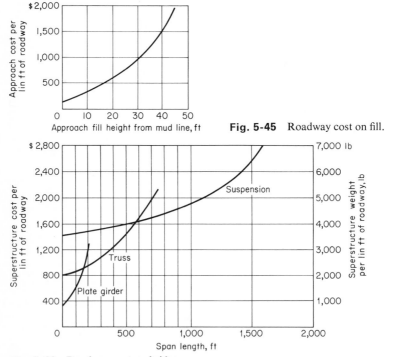

Fig. 5-45   Roadway cost on fill.

Fig. 5-46   Roadway cost on bridge.

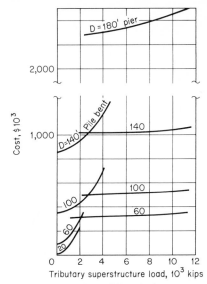

Fig. 5-47 Estimated foundation costs.

estimated foundation costs are shown as a function of superstructure load and depth D, from road level to dense sand, for hollow concrete pile trestle bents and for concrete piers. Pile bents can be used only for roadway heights less than 50 ft above water level.

From the given data, determine optimum lengths of the approach fills at each end of the bridge, optimum locations of all trestle-bent or pier supports, and optimum superstructure type along the length of the bridge. Assume for construction economy that no superstructure type would be used for a distance along the bridge of less than 1,200 ft.

5-34. Figure 5-48 shows the approximate soil-pressure distribution against braced sheet piling to be used for a subway excavation in loose sand. Assume that point A is sufficiently close to an inflection point on the resulting moment diagram of the piling to be considered as a hinge. The bracing consists of a horizontal wale, which acts as a continuous beam, supported by horizontal struts. Assume the estimated unit costs to be

$$C_p = 180 + 0.093M$$
$$C_w = 10 + 0.05m$$
$$C_s = 300 + 0.1f$$

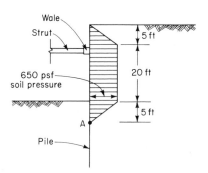

Fig. 5-48 Braced sheet piling.

where C_p, C_w, and C_s = costs/lin ft of trench for piling, wales, and struts, respectively, dollars

$\quad$ M = maximum bending moment in piling, kip-ft/lin ft of trench

$\quad$ m = maximum moment in wale, kip-ft

$\quad$ f = strut compression/lin ft of wall, kips

$\quad$ s = strut spacing, ft

Find the depth of wale and strut spacing which minimize total cost.

5-35. A precast-sandwich-panel design is required for the floors of a building. The panels, of autoclaved lime-fly ash, will have a solid mix for the compression face, a foamed mix for the core, and a mix reinforced with fiber glass mat for the tension face. The design variables are

$\quad$ t_c = compression face thickness, in.

$\quad$ t_t = tension face thickness, in.

$\quad$ t_o = core thickness, in.

$\quad$ d_o = core density factor (=lime-fly ash volume/total core volume)

The material properties are:

	Tensile or compressive strength, psi	Young's modulus, psi	Shear strength, psi	Shear modulus, psi
Compression face	$\sigma_c = \min \begin{cases} 3{,}000 \\ 20{,}000 t_c{}^2 \end{cases}$ *	$E_c = 8 \times 10^6$	—	—
Core	—	—	$\tau = 100 d_o{}^2$	$G = 1.3 \times 10^6 d_o$
Tension face	$\sigma_t = 5{,}000$	$E_t = 40 \times 10^6$	—	—

* Allowable stress for buckling of compression face.

$\quad$ A simply supported panel beam 20 ft long must carry 100 psf and satisfy constraints of the following form, which assumes thin faces with negligible shear modulus and negligible Young's modulus for the core:

$$\left. \begin{aligned} \frac{M}{t_o t_c} &\leqslant \sigma_c \\[2mm] \frac{M}{t_o t_t} &\leqslant \sigma_t \end{aligned} \right\} \quad \text{bending} \tag{1, 2}$$

$$\frac{V}{t_o} \leqslant \tau \qquad \text{shear} \tag{3}$$

$$\frac{5qL^4}{384EI} + \frac{qL^2}{8AG} \leqslant 0.5 \text{ in.} \qquad \text{deflection at midspan} \tag{4}$$

where $A = b[t_o + (t_c + t_t)/2]^2/t_o$

$\quad$ b = beam width

$\quad$ L = span length

$\quad$ M = maximum moment

$\quad$ q = uniform load per unit length of beam

$\quad$ V = maximum shear

$\quad$ $EI = \sum E_i I_i$, where E_i and I_i are the modulus of elasticity and the moment of inertia of each layer about the neutral axis. (Moments of the two faces about their own centroids may be neglected in computing EI.)

$\quad$ The tension face costs five times as much per unit volume as the compression face,

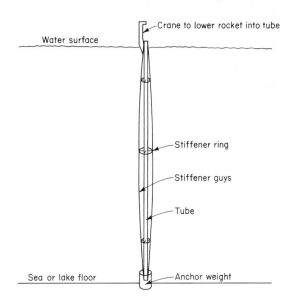

Fig. 5-49 Submarine launch tube.

and the core costs the same per unit *weight* as the compression face. Determine values of the four design variables which minimize total cost.

5-36. Fuel requirements for rocket launching could be reduced by providing initial acceleration from a launch tube, much as a bullet is fired from a gun barrel.[6] Consider the submarine tube shown in Fig. 5-49, for which external water pressure partially balances chamber pressure during firing and thereby reduces the required wall thickness. Vertical alignment is maintained by the combination of anchor weight at the bottom, center of buoyancy at midheight, and large ratio between tube length and maximum height.

From the following data, one can determine whether a submarine launch tube should be built and, if so, its optimum length and the tube wall thickness as a function of depth below water surface. Outline a solution in detail, without performing the computations. Assume present cost comparison at 8% interest.

Payload 14,000 lb, with maximum permissible acceleration of 10 g, maximum muzzle velocity of 2,000 mph, and required vertical burnout velocity at 200,000 ft of 9,000 mph.

Propellant Assume two burning stages: (1) a granular propellant placed in the bottom of the tube to provide initial acceleration and (2) a rocket engine which automatically ignites upon leaving the muzzle to provide acceleration in the atmosphere. The granular propellant costs $0.15 per lb. The rocket fuel costs $0.04 per lb and has a specific impulse of 300 sec (1 lb of fuel provides 300 lb-sec of thrust) and a relative exhaust velocity of 300 g (9,660 ft per sec).

The launch tube has a 6-ft internal diameter. Assume that hoop stress (compression or tension) determines wall thickness for the full length of the tube; i.e., neglect longitudinal buckling due to whip action when firing, radial buckling due to hydrostatic pressure, etc.

[6] Suggested by Jules Verne, "Voyage to the Moon," 1865.

Assume that wall thickness can vary continuously with depth. The tube metal has tensile and compressive strengths of 40,000 psi, weighs 490 pcf, and costs $2 per lb installed, which covers the cost of anchor, stiffeners, etc. (Salt water weighs 65 pcf.)

Fifteen uses per year are anticipated for 10 years, with zero maintenance and salvage value. Assume the same conditions for an existing atmospheric launch facility, and using the same rocket fuel.

Equations of motion

Inside the tube Use the following interior ballistic equations based on isothermal expansion, neglecting acceleration due to gravity, and assuming that propellant burnout occurs when the rocket reaches the muzzle.[7] (Subsequent studies could evaluate costs for the condition of burnout prior to muzzle exit.)

$$p = \frac{\lambda c(1 + c/w)}{AL(1 + c/3w)\,e^m} \qquad \text{peak pressure, psf} \tag{1}$$

$$a_1 = \frac{Ap}{(w/g)(1 + c/2w)} \qquad \text{max. acceleration, ft/sec}^2 \tag{2}$$

$$v_1 = \frac{A\beta}{w + c/2} \qquad \text{muzzle velocity, ft/sec} \tag{3}$$

$$L = le^m \qquad \text{barrel length, ft} \tag{4}$$

where λ = a constant (=300,000 ft)
c = weight of propellant charge
$w = w_1 + f$ = effective rocket weight, including frictional resistance f in barrel (assume $f = 100$ lb, constant)
w_1 = initial weight of rocket
A = bore area (= $6^2\,\pi/4$)
l = initial free length below rocket (assume 6 ft)
e = base of natural logarithms
β = a constant determined by burn rate and by size and geometry of the propellant granules (=60 lb/ft-sec)
m = a dimensionless ballistic parameter:

$$\frac{A^2\,\beta^2(1 + c/3w)}{(w/g)\,c\lambda(1 + c/2w)^2} \tag{5}$$

Assume that the maximum chamber pressure acts over the full length of tube.

In the atmosphere Use the impulse-momentum equation for varying mass, assuming constant burn-off rate:

$$v_2 = v_1 + v_e\left(2.30\log\frac{w_1}{w_1 - qt}\right) - gt - a_d t \qquad \text{velocity at burnout, ft/sec} \tag{6}$$

$$S_2 = v_1 t + v_e t\left[1 + \frac{1}{w_1/w_2 - 1}\left(2.30\log\frac{w_2}{w_1}\right)\right] - \frac{gt^2}{2} - \frac{a_d t^2}{2} \qquad \begin{array}{l}\text{altitude at}\\\text{burnout, ft}\end{array} \tag{7}$$

$$a_2 = \frac{[(w_1 - w_2)/t]\,I}{w_2/g} - g - a_d \qquad \text{acceleration at burnout, ft/sec}^2 \tag{8}$$

where v_e = relative exhaust velocity (=9,660 ft/sec)
w_1 = weight at muzzle, lb
w_2 = weight at burnout (=14,000 lb)
q = fuel burn-off rate, lb/sec

[7] See J. Corner, "Theory of the Interior Ballistics of Guns," John Wiley & Sons., Inc., New York, 1950.

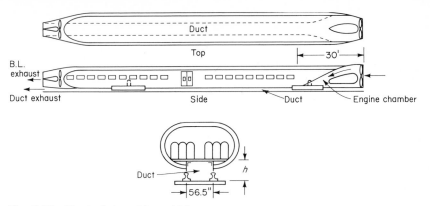

Fig. 5-50 Tracked air-cushion vehicle.

t = elapsed time from muzzle, sec

g = acceleration due to gravity

a_d = acceleration due to aerodynamic drag (assume 4.8 ft/sec², constant)

I = specific impulse (=300 sec)

The solution could be extended, by dynamic programming (Chap. 6), to include several rocket stages in atmosphere.

5-37. A tracked air-cushion vehicle for existing railroads (Fig. 5-50) is to be propelled by a turboprop engine which exhausts into a ducted space between the rails, the roadbed, and the bottom of the vehicle. The air mass acted upon by the engine thus provides both thrust and lift. Baffle strips on the bottom of the vehicle directly over the rails reduce the lateral leakage of air.

In addition, an exhaust pump sucks air through the perforated outer skin of the vehicle and discharges it at zero absolute velocity. This "boundary-layer suction" reduces the aerodynamic friction drag and also increases the lift on the roof of the vehicle, thereby further reducing the rolling friction.

The vehicle is suspended as a pendulum on two roller glides having positive attachment to the rails. Track improvements include additional anchoring of rails and ties on curves.

Given the following equations with coefficients for 250 mph at sea level, formulate a solution for the vehicle length L (ft), the duct height h (in.), and the boundary suction rate q (cfs per sq ft of surface) which minimize fuel rate per pound of loaded vehicle.

Weight of loaded vehicle 800 lb/lin ft.

Traction resistance $R = 0.0045W$ (lb), where W is the effective vehicle weight on the track.

Aerodynamic drag and boundary layer suction The friction drag with boundary layer suction is

$$D_f = (0.002q^3 - 0.04q^2 + 0.4q + 18)L \qquad \text{lb}$$

where D_f is the net drag after adding the equivalent of energy spent in sucking and q is the sucking rate (cfs/sq ft of surface area).

Assume that the remaining components of aerodynamic drag (pressure drag at the front, base drag at the rear, duct friction drag, and wheel ventilation drag) are negligible compared with the friction drag.

The added weight of pump and ducting for boundary-layer suction is

$$\Delta W = 1.2qL \qquad \text{lb}$$

To simplify, we neglect the reduction in traction resistance due to lift induced by boundary-layer suction on the vehicle roof.

Engine performance   The fuel consumption rate is

$$f = 0.001m(p_c - 14.7)^{1.8} \qquad \text{lb/hr}$$

where m is the mass flow rate (lb-sec/ft) of air (and fuel) entering the engine chamber and p_c is the chamber pressure (psia).

Duct   The constraints on duct height (Fig. 5-46) are 8 in. $\leqslant h \leqslant$ 24 in.   Assume that wind-tunnel tests show that flow from the engine chamber through the duct can be approximated by the equations for isentropic flow from a converging nozzle through a constant-area duct with adiabatic flow and friction (Fanno flow), by reducing the theoretical value of pressure through the duct and the thrust produced by the escaping air at the end of the duct each by one-half, to account for heat loss and lateral leakage.   The resulting equations are

$$p_c = p_i\left(1 + \frac{k-1}{2}M_i^2\right)^{k/(k-1)} \qquad\qquad \text{pressure at duct entrance}[8]$$

$$m = \frac{p_c A \sqrt{q}}{\sqrt{Rt_c}} M_i \sqrt{k}\left(1 + \frac{k-1}{2}M_i^2\right)^{(k+1)/(2-2k)} \qquad \text{mass flow rate}$$

$$4f\frac{l}{D} = \frac{1}{kM^2}\left(1 + \frac{k-1}{2}M_i^2\right)\left[1 - \left(\frac{V_i}{V_e}\right)^2\right] + \frac{k+1}{2k}\log_e\left(\frac{V_i}{V_e}\right)^2 \qquad \text{velocities in duct}$$

$$\frac{2p_e}{p_i} = \frac{V_i}{V_e}\left\{1 + \frac{k-1}{2}M_i^2\left[1 - \left(\frac{V_i}{V_e}\right)^2\right]\right\} \qquad\qquad \text{pressures in duct}$$

$$F = \frac{m}{2}V_a \qquad\qquad\qquad \text{exhaust thrust}$$

in which the Mach number is $M = V/a$, the acoustic velocity (fps) is

$$a = (gkRt)^{1/2}$$

and $A = 56.5h$, duct area, sq in.

  $D = 56.5h/2(56.5 + h)$ = area/perimeter, hydraulic diameter of duct, in.
  $f = 0.01$, effective duct friction factor ($f \simeq 0.001$ for rails and bottom of vehicle; $f \simeq 0.06$ for ties and roadbed)
  F = thrust of duct exhaust, lb
  $g = 32.2$ ft/sec²
  $k = 1.4$, specific heat ratio of air
  $l = L\text{-}360$, duct length, in.
  p = pressure, psia
  $p_e = 14.7$
  $R = 53.3$, gas constant for air
  t = temperature, °R

---

[8] For the unchoked condition ($M \leqslant 11$), $p_i/p_c \geqslant 0.528$.   Flow is approximated as being at rest in the engine chamber, which has much greater cross-sectional area than the duct.

$t_c = 250°R$, average gas temperature in engine chamber
V = gas velocity relative to vehicle, fps
$V_a = V_e - 250(1.47)$, absolute duct exhaust velocity, fps

The subscripts c, i, and e indicate engine chamber, duct inlet, and duct outlet, respectively. To simplify, assume that the average duct pressure is $(p_i + p_e)/3$.

REFERENCES

1. American Institute of Steel Construction, "Manual of Steel Construction," New York, 1963.
2. Andersen, P. A.: "Substructure Analysis and Design," The Ronald Press Company, New York, 1956.
3. Beale, E. M. L.: On Quadratic Programming, *Naval Res. Logistics Quart.*, vol. 6, pp. 227–244, September, 1959.
4. Bowles, J. E.: "Foundation Analysis and Design," McGraw-Hill Book Company, New York, 1968.
5. Soft Ground Tunnels for BART, pp. 52–59, and A Hill of Municipal Refuse, p. 50, *Civil Eng.*, June, 1968.
6. Denn, M. M.: "Optimization by Variational Methods," McGraw-Hill Book Company, New York, 1970.
7. Douty, R.: Optimization of a Two-span Cover-plated Steel Beam, *Computers in Engineering Design Education*, vol. III, pp. 34–50, Civil Engineering, University of Michigan, Ann Arbor, 1966.
8. Duffin, R. J.: Dual Programs and Minimum Cost, *J. Soc. Ind. Appl. Math.*, vol. 10, no. 1, pp. 119–123, March, 1962.
9. Duffin, R. J., E. L. Peterson, and C. Zener: "Geometric Programming—Theory and Application," John Wiley & Sons, Inc., New York, 1967.
10. Research Sparks Interest in New Solids Pipelines, *Eng. News Record*, pp. 36–37, Jan. 18, 1968.
11. Esthetic Reversal Ousts Arch—for Cable Stayed Girder Span, *Eng. News Record*, p. 16, Aug. 21, 1969.
12. Underground Pumped Storage, *Eng. News Record*, pp. 36–37, Aug. 29, 1968.
13. Oil Tank Goes to Sea and Sinks, *Eng. News Record*, p. 76, June 20, 1968.
14. Fan, L. T.: "The Continuous Maximum Principle," John Wiley & Sons, Inc., New York, 1966.
15. Frankus, A., and G. C. Lee: Automated Design for Dynamically Loaded Least Weight, *ASCE Joint Specialty Conf., EMD-STD, Optimization Nonlinear Probl.*, Chicago, Apr. 18–20, 1968.
16. Galler, W. S., and H. B. Gotaas: Optimization Analysis for Biological Filter Design, *Proc. ASCE*, vol. 92, no. SA1, pp. 163–182, February, 1966.
17. Hadley, G. R.: "Non-linear and Dynamic Programming," Addison-Wesley Publishing Company, Inc., Reading, Mass., 1962.
18. Hillier, F. S., and G. J. Lieberman: "Introduction to Operations Research, "Holden-Day, Inc., Publishers, San Francisco, 1967.
19. Hunt, W. A., and I. C. Hoffman: Optimization of Pipelines Transporting Solids, *Preprint 605, ASCE Natl. Meeting Transportation Eng.*, San Diego, Calif., Feb. 19–23, 1968.
20. Kelley, J. E.: The Cutting Plane Method for Solving Convex Programs, *J. SIAM*, vol. 8, no. 4, pp. 703–712, December, 1960.
21. Kuhn, H. W., and A. W. Tucker: Nonlinear Programming, *Proc. 2nd Berkeley Symp. Math. Statistics Probabilities*, J. Neyman (ed.), University of California Press, Berkeley, 1951.

22. Künzi, H. B., W. Krelle, and W. Oettli: "Nonlinear Programming," Blaisdell Publishing Company, Waltham, Mass., 1966.
23. Kutateladze, S. S., and V. M. Borishamskii: "A Concise Encyclopedia of Heat Transfer," translated from Russian, Pergamon Press, New York, 1966.
24. Levens, A. S.: "Graphical Methods in Research," John Wiley & Sons, Inc., New York, 1965.
25. Moses, F.: Optimum Structural Design Using Linear Programming, *Proc. ASCE*, vol. 90, no. ST6, pp. 90–104, December, 1964.
26. Neghabat, F.: "Optimization in Cofferdam Design," doctoral dissertation, University of Delaware, 1970.
27. Nicholls, R. L., and M. Izadi: Design and Model Tests of Cone and H-P Footings, *Proc. ASCE*, vol. 94, no. SM1, pp. 47–72, January, 1968.
28. Stout, J. J., and M. F. Thomas: Major Pumped Storage Projects in the United States, *Proc. ASCE*, vol. 94, no. PO1, pp. 85–104, May, 1968.
29. Teng, W. C.: "Foundation Design," Prentice-Hall, Inc., Englewood Cliffs, N.J., 1962.
30. Wilde, D. J.: "Optimum Seeking Methods," Prentice-Hall, Inc., Englewood Cliffs, N.J., 1964.
31. Wilde, D. J., and C. S. Beightler: "Foundations of Optimization," Prentice-Hall, Inc., Englewood Cliffs, N.J., 1967.
32. Woodworth, F.: "Graphical Simulation," International Textbook Company, Scranton, Pa., 1967.

6
Dynamic Programming

Dynamic programming depends upon the representation of a multistage decision problem as a sequence of single-stage problems; that is, one casts an N-variable problem into a sequence of N single-variable problems, which are solved successively. Therefore, dynamic programming is an approach to optimization rather than a series of theorems appropriate to a class of analytic expressions. Indeed, the particular optimization technique appropriate for each of the single-variable problems is somewhat irrelevant. It may range from complete enumeration to differential calculus or linear programming.

The basic work in dynamic programming, and much of the subsequent development, is credited to Bellman (since 1955) [2]. The notion of recursion, as implied above, is imbedded in the *principle of optimality*, upon which dynamic programming is based. Specifically,

An optimal policy has the property that whatever the initial state and decision are, the remaining decisions must constitute an optimal policy with regard to the state resulting from the first decision.

This principle and techniques for formulating dynamic-programming problems are illustrated in the examples which comprise this chapter. Consider the application of the principle of optimality to a familiar mechanics problem.

Example 6-1   Range of a projectile fired in a vacuum   Let $f(\dot{x}_0,\dot{y}_0)$ be the range of a projectile fired in a vacuum with initial velocity components $\dot{x}_0$ and $\dot{y}_0$. At time Δt after firing, the projectile has the abscissa $\dot{x}_0 \, \Delta t$ and its velocity components are $\dot{x}_0$ and $(\dot{y}_0 - g \, \Delta t)$ since the accelerations are $\ddot{x} = 0$ and $\ddot{y} = -g$. The principle of optimality is implied in the recursion relation

$$f(\dot{x}_0,\dot{y}_0) = \dot{x}_0 \, \Delta t + f(\dot{x}_0,\dot{y}_0 - g \, \Delta t)$$

Expanding the functional on the right-hand side in a Taylor series, one has

$$f(\dot{x}_0, \dot{y}_0 - g \, \Delta t) = f(\dot{x}_0,\dot{y}_0) + \frac{\partial f(\dot{x}_0,\dot{y}_0)}{\partial \dot{y}_0} g \, \Delta t + \phi(\Delta t)$$

where $\phi(\Delta t)$ denotes terms of higher order in Δt. Substituting,

$$f(\dot{x}_0,\dot{y}_0) = \dot{x}_0 \, \Delta t + f(\dot{x}_0,\dot{y}_0) + \frac{\partial f(\dot{x}_0,\dot{y}_0)}{\partial \dot{y}_0} g \, \Delta t + \phi(\Delta t)$$

Whence, in the limit,

$$\frac{\partial f(\dot{x}_0,\dot{y}_0)}{\partial \dot{y}_0} + \frac{\dot{x}_0}{g} = 0$$

Solving this (differential) equation yields

$$f(\dot{x}_0,\dot{y}_0) = - \int_{\dot{y}_0}^{-\dot{y}_0} \frac{\dot{x}_0}{g} \, d\dot{y}_0 = \frac{2\dot{x}_0 \dot{y}_0}{g}$$

a familiar kinematical result.

6-1   STRUCTURE OF DYNAMIC-PROGRAMMING PROBLEMS

Consider a sum of C dollars which can be allocated among m investments. Let $h_i(x_i)$ be the return from x_i dollars allocated to the ith investment, $i = 1,2, \ldots, m$. The total return is

$$\sum_{i=1}^{m} h_i(x_i)$$

The problem is to determine the levels of investment, x_i, which maximize the total return subject to constraints that the x_i be nonnegative and sum to C. Dynamic programming proceeds by representing this m-stage decision as a sequence of single-stage decisions. Let $f_m(C)$ be the maximum return from an allocation of C dollars among m investments (stages). Clearly, for a single stage,

$$f_1(C) = \max_{0 \leqslant x_1 \leqslant C} [h_1(x_1)]$$

If there are two possible investments then, using the principle of optimality we can write the functional relation

$$f_2(C) = \max_{0 \leqslant x_2 \leqslant C} [h_2(x_2) + f_1(C - x_2)]$$

In general,

$$f_i(C) = \max_{0 \leqslant x_i \leqslant C} [h_i(x_i) + f_{i-1}(C - x_i)] \qquad i = 1, 2, \ldots, m$$

with the initial condition $f_0(C) \equiv 0$. Computationally, these equations are solved recursively; i.e., having obtained $f_1(C)$, it is used to obtain $f_2(C)$, and so on, until the desired solution $f_m(C)$ is obtained. Thus a problem in m variables has been cast into a sequence of m problems in a single variable. The problem can be defined for any number of stages, and its structure is independent of that number. Note that the optimal allocations depend only upon the parameters m and C.

Only one *state variable* appeared above. That is, the required single-stage optimization was with respect to a single variable. In many practical instances, there are several such state variables. This means that enumerative optimization expands exponentially. Suppose that a single state variable takes on 10 values, so that 10 enumerations are required at each stage. If there are three such state variables, there are 10^3 enumerations (not 3×10) to perform at each stage. This exponential growth represents a serious limitation in the use of dynamic programming and is commonly called the "curse of dimensionality." There are, however, important advantages to dynamic programming, and Roberts [18] summarizes them well:

> Dynamic programming has become a refuge for problems unsolvable by other techniques, especially exact analytical techniques. Casting the problem into a dynamic programming guise may resolve problems that have previously defied solution. The consideration, for example, of many calculus of variations problems as multistage processes renders a solution not attainable by conventional techniques.
>
> ...The numerical approach makes it easy to test for inequality constraints. If the selection of a node on a grid causes the constraint to be violated, that node is rejected. Adjacent nodes are tested until it is possible to delineate the permissible region on the grid. The larger the number of constraints, the smaller is the permissible region with

no particular hardship computationally. In contrast to this, the resolution of problems by exact analytical methods becomes more and more involved as the number of constraints increases.

...Similarly, discontinuous functions are handled readily by numerical means. Price and cost structures are often discontinuous junctions of the cumulative volume of a product. The numerical evaluation of a cost can be done by a table-look-up or by equations fitted over separate parts of the discontinuous function.

6-2 APPLICATIONS OF DYNAMIC PROGRAMMING

An immense variety of problems can be formulated for solution by dynamic programming, as the following examples suggest.

Example 6-2 Least-cost path through a network Find a path between nodes m and d in the network of Fig. 6-1 such that the sum of the costs (or time or distance) which appear on each segment of path is a minimum. For simplicity, assume that at any node only a northbound or eastbound path can be chosen.

Note that any path from m to d will require six steps, three northbound and three eastbound. Thus there are 20 possible paths.[1] One might add the six cost values which appear on each of these paths and select the path having the smallest total cost. Instead, consider a dynamic-programming approach. Starting with the final node, d, we calculate the least-cost path for every node. The previous position must have been either at node c or at node h. The cost on path cd is 2 units, while on hd it is 4 units. Table 6-1 indicates this for the first (backward) step. Continuing this reverse expansion, one notes that the "two-step" position must be at either of nodes b, g, or l.

---

[1] The combination $\binom{6}{3} = \dfrac{6!}{3!(6-3)!} = 20$. See Chap. 8.

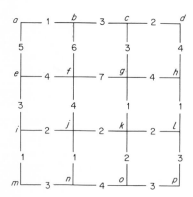

Fig. 6-1 A "3×3" network.

Table 6-1 Least-cost path in a network

Number of steps from node d	Costs to node d From node	Cost	Least cost to node d Cost	Path
1	c	2	2	cd
	h	4	4	hd
2	b	$3 + 2 = 5$	5	bcd
	g	$\begin{cases} 3 + 2 = 5 \\ 4 + 4 = 8 \end{cases}$	5	gcd
	l	$1 + 4 = 5$	5	lhd
3	a	$1 + 5 = 6$	6	abcd
	f	$\begin{cases} 6 + 5 = 11 \\ 7 + 5 = 12 \end{cases}$	11	fbcd
	k	$\begin{cases} 1 + 5 = 6 \\ 2 + 5 = 7 \end{cases}$	6	kgcd
	p	$3 + 5 = 8$	8	plhd
4	e	$\begin{cases} 5 + 6 \ = 11 \\ 4 + 11 = 15 \end{cases}$	11	eabcd
	j	$\begin{cases} 4 + 11 = 15 \\ 2 + 6 \ = 8 \end{cases}$	8	jkgcd
	o	$\begin{cases} 2 + 6 = 8 \\ 3 + 8 = 11 \end{cases}$	8	okgcd
5	i	$\begin{cases} 3 + 11 = 14 \\ 2 + 8 \ = 10 \end{cases}$	10	ijkgcd
	n	$\begin{cases} 1 + 8 = 9 \\ 4 + 8 = 12 \end{cases}$	9	njkgcd
6	m	$\begin{cases} 1 + 10 = 11 \\ 3 + 9 \ = 12 \end{cases}$	11	mijkgcd

From node b, the only available path is eastbound (at cost 3), and coupled with the (one-step) least cost from node c to node d, it yields a (two-step) least cost of 5 according to the principle of optimality.   A similar argument applies to the node at l.   From the node at g, however, two paths are possible. The eastbound path (at cost 4) coupled with the least-cost path from h yields a cost of 8 units.   This is to be compared with a northbound movement from node g at cost 3 added to a least cost of 2 from node c to yield a total of 5.   Clearly, the path gcd is preferred to ghd, as indicated in the final column of the table.   In a similar manner, the expansion continues back to node m, as indicated in Table 6-1.   The solution to the problem is the path $mijkgcd$, as indicated.

Those who find it convenient to summarize the preceding discussion symbolically can imagine that the network of Fig. 6-1 is placed on a cartesian coordinate system with node m as origin. Each node in the network can be described by the coordinates (x,y). For example, the coordinates of node f are $(1,2)$. Let $f(x,y)$ be the least cost of travel from the node at (x,y) to node d, and let $c(x,y;x',y')$ be the cost of travel along a single segment which begins at (x,y) and ends at $(x'y')$. For example, $f(1,2) = 11$ and $c(1,2:1,3) = 6$. Using the principle of optimality, as we implicitly have, we can write $f(x,y)$ = min $[c(x,y;x+1, y) + f(x+1, y); c(x,y;x, y+1) + f(x, y+1)]$, where the total cost is given by the first expression if the next step is eastbound and by the second expression if it is northbound. Starting from node d with coordinates $(3,3)$, one proceeds in reverse, as before. The entries in the third column of the table are values of $f(x,y)$. For example, the least cost from node a is $f(0,3) = 6$.

In the "3×3" network of Fig. 6-1, the total cost along any path is calculated with five additions (six terms). Therefore, solution by complete enumeration requires 100 additions for the 20 possible paths. The above dynamic-programming solution required only 24 additions (including evaluations at nodes c and h). If the network were a "10×10", there would be $\binom{20}{10}$, or about 184,000, paths with 19 ($=10 + 10 - 1$) additions each—about $3\frac{1}{2}$ million additions would be required for complete enumeration. For a "30×30" network, about 10^{30} additions are required for enumeration. A modern computer performs about 10^5 additions per sec. Thus, the "10×10" network would require about half a minute for complete enumeration. For the "30×30" network, an astronomical 10^{18} years are required. This illustrates the necessity for alternatives to complete enumeration for larger problems. The computational gains in dynamic programming arise because not every path is enumerated. The enumeration along a path continues only so long as that path holds promise of being optimal. When such promise is lost, the path is abandoned. In general, the computational effort increases

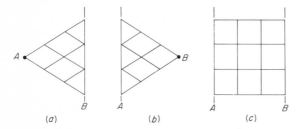

Fig. 6-2 Networks. (a) Initial-value problem; (b) final-value problem; (c) open boundaries.

Fig. 6-3   Two examples of branching.

exponentially with the number of variables in complete enumeration and linearly in the dynamic-programming formulation.

Many multistage decision processes, those with which dynamic programming is concerned, can be represented by networks. The network in Fig. 6-1 is a *two-point boundary* problem (nodes d and m). Figure 6-2 illustrates some other networks. For example, the problem in Fig. 6-2a is called an *initial-point boundary* problem because node A (the origin) is fixed but the final node is determined by the optimal solution. The situation in Fig. 6-2b is the reverse of that in Fig. 6-2a. Figure 6-2c illustrates *open boundaries*, and Fig. 6-3 illustrates *branching*. Techniques of numerical solution are not substantially different from those in the previous example.

Example 6-3   A combinatorial problem   An aggregate producer has four identical mobile crushing-screening plants and four sources of raw material which he can use during the coming construction season. Given the profit matrix below, how many plants should he assign to each site?

Profit matrix

No. of plants assigned	Raw-materials site			
	1	2	3	4
1	47	39	24	35
2	81	62	47	51
3	105	84	72	61
4	132	91	87	68

This problem suggests the transportation format of Sec. 4-1. The problem is combinatorial and, at first glance, may not appear reducible to a sequential solution. But dynamic programming offers an advantageous solution in which we first consider all possible plant assignments to site 1 and then find the optimum combination of assignments to sites 1 and 2, then the optimum among sites 1, 2, and 3, and finally the optimum among all four sites.

We could proceed by the tabular method used in Example 6-2 or, alternatively, by showing the computed results for each stage of the solution

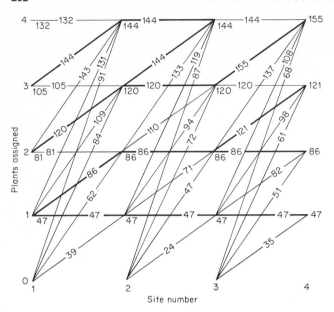

Fig. 6-4 Assignment network.

on the network, as in Fig. 6-4.   Trial assignments of 1, 2, 3, and 4 plants are
first made at site 1, and the profits 47, 81, 105, and 132 are written by the
appropriate nodes.   Next, the various combinations of assignments to sites
1 and 2 are evaluated, the profits are written on the corresponding diagonal
lines, and the maximum profit line to each new node is heavily drawn.   Its
value becomes the value at the new node.   The process is repeated through
the net, and the results are summarized in the table.

No. of plants assigned	Optimal assignments Site assignments	Profit
1	1 at #1	47
2	1 at #1, 1 at #2	86
3	1 at #1, 1 at #2, 1 at #4	121
4	2 at #1, 1 at #2, 1 at #4	155

Example 6-4 Replacement of tractor-scraper units   A contractor
has a fleet of tractor-drawn scrapers for moving earth on short hauls.   As a
tractor or scraper ages, the annual profit of the tractor-scraper unit decreases
due to increased maintenance costs.   To simplify for illustrative purposes,
assume that the contractor keeps a tractor no more than 4 years and a

scraper no more than 2 years. The contractor estimates his annual net return per tractor-scraper unit as:

Tractor age (years)	0	1	2	3	0	1	2	3
Scraper age (years)	0	0	0	0	1	1	1	1
Estimated net return of tractor-scraper unit for the following year ($10)	11	9	6	3	9	7	4	2

The cost of a new tractor is $9,000, and of a new scraper, $3,000. Replacements at the end of year i are changed to the ith year. At the end of each year, the contractor chooses one of the following policies for each tractor-scraper unit:

1. Replace neither.
2. Replace tractor only.
3. Replace scraper only.
4. Replace both.

What replacement policy maximizes profit for a given period (planning horizon)?

A profit table can be prepared for every current age combination and planning horizon (Table 6-2). For a 1-year horizon, no replacements are needed at the end of that year. The optimal replacement policy and corresponding profit are shown in the top row of Table 6-2.

For a 2-year horizon an optimal replacement policy is not so obvious. Policies 1 to 4 are evaluated in the second row. For example, the shaded equation in the row evaluates the profit for a new tractor and scraper and the adoption of policy 3 (replace scraper) at the end of this year. The current year's profit is $11 - 3 = 8$ ($\times$$1,000). Next year, the tractor will be 1 year old and the scraper will be new. In the next column, one finds a profit of 9 ($\times$$1,000) for a 1-year horizon of this equipment mix. The total profit for this replacement policy for a 2-year horizon is $11 - 3 + 9 = 17$.

Consider the evaluation of policy 2 for a 2-year-old tractor, a new scraper, and a 3-year planning horizon. The current-year profit is $6 - 9 = -3$ ($\times$$1,000). Next year, the tractor-scraper ages will be 0 and 1, respectively. For the second row, a profit of 15 ($\times$$1,000) is indicated corresponding to the optimal replacement policy 3 for this case. The maximum total profit for the 3-year horizon (shaded) is $6 - 9 + 15 = 12$ ($\times$$1,000).

Table 6-2 Dynamic-programming solution for tractor-scraper replacement[1]

Ages, yr								
Tractor	0	1	2	3	0	1	2	3
Scraper	0	0	0	0	1	1	1	1
1-yr horizon								
Policy 1	11	9	6	3	9	7	4	2
Optimum	1	1	1	1	1	1	1	1
2-yr horizon								
Policy 1	11+7=18	9+4=13	6+2=8	— —	— —	— —	— —	— —
Policy 2	11−9+9	9−9+9	6−9+9	3−9+9=3	— —	— —	— —	— —
Policy 3	11−3+9	9−3+6	6−3+3	— —	9−3+9=15	7−3+6=10	4−3+3=4	— —
Policy 4	11−12+11	9−12+11	6−12+11	3−12+11	9−12+11	7−12+11	4−12+11	2−12+11=1
Optimum	1	1	1	2	3	3	3	4
3-yr horizon								
Policy 1	11+10=21	9+4	6+1	— —	— —	— —	— —	— —
Policy 2	11−9+15	9−9+15=15	6−9+15=12	3−9+15=9	— —	— —	— —	— —
Policy 3	11−3+13=21	9−3+8	6−3+3	— —	9−3+13=19	7−3+8	4−3+3	— —
Policy 4	11−12+18	9−12+18	6−12+18	3−12+18	9−12+18	7−12+18=13	4−12+18=10	2−12+18=8
Optimum	1, 3	2, 4	2, 4	2, 4	3	4	4	4
4-yr horizon								
Policy 1	11+13=24	9+10=19	6+8	— —	— —	— —	— —	— —
Policy 2	11−9+19	9−9+19	6−9+19=16	3−9+19=13	— —	— —	— —	— —
Policy 3	11−3+15	9−3+12	6−3+9	— —	9−3+15=21	7−3+12=16	4−3+9	— —
Policy 4	11−12+21	9−12+21	6−12+21	3−12+21	9−12+21	7−12+21=16	4−12+21=13	2−12+21=11
Optimum	1	1, 2	2	2	3	3, 4	4	4

1 Profits are in thousands of dollars.

The analysis can be extended to any planning horizon. Some policies are omitted from the table (indicated by dashed lines) because tractors cannot be used for more than 4 years nor scrapers for more than 2 years. In some instances, the optimal policy is not unique. Note that a more precise analysis might take into account the time value of money (Sec. 1-5).

In a more general analysis, the replacement costs and production capacities may vary from year to year (see [3, p. 118]).

Example 6-5 Design of an irrigation system Hall used dynamic programming to size an irrigation aqueduct and allocate water from it among several irrigation districts [10]. A total anticipated annual profit objective was used.

An irrigation canal is to be designed to serve three districts whose head gates lie 30, 50, and 75 miles, respectively, downstream from the point of diversion. The available annual water supply is 800,000 acre-ft. Table 6-3 shows the anticipated annual irrigation benefits and the estimated annual cost of the aqueduct as functions of annual water delivery. The annual water delivery to each irrigation district and corresponding aqueduct capacity are to be chosen to maximize anticipated annual profit.

We use the notation:

i = irrigation district ($i = 1$ corresponds to the most upstream district, etc.)

q_i = water delivered to irrigation district i, acre-ft/yr

B_i = annual irrigation benefit to district i

b_i = annual net benefit to district i

c = amortized cost of aqueduct, $/mi-yr

c_i = total amortized cost of aqueduct from head gates ($i - 1$) to i, $/yr

The solution is obtained by first considering the size of the last segment of aqueduct (downstream district) and then proceeding stepwise to the first segment of aqueduct. Tables 6-4 to 6-6 show stepwise calculations for the

Table 6-3 Anticipated annual benefits and costs

q_i 10^3 acre-ft	B_1 $\$10^3$	B_2 $\$10^3$	B_3 $\$10^3$	c $\$10^3/mi$
200	600	400	900	7.6
400	980	760	1,250	10.7
600	1,310	1.090	1,500	13.2
800	1,600	1,380	1,690	15.2

Table 6-4   Costs and benefits for district 3

q_3 10^3 acre-ft	B_3 $\$10^3$	C_3 $(75 - 50)c = 25c$ $\$10^3$	b_3 $\$10^3$
200	900	190	710
400	1,250	268	982
600	1,500	330	1,170
800	1,690	380	1,310

Table 6-5   Costs and benefits for districts 3 and 2[1]

$q_2 + q_3$ 10^3 acre-ft	q_2	q_3	b_3 (from Table 6-4)	B_2	C_2 (=20c)	b_2	$b_2 + b_3$	Optimal allocation 10^3 acre-ft
	0	200	710	0	152	−152	558	$q_2 = 0$
200	200	0	0	400	152	248	248	
	0	400	982	0	214	−214	768	$q_2 = 200$
400	200	200	710	400	214	186	896	
	400	0	0	760	214	546	546	
	0	600	1,170	0	264	−264	906	
600	200	400	982	400	264	136	1,118	
	400	200	710	760	264	496	1,206	$q_2 = 400$
	600	0	0	1,090	264	826	826	
	0	800	1,310	0	304	−304	1,006	
	200	600	1,170	400	304	96	1,266	
800	400	400	982	760	304	456	1,438	
	600	200	710	1,090	304	786	1,496	$q_2 = 600$
	800	0	0	1,380	304	1,076	1,076	

[1] Sums are in thousands of dollars.

three irrigation districts, beginning downstream.   The reader can trace the solution through the tables.   Additional aspects are treated in [10].

Example 6-6   Construction staging in a transportation network

A highway department plans three new routes (dashed lines in Fig. 6-5) to connect communities A and D with industrial areas B and C.   Funding at a rate to build one route each year is anticipated.   Associated with each route is an average annual user cost per vehicle and an amortized construction and

Table 6-6   Costs and benefits for districts 3, 2, and 1[1]

$q_1 + q_2 + q_3$ 10^3 acre-ft	q_1	$q_2 + q_3$	$b_2 + b_3$	B_1	C_1 $(=30c)$	b_1	$b_1 + b_2 + b_3$	Optimal allocation, 10^3 acre-ft
	0	200	558	0	228	−228	330	$q_1 = 200$
200	200	0	0	600	228	372	372	$q_2 = 0$
								$q_3 = 0$
	0	400	896	0	321	−321	575	$q_1 = 200$
400	200	200	558	600	321	279	837	$q_2 = 0$
	400	0	0	980	321	659	659	$q_3 = 200$
	0	600	1,206	0	396	−396	810	
600	200	400	896	600	396	204	1,100	$q_1 = 400$
	400	200	558	980	396	584	1,142	$q_2 = 0$
	600	0	0	1,310	396	914	914	$q_3 = 200$
	0	800	1,496	0	456	−456	1,040	
	200	600	1,206	600	456	144	1,350	$q_1 = 400$
800	400	400	896	980	456	524	1,420	$q_2 = 200$
	600	200	558	1,310	456	854	1,412	$q_3 = 200$
	800	0	0	1,600	456	1,144	1,144	

[1] Sums are in thousands of dollars.

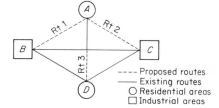

Fig. 6-5   Highway network.

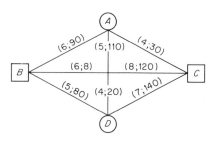

Fig. 6-6   User and capital costs for each route.

Table 6-7 Average daily traffic

| From | To | | | | |
	A	B	C	D	Total
A	– –	20	30	10	60
D	10	40	30	– –	80

maintenance cost.   Figure 6-6 indicates these costs, respectively, in parentheses for each route.   Average daily traffic volume from communities A and D is indicated in Table 6-7.   The sequence in which the three routes are constructed will influence the total system cost (construction, maintenance, and user costs) for the 3-year period.   Assume for illustrative purposes that traffic volume remains unchanged for the 3-year period and is unaffected by the construction sequence.   In what sequence should the new routes be built to minimize the total cost for the 3-year period?

There are 6(=3!) possible sequences in which the proposed routes can be constructed.   They appear in the *decision tree* of Fig. 6-7.   Annual construction and maintenance costs are obtained by adding the costs in Fig. 6-6 for the routes in service at the time.   Annual user costs are obtained by summing costs for all vehicles on their least-cost paths.   This assumes that the capacity of no route is exceeded.   Least-cost paths for the existing network of Fig. 6-5 can be identified by inspection.   For example, Table 6-8 shows annual user costs for the existing network.

User costs for the existing network plus possible combinations of proposed routes with the added construction and maintenance costs are indicated in Table 6-9.   Construction and maintenance costs for existing routes are assumed to be fixed and can be ignored in the computations.   As is customary in dynamic-programming problems, the optimization begins with the final decision, as shown in Tables 6-10 to 6-12.

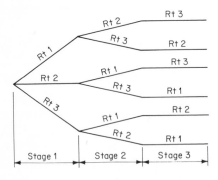

Fig. 6-7   Decision tree.

Table 6-8 Annual user costs for existing network

Origin	Destination	Least travel cost	Traffic volume	Total path cost
	B	11	20	220
A	C	13	30	390
	D	16	10	160
	A	16	10	160
D	B	5	40	200
	C	7	30	210

Total annual user costs = 1,340

Table 6-9 User and added construction and maintenance costs

New routes	User cost	Added construction and maintenance cost	Total cost
None	1,340	0	1,340
1	1,140	90	1,230
2	970	30	1,000
3	1,200	20	1,220
1,2	870	120	990
1,3	1,100	110	1,210
2,3	930	50	980
1,2,3	830	140	970

Table 6-10 System costs, stage 3

Existing routes	Added routes			
	None	1	2	3
None	1,340	1,230	1,000	1,220
1	1,230	– –	990	1,210
2	1,000	990	– –	980
3	1,220	1,210	980	– –
1,2	990	– –	– –	970
1,3	1,210	– –	970	– –
2,3	980	(970)	– –	– –

Table 6-11   System costs, stage 2

Existing routes	None	Added routes 1	2	3
None	1,340 1,000 2,340	1,230 990 2,220	1,000 980 1,980	1,220 980 2,200
1	1,230 990 2,220	– –	990 970 1,960	1,210 970 2,180
2	1,000 980 1,980	990 970 1,960	– –	980 970 1,950
3	1,220 980 2,220	1,210 970 2,180	980 970 1,950	– –

Table 6-12   System costs, stage 1

Existing routes	None	Added routes 1	2	3
None	1,340 1,980 3,320	1,230 1,960 3,190	1,000 1,950 2,950	1,220 1,950 3,170

The total cost at each stage is the cost at that stage plus the minimum cost for the stage resulting from the previous decision.   The optimal solution may be traced backward from Table 6-12 (circled entries).   The result is:

Year	Route to be constructed
1	2
2	3
3	1

Practical transportation networks are more complex: traffic generated increases with time and is affected by constructed routes; maintenance costs on existing routes are affected by new routes; route capacities may necessitate some vehicles to select more costly paths; and future costs should be discounted to their present worth. The model here can incorporate these factors [9].

Example 6-7 A warehouse problem We mentioned earlier that various optimization techniques may be appropriate at each stage of a dynamic-programming problem. Previous examples have used enumeration; this one uses linear programming.

A refinery orders crude oil on the fifth day of each month for delivery about the first of the following month. The cost of the crude oil and the income from refined products vary somewhat from month to month. For example, from a given crude, the refining process can produce different quantities of distillation cuts (gasoline, heating oil, asphalt, etc.) to meet seasonal demand. Ordering and refining policies are sought which maximize profit for a given horizon. It is convenient to assume that market demand is unlimited. The tank farm has a crude-oil storage capacity of 2 million bbl, and 1 million bbl are in storage initially. For a 4-month horizon, the estimated costs and sales prices are:

Month	Cost/bbl	Price/bbl
1	$0.90	$1.50
2	1.30	1.40
3	1.10	1.40
4	—	1.60

We use the notation:

$$i = \text{month}, \ i = 1, 2, 3, 4$$
$$s_i = \text{sales in month } i, \text{ bbl}$$
$$b_i = \text{order quantity for the fifth day of month } i, \text{ bbl}$$
$$p_i = \text{price in month } i, \text{ \$/bbl}$$
$$c_i = \text{cost of crude ordered in month } i, \text{ \$/bbl}$$
$$q_i = \text{storage on the first day of month } i, \text{ bbl}$$
$$Q = \text{tank-farm capacity, bbl}$$
$$f_{5-i}(q_i) = \text{maximum profit for a } (5 - i)\text{-month horizon when } i\text{th month begins with } q_i \text{ bbl of crude in storage}$$

The quantities s_i and b_i are to be chosen for each month subject to the restrictions

$$s_i \leqslant q_i \leqslant Q \qquad s_i, b_i, q_i \geqslant 0 \qquad i = 1, 2, 3, 4$$

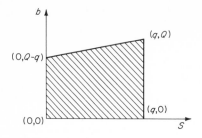

Fig. 6-8   A convex set.

On the first day of the final month,

$$f_1(q_4) = \max_{s_4, b_4} (p_4 s_4 - c_4 b_4)$$

subject to

$$0 \leqslant s_4 \leqslant q_4 \qquad 0 \leqslant b_4 \leqslant Q - (q_4 - s_4) \tag{1}$$

For the final month, the optimal policy is, obviously,

$$s_4 = q_4 \qquad b_4 = 0 \tag{2}$$

On the first day of the third month,

$$f_2(q_3) = \max_{s_3, b_3} [p_3 s_3 - c_3 b_3 + f_1(q_3 + b_3 - s_3)]$$

subject to

$$0 \leqslant s_3 \leqslant q_3 \qquad 0 \leqslant b_3 \leqslant Q - (q_3 - s_3)$$

We know from Eqs. (2) that $f_1(q_3 + b_3 - s_3)$ has the value $p_4(q_3 + b_3 - s_3)$. Therefore,

$$f_2(q_3) = \max_{s_3, b_3} [(p_3 - p_4) s_3 + (p_4 - c_3) b_3 + p_4 q_3] \tag{3}$$

where s_3 and b_3 have restrictions similar to those in Eqs. (1), that is,

$$0 \leqslant s_3 \leqslant q_3 \qquad 0 \leqslant b_3 \leqslant Q - (q_3 - s_3) \tag{4}$$

Since Eqs. (3) and (4) are linear in s_3 and b_3, we have a simple linear-programming problem. The (b,s) plane of the convex set appears in Fig. 6-8. Since $q_4 = q_3 + b_3 - s_3$, the policy for the fourth month, Eq. (2), can be stated in terms of q_3. The next iteration yields policies for the last 3 months in terms of q_2, and so on, until the policies for all months are in terms of q_1, the known initial storage of 1 million bbl. The general expression is

$$f_{n+1}(q) = \max_{\substack{0 < s < q \\ 0 < b < Q - q + s}} [p_{4-n} s - c_{4-n} b + f_n(q + b - s)]$$

Repeated iterations of this expression yield:

First day of month	Maximize	Policy	$f_{5-i}(q_i)$
4	$1.60s_4 - c_4b_4$	$s_4 = q_4; b_4 = 0$	$f_1(q_4) = 1.60q_4$
3	$-0.20s_3 + 0.5b_3 + 1.6q_3$	$s_3 = q_3; b_3 = Q$	$f_2(q_3) = 0.5Q + 1.4q_3$
2	$0.10b_2 + 1.4q_2 + 5Q$	$s_2 = q_2; b_2 = Q$	$f_3(q_2) = 1.4q_2 + 0.6Q$
1	$0.10s_1 + 0.50b_1 + 0.6Q + 1.4q_1$	$s_1 = q_1; b_1 = Q$	$f_4(q_1) = 1.1Q + 1.5q_1$

Since $q_1 = 10^6$ and $Q = 2 \times 10^6$, the maximum profit $f_4(10^6)$ is $10^6(1.5) + 2 \times 10^6(1.1) = \$3.7 \times 10^6$. The optimal policy can be summarized as:

Month	Initial storage	Sell	Order
1	1	1	2
2	2	2	2
3	2	2	2
4	2	2	0

Amounts in units of 10^6 bbl.

The form of this problem is well known and was extensively treated in a classic paper by Dreyfus [7].

Example 6-8 A tandem design

In previous examples, recursion relations have involved sums. Recursion relations involving products of design variables arise in the design and operation of drive systems which have several components in tandem. For example, a gasoline or hydraulic turbine–generator–electric motor system or a diesel engine–hydraulic pump–hydraulic motor system illustrates components in tandem. The efficiency of the components depends upon the levels at which they are operated. The operating levels, however, tend to be increasing functions of cost. Suppose that a total amount C is available to operate an n-component tandem system. The efficiencies of the components are related to the operating costs by the functions $E_1 = E_1(C_1), \ldots, E_n = E_n(C_n)$, where E_i is the efficiency of the ith component as a function of the operating cost $C_i, i = 1, \ldots, n$. We seek optimal operating costs $C_{01}, \ldots, C_{0n}$ such that

$$C = \sum_{i=1}^{n} C_{0i} \quad \text{and} \quad H_n(C) = \prod_{i=1}^{n} E_i(C_{0i})$$

where $H_n(C)$ denotes the maximum efficiency attainable in an n-component system when a total amount C can be allocated to operate the components. Clearly,

$$H_1(C) = \max_{0 \leqslant c_1 \leqslant C} E_1(C_1) = E_1(C)$$

that is, $C_{01} = C$ since $E_1(C_1)$ is assumed to be an increasing function. For a two-component system,

$$H_2(C) = \max_{0 \leqslant C_2 \leqslant C} [E_2(C_2) H_1(C - C_2)]$$

This equation follows from the principle of optimality; whatever the allocation to the second component, C_2, the remaining resource, $C - C_2$, is used in an optimal way for the remaining component. Note that the manner in which the single-stage optimization should be executed is not clear until the nature of the functions $E_1(C_1)$ and $E_2(C_2)$ is explicit. In general, we have the recursion relation

$$H_n(C) = \max_{0 \leqslant C_n \leqslant C} [E_n(C_n) H_{n-1}(C - C_n)]$$

In a simple case, the efficiency function is linear, that is, $E(C_i) = aC_i + b$, $i = 1, \ldots, n$, where a and b are constants. The case $a = 1, b = 0$ is well known (see Prob. 6-4). We illustrate a few steps of the optimization. First,

$$H_1(C) = \max_{0 \leqslant c_1 \leqslant C} [E_1(c_1) = C_1] = C$$

Next, for $n = 2$ we have

$$H_2(C) = \max_{0 \leqslant C_2 \leqslant C} [C_2(C - C_2)]$$

The required optimization is easily carried out using calculus. The maximum of the function $C_2(C - C_2)$ occurs when $C_2 = C/2$ and, hence,

$$H_2(C) = \left(\frac{C}{2}\right)^2$$

etc. An easy induction (Appendix 2) enables one to conclude that

$$H_n(C) = \left(\frac{C}{n}\right)^n \qquad n = 1, 2, \ldots$$

Recall that significant reductions in computational effort can accompany an increase in the number of constraints or other limitation of the range of the variables. The next example illustrates this and the handling of constraints in more general cases.

Example 6-9   A pipeline design   Dynamic programming is applicable to a wide variety of design and operating problems associated with gas and

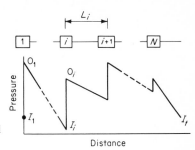

Fig. 6-9   Pressure distribution along a pumped
pipeline.

liquid pipelines ([18] and [13]).   The problem formulation depends upon
which parameters are fixed and which are selected to be variables.   We
define the parameters for an N-pump line as

$i =$ pump number, $i = 1, 2, \ldots, N$
$L_i =$ distance, pump i to $i + 1$
$D_i =$ pipe diameter, pump i to $i + 1$
$HP_i =$ delivered horsepower of pump i
$F_i =$ friction head loss, pump i to $i + 1$
$E_i =$ increase in elevation head, pump i to $i + 1$
$I_i =$ inlet pressure, pump i
$Q_i =$ flow rate, pump i to $i + 1$[2]
$O_i =$ discharge pressure, pump i
$C_i =$ initial cost of pump i
$C_{oi} =$ operating and maintenance cost of pump i
$CP_i =$ initial pipeline cost, pump i to $i + 1$
$CP_m =$ pipeline maintenance cost, pump i to $i + 1$
$I_t =$ terminal pressure

As a simplified example, consider a liquid pipeline having two pumps,
for which the pump horsepower and pipe diameter are variables on each
segment.   The pipeline will operate 4,000 hr per year.   Assume a 50-year
economic life, zero salvage value, and 8 % annual interest rate.

Suppose that the *ranges of the variables* are

$D_i = 10$ or 16 in.   pipes available in only 10- and 16-in. diameters
$HP_i = 200$ or 300 pumps available in only 200- and 300-hp sizes
$I_i \geqslant 3$ psi   to prevent cavitation at pump inlet
$O_i \leqslant 250$ psi

---

[2] The condition $Q_i \neq Q_{i+1}$ arises, for example, in oil-field pipelines where several wells
discharge into a single manifold or in refinery piping where portions of flow are removed
at various points along the line.

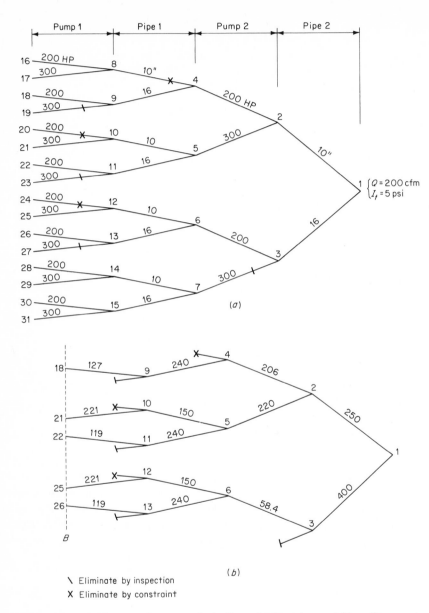

\ Eliminate by inspection
X Eliminate by constraint

Fig. 6-10 Decision tree for pumped pipeline. (*a*) Decision variables; (*b*) present-worth costs (thousands of dollars).

and that the *fixed parameters* are

$L_1 = 6$ mi $L_2 = 10$ mi
$E_1 = 250$ ft $E_2 = -10$ ft
$I_t = I_1 = 5$ psi
$Q_1 = Q_2 = 200$ cfm
$C_i = \begin{cases} \$10,000 & \text{for 200-hp installation} \\ \$16,000 & \text{for 300-hp installation} \end{cases}$
$C_{oi} = \$0.02/$delivered hp-hr
$CP_i = \begin{cases} \$25,000/\text{mi} & \text{for 10-in. pipe} \\ \$40,000/\text{mi} & \text{for 16-in. pipe} \end{cases}$ assume pipe cost independent of pressure head
$CP_m = 0$

Specific gravity of liquid $= 0.9$
while the *functional relationships* among variables are

$$F_i = \frac{0.60 L_i Q^2}{D_i{}^3} \qquad \text{friction loss} \tag{5}$$

where F_i is in pounds per square inch, L in miles, Q in cubic feet per minute, and D in inches.

$$I_{i+1} = O_i - F_i - 0.9\left(\frac{62.4}{144}\right) E_i \qquad \text{pressure balance} \tag{6}$$

$$HP_i = \frac{144(O_i - I_i) Q_i}{33,000} \qquad \text{required hp delivered} \tag{7}$$

The alternatives are shown in the decision tree of Fig. 6-10a. We recognize this as a final-value problem of the simple branching type shown in Fig. 6-3. This is a four-stage problem in a single variable, since at each of the four decision stages we choose the size of only one component, a pump or a pipe. One wonders whether the pump-pipe combinations indicated by the branches in Fig. 6-10a are feasible. For example, a combination of pump and pipe sizes along the top branch might be incapable of yielding 200 cfm at 5-psi discharge. Constraints evolve in the course of solution. When a constraint is violated, one simply eliminates further analysis of the offending branch.

To illustrate the calculations for the second pump, we use Eqs. (5) and (6):

$$O_2 = 5 + F_2 + 0.9\left(\frac{62.4}{144}\right) E_2$$

$$= 5 + \frac{0.6(10)(200)^2}{D^3} + 0.390(-10)$$

which yields $O_2 = 241.1$ for $D_2 = 10$ in. and $O_2 = 59.6$ for $D_2 = 16$ in.　Using Eq. (7), we form the following table:

For D_2	and HP$_2$,	obtain I_2.
10 in.	200 300	12.1 psi <3
16 in.	200 ~~300~~	<3 ~~<3~~

We delete the combination $D_2 = 16$ in., HP$_2 = 300$ hp since a lower-cost alternative is available.　We discontinue computation along the associated branch (diagonal slash in Fig. 6-10a).　For the remaining three pump and pipe combinations, feasible pump sizes have been established.　However the operating levels, I_2, are to be selected.　Observing that efficiency is independent of operating level ($C_{oi} = \$0.02$ per delivered hp-hr), we operate at maximum pump output ($I_2 = 12.1$, 3, and 3 psi, respectively).　These are the operating levels which are most likely to require only 200 hp for pump 1.

　　The computations are repeated for pump 1 with $I_1 = 5$ psi:

	and D_1,	obtain O_1.	With HP$_1$,	obtain I_1.
12.1 psi	~~10 in.~~ 16	~~253.5 psi~~ 144.6	⎰200 ⎱300	<3 psi ~~<3~~
3 psi	10	244.4	⎰200 ⎱300	~~15.4~~ <3
	16	135.5	⎰200 ⎱300	<3 ~~<3~~

Delete the combination which yields $O_1 = 253.5$ psi since this violates the constraint $O_i \leqslant 250$.　This constraint violation is indicated by a crossed branch in Fig. 6-10a.　Likewise, delete combinations which yield $I_1 = 15.4$ because they do not satisfy the condition $I_1 = 5$ (two additional crosses on branches in Fig. 6-10a).　We delete by inspection (as being more costly than necessary) all combinations of $D_1 = 16$ in. and HP$_1 = 300$, indicated by further slashes on branches in Fig. 6-10a.　Now compute present-worth costs (Table 6-13) for the remaining portion of the decision tree.　The results appear in Fig. 6-10b.

　　The solution (Table 6-14) employs the tabular format of Example 6-2.

Table 6-13 Determination of present costs[1]

D_2, in.	O_2	HP_2	Cost	I_2	Reqd. oper. hp[2]	Present worth of oper. cost	Total present cost
10	241.1	200	10	21.1	200	196	206
		300	16	3	208	204	220
16	59.6	200	10	3	49.4	48.4	58.4

D_1, in.	O_1	HP_1	Cost	Reqd. oper. hp[2]	Present worth of oper. cost	Total present cost
16	141	200	10	119	117	127
10	244.4	300	16	209	205	221
16	131.9	200	10	111	109	119
10	244.4	300	16	209	205	221
16	131.9	200	10	111	109	119

[1] Costs are in thousands of dollars.

[2] From Eq. (7), with pump 2 carrying maximum load and pump 1 carrying remainder.

Table 6-14   Least-cost path[1]

Stage	Cost to line B From node	Cost	Least cost from the node to line B Cost	Along path
1	9	127	127	9,18
	10	221	221	10,21
	11	119	119	11,22
	12	221	221	12,25
	13	119	119	13,26
2	4	367	367	4,9,18
	5	$\begin{cases}371\\359\end{cases}$	359	5,11,22
	6	$\begin{cases}371\\359\end{cases}$	359	6,13,26
3	2	$\begin{cases}573\\579\end{cases}$	573	2,4,9,18
	3	417	417	3,6,13,26
4	1	$\begin{cases}823\\817\end{cases}$	817	1,3,6,13,26

[1] Sums are in thousands of dollars

From Table 6-14 and Fig. 6-10b, we have the optimal solution:

Pump 1:   200 hp
Pipe 1:   16 in. diameter
Pump 2:   200 hp
Pipe 2:   16 in. diameter

SUMMARY

The key to the use of dynamic programming is to identify a repetitive or multistage character in the desired decisions.   After identifying the decision variables, one focuses on the single-stage decision problem for the last stage for all possible initial-state variables.   Then one carries out the single-stage optimization, subject to constraints, to yield the optimal single-stage policy. For example, the first block of Table 6-1 in Example 6-2 and Eqs. (1) and (2) of Example 6-7 are the optimal one-step policies for the possible values of the initial-state variables c, h, and q_4 in the respective examples.

Having formulated an optimal single-stage decision, one focuses on the two-stage decision problem associated with the final two stages.   The objective function is composed of two parts; one part is the objective function for the current state, and the second part is the optimal one-part policy for the final stage (above paragraph).   The optimization is carried out, subject to constraints and using the principle of optimality, and an optimal two-stage policy is obtained for an arbitrary initial state.   This corresponds to the second step in Table 6-1 and Eqs. (3) and (4) of Example 6-2.

The procedure continues in this fashion until the initial state for the entire optimization is reached.   The initial-state value for the entire optimization is known, and therefore the optima associated with the subsequent stages are computed to yield the entire decision.   This corresponds to step 6 in Table 6-1 and the tabulations in Example 6-7.

The computational advantage of dynamic programming becomes more significant for problems having many stages.   Computational effort by enumeration tends to increase exponentially with the number of stages while for the same problem solved by dynamic programming, the effort tends to increase only linearly with the number of stages.

The examples illustrated the diversity of dynamic-programming applications.   They include problems in assignments, allocation, scheduling, structural and water-resources design, and engineering mechanics.

PROBLEMS[3]

6-1.   Find the least-cost path between the vertical lines A and B.

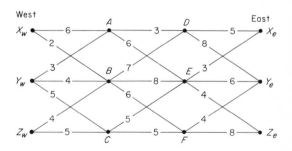

6-2.   Find the least-cost path from each western node to an eastern node.

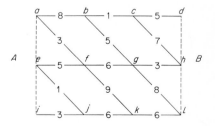

Many of these problems can be solved by techniques other than dynamic programming.

6-3. For the above problem, find the shortest path from west to east under the loop constraint of beginning and ending at the same node (cyclic optimization).

6-4. A line segment of length L is to be divided into n subsegments such that the product of the lengths is a maximum. Using a dynamic-programming argument, conclude that for an optimum division the subsegments should be of equal length. ◆

6-5. Using a dynamic-programming approach, show that the n-sided polygon having the largest perimeter which can be inscribed in a given circle is regular.

6-6. Using an approach similar to that in Example 6-6, show that the maximum height of the projectile is $\dot{y}_0{}^2/2g$.

6-7. For a projectile fired vertically upward, the equation of motion can be written

$$\ddot{y} = -g - h(\dot{y})$$

where $h(\dot{y})$ is the aerodynamic drag as a function of velocity. Find the maximum height of a projectile fired with initial velocity $\dot{y}_0$.

6-8. Consider the linear-programming problem:

Max: $z' = c_1 x_1 + c_2 x_2$
Subject to: $a_{11} x_1 + a_{12} x_2 \leqslant b_1$
             $a_{21} x_1' + a_{22} x_2 \leqslant b_2$
             $x_1, x_2 \geqslant 0$

Solve the problem by a two-stage dynamic program. For simplicity, assume that all parameters nonnegative. Test your program for the following data:

   (a) $c_1 = 2$, $c_2 = 6$; $a_{11} = a_{21} = 3$, $a_{12} = 6$, $a_{22} = 12$; $b_1 = 24$, $b_2 = 36$.
   (b) $c_1 = 2$, $c_2 = 3$; $a_{11} = 3$, $a_{12} = 4$, $a_{21} = a_{22} = 0$; $b_1 = 10$, $b_2 = 0$.

6-9. Consider the nonlinear problem:

Min: $z = c_1 x_1{}^2 + c_2 x_2$
Subject to: $a_1 x_1 + a_2 x_2 \geqslant b$
             $x_1, x_2 \geqslant 0$

Solve this quadratic-programming problem by a two-stage dynamic program. For simplicity, assume that all parameters are positive. ◆

6-10. Consider the integer-programming problem

Max: $z' = 3x_1 - x_2 + 2x_3$
Subject to: $x_1 + 2x_2 \leqslant 6$
             $2x_1 - 3x_2 \leqslant 6$
             $x_3 \leqslant 2$
             x_1, x_2, x_3 nonnegative integers

Develop a solution using dynamic programming and compare with the result using the integer-programming algorithm in Chap. 4.

6-11. A commercial pilot uses a single seven-passenger plane to operate a charter flight service between three cities. He lives in a fourth city, equidistant from the others, and returns home each night. The incremental operating cost between each of the three cities is \$60, the fare is \$15, and flight time is approximately 40 min. A change from charter to scheduled flights is being considered. Estimates of average daily travel demand are tabulated. Find a daily schedule between the three cities having on-the-hour departures between 10 A.M. and 2 P.M. which maximizes total profit. Neglect the cost of letting the plane be idle.

   (a) Assume that all passengers take alternate transportation rather than wait more than 1 hr.

Origin	Destination	Estimated travel demand time				
		10 A.M.	11	12	1 P.M.	2
A	B	5	7	2	1	4
	C	6	3	8	2	1
B	A	4	2	7	9	2
	C	1	5	5	3	2
C	A	7	6	6	7	3
	B	1	3	1	4	4

(b) Assume that all passengers take alternate transportation rather than wait more than 2 hr.

(c) Assume that all passengers take alternate transportation rather than wait more than 3 hr.

Hint: A solution by dynamic programming requires division of the problem into uncoupled stages. Which of parts a, b, and c can meet this criterion?

6-12. Try to extend the dynamic-programming approach to the minimum-cost design of a bridge where the pier spacing is the design variable and the costs per running foot of superstructures vary with the square of the span length.

6-13. Pumps are to be placed at the ends of a natural-gas pipeline. Using the notation of Example 6-9 and the following data, determine the optimal pipe diameter and pump sizes. Assume a 50-year life, zero salvage value, and 8% required interest.

Constraints
   Pipes available in 8-, 9-, and 10-in. diameters.
   Pumps available in 150- and 200-hp sizes.
   $I_2 \geqslant 20$ psi
   $O_1 \leqslant 600$ psi

Fixed parameters
   $L = 100$ miles
   $E = 0$ (for gas pumping)
   $I_1 = 30$ psi
   $O_2 = 300$ psi
   $Q = 2,000$ cfm at atmospheric pressure (assume 15 psi)
   $C_i = \begin{cases} \$35,000 & \text{for 150 hp} \\ \$50,000 & \text{for 200 hp} \end{cases}$
   $\left. \begin{array}{l} C_{01} = \$0.014/\text{delivered hp-hr} \\ C_{02} = \$0.020/\text{delivered hp-hr} \end{array} \right\}$ continuous operation
      (Natural gas used for fuel costs more at pump 2.)
   $CP = \begin{cases} \$10,000/\text{mile} & \text{for 8-in. pipe} \\ \$11,000/\text{mile} & \text{for 9-in. pipe} \\ \$12,000/\text{mile} & \text{for 10-in. pipe} \end{cases}$
      (Assume pipe cost independent of operating pressure.)
   $CP_m = 0$

Functional relationships

$$F = 0.005 \, L \frac{Q^2}{D^4}$$

where F is in pounds per square inch, L in miles, Q in cubic feet per minute at 15 psi, and D in inches.

$$I_2 = O_1 - F$$

$$HP_i = \frac{144(O_i - I_i)(Q_i)}{0.8(33,000)}$$

where $Q_i = $ cfm at O_i.   Assume a perfect gas and isothermal operation ($P_1 \, V_1 = P_2 \, V_2$).

6-14.   Crude oil is to be pumped through a collapsible (flexible-wall) submarine pipe in lieu of transportation by oil tankers.   The pipe diameter and the size of two identical pumps are to be determined, as well as the distance x from the pump at the starting point to the second one (at a 1,000-ft depth) to minimize total pumping cost.   A life of 50 years, zero salvage, and 8% interest are assumed.

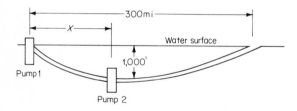

Seawater density: 65 pcf
Oil density: 58 pcf
$Q = 20$ cfm

Friction loss in psi: $F = \dfrac{3.0LQ^2}{D^2}$

where L is in miles, Q in cfm, and D in inches.

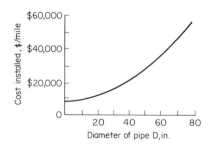

Pipe installation cost (assumed to be independent of internal operating pressure). Assume no pipe maintenance cost.

Pump installation cost.

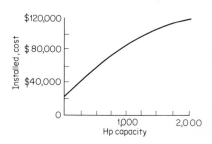

Pump operating costs:
    Pump 1: $0.01/delivered hp-hr
    Pump 2: $0.015/delivered hp -hr
Pipeline will operate 8,000 hr/year

6-15. An airline pilot at 10,000 ft must return to the same altitude at a point 1,000 miles away before reducing power to land. He wishes to fly the distance in minimum time at a fixed throttle setting. Greater altitude allows greater speed, but speed is reduced while climbing. For the given data, what should be the altitude profile?

Data The service ceiling is 40,000 ft, and there are no winds. For this aircraft in level flight, velocity increases with altitude approximately as the decrease in square root of air density. The heavy curve shows this relationship for specified throttle settings. Ascending and descending performance characteristics are shown by the lighter curves. For simplicity, assume gross aircraft weight remains constant.

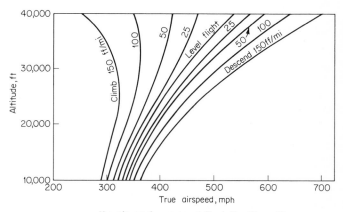

Aircraft performance at fixed throttle setting

6-16. An irrigation aqueduct is to be built between points A and F along one of the routes shown. Estimated construction, operation, and maintenance costs for each link are tabulated. What is the optimal route? Assume 60-year economic life, zero salvage, and a 3% annual interest rate.

Problems 6-17 to 6-19 are *variational* problems, which can be solved using the calculus of variations. Such problems can also be solved using dynamic programming. Variational

Link	Construction cost	Operating and maintenance cost per year
A–B	100	3
A–C	180	4
A–D	200	7
B–C	80	4
B–E	120	5
C–D	90	6
C–E	70	2
C–F	120	7
D–F	70	5
E–F	100	3

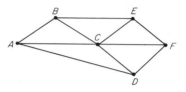

problems involve the optimization of a definite integral containing a function and its derivative. For example, let $F(x,y,dy/dx)$ be a cost function in which y is a function of the controllable variable x. The optimization is

$$\text{Min:} \quad J = \int_{x_1}^{x_2} F\left(x, y, \frac{dy}{dx}\right) dx$$

$$\text{Subject to:} \quad y \leqslant c_1 \qquad \frac{dy}{dx} \leqslant c_2$$

or, alternatively,

$$\text{Subject to:} \quad \int_{x_1}^{x_2} G\left(x, y, \frac{dy}{dx}\right) dx = c_3$$

An equality constraint involving an integral over the same range of x as the objective function is called an *isoperimetric* constraint. In contrast to problems of differential calculus, the function $F(x,y,dy/dx)$ is not known and is to be determined such that J is a minimum. See [8] and [18].

6-17. Several 24-ft-long laminated timber beams are to be made from 8-in.-wide, 1-in. actual thickness, southern pine boards. The beams will be simply supported at their ends and will carry uniform loads of 400 lb per lin ft. They must have minimum depth over the supports of 8 in. for shear and bearing requirements. Find the beam-depth profile which permits a maximum (center span) deflection of 1.5 in. with the minimum volume of lumber. The boards have a Young's modulus of 1,760,000 psi and allowable bending fiber stress of 2,000 psi.

    Hint: Use the moment-area method to obtain deflections and rotations of successive segments of the beam. Start at the center, where the slope is zero, and work toward an end.

6-18. A simply supported beam must be 20 ft long, support a single load of 50 kips at its center, and not deflect more than 0.25 in. due to the load. The available materials are a 1- by $11\frac{1}{2}$-in., 96-lb wide flange beam ($I = 1,355$ in.) and $\frac{1}{8}$-in.-thick plates which can be welded to the flanges of the beam to stiffen it. How many cover plates should be used, how long should they be, and where should they be located to obtain required stiffness with minimum beam weight?

    Young's modulus for steel is 30×10^6 psi, and the allowable fiber stress is 30×10^3 psi.

6-19. Construct a dynamic-programming solution for the design of a minimum-cost flagpole, given its height, static wind loading, allowable top deflection, available sizes and costs of nesting steel tubes for its construction, and Young's modulus and allowable stress of the steel.

    Hint: Consider a pole of n segments, each of which may be a different size of steel tubing. Set up equations for the cumulative cost, slope, and deflection at the top of each segment. Assume a fixed ratio between tube diameter and wall thickness. Use small-deflection theory.

REFERENCES

1. Ackoff, R. L., and M. W. Sasieni: "Fundamentals of Operations Research," John Wiley & Sons, Inc., New York, 1968.
2. Bellman, R.: "Dynamic Programming," Princeton University Press, Princeton, N.J., 1957.
3. Bellman, R., and S. E. Dreyfus: "Applied Dynamic Programming," Princeton University Press, Princeton, N.J., 1962.
4. Bellman, R.: "Adaptive Control Processes: A Guided Tour," Princeton University Press, Princeton, N.J., 1962.
5. Cartaino, T. F., and S. E. Dreyfus: Application of Dynamic Programming to the Airplane Minimum Time-to-climb Problem, *Aeron. Eng. Rev.*, vol. 16, pp. 74–77, June, 1957.
6. Carver, D. R.: Dynamic Programming and Mechanics, *Eng. Educ.*, pp. 631–635, May, 1967.
7. Dreyfus, S. E.: An Analytic Solution of a Warehouse Problem, *Management Sci.*, vol. 4, no. 1, October, 1957.
8. Dreyfus, S. E.: "Dynamic Programming and the Calculus of Variations," Academic Press, Inc., New York, 1965.
9. Funk, M. F., and F. A. Tillman: A Dynamic Programming Approach to Optimal Construction Staging, *Preprint* 613, *ASCE Natl. Meeting Transportation Eng.*, San Diego, Calif., Feb. 19–23, 1968.
10. Hall, W. A., and J. Dracup: "Water Resources Systems Engineering," McGraw-Hill Book Company, New York, 1970.
11. Howard, R.: "Dynamic Programming and Markov Processes," Technology Press and John Wiley & Sons, Inc., New York, 1960.
12. Jacobs, O. L.: "An Introduction to Dynamic Programming: The Theory of Multistage Decision Processes," Chapman & Hall, Ltd., London, 1967.
13. Jefferson, J. T.: "Dynamic Mathematical Programming for Power Cost Optimization," *IBM Liquid Pipeline Computer Workshop*, Chicago, November, 1960.
14. Lewis, A. D.: Optimal Design of Structural Steel Framing for Tier-type Buildings, *Computers in Engineering Design Education*, vol. III, pp. 64–88, Civil Engineering, University of Michigan, Ann Arbor, 1966.
15. Liebman, J. C., and W. R. Lynn: The Optimal Allocation of Stream Dissolved Oxygen, *Water Resources Research*, vol. 2, no. 3, pp. 581–591, 3d quarter, 1966.
16. Nemhauser, G. W.: "Introduction to Dynamic Programming," John Wiley & Sons, Inc., New York, 1966.
17. Palmer, A. C.: Optimal Structure Design by Dynamic Programming, *Proc. ASCE*, vol. 94, no. ST8, pp. 1887–1906, August, 1968.
18. Roberts, S. M.: "Dynamic Programming in Chemical Engineering and Process Control," Academic Press, Inc., New York, 1964.

7
Sequencing, Routing, and Scheduling

Sequencing problems arise when one must order several tasks sequentially to minimize total time or effort in performing them. A typical example is the sequencing of odd jobs through various machine tools in a shop in order to minimize total processing time.

In *routing* problems, one seeks to identify a path through a network which minimizes travel time, cost, or distance. An example is the routing of a truck to several sites with minimum total travel distance.

In *scheduling* problems, the task sequence is fixed. However, the task cost is time-dependent, and one wishes to allot times to each task which minimize total cost for a specific total completion time. Applications include the scheduling of tasks in most civil engineering construction projects.

PART I
Sequencing

Sequencing problems arise in a wide variety of contexts.   They are conveniently classified according to characteristics related to jobs in a machine shop [2]:

1. The job *arrival process.*   In *static* problems, jobs arrive simultaneously
    and no further arrivals occur.   In deterministic *dynamic* problems, they
    arrive at different but predictable times.   In stochastic dynamic prob-
    lems, they arrive at different times and these times are unknown in
    advance except in a statistical sense.
2. The *number and type of machines* in the shop.   In one case, two or more
    machines may be used in parallel to process jobs.   In another, the
    machine setup time between jobs is dependent on the job sequence, etc.
3. The *flow discipline.*   Principal disciplines are the *flow shop*, where all
    jobs proceed through the various machines in the same sequence; the
    randomly routed shop, in which machine sequences for the various jobs
    are specified but not identical; and *arbitrary flow*, where machine sequence
    is not specified for any of the jobs.   When arrivals are dynamic, the
    flow discipline may be further classified according to whether *preemption*
    is allowed, i.e., whether one job temporarily displaces another on a
    particular machine.
4. The *criterion* for evaluating the schedule, e.g., to complete the final job
    as early as possible, to minimize the flow time for all jobs or the time
    cost of all jobs.   Criteria may refer to the shop, rather than the jobs
    (e.g., to minimize idle machine time).

Variations of these characteristics also arise.   For example, a processing
operation may simultaneously require a specific man, machine, and tool
instead of only a specific machine.   Also, incoming jobs may be aggregated
into priority groups.

Sequencing problems are easy to state, but solutions of almost all but
the simplest cases are difficult.   General nonenumerative solutions are
presently available for only three special cases:

1. Two units are processed through a number of stations in the same or
    a different sequence.
2. A number of units are processed in the same order through two stations.
3. A number of units are processed through three stations in the same order
    if the maximum time spent by any unit in the middle station is less than

the least time spent by any unit in either the first or the last station [3]. This condition enables transformation into the two-station problem 2.

Consider some examples.

Example 7-1 Two units, *n* **stations (case 1)** In a prefabricated housing plant, two house units must be processed through several machines in the indicated sequence:

		Machines			
Unit 1	Sequence	C	A	D	B
	Time	2	1	4	1
Unit 2	Sequence	A	B	C	D
	Time	5	2	2	1

Determine the minimum completion time.

Although the problem may be solved by simple enumeration, a graphic technique depicts alternate optima more clearly [1]. Required sequencing times for the two units are indicated along the coordinate axes in Fig. 7-1. The rectangles represent periods of conflict for machine time, which must be avoided. The heavy lines at a 45° angle represent simultaneous work on both units. Vertical lines represent work on unit 1 while unit 2 is idle, and horizontal lines represent work on unit 2 while unit 1 is idle. The optimal sequencing is indicated by the shortest line from start to finish—in this case, containing either of the alternate branches *a* and *b*. The shortest line has the

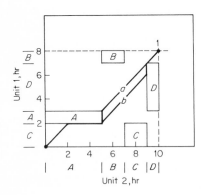

Fig. 7-1 Two units—*n*-phase sequencing.

least length of vertical and horizontal segments, because these correspond to idleness. The optimal completion time is obtained by adding the lengths of vertical segments to the projection of the selected line or the horizontal axis $(1 + 10 = 11)$, or by adding the length of horizontal segments to the projection of the line on the vertical axis $(3 + 8 = 11)$.

Example 7-2 *n* **units, two stations (case 2)** Steel construction for penstocks, draft tubes, surcharge tower, etc., for a hydroelectric dam consists of two phases: (1) on-site shop fabrication and (2) erection. One crew is available for fabrication, and one crew for erection. Erection on each job cannot begin until fabrication is completed. The contractor scheduled the jobs in the indicated sequence. How should they have been scheduled?

| | Phase | |
| | 1 | 2 |
Job	Fabrication	Erection
1	4 days	5 days
2	12	2
3	10	8
4	3	6
5	7	11

The procedure to obtain an optimal sequence is:

1. Select the smallest processing time in the matrix. If the smallest entry is in the first column, place that unit first in the sequence; if it is in the second, place the unit last in the sequence.
2. For a tie, if the two smallest times are in column 1, select first the entry with the smallest time in column 2. If equal smallest times occur in column 2, select that with the smallest time in column 1.
3. Repeat until all units are sequenced.

Table 7-1

Phase 1	Phase 2
2← 4	5
12	2 →5
10	8 →4
1← 3	6
3← 7	11

Table 7-2

	Original sequence times			Rescheduled sequence times	
Job	Phase 1	Phase 2	Job	Phase 1	Phase 2
1	4^4	5^9	4	3^3	6^9
2	12^{16}	2^{18}	1	4^7	5^{14}
3	10^{26}	8^{34}	5	7^{14}	11^{25}
4	3^{29}	6^{40}	3	10^{24}	8^{33}
5	7^{36}	11^{51}	2	12^{36}	2^{38}

Specifically, the minimum time of 2 days occurs in phase 2 of job 2; schedule it last, and so on. The optimum sequence, indicated by arrows, appears in Table 7-1. The superscripted numbers in Table 7-2 indicate the completion times for each job in the original sequence and in the rescheduled sequence. Note the saving of $51 - 38 = 13$ days. Note that no job can begin in phase 2 until the previous job has completed phase 2 and the current job has completed phase 1.

Example 7-3 Transforming three stations into two stations
(**case 3**) Blocks in the gravity section of a dam are poured in 5-ft lifts. The construction cycle for each lift includes eight steps:

Phase A
1. Sandblast and wash top of preceding lift to remove laitance
2. Lay cooling pipes
3. Erect exterior formwork and formwork for inspection galleries, draft tubes, etc.

Phase B
4. Install instrumentation for measuring stresses and temperatures
5. Wash top of preceding lift to remove construction debris

Phase C
6. Pour concrete
7. Allow 2 days cure
8. Strip and clean forms

The time required for the eight steps on each lift depends upon factors such as the number and sizes of interior cavities to be formed and total volume of concrete to be poured. To simplify the problem, the construction steps are grouped into the three phases A, B, and C. Blocks 9 to 17 are ready to begin phase A.   The estimated times for each phase of the next lift on these blocks are:

| | Time for construction phase, hr | | |
Block	A	B	C
9	58	49	74
10	61	52	56
11	51	32	68
12	50	45	64
13	57	20	56
14	60	37	71
15	60	29	57
16	60	41	59
17	66	26	72

Determine a construction sequence that minimizes completion time for the nine pours.

In this problem, there are three phases (stations) and the maximum time for any block in phase B is less than the minimum time for any block in phase C (case 3, above).   To convert to a two-phase problem, phases A and B are combined into a new phase (call it 1) and phases B and C are combined into phase 2 (Table 7-3).

The solution is indicated in Table 7-4 [4].   Substitution into the original three-phase matrix (Table 7-5) yields a total of 660 hr for the minimum completion time of one lift in all nine blocks.

Table 7-3

| | Phase | |
| | 1 | 2 |
Block	(A + B)	(B + C)
9	107	123
10	113	108
11	83	100
12	95	109
13	77	76
14	97	108
15	89	86
16	101	100
17	92	98

MATHEMATICAL FOUNDATIONS FOR DESIGN

Table 7-4

Phase 1	Phase 2
5 ← ~~107~~	~~123~~
~~113~~	~~108~~ → 6
1 ← ~~83~~	~~100~~
3 ← ~~95~~	~~109~~
~~77~~	~~76~~ → 9
4 ← ~~97~~	~~108~~
~~89~~	~~86~~ → 8
~~101~~	~~100~~ → 7
2 ← ~~92~~	~~98~~

Table 7-5

Block	A	B	C
11	51^{51}	32^{83}	68^{151}
17	66^{117}	26^{143}	72^{223}
12	50^{167}	45^{212}	64^{287}
14	60^{227}	37^{264}	71^{358}
9	58^{285}	49^{334}	74^{432}
10	61^{346}	52^{398}	56^{488}
16	60^{406}	41^{447}	59^{547}
15	60^{466}	29^{495}	57^{604}
13	57^{523}	20^{543}	56^{660}

The research status of more complicated sequencing problems has been summarized by Sisson [5].

PART II
Routing

In routing problems, one seeks an optimal route in a network for the selected measure of performance (e.g., cost, time, or distance). It is convenient to divide routing problems into two cases:

1. *Minimal-path* problems, where the terminal node differs from the starting node.
2. *Traveling-salesman* problems, where the terminal node and the starting node coincide.

We consider both cases briefly.

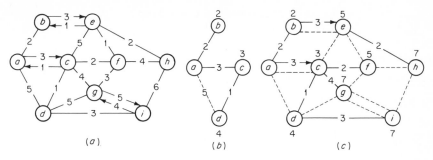

Fig. 7-2 Minimal-path problem.

7-1 MINIMAL-PATH PROBLEM

Minimal-path problems arise in urban and rural road networks, in rail freight classification and routing, in mailing systems, and in the transshipment of materials through conveyors and other delivery systems.

Consider the problem of finding alternate paths from node a to node h in the network of Fig. 7-2a, where numbers indicate path costs in the directions shown. We illustrate graphic and matrix methods of solution [1]. The recursion concept will be apparent in both methods. In fact, the only features not already familiar to us from the dynamic-programming examples of Chap. 6 are that the network is geometrically irregular and that the matrix method gives the least-cost paths between all pairs of nodes in the network, not just between two specified nodes. Such network information is useful for transportation problems like Example 4-5.

GRAPHICAL METHODS

1. Draw all links from the origin at node a and indicate their corresponding costs (Fig. 7-2b).
2. If links exist between any of the nodes obtained in step 1, determine the costs for the indirect routes from node a and for the direct route. Identify the least expensive route by a solid line and the more costly routes by dotted lines, and write the lowest internodal route cost near the node (Fig. 7-2b).
3. Repeat steps 1 and 2 for all links emanating from each newly exposed node (b, c, and d). Continue this procedure throughout the network. Figure 7-2c shows a completed diagram, with the solid lines indicating the least-cost routes from node a to every other node.

MATRIX METHOD

The graphic method is tractable only for simpler nets. A matrix method developed by Shimbel [7] yields the least-cost route between every pair of nodes. The steps follow:

Step 1   Represent the network of nodes from *a* to *i* by an $i \times i$ matrix. Infinite costs indicate the absence of links.

From	To								
	a	*b*	*c*	*d*	*e*	*f*	*g*	*h*	*i*
a	0	2	3	5	∞	∞	∞	∞	∞
b	2	0	∞	∞	3	∞	∞	∞	∞
c	1	∞	0	1	5	2	4	∞	∞
d	5	∞	1	0	∞	∞	5	∞	3
e	∞	1	5	∞	0	1	∞	2	∞
f	∞	∞	2	∞	1	0	3	4	∞
g	∞	∞	4	5	∞	3	0	∞	5
h	∞	∞	∞	∞	2	4	∞	0	6
i	∞	∞	∞	3	∞	∞	4	6	0

Step 2   The least-cost route between any two nodes may, in general, consist of any number of links from *n* to $(j-1)$, where *n* is the smallest possible number of links between the two nodes (as three links from *a* to *h*) and *j* is the number of nodes.   Routes with more than $j-1$ links must contain a loop and will, therefore, necessarily be more expensive than the least-cost path containing $j-1$ links.

To identify the least-cost route from among all possible $n, n+1, \ldots, j+1$ link routes, we could determine in sequence the available least-cost one-link route between each pair of nodes, the available least-cost one- or two-link route, the available least-cost one-, two-, or three-link route, etc., until the cost of no route can be reduced by adding more links.   For example, between nodes *a* and *d*, the route cost cannot be reduced by link routes longer than *a–c* and *c–d*.   To accomplish this, we could prepare from the initial one-link matrix the matrices representing the least cost of one- or two-link routes, one-, two-, or three-link routes, etc., until two succeeding matrices are identical. This indicates that routes having larger numbers of links do not further reduce the cost.

Matrix elements are the minimums of the sums of corresponding row and column elements.   For example, element *ad*(=4) in the next matrix is obtained from the following entries in the previous matrix:

Row *a*:	0	2	3	5	∞	∞	∞	∞	∞
Col. *d*:	5	∞	1	0	∞	∞	5	∞	3
Σ:	5	∞	4	5	∞	∞	∞	∞	∞

                            ↑
                        Minimum

Continuing in this way yields the matrix:

Least-cost routes, two or fewer links

From	a	b	c	d	e	f	g	h	i
					To				
a	0	2	3	4	5	5	7	∞	8
b	2	0	5	7	3	4	∞	∞	∞
c	1	3	0	1	3	2	4	6	4
d	2	7	1	0	6	3	5	9	3
e	3	1	3	6	0	1	4	8	2
f	3	2	2	3	1	0	3	3	8
g	5	∞	4	5	4	3	0	7	5
h	∞	3	6	9	2	3	7	0	6
i	∞	∞	4	3	8	7	4	6	0

Repeating the operation upon the second matrix, we obtain the third matrix as:

Least-cost routes, four or fewer links

From	a	b	c	d	e	f	g	h	i
					To				
a	0	2*	3*	4	5	5	7	7	7
b	2*	0	5	6	3*	4	7	5	9
c	1*	3	0	1*	3	2*	4*	6	4
d	2	4	1*	0	4	3	5*	7	3
e	3	1*	3	4	0	1*	4	2*	8
f	3	2	2*	3	1*	0	3*	3	6
g	5	5	4*	5*	4	3*	0	7	5*
h	5	3	6	6	2*	3	6	0	6*
i	5	9	4	3*	7	6	4*	6*	0

Continuation yields a matrix of least-cost routes of up to eight links and is identical to the preceding matrix. Therefore, the matrix for four-link routes is the optimal solution. Notice that the number of links per route considered in each succeeding matrix doubles. This procedure converges more rapidly to an optimum solution than does the method of evaluating paths with one link, two links, three links, and so on. For example, if the least-cost route between two nodes happens to be a 10-link route, we discover its cost in 5 cycles (1,2,4,8,16), whereas 10 cycles would be required if routes of 1, 2, ..., 10 links were evaluated.

The least-cost routes are identified by comparing the initial and final matrices. Identical elements (a_{ij}) in each constitute one-link least-cost paths. Every other least-cost path must be made up of these elements, and we have starred them in the final matrix.

7-2 TRAVELING-SALESMAN PROBLEM

In the *traveling-salesman* problem, a minimum-cost route is sought which passes through each node once, and only once, and returns to the starting node. The problem has puzzled researchers for years, and an analytic solution is not available. An iterative procedure developed by Little and coworkers [6] is generally regarded as one of the more efficient currently available. The traveling-salesman problem is of interest to pickup and de-livery services, (e.g., trash collection) and for transportation-routing problems in construction. Solutions could be obtained by enumeration. Since there are $(n - 1)!$ routes in an n-node problem, this is feasible only for small values of n.

The crux of the procedure of Little et al. is to partition the $(n - 1)!$ tours into two distinct groups and calculate a lower-bound cost to the routes in each group. The group having the larger lower-bound cost is discarded, and the surviving group is again partitioned, and so on. The procedure continues until a single route remains. It is the optimal route. This pro-cedure is commonly called a *branch-and-bound* technique, and the idea is sometimes used in solving difficult nonlinear-programming problems.

Following the algorithm given by Ackoff and Sasieni [1], we solve the traveling-salesman problem for the cost matrix (c_{ij}):

From	To			
	1	2	3	4
1	∞	9	8	25
2	3	∞	29	7
3	14	12	∞	9
4	37	22	11	∞

Note that diagonal entries, c_{ii}, are infinite to preclude travel from a node to itself in one step. The matrix represents an asymmetrical traveling-salesman problem, since the cost of travel from node 3 to node 2, for example, differs from the cost of travel from node 2 to 3 (see Prob. 7-4). A symmetrical traveling-salesman problem may be solved by the same technique. The steps follow.

Step 1   The cost matrix is "reduced" by subtracting the smallest element in each row from every element in the corresponding row and similarly for each column.   The total reduction r_0 is the sum of the amounts subtracted. This is the lower bound to every route in the original group, which we denote by $G(0)$.   Hence:

Row subtraction

From	To			
	1	2	3	4
1	∞	1	0	17
2	0	∞	26	4
3	5	3	∞	0
4	26	1	0	∞

Column subtraction

From	To			
	1	2	3	4
1	∞	0	0	17
2	0	∞	26	4
3	5	2	∞	0
4	26	0	0	∞

and $r_0 = 8 + 3 + 9 + 11 + 0 + 1 + 0 + 0 = 32$.

Step 2   For each zero element, we calculate a "penalty," p_{hk}, as follows:

$$p_{hk} = \min_{j \neq k}(c_{hj}) + \min_{i \neq h}(c_{ik})$$

For example, for the zero element at $(2,1)$,

$$P_{2,1} = \min(\infty, 26, 4) + \min(\infty, 5, 26) = 9$$

In words, p_{hk} is the penalty if a zero element is not used in a route.   If we do not use the link hk in the route, then we must use some other link from h and another link to k.   Thus, the cost for not using the link hk at zero cost must be at least the cost of going from h to the least expensive node plus the cost to k from the least expensive node.   The penalty is calculated for each zero element in the reduced matrix and appears in the upper left-hand corners of these cells in the following matrix.

From	To 1	2	3	4
1	∞	$^0 0$	$^0 0$	17
2	$^9 0$	∞	26	4
3	5	2	∞	$^6 0$
4	26	$^0 0$	$^0 0$	∞

Thus, for the zero-element positions, we have

$$\begin{aligned} p_{12} &= 0 + 0 = 0 \\ p_{13} &= 0 + 0 = 0 \\ p_{21} &= 4 + 5 = 9 \\ p_{34} &= 2 + 4 = 6 \\ p_{42} &= 0 + 0 = 0 \\ p_{43} &= 0 + 0 = 0 \end{aligned}$$

(The first cost figure is the row minimum)

If this is not the first cycle, then skip to step 6.

Step 3   Select the zero-element position, say h, k, with the largest penalty (in the event of a tie, select any tieing position). We partition according to the rule: divide the routes $G(0)$ into two groups, those which include (h,k) $[G(h,k)]$ and those which do not $[G(\overline{h,k})]$. [Of course, $G(h,k) + G(\overline{h,k}) = G(0)$.]   In the example, $h = 2$ and $k = 1$ for the largest penalty of 9.

Step 4   Now we compute the lower bounds in each group.

    a. Group $G(\overline{h,k})$.   If a zero element position, h, k, is not used, there is a cost of at least p_{hk}, which is added to r_0 to yield the lower bound $l(\overline{h,k}) = p_{hk} + r_0$ for the group.

    b. Group $G(h,k)$.   Since we use link hk in each route of this group, we cannot use any other link in row h or column k, so we delete the hth row and kth column.   The use of link hk also precludes the use of link kh, because this results in a subroute, so we set $c_{kh} = \infty$.   In the remaining matrix, i.e., without the hth row and kth column, we perform a "reduction" and calculate the reduction r_{hk} as in step 1.   Thus we have $l(h,k) = r_{hk} + r_0$ as the lower bound for $G(h,k)$.

In the example we have

	To			
From	1	2	3	4
1		∞	0	17
2				
3		2	∞	0
4		0	0	∞

in which all rows and columns still contain at least one zero element.   In this instance, no additional subtractions can be made and $r_{hk} = 0$.   Then,

$$l(\overline{2,1}) = 9 + 32 = 41$$

and

$$l(2,1) = 0 + 32 = 32$$

It is convenient to indicate our results thus far by

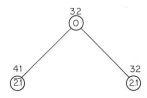

Step 5   To partition further, we choose the branch representing the group with the least lower bound.

a. If group (h,k) is selected, return to step 2 and proceed using the second reduced matrix just computed.

b. If group $\overline{(h,k)}$ is selected, set $c_{hk} = \infty$ in the first reduced matrix, reduce this matrix again, and return to step 2 with the matrix thus obtained.

In the example we select $G(2,1)$ and the last matrix above before proceeding to step 2.   We recalculate the penalties as

$$p_{13} = 17 + 0 = 17$$
$$p_{34} = 2 + 17 = 19$$
$$p_{42} = 0 + 2 = 2$$
$$p_{43} = 0 + 0 = 0$$

so that

From	To 2	3	4
1	∞	$^{17}0$	17
3	2	∞	$^{19}0$
4	$^{2}0$	$^{0}0$	∞

Step 6   Again, select the zero-element position (p,q) having the largest penalty and partition into groups $G(p,q)$ and $G(\overline{p,q})$ as before.   In the example $p = 3$, $q = 4$, and $p_{34} = 19$.

Step 7   To obtain the lower bounds for the new groups, let l denote the lower bound of the selected group.

a. For the group $G(\overline{p,q})$, the lower bound is

$$l(\overline{p,q}) = l + p_{pq}$$

b. For the group $G(p,q)$, delete the pth row and qth column in step 4b. In addition, set the cost element in the (q,p) to infinity.   Now, however, we must search for the additional link which could complete a subroute.   To avoid a subroute, we set the cost element of that link to infinity.   The resulting matrix is reduced, and to the reduction r_{pq} we add l to obtain the lower bound for the group.

In the example,

$$l = \min [l(2,1), l(\overline{2,1})] = l(2,1) = 32$$

We delete the third row and fourth column and change the (4,3) element to infinity.

From	To 2	3
1	∞	0
4	0	∞

Since $p_{34} = 19$, we have $l(\overline{3,4}) = 32 + 19 = 51$.   Since the matrix is already reduced, we have $r_{34} = 0$.   Hence $l(3,4) = 32 + 0 = 32$, and we include link (3,4).

Our route thus far includes links (2,1) and (3,4):

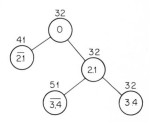

Having selected link 3, 4, we return with the last matrix to step 2 for computation of penalties, and we obtain:

From	To 2	3
1	∞	$^{\infty}0$
4	$^{\infty}0$	∞

Here there is a tie among penalties, and we select link 1, 3 arbitrarily, giving the lower bounds

$$l(\overline{p,q}) = l + p_{pq} = 32 + \infty = \infty$$

and

$$l(p,q) = l + r_{pq} = 32 + 0 = 32$$

Adding link 1, 3, we obtain:

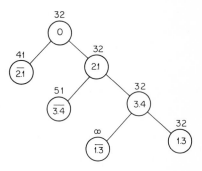

We observe from the previous matrix that the final link must be 4, 2 and that its reduced cost is also zero, to yield:

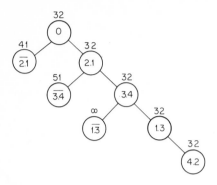

Our optimal route contains the lower-bound links indicated in the diagram, and since the route is cyclic, the starting point is irrelevant. Arbitrarily starting at node 1, we have

$$1 \rightarrow 3 \rightarrow 4 \rightarrow 2 \rightarrow 1$$

Note that the lower-bound links all contain the zero element selected in step 3 (none is designated with bars). This result frequently (but not always) occurs, due to the rule-of-thumb highest-penalty selection procedure.

If alternative optimal solutions exist, they will always be revealed by equal lower-bound costs shown on the final symbolic diagram.

It is worthwhile to return to subroutes mentioned in step 7. By a subroute, we mean a route from *start* to *start* which does not include every node. Naturally, we eliminate subroutes by setting the associated cost to infinity. The need to locate subroutes is not apparent in our example because of its small size. Suppose that the example had included more nodes, so that the link 4, 2 was not the final one and the route thus far was $2 \rightarrow 1 \rightarrow 3 \rightarrow 4$. If the next link by chance linked node 4 to node 2, then we would have a subroute. To avoid this, we set the element in the 4, 2 position to infinity and proceed with the algorithm.

PART III
Critical-path Scheduling

The essence of construction management is to schedule men, money, and materials. The *arrow diagram* in Fig. 7-3 indicates an activity sequence for construction of building footings. The diagram is prepared from a list of

Table 7-6 Activities list for footing construction

Activity	Prerequisite	Arrow-diagram node link
a. Procure steel reinforcement	None	1–2
b. Procure tile and granular backfill for perimeter drains	None	1–9
c. Stake out foundations and perimeter drains	None	1–3
d. Excavate for foundations and perimeter drains	c	3–4
e. Place foundation formwork	d	4–5
f. Cut and bend reinforcement	a	2–5
g. Place reinforcement	e, f	5–6
h. Place concrete	g	6–7
i. Cure concrete	h	7–8
j. Strip forms	i	8–9
k. Place perimeter drains and granular backfill	b, j	9–10
l. Place compacted backfill to first floor level	k	10–11

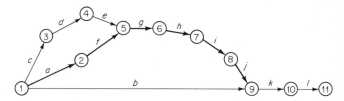

Fig. 7-3 Arrow diagram for footing construction.

activities and their prerequisites (Table 7-6). A schedule of prerequisites (Table 7-7) is useful to prepare more complex arrow diagrams. Figure 7-4 shows a trial arrow diagram prepared from Table 7-7. Misplaced nodes in Fig. 7-4 are connected by dotted lines. The trial arrow diagram is then rearranged to the final form of Fig. 7-3.

The *critical-path* problem is one of allocating resources to activities to minimize the total construction cost. For example, if two simultaneous activities require carpenters, how many should be assigned to each to complete the contract in a specified time at least cost? The logic and techniques for such questions are the subject of the remainder of the chapter.

Numerous techniques for solving these problems are known. They are offspring of the original developments, *PERT* (program evaluation and review technique) and *CPM* (critical-path method). The primary difference between PERT and CPM is that PERT employs statistically related time estimates (a range of possible activity completion times) whereas CPM uses a single-value time estimate for each activity. PERT-related techniques are more useful for research and development projects, for which there is little or no prior

Table 7-7 Activities schedule

		From										
	0	a	b	c	d	e	f	g	h	i	j	k
a	×											
b	×											
c	×											
d				×								
e					×							
f		×										
g						×	×					
h								×				
i									×			
j										×		
k		×									×	
l												×

To appears to the left of rows.

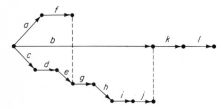

Fig. 7-4 Trial arrow diagram.

experience. CPM techniques are more useful for projects having more predictable activities, such as those in most construction.

In CPM one assumes that the cost of an activity depends upon the allotted time—as, for example, the curves joining points *A* and *B* in Fig. 7-5.   Point *A* is the lowest cost or *normal time* to complete the activity.   Point *B* is the shortest practical time, or *crash time*.   Crash cost is generally higher than normal cost, due to such factors as increased unit labor costs (overtime) and reduced efficiency of men and equipment due to interference as more units are added

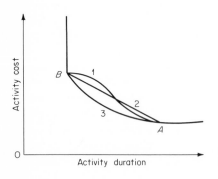

Fig. 7-5   Activity duration-cost relationship for CPM.

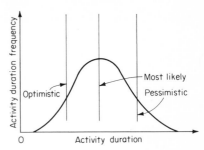

Fig. 7-6 Frequency diagram for activity duration in PERT.

to the job. In contrast, PERT assumes a random activity time and represents it by the mean and standard deviation. Another popular representation is an optimistic time, a most likely time, and a pessimistic time (Fig. 7-6). The total project duration is also a random variable. Pessimistic, most likely, and optimistic project-completion times are determined by summing the corresponding times for individual activities. In short, PERT is time-oriented while CPM is cost-oriented. Civil engineering projects are generally more cost-oriented, and CPM is widely used.

7-3 NETWORK LOGIC

To prepare an arrow diagram (Fig. 7-3), one decides upon a useful level of detail. A high level of detail, showing many activities, can make the diagram incomprehensible to users. Too few activities do not adequately expose the cost and time relationships between subordinate activities. To decide upon a level of detail, one asks: Who will use the network, why, and what level of project decisions do they make? For complex projects, several hierarchies of arrow diagrams can be prepared. A small portion of the project can be shown in greater detail for operating personnel. At the other extreme, the entire project with little detail is better suited for management.

Arrow-diagram logic (network logic) may sometimes be maintained by the use of *dummy* activities. Dummy activities require neither time nor resources. They ensure that only one link passes between each pair of nodes, as indicated by the change in Fig. 7-7. They are also used to indicate that an activity may be started before the preceding activity is complete. For example, in Fig. 7-8, $B1$ may begin when portion $A1$ of activity A has been completed and $B2$ may begin when portion $A2$ is complete. *Artificial*

Fig. 7-7 Use of dummy node for a single link between node pairs.

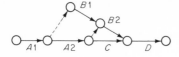

Fig. 7-8 Use of dummies to start an activity after a prior activity is partially complete.

activities are used to secure a time delay in an activity—for example, when men or equipment required to start an activity are still occupied elsewhere. Artificial activities require time but no resources.

7-4 FINDING THE CRITICAL PATH

The heavy arrows in Fig. 7-3 indicate the critical path. Any delay on this path is reflected by a like delay in project completion. Light arrows appear on noncritical paths, i.e., paths where a delay may not delay the project completion. One may verify this by adding the activity times from start to finish on these paths. Sometimes the critical path has parallel segments. A tabular method for identifying parallel paths appears in Table 7-8. Each activity is designated by the ordered tail-head node pair in Fig. 7-3. The estimated least-cost duration, or normal duration, is entered in the "*Duration*" column. Values in the *earliest start time* ("*EST*") and *earliest finish time* ("*EFT*") columns represent the total duration times for prior activities along each network path. The EST at a node is the largest EFT of activities which terminate at that node. To obtain EFT, the activity duration is added to its EST. For example, the EST of activity 5–6 is 14 days since this is the larger EFT for the activities 2–5 (14 days) and 4–5 (12 days). The EFT of 5–6 is then $14 + 4 = 18$ days. The EFT of the final activity is the EFT of the project.

The *latest finish time* ("*LFT*") and *latest start time* ("*LST*") entries are obtained in the same manner except that one proceeds from the bottom of the table (final node in Fig. 7-3) to the top. The LFT of the last activity is first set equal to its EFT. In order to complete activity 10–11 at 29 days, it must be started at $29 - 3 = 26$ days, so 26 is entered in the LST column for activity 10–11. Hence one proceeds backward to activity 0–1. Notice at node 1 that the earliest LST of activities 1–2, 1–3, and 1–9 is 0 days. Therefore, the LFT of any activity prior to point 1 (not shown) must be zero. In general, branch nodes (such as node 1) occur throughout the arrow diagram. LST and LFT columns give the latest times at which each activity can begin and finish without increasing the project duration.

The *float* ("*F*") column is obtained by

$$L = LST - EST = LFT - EFT$$

Float is the slack time for the start of an activity without delaying the project (although it delays subsequent activities on its branch of the diagram). The

Table 7-8 Activity-schedule tabulation and bar chart

Activity	Duration	EST	EFT	LFT	LST	F	Critical path	Time, days
1-2	7	0	7	7	0	0	×	
1-3	2	0	2	4	2	2		
1-9	4	0	4	23	19	19		
2-5	7	7	14	14	7	0	×	
3-4	5	2	7	9	4	2		
4-5	5	7	12	14	9	2		
5-6	4	14	18	18	14	0	×	
6-7	2	18	20	20	18	0	×	
7-8	2	20	22	22	20	0	×	
8-9	1	22	23	23	22	0	×	
9-10	3	23	26	26	23	0	×	
10-11	3	26	29	29	26	0	×	

critical activities, i.e., those on the critical path, are identified by zeros in the float column. Float time is a margin within which activities on noncritical paths may be scheduled to offset unforeseen delays or to reduce resources expended.

The bar chart on the right in Table 7-8 is a convenient way to present the results. Note that the foregoing procedure has been based on normal completion times of individual activities, as represented by point A in Fig. 7-5.

7-5 COST CONSIDERATIONS

Now that we have the critical-path arrow diagram and bar chart, we consider questions of cost:

1. Is more of some resource required than is available? For example, if two backhoes are available, does the schedule call for more than two? If so, can noncritical activities be shifted within their available float? Can some activities be divided into two time intervals to satisfy a resource constraint? This is called *scheduling under resource constraints*.
2. Having satisfied resource constraints, can the project cost be reduced by a time-leveling of resource requirements? Besides the hourly costs of manpower and equipment, there are costs associated with the hiring and firing of men or with idle men and equipment between peak demands. Can these costs be reduced by leveling the resource demands, as suggested in Fig. 7-9a and b? This is called *resource leveling*.
3. Project costs also include overhead costs (administrative costs, interest charges, contract penalties for delay or bonuses for early completion, etc.). Overhead tends to increase with project duration, whereas direct costs tend to decrease, as indicated in Fig. 7-10. One recognizes the lot-size model rationale of Sec. 5-1 in this *time-cost trade-off*.

In the remainder of the chapter, we consider techniques for scheduling with resource constraints, for resource leveling, and for making time-cost trade-offs. For simple critical-path problems, these procedures are done by inspection. For complex arrow diagrams, various algorithms are available. Scheduling under resource constraints has been described by Shaffer, Ritter, and Meyer [26, pp. 89–108], Perk [23], Kelley [18], Berman [9], and Royer [25]. Resource leveling is described by Burgess and Killebrew [10]. Fulkerson

Fig. 7-9 Resource leveling with respect to time.

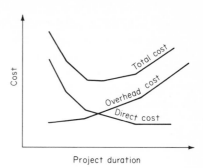

Fig. 7-10 Project costs.

[14] and Ford and Fulkerson [13] developed an efficient flow-net-theory technique for time-cost trade-off studies. The following algorithm can be used for these three cost problems. It incorporates features of the referenced methods for solving the individual problems. Although most practical problems contain enough activities to justify computer solution, the method is best illustrated with a simple diagram, as in Fig. 7-11a. The next section outlines computational steps.

7-6 COST MINIMIZATION

REMOVE RESOURCE CONSTRAINTS

Step 1   List activities, draw arrow diagram, draw activity duration-cost curves, prepare activity-schedule table and bar chart (Figs. 7-3 and 7-5 and Tables 7-6 and 7-8).

Step 2   Add *activity resource requirements, total available resources,* and *total required resources* to the bar chart (shaded portion of the example in Fig. 7-11a). *Total available resources* may indicate a sharp increase in unit cost for additional units.   Check that no single activity resource requirement exceeds the total available of the resource.   If it does, either the activity resource requirement must be reduced (by lengthening or shifting activity durations) or the resource constraint must be relaxed.

Total required resources (Fig. 7-11a) are obtained by summing the resources required by activities for each unit of time on the bar chart.   Circled numbers indicate periods in which resource constraints have been violated. Resources with critical constraints are listed near the top in the "total available resources" section so that they may be satisfied if subsequent scheduling conflicts arise.   Constraints that are expensive to violate are called *critical constraints.*

Step 3   Remove any resource-constraint violations (circled numbers) for the first listed resource by the following steps, as necessary, in the order indicated.

a. If any activities which require the resource during the constraint-violation period have a later LST than the end of the violation, reschedule the minimum required number of these activities to begin at the end of the constraint-violation period.

In the example, the violation of 4 units of resource *a* may be removed by either delaying activity 1–5 by 3 days or delaying activity 2–5 by 1 day.

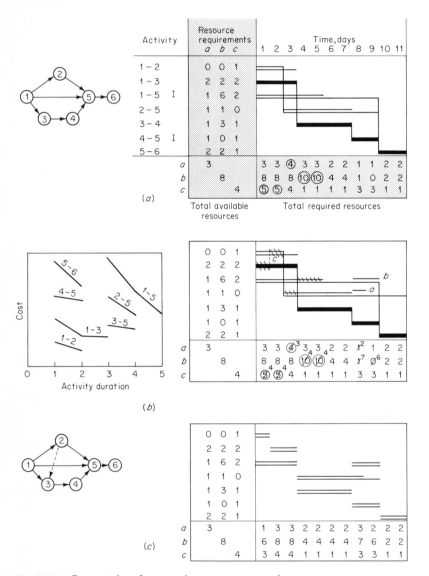

Fig. 7-11 Computations for removing resource constraints.

Activity 2–5 was delayed as shown by the line labeled "*a*" on the bar chart and by the two corrections to the required-resources row *a* of Fig. 7-11*b*.

b. If a violation(s) still exists, sometimes the constraint can be relaxed by interrupting a resource-competing activity. Interrupt activities so that the finish times are as early as possible (consistent with removal of the constraint violation).

In the example, it is found that the violation of 10 units of resource *b* cannot be removed by delaying any activity. However, activity 1–5 has been designated as one being capable of interruption by an "I" in the activity column. Therefore, the resource *b* constraint violation may be removed by interrupting activity 1–5 as shown by the line labeled "*b*" in Fig. 7-11*b*. Finally, a check indicates that this did not result in a new violation of the constraint of 3 available units of resource *a*.

c. If violations still exist, find from the activity cost-duration curves (Fig. 7-11*b*) the competing activities which can be shortened (and possibly delayed) to remove the violation at least cost. Record any changes in required resource levels resulting from the shortened activity durations.

In the example, complete the preceding steps and note that the violation of 5 units of resource *c* cannot be removed by any combination of delay and interruption of activities. Therefore, the remaining choice is to shorten the duration of one or more activities (and increase direct costs). The activities responsible for the violation are 1–2, 1–3, and 1–5. Observe in the activity cost-duration curves of Fig. 7-11*b* that shortening by 1 day is achieved at least cost on activity 1–3 and that a second day can be cut at least expense from activity 1–2. Therefore, activities 1–2 and 1–3 are each shortened by 1 day in order to delay the start of 1–3 until the finish of 1–2, as shown by the dummy (dotted) line labeled "*c*" in Fig. 7-11*b*.

Step 4 Repeat step 3 for succeeding resource rows, one at a time. Remember to shift, or to interrupt and shift, activity times to the right only, since a shift to the left is likely to violate a resource constraint removed in a previous resource row. Also, after each resource row has been treated in this manner, possible secondary violations of previous resource constraints may arise. If a secondary violation is identified, the method in step 3 should be used for removing the resource constraint in the current step. For example, if in resource row *c* step 3*b* produced a secondary constraint in resource row *a*, the constraint in row *c* should be removed by step 3*c* instead of by step 3*b*.

Results of steps 3 and 4 are shown in Fig. 7-11*c*. Observe that steps 3 and 4 in the arrow diagram involve shifting activities to the right. The effect of these steps is to delay certain noncritical activities, thus postponing the times at which certain resources must be committed to the project but also reducing the completion-time safety margin in regard to unforeseen delays on the noncritical paths.

LEVEL RESOURCES

The sum of the squares of a total resource requirement in successive time increments may be used as an indicator of the extent of resource leveling. The sum is minimum when leveling is maximum. For example, consider a 2-day assignment which requires any combination of 6 machine-days for which the sums of squares for alternate schedules are shown in Fig. 7-12. Applying this measure, resource a of Fig. 7-11c gives

$$1^2 + 2(3)^2 + 4(2)^2 + 3^2 + 3(2)^2 = 56$$

Resource leveling will be improved if activities can be shifted in such a way as to reduce this sum of squares without violating any resource constraints just satisfied in steps 2 to 4. Resource leveling may be accomplished by the following step.

Step 5   Taking the first-row resource first, test to see if the sum of the squares can be reduced by shifting activities left or right, away from the major resource peaks. Perform those shifts which reduce the sum of squares for the resource in question and which do not violate the constraints of any other resource.

For the example, observe from Fig. 7-11c that after satisfying resource constraints, activity 2–5 is the only one which can still be shifted within its float. Since activity 2–5 requires only resources a and b, the sums of the squares for these two resources may be compared with their sums of squares when activity 2–5 is shifted to its alternate position 1 day to the right. Since the shift changes resource requirements only on the first and last days of the activity, the comparison may easily be made as follows:

	Current schedule	*New schedule*
Resource "a"		
Day 4 requirement	2	1
Day 9 requirement	2	3
	$2^2 + 2^2 = 8$	$1^2 + 3^2 = 10$
Resource "b"		
Day 4 requirement	4	3
Day 9 requirement	6	7
	$4^2 + 6^2 = 52$	$3^2 + 7^2 = 58$

Hence the current schedule is retained since it yields a smaller sum of squares for both resources a and b.

Step 6   Determine total project direct cost by summing costs for appropriate activity durations in Fig. 7-11b.

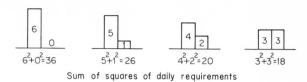

Sum of squares of daily requirements

Fig. 7-12 Variation of sum of squares with resource-time distribution.

PERFORM TIME-COST TRADE-OFF STUDY

If project shortening can be accomplished without violating resource constraints, it may be possible to further reduce costs, due to the reduction in overhead cost, as shown in Fig. 7-10. Since the time-cost trade-off study is more complex than were the resource constraint and leveling steps, the simpler arrow diagram shown in Fig. 7-13a is used for illustration. In this diagram, each activity is designated by a three-digit number. The three digits indicate the cost slope c, normal duration d_a, and crash duration d_b, respectively, shown in Fig. 7-13b. For simplicity, the activity cost-duration curves will all be assumed to be linear functions between normal cost and crash cost. The procedure can also handle piecewise linear cost functions. The computation includes iterations in which each successive reduction in project duration is obtained by shortening the activity (or activities) on the critical path which incurs the least cost increase. An alternative method is the flow-net-theory algorithm of Ford and Fulkerson [13]. The steps follow:

1. Enter in the "Normal" column of Table 7-9 the activity durations and ESTs obtained from previous steps, and identify the critical path by inspection or by the method of Table 7-8.
2. To start the first iteration, enter the critical path just determined into the "Critical path" row of column 1.
3. The "Activity to shorten" is identified as that activity on the critical path which has the lowest cost slope c and which has not yet been shortened to its crash duration. When the critical path has parallel branches (Fig. 7-14), the activity(ies) to shorten is determined by comparing the minimum cost slope of activities on the single branches of the critical path (branch f) with the *sum of cost slopes* for the optimal activities on each of the parallel branches (branches b and e). Thus, activities b and e are shortened because the sum of their cost slopes $2 + 3 = 5$ is less than 6, the cost slope of f.
4. The "Activity duration" for the activity determined in step 3 is reduced until:
   a. An activity crash duration is reached, or

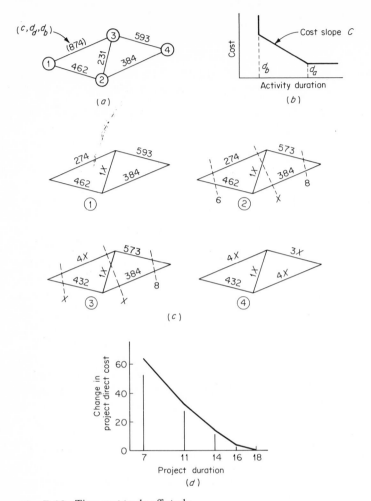

Fig. 7-13 Time-cost trade-off study.

b. An alternate path becomes critical.

Thus activity 2–3 may be shortened from 3 days to 1 day in the first iteration because 1 day is its crash duration. By coincidence, 1 day also makes path 134 critical, satisfying both conditions *a* and *b*.

5. Adjusted values of "EST" are entered, by the normal method, in order to obtain the new final EST, or project duration time.

6. The cost increase, ΔC, due to activity shortening is entered in Table 7-9. ΔC = cost slope c multiplied by the number of days shortened.

7. The cumulative cost increase, $\sum \Delta C$, is recorded, and additional critical paths which may result from step 4*b* are determined.   Steps 2 to 7 are

Fig. 7-14 Critical path with parallel branches.

repeated until no remaining path which can be shortened will cause a reduction in project time.

8. The results may be presented graphically by plotting the terminal EST (project duration) against $\sum \Delta C$, as in Fig. 7-13d. To this curve would be added the overhead-costs curve to determine project duration at which minimum total cost could be obtained.

If hand computation is used, it is helpful to draw the arrow diagrams of Fig. 7-13c after each of the corresponding tabular iteration columns has been completed. This may be done simply by adding corrected activity durations to the single arrow diagram of Fig. 7-13a, but separate diagrams are used here for clarity. Each diagram facilitates choosing the activity to shorten and the activity duration in the succeeding column. An "X" indicates that the activity has been shortened to its crash point and is, therefore, no longer a candidate for shortening. The number preceding an X is the crash duration.

Table 7-9 Time-cost trade-off study

		Normal	1	*Cycle* 2	3	4
Critical path				134		
			1234	1234	All	All
Activity to shorten					1–2	2–4
			2–3	3–4	1–3	3–4
Activity duration	1–2	6			3	
	1–3	7			4	
	2–3	3	1			
	2–4	8				4
	3–4	9		7		3
EST	2	6			3	3
	3	9	7		4	4
	4	18	16	14	11	7
ΔC			4	10	18	32
$\sum \Delta C$			4	14	32	64

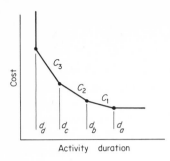

Fig. 7-15 Piecewise-linear activity cost-duration curve.

Finally, when all paths become critical, a simple procedure using *cut lines* (dotted lines in Fig. 7-13c) is used to determine which activities to shorten. The project duration is shortened if all activities on any single cut line are shortened. Cut lines are labeled either with a number, which equals the sum of cost slopes of activities cut by the line, or by an X, which indicates that the line cuts at least one crashed activity which cannot be further shortened. Therefore, the activities to shorten for optimality are those intersected by the cut line having the smallest numerical label.

An alternative hand computation useful for nets of slightly greater complexity is to add LST and float data to the EST rows. This is illustrated in Table 7-10 for a portion of the example. The activities having zero total float identify the critical path for the next iteration. The activity having the smallest nonzero float sets the limit for step 4b in the next iteration. For all but small nets, computer solution is the only practical method.

For piecewise-linear activity cost-duration curves, the only modification to the above procedure is to relabel the activity $c_2 d_c d_b$ (see Fig. 7-15) when d_b has been reached, rather than to label it $d_b x$, as in Fig. 7-13. This procedure is continued for each linear segment of the curve until the crash duration is reached.

Table 7-10   Time-cost trade-off tabulation format

| | | Cycle | | | | | |
		Normal			1		
	1–2	0	0	0	0	0	0
	1–3	0	2	2	0	0	0
EST-LST-Float	2–3	6	6	0	6	6	0
	2–4	6	10	4	6	8	2
	3–4	9	9	0	7	7	0
	4	18	18	0	16	16	0

7-7 LINEAR- AND DYNAMIC-PROGRAMMING TECHNIQUES

Critical-path scheduling problems can often be formulated as linear- and dynamic-programming problems.

A LINEAR-PROGRAMMING MODEL FOR CRITICAL-PATH DETERMINATION

Moder and Phillips [21] determined the activities on the critical path and their durations using a linear-programming model. The project is viewed as a flow net in which units flow from a source (start) to a sink (finish) on the arrow diagram. The activity durations are considered to be times for transporting one unit of flow between adjacent nodes. The critical path then becomes the route from source to sink which requires a maximum flow time. The linear-programming formulation for locating the critical path for the example of Fig. 7-13a is

$$\text{Max:} \quad z' = 6x_{12} + 7x_{13} + 3x_{23} + 8x_{24} + 9x_{34} \tag{1a}$$
$$\text{Subject to:} \quad x_{12} + x_{13} = 1 \tag{1b}$$
$$-x_{12} + x_{23} + x_{24} = 0 \tag{1c}$$
$$-x_{13} - x_{23} + x_{34} = 0 \tag{1d}$$
$$-x_{24} - x_{34} = -1 \tag{1e}$$
$$x_{12}, x_{13}, x_{23}, x_{24}, x_{34} \geq 0$$

where z' = total project duration and x_{ij} takes the value zero if there is no flow on path ij and unity otherwise. The coefficients in the objective function are the scheduled activity flow durations. The constraints (1b) and (1e) indicate that a unit of flow leaves source 1 and enters sink 4, while constraints (1c) and (1d) are the Kirchhoff node equations for flow conservation at internal nodes.

More complex nets often lead to linear-programming formulations which suggest solving the dual (Sec. 4-3).

A DYNAMIC-PROGRAMMING MODEL FOR TIME-COST TRADE-OFF STUDY

The following example is adapted from Butcher [11] to illustrate potential applications of dynamic programming in time-cost trade-off studies. For a fixed expenditure, we want to allocate funds to three sequentially performed tasks (Fig. 7-16) so that total construction time is a minimum.

Cost-time relationships for each task appear in Fig. 7-17. The cost-time functions differ for the individual tasks. For example, the step function in Fig. 7-17a can represent a choice between one or two machines for stage 1. The curve in Fig. 7-17b could represent work done by the contractor's own

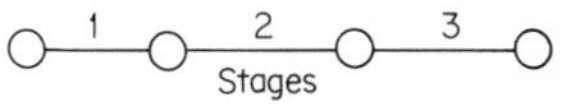

Fig. 7-16 CPM network.

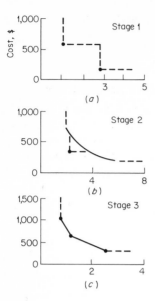

Fig. 7-17 Time-cost relationships for three stages.

forces, and the dot could represent cost and time quoted by a subcontractor for doing the same task. The data of Fig. 7-17 are tabulated in Table 7-11. The choice of $200 increments is a compromise between smaller increments, which improve accuracy, and larger increments, which reduce computations.

Table 7-11   Time-cost relationships

	Cost	Time, days
	Stage 1	
(a)	$ 200	3
	400	3
	600	1
	800	1
	Stage 2	
(b)	$ 200	5
	400	3
	600	3
	800	2
	1,000	2
	Stage 3	
(c)	$ 200	3
	400	2
	600	1
	800	1

Table 7-12 Optimum allocation of funds to stages 1 and 2

Funds allocated, $	Stage 1 $	Stage 1 Time, days	Stage 2 $	Stage 2 Time, days	Total time, days
400	200	3	200	5	8
600	200	3	400	3	6
800	200–600	3	600–200	3	6
1,000	600	1	400	3	4
1,200	600–800	1	600–400	3	4
1,400	600	1	800	2	3

In Table 7-11b, the subcontractor's performance is tabulated for the range where his performance is superior (dotted lines in Fig. 7-17).

A tabular solution is developed by finding (for fixed level of expenditure) the allocation between stages 1 and 2 which minimizes their completion time. Next, find the allocation between stages (1 + 2) and 3 which minimizes completion time for all three stages. The process can clearly be extended to any number of sequential stages.

The left-hand column of Table 7-12 gives funds (in $200 increments) allotted to stages 1 and 2. We start with $400 ($200 + $200), the smallest sum for these two stages, and end with $1,400 ($500 + $800), an amount beyond which there are no further decreases in the completion time for stages 1 and 2.

To obtain the row entries in Table 7-12, consider, for example, the fourth row, where a total allocation of $1,000 is being studied. Possible allocations are:

$	Stage 1 Time, days	Stage 2 $	Stage 2 Time, days	Total time, days
200	3	800	2	5
400	3	600	3	6
600	1	400	3	4←
800	1	200	5	6

The allocation giving minimum total time is $600 for stage 1 and $400 for stage 2. This result is entered in Table 7-12, and the procedure is repeated to yield the remaining rows.

Table 7-13 is obtained from Tables 7-11c and 7-12 in the same manner that Table 7-12 was obtained from Table 7-11a and b. Finally, we complete the example by plotting in Fig. 7-18 the results given in Table 7-13.

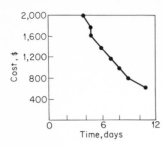

Fig. 7-18 Time-cost relationship for project.

The example used the idea of dynamic programming to allocate funds to stages of a construction project.   For parallel stages, such as stages 1 and 2 in Fig. 7-19a, the division of funds between the two stages is made so that their construction times are equal.   Thus any CPM net containing simple combinations of sequential and parallel links can be handled by dynamic programming.   For example, a suitable sequence for the net in Fig. 7-19b is

$1 + 2$	sequential
$(1 + 2) + 3$	parallel
$(1 + 2 + 3) + 4$	sequential
$5 + 6$	sequential
$(1 + 2 + 3 + 4) + (5 + 6)$	parallel

Butcher [11] notes that this method is not directly applicable to nets without pure combinations of sequential and parallel links—as, for example, the net in Fig. 7-19c.

7-8 APPLICATIONS

Consider the construction of a three-span concrete girder bridge having two pile-supported abutments at the banks of a river and two pile-supported

Table 7-13 Optimum allocation of funds to stages 1, 2, and 3

Funds allocated $	Stage 1 + 2 $	Time, days	Stage 3 $	Time, days	Total time, days
600	400	8	200	3	11
800	600	6	200	3	9
1,000	600	6	400	2	8
1,200	600, 1,000	6, 4	600, 200	1, 3	7
1,400	1,000	4	400	2	6
1,600	1,000	4	600	1	5
1,800	1,000–1,400	4, 4, 3	800–400	1, 1, 2	5
2,000	1,400	3		1	4

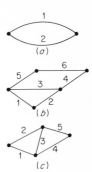

Fig. 7-19 Types of nets. (*a*) Parallel net; (*b*) net with pure sequential-parallel links; (*c*) net with mixed sequential-parallel links.

piers midstream. Figure 7-20 is a simplified arrow diagram for this construction. Two or more alternative arrow diagrams are often prepared for such projects in order to ascertain an optimal construction program. For example, initial planning might reveal the following alternatives:

1. Casting piles at the site is less expensive than buying them some miles away, but buying them allows an earlier start and thereby more time for pile-driving operations. The added time could reduce the need for pile drivers from two to one.
2. Construction could proceed from both banks of the river to the middle to permit simultaneous activities on both sides. However, if construction proceeds from only one bank, the supervision and transportation costs can be reduced.

Arrow diagrams would be prepared for each alternative plan, and the resulting duration-cost comparisons would guide the choice of construction program.

Construction often requires initial assessment of site hazards. For example, in dam construction some activities must be completed in a low-flood-risk season. A site hazard can be represented in an arrow diagram as an artificial hazard activity whose duration-cost curve (a risk cost) may be based

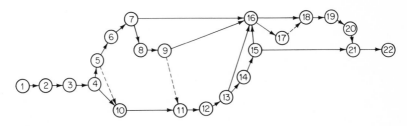

Fig. 7-20 Arrow diagram for construction of a three-span bridge.

Table 7-14   Activities for construction of a three-span bridge

Access roads, site clearing and preparation	1–2
Move in, set up casting yard for piles, girders	2–3
Cast piles for abutments	3–4
Cast piles for piers	4–11
Cast girders for end spans	10–16
Cast girders for center span	16–17
Drive piles for abutments	4–5
Drive piles for piers	10–11
Place sheet-pile cofferdam, abutment 1	5–6
Steel, formwork, and pour concrete for abutment 1 to above waterline	6–7
Move cofferdam to abutment 2	7–8
Steel, formwork, and pour concrete for abutment 2 to above waterline	8–9
Move cofferdam to pier 1	11–12
Formwork and pour concrete pile cap and pier 1 to above waterline	12–13
Move cofferdam to pier 2	13–14
Formwork and pour concrete pile cap and pier 2 to above waterline	14–15
Remove cofferdam	15–21
Form and concrete abutment 1 to full height	7–16
Form and concrete abutment 2 to full height	9–16
Form and concrete pier 1 to full height	13–16
Form and concrete pier 2 to full height	15–16
Place precast girders on 2 end spans	16–18
Place precast girders on midspan	18–19
Steel, formwork, and pour concrete deck	19–20
Attach guardrail, lighting	20–21
Clean up and move from site	21–22

on previous records, such as stream hydrographs (see Example 10-2). It may be optimal to complete certain activities on a crash program between two flood seasons.

SUMMARY

Sequencing theory orders "jobs" through "machines." Analytic solutions are available for three special cases:

1. Any number of units processed in the same order through two stations.
2. Two units processed in any order through any number of stations.
3. Any number of units processed in the same order through three stations if the maximum time (or cost) of any unit in the middle station is less than the minimum time of any unit in either the first or last station (reduces to case 1).

Routing problems require the identification of an optimum path through a network. When the object is to find the path between two nodes, dynamic programming may be used. Two methods, one graphical and one matrix, both based on the dynamic-programming principle of recursion, were demonstrated. The matrix method is especially useful for various types of transportation studies because it gives the shortest path lengths between all pairs of nodes in the network.

A second type of routing problem is to find the optimum cyclic path from any point in the network through all nodes and back to the starting point (traveling-salesman problem). The branch-and-bound algorithm is used to obtain solutions.

Scheduling problems arise when the task sequence is fixed but the allotted times to perform tasks can be varied. The object is to allocate task times which minimize total project cost or minimize cost for a specified total completion time. PERT (program evaluation and review technique) and CPM (critical-path method) and their modifications may be used. PERT is better suited to research and development projects, for which little prior experience exists; CPM is better suited to routine construction projects.

The critical (longest-time) path through a network of tasks may be determined by tabular or computer methods. The computer is needed except for small networks. An algorithm was illustrated for scheduling under resource constraints, for resource leveling, and for performing time-cost trade-off studies. Critical determinations are possible using linear programming, and dynamic programming can be used for time-cost trade-off studies.

PROBLEMS

7-1. Two jobs are to be processed through five machines (A, B, C, D, and E) in a machine shop. The processing orders and times required in each machine are given below:

    Job 1:   C-3, D-9, A-6, B-11, E-4
    Job 2:   A-5, C-7, D-7, E-2, B-7

What is the minimum time required to complete both jobs?

7-2. A steel fabricator has seven assemblies to fabricate. Each will require cutting and bending, followed by welding. Based on the estimated time requirements, determine the order in which the assemblies should be fabricated to minimize total completion time.

Assembly	Cutting and bending	Welding
1	3	5
2	2	4
3	9	7
4	8	12
5	11	8
6	6	6
7	7	9

7-3. A contractor wishes to inspect six construction sites in such a manner that his total travel distance is minimized. The travel distances between each pair of sites (including the home office) are given in the matrix below. In what sequence should he visit the six sites?

Site	1	2	3	4	5	6
1	×					
2	5	×				
3	15	12	×			
4	25	8	7	×		
5	20	18	13	36	×	
6	10	14	28	9	6	×

7-4. A plant manufactures five shapes of concrete block with a single-block machine. The setup costs for changing from one mold to another are given in the matrix. In what sequence should the various molds be used in the machine?

Setup costs

From mold No.	To mold No.				
	1	2	3	4	5
1	×	9	12	9	17
2	5	×	6	3	14
3	8	2	×	13	5
4	6	14	7	×	4
5	12	3	9	1	×

7-5. Draw an arrow diagram for each set of sequence constraints shown. Capital letters indicate activities.

(a)	(b)	(c)
A < B, D	A < C, E	A < B, F
B < D, F	B < C, D	B < C, D
C < D, E, F	C < D	C < E
D < E, G	D < F	D < E, G
E < G	E < F, G	E < G
F < G	F < G	F < G

7-6. Prepare an activity-schedule tabulation and bar chart for the following arrow diagram.

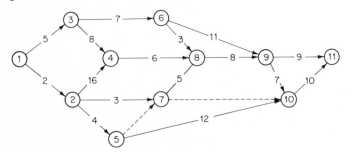

7-7. Given the following activities, estimated durations, and sequence constraints, draw an arrow diagram and prepare an activity schedule and bar chart.

Activity	Duration	Prerequisites
A	2	None
B	5	A
C	4	None
D	7	A
E	12	A
F	6	B
G	3	C, D
H	9	B
I	4	E, F, G
J	1	E, F, G
K	8	C, D
L	11	None
M	6	J, K, L

7-8. Eleven plumbers and nine laborers are available for a project (see arrow diagram below). The estimated duration is shown on each activity, followed by the required numbers of plumbers and laborers. Plumbers and laborers must both work at the same time when assigned to the same activity. Prepare an activity schedule, bar chart, and resources (plumbers and laborers) table which satisfies the resource constraints. Assume that interruption of jobs is permitted, if necessary.◆

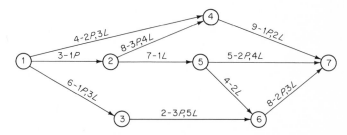

7-9. In the arrow diagram below, the duration of each activity is followed by the number of laborers required. The letter c indicates that a crane is required for the duration of the activity. Only one crane is available for daily rental. Schedule the project for minimum cost. Laborers are paid $45 per day, and the crane rental is $120 per day. A constant number of laborers are employed for the project. Interruption of jobs is permitted.

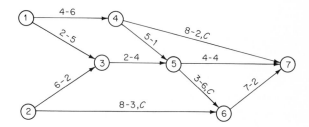

7-10. Trains must be scheduled between terminals A and B, 325 miles apart. The line is double-track except for a 5-mile-long tunnel and a 60-mile single-track section through mountains (Fig. 7-21). Train speeds average 80 mph on the double-track line and 50 mph through the tunnel and single-track section. Given the following constraints on departure times, how should trains be scheduled to minimize total en route train time?

Departure constraints

Train No.	Departure point	Earliest departure time	Latest departure time
1	A	1:00	2:30
2	A	1:30	3:00
3	B	2:00	4:00
4	A	3:30	6:00
5	B	4:00	5:00
6	B	5:30	7:00

Fig. 7-21 Trackage.

7-11. The Federal Aviation Agency studies various plans for increasing the efficiency and safety of air-traffic movements near large terminals. One such plan is described here.

When an arriving aircraft is within 50 miles of the airport, the pilot reports his craft and position to the control tower. This information is entered to a computer, and an operator locates the approaching aircraft on a radar screen. Likewise, when a departing plane is ready to taxi, the pilot identifies his craft to ground control and this information is also entered to the same computer.

Various aircraft have differing costs associated with their flying and ground times. The object is to minimize the total costs for all aircraft, arriving and departing, emergencies excepted. Programmed data include, for each class of aircraft, the minimum and maximum safe airspeeds for approach, the minimum safe distance from final-approach turn to end of runway, and the cost per hour airborne and on ground. Two or more radio localizers having different transmission frequencies, so-called "turning posts," are spaced at various distances from the approach end of the runway (Fig. 7-22). Planes may fly to the vicinity of one of these localizers before making the turn for final approach.

The computer program seeks to minimize $\sum_{i=1}^{n} c_i t_i$, where n is the total number of arriving planes in the 50-mile radius and departing planes on the ground, c_i is the cost per minute for the ith plane (whether airborne or on the ground), and t_i is the time remaining until landing or takeoff for the ith plane.

Additional data and restrictions are:

(*a*) Minimum intervals between landings and takeoffs are 40 sec.
(*b*) The taxiway hold area is laid out so that planes may take off in any desired sequence.

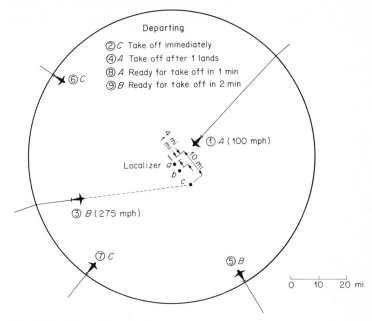

Fig. 7-22 Air-traffic control.

(*c*) Departing pilots are given the identification of the landing or departing aircraft they are to follow.

(*d*) Approaching pilots entering the 50-mile radius are given the turning-post transmission frequency, required airspeed, and required altitude upon arrival at the turning post.

(*e*) Initial instructions to pilots remain unchanged except for an emergency.

A hypothetical case is shown in Fig. 7-22 for the data in Table 7-15. Assignments already completed are indicated on aircrafts 1 to 4. Assume, for greater system efficiency, that the computer "digests" information and makes assignments only at 2-min intervals. During the last 2-min interval, planes 5 to 7 enter the 50-mile radius and planes 8 and 9 arrive at the taxiway hold area.

Table 7-15 Aircraft characteristics

Aircraft class	Min. safe approach airspeed, mph	Max. safe approach airspeed, mph	Min. safe distance from end of runway for final turn, miles	Cost/hr, airborne	Cost/hr, on ground
A	50	120	$\frac{1}{4}$	$ 25	$ 16
B	125	300	1	80	45
C	200	500	$2\frac{1}{2}$	900	500

Devise a general solution method and indicate in the following table the computed assignments for planes 5 to 9.

Computed assignments, aircrafts 5 to 9

Aircraft	Departing Takeoff after plane No.	Landing Assume heading on localizer No.	At an airspeed of
5			
6			
7			
8			
9			

7-12. Ships pass through a 30-mile-long canal at a speed of 10 mph. Two passing lanes at the 10- and 20-mile points allow ships going in opposite directions to pass one another. Assume that ships traveling in the same direction can be grouped into convoys and that any number of ships can pass in the passing zones. Develop an algorithm, or set of operating rules, to minimize total ship waiting cost, and determine a schedule which minimizes cost for the following data.

Ship No.	Cost per hr	Direction[1]	Est. arrival time at canal entrance
1	$400	E	1.00
2	200	W	1.15
3	50	E	1.30
4	500	E	2.00
5	300	W	3.00
6	200	E	3.15
7	400	W	3.30
8	300	W	3.45

[1] "E" represents eastbound, and "W," westbound.

REFERENCES

Sequencing

1. Ackoff, R. L., and M. W. Sasieni: "Fundamentals of Operations Research," John Wiley & Sons, Inc., New York, 1968.
2. Conway, R. W., L. Maxwell, and L. W. Miller: "Theory of Scheduling," Addison-Wesley Publishing Company, Inc., Reading, Mass., 1967.
3. Johnson, S. M.: Optimal Two- and Three-stage Production Schedules with Setup Times Included, *Nav. Res. Log. Quart.*, vol. 1, no. 1, March, 1954.

4. Nicholls, R. L.: Operations Research in Construction Planning, *Proc. ASCE*, vol. 89, no. CO2, pp. 59–73, September, 1963.
5. Sisson, R. L.: Sequencing Theory, in R. L. Ackoff (ed.), "Progress in Operations Research," vol. 1, pp. 293–326, John Wiley & Sons, Inc., New York, 1961.

Routing

6. Little, J. D. C., K. G. Murty, D. W. Sweeney, and C. Karel: An Algorithm for the Traveling Salesman Problem, *Operations Res.*, vol. 11, pp. 972–989, 1963.
7. Shimbel, A.: Structure in Communication Nets, *Proc. Symp. Inform. Networks*, Polytechnic Institute of Brooklyn, New York, April, 1954.

Critical-path scheduling

8. Antill, J. M., and R. W. Woodhead: "Critical Path Methods in Construction Practice," John Wiley & Sons, Inc., New York, 1965.
9. Berman, H.: The Critical Path Method for Project Planning and Control, *The Constructor*, pp. 88–94, September, 1961.
10. Burgess, A. R., and J. B. Killebrew: Variation in Activity Level on a Cyclical Arrow Diagram, *J. Ind. Eng.*, vol. 13, no. 2, March–April, 1962.
11. Butcher, W. S.: Dynamic Programming for Project Cost-Time Curves, *Proc. ASCE*, vol. 93, no. CO1, pp. 59–73, March, 1967.
12. Charnes, A., and W. W. Cooper: A Network Interpretation and a Directed Subdual Algorithm for Critical Path Scheduling, *J. Ind. Eng.*, vol. 13, no. 4, pp. 213–218, 1962.
13. Ford, L. R., and D. R. Fulkerson: "Flows in Networks," Princeton University Press, Princeton, N.J., 1962.
14. Fulkerson, D. R.: A Network Flow Computation for Project Cost Curves, *Management Sci.*, vol. 7, no. 2, pp. 167–179, January, 1961.
15. Galbrath, R. V.: Computer Program for Leveling Resource Usage, *Proc. ASCE*, vol. 91, no. CO1, pp. 197–124, March, 1965.
16. Gleason, W. J., and J. J. Ranieri: First Five Years of the Critical Path Method, *Proc. ASCE*, vol. 90, no. CO1, pp. 27–36, March, 1964.
17. Holroyd, E. M.: The Optimum Bus Service: A Theoretical Model for a Large Uniform Urban Area, in L. C. Edie, R. Herman, and R. Rothery (eds.), "Vehicular Traffic Science," Elsevier Publishing Company, Amsterdam, 1967.
18. Kelley, J. E.: Critical Path Planning and Scheduling: Mathematical Basis, *J. ORSA*, vol. 9, no. 3, pp. 296–320, 1961.
19. Levin, R. I., and C. A. Kirkpatrick: "Planning and Control with PERT/CPM," McGraw-Hill Book Company, New York, 1966.
20. Meyer, W. L., and L. R. Shaffer: Extending CPM for Multiform Project Time-Cost Curves, *Proc. ASCE*, vol. 90, no. CO1, pp. 45–67, March, 1965.
21. Moder, J. J., and C. R. Phillips: "Project Management with CPM and PERT," Reinhold Publishing Corporation, New York, 1964.
22. Muth, J. F., and G. L. Thompson: "Industrial Scheduling," chap. 21 by J. E. Kelley, Jr., Prentice-Hall, Inc., Englewood Cliffs, N.J., 1963.
23. Perk, H. N.: Man-scheduling, file 10.3.009, *IBM* 650 *Program Library*, file 10.3.013, *IBM* 1620 *Program Library*.
24. Riggs, J. L.: "Economic Decision Models for Engineers and Managers," McGraw-Hill Book Company, New York, 1968.
25. Royer, K.: CPM vs. Cost Control, *Bldg. Construct.*, pp. 62–70, November, 1963.
26. Shaffer, L. R., J. B. Ritter, and W. L. Meyer: "The Critical Path Method," McGraw-Hill Book Company, New York, 1965.

8
Random Variables and Probability

Every aspect of our environment possesses characteristics of uncertainty. The strength of a beam, streamflow, numbers of vehicles on a highway, opponents' bids for a construction job, ground displacement in an earthquake, and the loading cycle at which failure occurs are all examples of *chance*, or *random phenomena*. This chapter is an introduction to applied probability. It is not necessary to master the entirety before taking up subsequent chapters. However, a thorough study of the first few sections and at least a familiarity with the later sections are helpful. The references list several well-known texts for additional study, particularly for readers without previous exposure to the subject.

8-1   NATURE OF RANDOM VARIABLES AND PROBABILITIES

A *random variable* describes a possible outcome (or event) of a chance experiment.   For a given Hooke's law spring, the displacement is taken to be a deterministic (or nonchance) variable for known applied forces.   However, if the applied forces arise from a chance mechanism, then the displacement is a random variable.   Nonrandom variables can take on any values selected by the experimenter, but values of a random variable are determined by chance.

A random variable may be discrete, continuous, or mix-valued.   To some extent, the choice belongs to the modeler.   Numbers of vehicles suggest a discrete-valued random variable, while streamflows suggest continuous random variables.   Sometimes streamflow is considered as a continuous-valued random variable in a particular range of interest and as discrete (rounded to the nearest whole unit) outside this range.   Such a random variable is called *mix-valued.*

The set of all possible values of the random variable is called the *sample space*.   The sample space describing the outcome of the flip of a coin consists of "heads," "tails," and "edge."   However, the modeler may decide that the event "edge" is not important to his purpose and therefore may count the flip a mistrial.   It is the modeler, not probability theory, who determines which sample space is more appropriate.

Associated with each outcome of a random experiment is a *measure* of the likelihood of occurrence, or *probability*.   For a fair coin, the probability for heads or tails is $\frac{1}{2}$.   Intuitively, this is understandable since it is convenient to think of probabilities as *frequencies*.   If n_h and n_t represent the numbers of heads and tails that result from $N(=n_h + n_t)$ flips, the ratios n_h/N and n_t/N are called the frequencies of the respective occurrences.   The limits

$$p_h = \lim_{N \to \infty} \frac{n_h}{N} \quad \text{and} \quad p_t = \lim_{N \to \infty} \frac{n_t}{N}$$

are the classic definitions for the respective probabilities.[1]   Note that a frequency only approximates a probability.   Although an approximation may be exceedingly good, one can never determine probabilities by experiment since it requires infinite repetition.   One can consider the probabilities associated with points in the sample space as either weights (in the gravitational sense) or weight functions (in the mathematical sense).   The sum of the probabilities (weights) over the sample space is unity.   The requisite properties of probabilities for points in the sample space are

$$0 \leqslant p_k \leqslant 1 \quad \text{and} \quad \sum_k p_k = 1 \quad k = 0, 1, \ldots, n \tag{1}$$

[1] An assumption of equilikelihood in the experiments described here will be considered in Sec. 8-4.

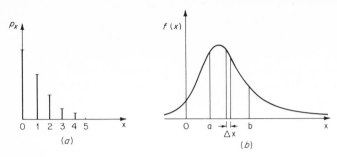

Fig. 8-1   Probability functions. (*a*) Discrete; (*b*) continuous density.

where the sum extends over the n (possibly infinite) points of the sample space (see Fig. 8-1*a*).   We interpret a probability of 0 as an impossible event and a probability of 1 as a certain event.

The preceding discussion applies to discrete nonnegative random variables.   For continuous random variables, since there are infinitely many points in a continuum, the above frequency notion breaks down.   It can be given meaning by imagining outcomes to consist of groups of sample points, such as areas on a plane, lengths on a line, or volumes in a space.   The ratio of the "weight" of a specific outcome to the total "weight" is the frequency (or probability) of the group.

Let X be a continuous random variable and $f(x)$ its associated weight function, or *probability density*.[2]   The function $f(x)$ is not a probability; it is a kind of "probability per unit length."   The probability that a random outcome will be in the interval $\{a,b\}$ is represented by

$$P(a \leqslant X \leqslant b) = \int_{a}^{b} f(x)\, dx \tag{2}$$

Thus, if x represents the random time to complete a phase of a construction project, then the probability that the actual completion time will be between times a and b is given by Eq. (2).   Note that the probability that the project will be completed at any specific time is zero.   Also, if $a = 0$ and $b \to \infty$, we expect the probability to be unity since it is certain that the project will be completed at some time in $\{0,\infty\}$.   The sample space is the X axis, the outcomes are of length x, and the weights equal $f(x)$ (see Fig. 8-1*b*).   While random variables can assume negative values, the density function must always be nonnegative.

The analogy to Eq. (1) for a density function is

---

[2] In general, we shall use capital letters to designate random variables and lowercase letters for particular values.

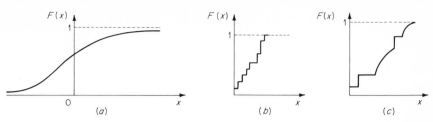

Fig. 8-2 Distribution functions. (*a*) Continuous random variable; (*b*) discrete random variable; (*c*) mixed random variable.

$$f(x) \geqslant 0 \quad \text{and} \quad \int_{-\infty}^{\infty} f(x)\,dx = 1 \quad -\infty < x < \infty \tag{3}$$

The function $F(x)$, called the *distribution function*, is the probability that the random variable X takes a value less than or equal to x, that is,

$$P(X \leqslant x) = F(x) \quad -\infty \leqslant x \leqslant \infty$$

Its properties are:

1. $0 \leqslant F(x) \leqslant 1$.
2. $F(-\infty) = 0$; $F(\infty) = 1$.
3. When $x < x'$, then $F(x) \leqslant F(x')$; that is, $F(x)$ is a nondecreasing function.
4. $F(x)$ is right-hand continuous; that is, it has a left-hand limit but not necessarily a right-hand limit.

Figure 8-2 illustrates distribution functions.

A continuous distribution function corresponds to a continuous random variable. If $F(x)$ is continuous, then

$$F(x) = \int_{-\infty}^{x} f(t)\,dt$$

where $f(t)$ is the density function. Note that $f(x)$ is the derivative of $F(x)$. If the variable is discrete, then

$$F(k) = \sum_{i=-\infty}^{k} p_i$$

where p_i is the probability that the random variable takes the integer value i.

8-2 COMPOSITE EVENTS

Complicated random phenomena are more easily described by set combinations of simpler events or sets. Hence this section deals with the algebra

Fig. 8-3 Complementary events.

of sets.   This enables us to determine the probabilities of complicated events in terms of probabilities for simpler events.

COMPLEMENTARY EVENTS

If this page is the sample space S and the region in Fig. 8-3 is an event X, the remainder of the page, X', is the *complement*, or *negation*, of X.   It indicates that X did not occur.   The sample space S, therefore, consists of the two events X and X'.   If $P(X)$ and $P(X')$ denote the respective probabilities, then according to Eq. (1),

$$P(X) + P(X') = 1$$

COMPOUND (JOINT) EVENTS

Let X and Y denote two events.   Their simultaneous occurrence is an event called the *compound event*, or *joint event*, or *intersection event*.   The notations (X,Y), (XY), and $(X \cap Y)$ are used interchangeably.

If the events X and Y cannot occur simultaneously, they are called *mutually exclusive* and their joint probability is zero, that is, $P(X,Y) = 0$. For example, if X and Y represent the events "failure in tension" and "failure in compression" of a structural member, they are mutually exclusive.

UNION OF EVENTS

An important composite event is an outcome in which either X or Y or XY occurs.   It is called the *union* of X and Y, denoted by $(X \cup Y)$.   For example, if X and Y are the events "first member fails" and "second member fails," the union is the event "first member fails or second member fails or both fail."   The probability of the union event is

$$P(X \cup Y) = P(X) + P(Y) - P(XY) \tag{4}$$

It is acceptable to regard Eq. (4) as an axiom.   In a Venn diagram, i.e., a geometric representation of the sample space (Fig. 8-4a), the outer boundary

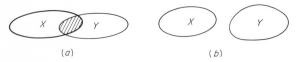

(a)   (b)

Fig. 8-4   Venn diagrams for two events.   (a) Intersecting; (b) mutually exclusive.

of the two intersecting sets is the union since any point within the outer boundary satisfies the definition. The probability of the compound event, the shaded region in Fig. 8-4a, is subtracted in Eq. (4) because it is included twice in the sum $P(X) + P(Y)$.

In Fig. 8-4b, the events X and Y are mutually exclusive and the probability of the joint event is zero. Equation (4) then becomes $P(X) + P(Y)$.

CONDITIONAL EVENTS

The event that X occurs when it is known that Y has occurred defines the *conditional* event denoted by $(X|Y)$. The probability of the conditional event is

$$P(X|Y) = \frac{P(X,Y)}{P(Y)} \qquad P(Y) \neq 0 \tag{5}$$

Equation (5) can be regarded as axiomatic. In Fig. 8-4a, since it is known that Y has occurred, the portion of X which is unshaded is no longer pertinent. If X occurs, given that Y has occurred (shaded region in Fig. 8-4a), the conditional probability is the ratio of the probability of the joint event to the probability of the entire space of Y. For mutually exclusive events (Fig. 8-4b), the conditional probability is zero.

An important special case of Eq. (5) arises if the occurrence of Y in no way affects the probability that X will occur, that is, when $P(X|Y) = P(X)$. Then events X and Y are said to be *independent*, and Eq. (5) can be written

$$P(X,Y) = P(X)P(Y) \tag{6}$$

Note that Eq. (6) is a necessary condition for independence. For sufficiency, the sample space of one variable is not influenced by the sample space of the other.

Example 8-1 Sample space for a two-member truss For a two-member truss, let X be the event "the tension in member B exceeds β" and Y the event "the tension in member A exceeds α" (see Fig. 8-5).

1. The complement of X (regions I and II) is the event X' {the tension in member B does not exceed β}. Since the tension in member B either does or does not exceed β, $P(X) + P(X') = 1$.
2. The joint event (X, Y) is region III.
3. The union $(X \cup Y)$ is represented by regions II, III, and IV.
4. The conditional event $(X|Y)$ occurs in region III, which is also the region corresponding to the joint event. However, the probability of the conditional event is not the same as the probability of the joint event. The joint probability is the chance that region III will be the outcome

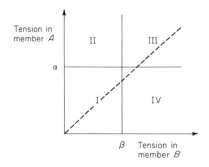

Tension in member A

II   III

α

I   IV

β Tension in member B

Fig. 8-5 Tension quadrant for a two-member truss.

in the sample space consisting of the four regions, I to IV. The conditional probability is the chance that the outcome is in region III in the sample space consisting of regions II and III. Similarly, the conditional probability $P(Y|X)$ is the chance that region III will be the outcome in the space of regions III and IV. The effect of the denominator in Eq. (5) is to normalize the new sample space.

One may analyze other events. For example, the region to the right of the (dashed) 45° line means that B bears the greater tension.

So far, we have defined events complementary, compound, union, and conditional which arise from basic set combinations of events. These can be combined to yield still other set combinations. For example, the event $(X \cup Y)Z$ is caused by compounding the union of the events X and Y with another event Z. It is easy to conclude that

$$(X \cup Y)Z = XZ \cup YZ \tag{7}$$

using the Venn diagram in Fig. 8-6. Using Eq. (7), one can show that

$$P(X \cup Y \cup Z) = P(X) + P(Y) + P(Z) - P(XY) - P(XZ) \\ - P(YZ) + P(XYZ) \tag{8}$$

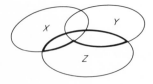

X Y

Z

Fig. 8-6 A three-event Venn diagram.

Another useful set relation follows from Eq. (7). If $Y = X'$, then $(X \cup Y)$ is an entire sample space. It can be omitted from the left side of Eq. (7) to yield

$$Z = XZ \cup X'Z \tag{9}$$

Using a Venn diagram, or an analytic argument, one can show that

$$Z = X_1 Z \cup X_2 Z \cup \cdots \cup X_n Z \tag{10}$$

is the generalization of Eq. (9) assuming that at least one of the events $X_1, X_2, \ldots, X_n$ occurs, i.e., that the events are collectively exhaustive.

BAYES' RULE

From Eqs. (5) and (10) and assuming the events $X_1, X_2, \ldots, X_n$ to be mutually exclusive, the probability of the event Z is written

$$P(Z) = \sum_{k=1}^{n} P(X_k Z) = \sum_{k=1}^{n} P(Z|X_k) P(X_k)$$

Using this result, we write

$$P(X_k|Z) = \frac{P(X_k Z)}{P(Z)} = \frac{P(Z|X_k) P(X_k)}{\sum_k P(Z|X_k) P(X_k)} \tag{11}$$

which is *Bayes' rule*, one of the most useful formulas in applied probability. For example, suppose that several crews have recently poured separate sections of a concrete road. Here $X_1, \ldots, X_n$ are the events "first crew poured," "second crew poured,"..., "nth crew poured." Let Z be the event that a defective section is discovered. Clearly, it was the work of one of the crews. Equation (11) relates the probability $P(X_k|Z)$ that the kth crew poured the defective section to the probabilities $P(Z|X_k)$ that the kth crew's work is defective and $P(X_k)$ that the kth crew poured the section. Bayes' rule is useful because the right side of Eq. (11) relates probabilities for which data are more likely to be available than the conditional probability on the left. Examples of Bayes' rule and other set relations appear in the Problems. Bayes' rule is the motivation for defining probabilities without reference to the frequencies mentioned in Sec. 8-1. This has obvious advantages for many situations of interest to engineers (see [1] and [12]).

SEVERAL VARIABLES

It is easy to generalize to a finite number of random variables. As with joint probabilities, one also speaks of joint density functions. For example,

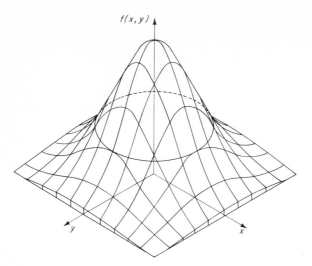

Fig. 8-7 A two-dimensional density function. (*Adapted from A. Hald, "Statistical Theory with Engineering Applications," John Wiley & Sons, Inc., New York, 1952.*)

let $f(x,y)$ be the joint density for the random variables X and Y. It has the properties

$$f(x,y) \geqslant 0 \qquad \text{and} \qquad \iint f(x,y)\, dx\, dy = 1$$

where the integration extends over the entire sample space of X and Y. Figure 8-7 illustrates a two-dimensional density function.

Joint densities with many variables are common. The *marginal density* of Y, $q(y)$, is defined by

$$q(y) = \int_x f(x,y)\, dx$$

and similarly for the marginal density of X. Thus single-variable densities can be obtained from joint densities, but the converse is true only when the variables are independent.

8-3 COMBINATORIAL ANALYSIS

In many situations, each point in the sample space has the same probability. The probability of an event is calculated by dividing the number of points for the corresponding event by the total number of points in the sample space. In principle, one can always obtain these numbers by enumeration. For example, the event "ace" arises four times in the sample space of 52 cards, so the associated probability is $4/52 = 1/13$. In practice this is feasible only for simple cases. In this section we derive rules to enumerate more efficiently.

Suppose that four engineers (E_1, E_2, E_3, and E_4) are available for assignment to two jobs (J_1 and J_2). How many possible assignments are there of an engineer to a job? A direct enumeration yields the eight possibilities: (E_1,J_1), (E_2,J_1), (E_3,J_1), (E_4,J_1), (E_1,J_2), (E_2,J_2), (E_3,J_2), and (E_4,J_2). A more efficient way to reason is: there are two jobs, each of which can be assigned to any of four men, so that $4 + 4 = 8$. For more jobs and more engineers, the number of possible assignments grows rapidly. With m elements of one type and n elements of a second type, there are mn pairs consisting of an element of each type. We call this the *theorem on pairs*.

A generalization to k types of elements is given by the *theorem on multiplets*:

With n_1 elements of the first type, n_2 of the second type, . . . , n_k of the kth type, there are exactly $n_1 n_2 \ldots n_k$ multiplets consisting of one element of each type.

A simple proof of this theorem is suggested in Prob. 8-13.

Consider next the number of ways in which k distinct objects can be selected from a population of n ($\geqslant k$) distinct objects, e.g., a deck of cards. The first object can be selected from any of n, the second from the remaining $n - 1$, and so on. The required number of ways is the product $n(n - 1) \ldots (n - k + 1)$. This product of k integers is called a *permutation* and is denoted by ^nP_k. Note that once an object has been selected, it is no longer available for subsequent selections. This is referred to as *sampling without replacement*. Actually, this is not a new result since it follows from the theorem on multiplets. Imagine k identical sets of the n objects, e.g., decks of cards. After drawing from the first deck, remove the corresponding card in each of the other $k - 1$ decks. After drawing from the second deck, the corresponding card is removed from each of the $k - 2$ remaining decks, and so on. Now, there are n cards of the first type, $n - 1$ of the second, etc., and the result is ^nP_k, using the theorem on multiplets.

Consider again the number of ways in which k objects can be selected from a population of n distinct objects. However, assume that after it is drawn and recorded, the object is returned to the population before the next draw. This is *sampling with replacement*. Reasoning as before, we conclude that there are n^k ways to select the k objects. For example, from a population of $n = 4$ sizes (S_1, S_2, S_3, S_4) of beams, a sequence of $k = 2$ sizes can be selected with replacement in $4^2 = 16$ ways as follows:

$$
\begin{array}{cccc}
S_1 S_1 & S_1 S_2 & S_1 S_3 & S_1 S_4 \\
S_2 S_1 & S_2 S_2 & S_2 S_3 & S_2 S_4 \\
S_3 S_1 & S_3 S_2 & S_3 S_3 & S_3 S_4 \\
S_4 S_1 & S_4 S_2 & S_4 S_3 & S_4 S_4
\end{array}
$$

Sampling without replacement, there are $4 \cdot 3 = 12$ selections. This corresponds to eliminating the possibilities $S_1 S_1$, $S_2 S_2$, $S_3 S_3$, and $S_4 S_4$ from the list. Pairs with different orderings are counted twice, for example, $S_3 S_4$ and $S_4 S_3$. When the order of selection is not important, the number of ways that the k objects can be selected is called the *combination* ^nC_k or $\binom{n}{k}$. For example, in five-card poker, card order is immaterial and AAKKK $=$ AKKKA $=$ KKKAA, and so on.

If ^nC_k is multiplied by $k!$, we have the number of ways without replacement including order, that is, ^nP_k. Therefore,

$$^nC_k = \frac{^nP_k}{k!} = \frac{n(n-1) \cdots (n-k+1)}{k!} \frac{(n-k)(n-k-1) \cdots 1}{(n-k)(n-k-1) \cdots 1}$$

$$= \frac{n!}{k!(n-k)!} \equiv \binom{n}{k} \tag{12}$$

where $^nP_k = n!/(n-k)!$.

For example, for four beams, $^4C_2 \equiv \binom{4}{2} = 6$ is the number of distinct pairs of beams exclusive of ordering and $\binom{4}{2}2! = 12 = {}^4P_2$ is the number of pairs with regard to order. The reader may recognize that the combination ^nC_k is a binomial coefficient. There is a large literature dealing with combinational identities (see Chap. II of [3]). Several results used in subsequent sections appear as problems at the end of the chapter.

8-4 PROBABILITY FUNCTIONS BY ENUMERATION

UNIFORM LAW

Everyone has solved probability puzzles—as, for example, the chance for throws of a fair die. The ratio of "favorable" points to the total number yields the probability of ace as $1/6$; of deuce, $1/6$; and so on. In short,

$$p_k = \begin{cases} 1/6 & k = 1, 2, \ldots, 6 \\ 0 & \text{otherwise} \end{cases}$$

where k represents the random variable for the outcome of a throw and p_k the probability function.

For a sample space of n points which are equally likely outcomes of an experiment, let $k = 1, 2, \ldots, n$ designate the points. The probability function $un(k,n)$ is

$$un(k,n) = \begin{cases} \dfrac{1}{n} & k = 1, 2, \ldots, n \\ 0 & \text{otherwise} \end{cases} \qquad (13)$$

where n is its parameter. The die example is the case $n = 6$. The probability function in Eq. (13) is called the *uniform probability law*. Incidentally, probability functions which have something of a general character are referred to as *probability laws*.

Consider a sample space of n equally likely points, and suppose that the experiment is repeated k times. What is the probability that no point is selected more than once? The number of "favorable" ways, i.e., a sample without duplication, is ^nP_k, and the total number of sample points is n^k. Thus, by enumeration, we conclude that the required probability is

$$\frac{n(n-1)\cdots(n-k+1)}{n^k} \qquad k = 0, 1, \ldots, n \qquad (14)$$

HYPERGEOMETRIC LAW

Consider a quality-control situation for a population of n items which include $m(\leqslant n)$ defectives. A sample of $r(\leqslant n)$ items is drawn at random. What is the probability that k of those drawn are defective? We reason as follows: The number of ways that k defective items can be drawn from the total of m defectives is

$$\binom{m}{k} = \frac{m!}{k!(m-k)!}$$

Similarly, $r - k$ nondefective items can be drawn from the total of $n - m$ nondefectives in $\binom{n-m}{r-k}$ ways. From the theorem on pairs (Sec. 8-3), the number of ways that the sample of size r with k defectives can arise is the product $\binom{m}{k}\binom{n-m}{r-k}$. This is the number of "favorable" cases. The sample space is the number of ways that a sample of size r can be drawn from a population of n elements, namely $\binom{n}{r}$. Thus, by enumeration, we have the probabilities

$$hy(k;r,m,n) = \frac{\binom{m}{k}\binom{n-m}{r-k}}{\binom{n}{r}} \qquad k = 0, 1, \ldots, r \qquad (15)$$

This is called the *hypergeometric probability law*. Problem 8-16 asks the reader to prove that these probabilities sum to unity. In practice, the observed frequency of defective items is compared with the range of frequencies for normal circumstances. Using various techniques, statisticians decide whether there is an abnormal number of defectives in the lot being inspected.

The hypergeometric law also arises in estimating the sizes of populations for which direct enumeration is not practical—as, for example, the number of fish in a lake [3]. Suppose that we catch and mark m fish and return them to the lake. When the marked fish have thoroughly mixed with the other fish, another catch of r fish is made and the number of marked ones, k, is observed. We are certain that there are at least $m + (r - k)$ fish in the lake, but we cannot know the total number n. How should we estimate n from the data on m, r, and k? We could assume that $n = m + r - k$, a very unlikely event. For example, for $m = r = 1,000$ and $n = 1,900$, the probability that $k = 100$ marked fish will turn up in the second catch is of the order 10^{-430}.

Rather than assume that our experience was an extremely rare event, it is more reasonable to assume that the most likely event has occurred. This most likely event corresponds to the value of k for which $hy(k)$ takes its largest value. The reader can show that the maximum is attained for the value $n \sim mr/k$ (see [3]). This criterion has a principal role in statistics as the principle of maximum likelihood [13]. Thus, a maximum-likelihood estimate of n for the given data is 10,000.

We have illustrated how probability laws can arise from enumerative arguments. Enumeration, however, has limitations. First, for continuous random variables it is not clear how to derive density functions. Second, even for discrete probability laws enumeration is useful only if each of the sample points is equally likely. For example, our enumerative argument breaks down if a die is not a fair one. Note that in each derivation we have included the "equally likely" qualification. For most random phenomena of engineering interest, an enumerative method is of limited usefulness.

8-5 PROBABILITY FUNCTIONS BY FORMAL ARGUMENTS

In the last section we found probability laws which are useful for equally likely outcomes. Since probability functions can be represented by any set of numbers or functions which satisfy Eqs. (1) or (3), there is no end to their number and variety. In this section we introduce additional probability laws largely by using Eqs. (1) and (3). The following chapters make clear why they are useful.

BINOMIAL LAW

Recall from algebra the binomial theorem:

$$(p + q)^n = \sum_{k=0}^{n} \binom{n}{k} p^k q^{n-k}$$

The terms

$$b(k;p,n) = \binom{n}{k} p^k q^{n-k} \qquad k = 0, 1, \ldots, n \tag{16}$$

can represent discrete probabilities since Eq. (1) is satisfied if $p + q = 1$, for $p,q > 0$. This probability law, called the *binomial law*, is very important because it arises from a versatile conceptual model (to be considered in detail in the next chapter).

For example, suppose that a new technique for pouring concrete slabs is to be tested. In each of n pours we note whether the new technique has produced a better than standard slab. If B_i denotes the event that the ith slab is better than standard, a typical outcome can be represented by the compound event $(B_1, B_2, B_3', \ldots, B_n')$; that is, the first and second slabs are better, the third is not better, . . . , the nth slab is not better. We seek the probability of possible outcomes. The conditional probability enables us to decompose such compound events into more manageable sizes. Using Sec. 8-2, we write

$$P(B_1, B_2, B_3', \ldots, B_n') = P(B_n' | B_1, B_2, \ldots, B_{n-1}')$$
$$P(B_{n-1}' | B_1, \ldots, B_{n-2}') \cdots P(B_1)$$

If a knowledge of the condition of the first, second, . . . , $(n-1)$st slabs has no bearing on the condition of the nth slab, the outcomes are independent in the sense of Eq. (6). In other words, $P(B_n' | B_1, \ldots, B_{n-1}') = P(B_n'), \ldots,$ $P(B_2 | B_1) = P(B_2)$, and so on. Thus, the joint event is written

$$P(B_1, B_2, B_3', \ldots, B_n') = P(B_1) P(B_2) P(B_3') \cdots P(B_n') \tag{17}$$

The probabilities on the right in Eq. (17) are that specific pours will or will not be better. Usually we are interested in the probability for the total number of better slabs without regard to the order in which they were poured. To eliminate the ordering, we multiply Eq. (17) by $\binom{n}{k}$ (recall Sec. 8-3). Furthermore, if $P(B_i) = P(B)$ for all $i = 1, \ldots, n$, the probability that exactly k of the n slabs will be better, assuming constant probabilities from pour to pour, is

$$\binom{n}{k} [P(B)]^k [1 - P(B)]^{n-k} \qquad k = 0, 1, \ldots, n$$

which is the *binomial law*.

POISSON LAW

Substituting the Maclaurin series for e^v into the identity $e^v e^{-v} = 1$, we obtain

$$1 = e^{-v} + v e^{-v} + \frac{\mu^2}{2!} e^{-v} + \cdots + \frac{v^k}{k!} e^{-v} + \cdots$$

where $v > 0$. The terms clearly satisfy Eq. (1), and therefore we have the probability law

$$p(k;v) = \frac{v^k}{k!}e^{-v} \qquad k = 0, 1, \ldots \tag{18}$$

This is the *Poisson law* and is of marked importance.

For example, to examine a steel bar for a microscopic flaw, the bar is divided into a number n of independent and nominally identical segments of length l. Let p denote the probability that a segment is flawed. The probability that exactly $k(\leqslant n)$ flawed segments are discovered is clearly the binomial law with parameters p and n. To illustrate the approximation to the Poisson law, we form the ratio

$$\frac{b(k)}{b(k-1)} = \frac{\binom{n}{k}p^k q^{n-k}}{\binom{n}{k-1}p^{k-1}q^{n-k+1}} = \frac{n-k+1}{k}\frac{p}{q} \qquad k = 1, 2, \ldots$$

As the segment length l is made smaller, the number of segments n becomes larger. Intuitively, as l becomes small, p does also, but the product $np = v$ remains finite. The ratio in the last expression may thus be approximated by v/k since $q \to 1$. From a simple induction (Appendix 2), one concludes that

$$b(k) \sim \frac{v^k}{k!}b(o)$$

Since $b(o) = (1-p)^n = \left(1 - \dfrac{v}{n}\right)^n \sim e^{-v}$ for large n and small p, one has the approximation

$$b(k) \sim \frac{v^k}{k!}e^{-v} \qquad k = 0, 1, \ldots$$

The right side is the Poisson law. The approximation improves as $n \to \infty$ and $p \to 0$ while $v = \lim_{\substack{n\to\infty \\ p\to 0}}(np)$ exists.

The Poisson law can be regarded as a convenient approximation to the binomial law for some computational purposes. Its more important roles, however, stem from its being a continuous analog to the binomial law. The Poisson law is often used to describe numbers of vehicles, earthquakes, floods, etc., occurring in a period of time. Cumulative probabilities for the Poisson law appear in Appendix 4.

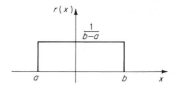

Fig. 8-8 Rectangular probability law.

RECTANGULAR LAW

Consider a continuous random variable X on the interval $a \leqslant x \leqslant b$. The function

$$r(x;a,b) = \begin{cases} \dfrac{1}{b - a} & a \leqslant x \leqslant b \\ 0 & \text{otherwise} \end{cases} \tag{19}$$

satisfies Eq. (3) and is called the *rectangular law* (see Fig. 8-8).

For example, consider a metal part which is subject to fatigue failure. The practice is to replace the part upon failure or after T hours of service, whichever occurs first. If the data suggest that the probability of a fatigue failure depends linearly upon the age of the part, then the rectangular law governs the random time in service. To prove this, let $a = 0$, $b = T$, and X be the random time in service in Eq. (19). Now, the distribution function $F(t)$ is the probability that failure occurs before time $t < T$, that is,

$$F(t) = \int_0^t \frac{dx}{T} = \frac{t}{T}$$

which is linear in t. Another way to describe the fatigue is to note that the probability of failure in an interval $\{t_0, t_1\}$, that is,

$$\int_{t_0}^{t_1} \frac{dx}{T} = \frac{t_1 - t_0}{T}$$

depends only upon the interval $t_1 - t_0$ and not upon its age.

EXPONENTIAL LAW

The function

$$e(x;\lambda) = \lambda e^{-\lambda x} \qquad x > 0 \tag{20}$$

where λ is a positive constant, also satisfies Eq. (3) and is called the *exponential probability law*. The exponential law also arises in a remarkable variety of problems. The gap length between vehicles in a traffic stream, the life of electronic equipment, and the time between consecutive floods are often described by the exponential law. In a subsequent chapter the reasons will become clearer. A remarkable property of the exponential law is unique

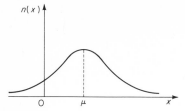

Fig. 8-9 Normal probability law.

among continuous probability laws. It is called the "memoryless" or Markov property.

Let τ, the random time to failure, be governed by the exponential law. We assert

$$P(\tau > t + t_0 | \tau > t_0) = P(\tau > t) \tag{21}$$

In words, the probability that the equipment will "live" at least for an additional time t, given that it is already aged t_0, is the same as the probability that a new item will have a "life" of at least t. The proof is an easy calculation suggested in Prob. 8-20.

NORMAL (GAUSSIAN) LAW

Finally, we introduce the function

$$n(x;\mu,\sigma) = \frac{1}{\sqrt{2\pi}\sigma} e^{-[(x-\mu)^2/2\sigma^2]} \qquad -\infty < x < \infty \tag{22}$$

where μ and $\sigma(>0)$ are constants, which also satisfies Eq. (3) and is called the *normal*, or *gaussian*, *probability law* (see Fig. 8-9).[3]

The normal law finds wide application. It is used to describe complex phenomena such as wind loads, strengths of steel bars, jet noise, and amplitudes of ship oscillations.

An important property of the normal law is that it can be standardized. For example, if the strength of a steel bar follows a normal law, the probability that its strength exceeds S is

$$\int_S^\infty n(x)\,dx = \frac{1}{\sqrt{2\pi}\sigma} \int_S^\infty e^{-[(x-\mu)^2/2\sigma^2]}\,dx$$

Consider the transformation

$$Z = \frac{X - \mu}{\sigma} \tag{23}$$

---

[3] The proof that the integral of Eq. (22) over the real line is unity is more easily done in polar coordinates (e.g., see [9]). It also appears in tables of definite integrals.

Substituting, we get

$$\int_s^\infty n(x)\,dx = \frac{1}{\sqrt{2\pi}} \int_{\frac{s-\mu}{\sigma}}^\infty e^{-z^2/2}\,dz$$

This integrand is also a normal law with parameters $\mu = 0$ and $\sigma = 1$. In fact, the integral of any normal law can be transformed using Eq. (23) into the integral of a *unit normal law*, that is, $\mu = 0$ and $\sigma = 1$, with revised limits of integration. This property enables one to form a table for the unit normal law which can be used for any normal law. This is especially useful since the normal law cannot be integrated in closed form. We illustrate the use of the unit normal table appearing in Appendix 4 with an example.

Example 8-2 Using a unit normal table The time to complete a certain phase of a construction project is a random variable t governed by the normal law. Two construction methods are available. For the first method, the completion time is normal with parameters $\mu_1 = 33.9$ and $\sigma_1 = 11.8$, and for the second method, $\mu_2 = 29.3$ and $\sigma_2 = 17.5$. If 44 days are available to complete this phase of the project, which of the methods should be used?

As a criterion, we choose the method which has the greater probability of being completed within the allotted time. Thus,

First method: $P(t_1 < 44) = \displaystyle\int_{-\infty}^{44} n(t;33.9,11.8)\,dt$

$$= \int_{-\infty}^{0.86} n(z;0,1)\,dz = 0.802$$

Second method: $P(t_2 < 44) = \displaystyle\int_{-\infty}^{44} n(t;29.3,17.5)\,dt$

$$= \int_{-\infty}^{0.84} n(z;0,1)\,dz = 0.799$$

The upper limits of 0.86 and 0.84 arise from the transformation in Eq. (23), that is,

$$\frac{44 - 33.9}{11.8} = 0.86 \quad \text{and} \quad \frac{44-29.3}{17.5} = 0.84$$

Using the unit normal table (Appendix 4) and interpolating linearly between $z = 0.8$ and 0.9 yields the probability 0.802, and so on. Both methods have about the same probability of completion within the allowed time.

Now, suppose that only 42 days, rather than 44 days, are available to

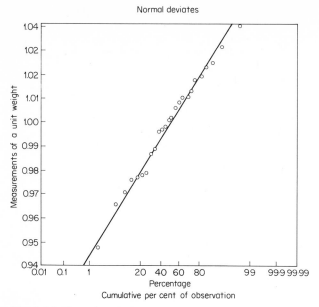

Fig. 8-10 Normal probability paper. (*Adapted from Hahn and Shapiro* [6].)

complete the construction.   Again we calculate the probabilities of completion within the allotted time to be

$$\text{First method:} \quad P(t_1 < 42) = \int_{-\infty}^{42} n(t;33.9,11.8)\, dt$$

$$= \int_{-\infty}^{0.69} n(z;0,1)\, dz = 0.755$$

$$\text{Second method:} \quad P(t_1 < 42) = \int_{-\infty}^{42} n(t;29.3,17.5)\, dt$$

$$= \int_{-\infty}^{0.73} n(z;0,1)\, dz = 0.767$$

The probabilities for a 42-day completion time give preference to the second method, other things being equal.   The specific values are arbitrary, so the example can be made more dramatic to illustrate that intuition cannot always be trusted when dealing with randomness.   Note that the integration range included negative values of time.   This unsettling feature is only a technicality of using the normal law, which has a range of $-\infty$ to ∞, for positive-valued data.   Some workers use a truncated normal law.   Also, the *normal probability paper* illustrated in Fig. 8-10 is useful for observing how well the data are described by a normal law with parameters μ and σ.   The paper is designed so that perfectly normal data fall on a straight line [6].

8-6 EXPECTED VALUES

A probability function provides a complete description of the random variable it represents. For some purposes a less complete but more convenient description is useful. The average value of the random variable is one of many possibilities. We define the *expected value* of a continuous (or discrete) random variable X with an associated probability function $f(x)$ (or p_k) as

$$\mu = E(X) \int_x xf(x)\,dx \qquad \left(\text{or } \sum_k kp_k\right) \tag{24}$$

where the integration (or summation) is understood to be over the domain of X. Commonly, the symbols μ and $E(X)$ are used for the mean value. Note that $E(X)$ does not mean "a function of X." Expected value is a synonym for the terms "average value," "mean value," and "first moment."

The rationale for Eq. (24) is familiar. Consider a beam with a total distributed load of unity and a load intensity, $f(x)$, at a distance x from one end. The distance from that end to the center of gravity of this load is

$$\mu = \frac{\int_x xf(x)\,dx}{\int_x f(x)\,dx}$$

where the integration is over the entire beam. Since the denominator is unity, we have

$$\mu = \int_x xf(x)\,dx$$

which is Eq. (24). Clearly, similar remarks hold for a discrete load.

Example 8-3 Calculating Means

1. The wind load on a tower is a random variable described by the normal probability law of Eq. (22). To calculate the average load, we use the definition

$$E(X) = \int_{-\infty}^{\infty} xn(x)\,dx = \frac{1}{\sqrt{2\pi}\sigma} \int_{-\infty}^{\infty} x \exp\left[\frac{-(x-\mu)^2}{2\sigma^2}\right]dx$$

$$= \frac{1}{\sqrt{2\pi}} \int_{-\infty}^{\infty} (\sigma z + \mu) \exp\left(\frac{-z^2}{2}\right)dz = \mu$$

where $z = (x - \mu)/\sigma$. Thus the parameter μ in the normal law can be interpreted as the mean value.

2. Let p be the constant probability that annual rainfall exceeds a fixed amount. If rainfall in successive years is assumed to be independent

(in the probability sense), then the binomial law gives the probability that the amount will be exceeded in k of the next n years, that is,

$$P\{X = k\} = \binom{n}{k} p^k q^{n-k} \qquad k = 0, 1, \ldots, n$$

and

$$E(X) = \sum_{k=0}^{n} k \binom{n}{k} p^k q^{n-k} = p \sum_{k=0}^{n} \frac{n!}{(k-1)!(n-k)!} p^{k-1} q^{n-k}$$

$$= np \sum_{k=1}^{n} \binom{n-1}{k-1} p^{k-1} q^{n-k} = np$$

Thus the mean of a binomial variable is np. This agrees with the intuition that if a fair coin ($p = 1/2$) is tossed n times, the average number of heads should be $n/2$. A similar calculation shows that the mean of the Poisson variable in Eq. (18) is ν.

In addition to the mean, one is frequently interested in the expected value of other functions of a random variable. If $g(x)$ is some function of X, then its average value is defined by

$$E(g(x)) = \int_x g(x) f(x)\, dx \qquad (25)$$

where $f(x)$ is the density for the continuous random variable X. The mean is the special case $g(x) = x$.

THE VARIANCE

An important descriptor of a random variable is the *variance*, which is defined as the average value of the square of the deviations from the mean:

$$\mathrm{Var}(X) = \sigma^2 = E\{(X - \mu)^2\} = \int_x (x - \mu)^2 f(x)\, dx \qquad (26)$$

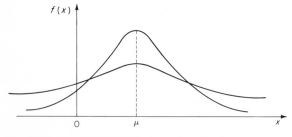

Fig. 8-11 Two densities with a common mean.

Variance measures the "breadth" of a density function.   The variance of its density function is analogous to the moment of inertia of a weight about its centroid.   Figure 8-11 shows two density functions with a common mean μ and unequal variance.   In the limiting case of zero variance, the random variable takes on a single value with probability 1, i.e., it is deterministic.   A similar analysis applies for the discrete case.

Example 8-4   Calculating Variances

1.   For a normal variable,

$$E\{(X - \mu)^2\} = \int_{-\infty}^{\infty} (x - \mu)^2 \, n(x) \, dx = \frac{\sigma^2}{\sqrt{2\pi}} \int_{-\infty}^{\infty} z^2 \exp\left(\frac{-z^2}{2}\right) dz = \sigma^2$$

An integration by parts and the result in the previous example are used to evaluate the last integral.   Again, the parameter in the normal law has an interpretation; in this instance, σ^2 is the variance.

2.   A useful general result is easily derived:

$$\sigma^2 = E\{(X - \mu)^2\} = E\{(X^2 - 2\mu X + \mu^2)\} = E(X^2) - 2\mu E(X) + \mu^2$$
$$= E(X^2) - \mu^2$$

That is, the variance can be obtained by subtracting μ^2 from the expected value of the square of the random variable, $E(X^2)$, i.e., $g(x) = x^2$ in Eq. (25).
For the binomial law in particular,

$$E(X^2) = \sum_{k=0}^{n} k^2 \frac{n!}{k!(n-k)!} p^k q^{n-k} = \sum_{k=0}^{n} \frac{[(k-1)+1]n!}{(k-1)!(n-k)!} p^k q^{n-k}$$

$$= n(n-1)p^2 \sum_{k=2}^{n} \binom{n-2}{k-2} p^{k-2} q^{n-k} + np \sum_{k=1}^{n} \binom{n-1}{k-1} p^{k-1} q^{n-k}$$

$$= n(n-1)p^2 + np = (np)^2 + npq$$

and $\mu = np$.
Clearly,

$$\sigma^2 = E\{(X - np)^2\} = npq$$

Similarly, the variance of the Poisson variable in Eq. (18) is equal to its mean, namely, ν.

EXPECTED VALUES OF MULTIVARIATE FUNCTIONS

One is frequently interested in the expected value of a function of several random variables, say $g(x_1, x_2, \ldots, x_n)$.   Consider the case $n = 2$.   The expected value of $g(x_1,x_2)$, with X_1 and X_2 described by the joint density function $f(x_1,x_2)$, is defined by

$$E\{g(x_1,x_2)\} = \int_{x_1} \int_{x_2} g(x_1,x_2) f(x_1,x_2)\, dx_1\, dx_2 \qquad (27)$$

If $g(x_1,x_2) = x_i$, then Eq. (27) defines its mean, μ_i, $i = 1, 2$. Similarly, if $g(x_1,x_2) = (x_i - \mu_i)^2$, then Eq. (27) gives the variance σ_i^2, $i = 1, 2$. If $g(x_1,x_2) = (x_1 - \mu_1)(x_2 - \mu_2)$, the expectation is called the *covariance* of X_1 and X_2, that is,

$$E\{(X_1 - \mu_1)(X_2 - \mu_2)\} = \sigma_{1,2}^2 = \mathrm{cov}(X_1, X_2) \qquad (28)$$

Note that the covariance is the analog of the product of inertia. The *correlation coefficient* $\rho_{1,2}$ is related to the covariance by

$$\rho_{1,2} = \frac{\sigma_{1,2}^2}{\sqrt{\sigma_1^2 \sigma_2^2}} \qquad (29)$$

It is useful to interpret the correlation coefficient and covariance as a measure of the dependence between two linearly related random variables. If the random variables are independent, then the correlation coefficient vanishes; however, the converse is not always true. At the other extreme, if the random variables are completely dependent, the covariance equals the variance and the correlation coefficient is unity.

We summarize several simple results which arise often:

1. $E(aX) = aE(X)$; a is a constant.
2. $E(X_1 \pm X_2) = E(X_1) \pm E(X_2)$. $\qquad\qquad (30)$
3. $\mathrm{Var}(a_1 X_1 + a_2 X_2) = a_1^2 \mathrm{var}(X_1) + a_2^2 \mathrm{var}(X_2) + 2a_1 a_2 \mathrm{cov}(X_1, X_2)$; a_1, a_2 are constants.
4. $\mathrm{Cov}(X_1, X_2) = 0$ if X_1 and X_2 are independent.
5. $-1 \leqslant \rho_{1,2} \leqslant 1$.

Proofs are left as problems. Each result follows from the definition of expected value, and many mistakes can be traced to carelessness. For example, the assertion that $E(1/X) = 1/E(X)$ is not generally true. The latter is the definite integral

$$\frac{1}{E(X)} = \frac{1}{\int_x x f(x)\, dx}$$

whereas the former is

$$E\left(\frac{1}{X}\right) = \int_x \frac{f(x)}{x}\, dx$$

and one cannot expect these to be equal. A useful way to obtain the expectations of more complicated analytic functions is to expand them in a Taylor series and take a termwise expectation.

8-7 APPROXIMATIONS OF PROBABILITIES

The last section noted that expected values are incomplete but convenient descriptions of a random variable. In this section we use expected values to approximate probabilities.

If probability functions were available for all random variables, we could calculate probabilities of events as they were needed. In practice, the random variable of interest is often a function of other random variables and its probability function is not available. Although we shall study techniques for deriving probability functions, the required calculations are not always trivial. An ability to form estimates of probabilities from available data is very useful.

CENTRAL LIMIT THEOREM

The most important approximation in the theory of probability is the *central limit theorem*. Consider a sequence of independent random variables $x_1, x_2, \ldots, x_n$ with arbitrary probability functions $f_1(x_1), f_2(x_2), \ldots, f_n(x_n)$ and respective means and variances $\mu_1, \mu_2, \ldots, \mu_n$ and $\sigma_1^2, \sigma_2^2, \ldots, \sigma_n^2$. The random variable Y,

$$Y = X_1 + X_2 + \cdots + X_n$$

is *approximately* described by the normal law with mean $\mu = \mu_1 + \mu_2 + \cdots + \mu_n$ and variance $\sigma^2 = \sigma_1^2 + \sigma_2^2 + \cdots + \sigma_n^2$. For a standarized variable, $\dfrac{Y - E(Y)}{\sigma_y}$, the approximation becomes exact as $n \to \infty$. This is the essence of the central limit theorem, one of the most remarkable in mathematics. A proof and more precise statement are beyond our scope. Note that the random variables can be discrete and/or continuous and that mention of their probability functions is not necessary. Actually, not all the variables need be independent since a sum of dependent variables can be replaced by a single variable which is independent of the remaining ones. It is the central limit theorem which accounts for the importance of the normal law in engineering problems. Such complex phenomena as wind loads, errors of measurement, Brownian motion, and the like, stem from the additive effect of many random variables, and the central limit theorem explains the experimental result that the normal law provides a "good fit." While the theorem requires that $n \to \infty$ for exact normality, a value of n as small as 10 is often adequate.

CHEBYSHEV INEQUALITY

Another widely used approximation is the *Chebyshev inequality*. It states that

$$P\{|X - \mu| \geqslant c\sigma\} \leqslant \frac{1}{c^2} \tag{31}$$

or, equivalently,

$$P\{|X - \mu| \leqslant c\sigma\} \geqslant 1 - \frac{1}{c^2} \tag{32}$$

where c is a constant. In words, inequation (32) states: the probability that the absolute difference between the random variable and its mean exceeds the product of a constant c and the *standard deviation* (i.e., square root of the variance) is not greater than c^{-2}. It is worthwhile to prove this result because inequations (31) and (32) are apt to be misremembered. Also, the proof suggests improvements in the approximation for particular cases.

By definition,

$$\sigma^2 = \int_{-\infty}^{\infty} (x - \mu)^2 f(x)\, dx$$

$$= \int_{-\infty}^{\mu - c\sigma} (x - \mu)^2 f(x)\, dx + \int_{\mu - c\sigma}^{\mu + c\sigma} (x - \mu)^2 f(x)\, dx$$

$$+ \int_{\mu + c\sigma}^{\infty} (x + \mu)^2 f(x)\, dx$$

Since the integrals are nonnegative, we have

$$\sigma^2 \geqslant \int_{-\infty}^{\mu - c\sigma} (x - \mu)^2 f(x)\, dx + \int_{\mu + c\sigma}^{\infty} (x - \mu)^2 f(x)\, dx \tag{33}$$

In addition, the integrals take on their smallest values at the finite limits. That is, each of the integrals in inequation (33) is greater than

$$c^2 \sigma^2 \int_{-\infty}^{\mu - c\sigma} f(x)\, dx = c^2 \sigma^2 P\{x \leqslant \mu - c\sigma\}$$

and

$$c^2 \sigma^2 \int_{\mu + c\sigma}^{\infty} f(x)\, dx = c^2 \sigma^2 P\{x \geqslant \mu + c\sigma\}$$

respectively. Substituting the right-hand side of these expressions into inequation (33) yields inequation (31).

The simplicity and generality of the Chebyshev inequality account for its popularity in spite of its conservative estimates. To use the Chebyshev inequality in estimating probabilities, one only needs to specify the constant c with given mean and variance. The constant c is related to the "safety" of a design. For example, let X be the random stress and μ and σ^2 its mean

Fig. 8-12 Region of safety.

and variance, respectively. A specified minimum probability of survival is equated to the right-hand side of inequation (32), which is written

$$P\{\mu - c\sigma \leqslant X \leqslant \mu + c\sigma\} \geqslant 1 - \frac{1}{c^2}$$

The design strength of a steel member might thus be $\mu \pm c\sigma$ for tension and compression, respectively. Increasing c increases the probability that a random stress is within a safety region (see Fig. 8-12). For $c = 10$, the probability of a stress level in a safety region $\mu - 10\sigma < X < \mu + 10\sigma$ is at least 0.99. Occasionally, the random stress can be controlled—as, for example, by prohibiting certain types of vehicles from bridges. For a structure having a steel member whose nominal tensile strength is $D^+ > \mu + c\sigma$ (and compressive strength $D^- < \mu - c\sigma$) and whose safety has been specified by c, any alteration of the stress-producing environment is permissible provided that D^+ and D^- are not exceeded.

To show the conservativeness of the Chebyshev inequality, suppose that X is a unit normal variable. Table 8-1 compares the Chebyshev approximation with the corresponding values from the unit normal table in Appendix 4.

Not only the probability function but also the mean and variance may be unknown. The mean can be estimated by averaging sample values (measurements). The variance can be estimated from the same data by averaging the square of the difference between the sample value and the mean overall data. The specific procedures for this, again, constitute a topic in statistics [13].

GAUSS' INEQUALITY

Although a probability function may be unknown, a particular situation may suggest some of its characteristics. For example, it is natural to assume that

Table 8-1 Chebyshev approximation to normal values

c	Chebyshev inequality	Normal table value
1	1	0.32
2	0.25	0.05
3	0.11	0.001

the random strength of a steel member is described by a unimodal probability function. For unimodal probability functions, the *Gauss inequality* is a better approximation than the Chebyshev inequality.

Letting m denote the abscissa of the mode,

$$P\{|X - \mu| \geq c\sigma\} \leq \frac{4(1 + \lambda^2)}{9(c - |\lambda|)^2} \tag{34}$$

for $c > |\lambda|$, where $\lambda = (\mu - m)/\sigma$. This is Gauss' inequality [13].

CAMP-MEIDELL INEQUALITY

If the probability function is symmetric and unimodal, the mean and mode coincide, $\lambda = 0$, and the Gauss inequality becomes

$$P\{|X - \mu| \geq c\sigma\} \leq \frac{4}{9c^2} \tag{35}$$

Inequation (35) is called the *Camp-Meidell inequality* [13]. Note that if the assumptions for inequation (35) can be justified, then the upper-bound estimate of the probability in inequation (31) is more than halved.

TWO-DIMENSIONAL CHEBYSHEV INEQUALITY

Generalizations to more than one random variable are of use in applications. The two-dimensional Chebyshev inequality is

$$P\{|X_1 - \mu_1| \geq c\sigma_1 \text{ or } |X_2 - \mu_2| \geq c\sigma_2\} \leq \frac{1}{c^2}\{1 + \sqrt{1 - \rho^2}\} \tag{36}$$

where ρ is the correlation coefficient defined by Eq. (29). For example, consider two structural members under random stresses X_1 and X_2 with respective means μ_1 and μ_2, variances σ_1 and σ_2, and correlation coefficient ρ. For a selected value of c, the probability that at least one member "fails" is not greater than the right-hand side of inequation (36).

While the Chebyshev inequality is quite old, its generalizations are recent. The literature on approximation of probabilities is not abundant, and as applications become more common, additional techniques are likely to be devised. The proof of inequation (36), as well as other generalizations of the Chebyshev inequality, can be found in Olkin and Pratt [8].

MONTE CARLO APPROXIMATION

Sometimes quick answers are needed for a problem and an adequate analytic model is not readily available. *Monte Carlo techniques* can provide answers to specific problems for which data can be collected. The Monte Carlo technique requires a distribution function(s) and a source of *random numbers*.

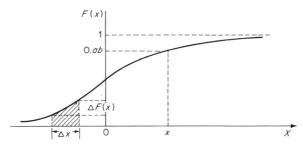

Fig. 8-13 Generating sample values.

The widely used table of 1 million random digits developed at the RAND Corporation describes how they can be generated [11]. The random-number table in Appendix 4 is taken from the "RAND Table."

Let X be the random variable of interest and $F(x)$ its distribution function. The abscissa corresponding to the ordinate $0.ab$, which is a two-digit random number selected from the table in Appendix 4, is the sample value, x, of X (see Fig. 8-13). The procedure is repeated to obtain additional sample values as needed. If more precision is desired, a *three-digit* random number is used, and so on.

Example 8-5 Monte Carlo design of a two-member truss

Consider a two-member truss (Fig. 8-14) bearing random loads L_1 and L_2 (in kips). Let L_1 and L_2 have rectangular probability functions $r_1(l_1) = 1$, $0 \leqslant L_1 \leqslant 1$, and $r_2(l_2) = \frac{1}{2}$, $0 \leqslant L_2 \leqslant 2$, respectively. From the random-number table in Appendix 4, we select a two-digit random number and divide by 100. Since the distribution function for L_1 is a line with unit slope passing through the origin, the random decimal equals the sample value of L_1. Another random decimal is selected for L_2. This decimal is multiplied by 2 since the domain of L_2 is $\{0,2\}$.

Six possible designs appear in Table 8-2. Sample values of loads L_1 and L_2 can be used to compute the forces in the members using simple

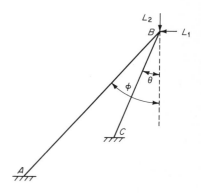

Fig. 8-14 Two-member truss with random loads.

Table 8-2   Monte Carlo failure frequencies

Design No.	Member capacity, kips AB	BC	Truss angles θ	ϕ	Failure frequency (100 trials)
1	2	2	30°	45°	0.35
2	2	2	45°	75°	0.00
3	2	1	30°	45°	0.51
4	2	1	45°	75°	0.27
5	3	3	30°	45°	0.00
6	3	3	45°	75°	0.00

statics.   If either load exceeds the design value, then the member (and the truss) is assumed to fail.   One hundred trials for each design yielded the listed failure frequencies.

Incidentally, an analytic expression for the failure probability of the two-member truss is surprisingly cumbersome.   Tractable expressions for the probability of failure of larger trusses are not available.

Monte Carlo is not restricted to situations with randomness.   An imaginative twist will often enable one to replace a deterministic problem by a random one with the same solution.   This idea is used for Monte Carlo solutions to difference and partial differential equations, inversion of matrices, evaluation of integrals, and so on (also see Sec. 11-2).

Example 8-6   Monte Carlo estimation of an area   Planimeters are instruments to measure irregular areas.   However, a simple Monte Carlo may be more convenient, particularly where speed is desired and a rough estimate is adequate.   For example, suppose that we wish to estimate the shaded area with three irregular "holes" on the map of Fig. 8-15.   We proceed by enclosing the area in a square and selecting two orthogonal sides for a cartesian coordinate system.   Assume that the square has unit sides. Select a pair of random decimals to represent the sample values of X and Y, and note whether the point (x,y) is in the desired area.   A value of unity is assigned when the random point falls in the shaded area, and zero otherwise. The cumulative score, divided by the total number of random points, is an estimate of the fractional area of the square that is shaded.   The area of the square can be obtained from the map scale.

The number of replications required in a Monte Carlo depends upon the desired precision.   One procedure is to plot the *moving average* and to sample until it settles within acceptable bounds.   There may be no guarantee, unfortunately, that it will continue to remain within bounds if the sampling

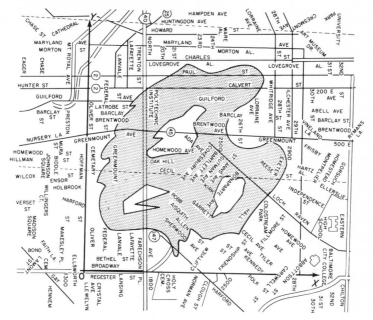

Fig. 8-15 Monte Carlo estimation of an area.

continues. The unattractive feature of the Monte Carlo technique is its inefficiency. The number of replications required to obtain acceptable results is usually large. In this case, Monte Carlo is practical only for the more complex problems which are otherwise unmanageable. While this discussion of Monte Carlo is adequate for casual work, more detailed considerations appear in [7].

SUMMARY

This chapter developed and reviewed the elements of probability theory with a view to applications.

Notions were developed of random variables as descriptions of chance events and of probabilities as measures of their likelihood of occurrence. An algebra of events was described in Sec. 8-2 in order to permit the description of more complicated events in terms of simpler ones. Also, the elements of combinatorial analysis were developed to calculate probabilities of equally likely events.

Several basic probability functions were developed in Secs. 8-4 and 8-5 by enumeration and by formal arguments. In subsequent chapters they will arise as solutions of random models.

The concept of expected value is important to understanding probability and design applications.   The rudiments appeared in Sec. 8-6, while Sec. 8-7 indicated their use in approximating probabilities and in Monte Carlo approximations.

PROBLEMS[4]

8-1.   Use a Venn diagram to verify the set relation

$$Y = YX \cup YX'$$

where X' is the complement of X.

8-2.   Use a Venn diagram to conclude the set relation

$$Y = YX_1 \, YX_2 \cdots YX_n$$

for arbitrary n, assuming that the $X_1, \ldots, X_n$ are mutually exclusive and collectively exhaustive.

8-3.* Verify the following set relations:

(a) $(A \cup B)' = A' B'$ (b) $(A \cup B) - B = A - AB = AB'$
(c) $AA = A \cup A = A$ (d) $(A - AB) \cup B = A \cup B$
(e) $(A \cup B) - AB = AB' \cup A' B$ (f) $A' \cup B' = (AB)'$
(g) $(A \cup B)C = AC \cup BC$ ◆

8-4.* State which of the following relations are correct:

(a) $(A \cup B) - C = A \cup (B - C)$
(b) $ABC = AB(C \cup B)$
(c) $A \cup B \cup C = A \cup (B - AB) \cup (C - AC)$
(d) $A \cup B = (A - AB) \cup B$
(e) $AB \cup BC \cup CA = ABC$
(f) $(AB \cup BC \cup CA) \subset (A \cup B \cup C)$
(g) $(A \cup B) - A = B$
(h) $AB' C \subset A \cup B$
(i) $(A \cup B \cup C)' = A' B' C'$
(j) $(A \cup B)' C = A' C \cup B' C$
(k) $(A \cup B)' C = A' B' C$
(l) $(A \cup B)' C = C - C(A \cup B)$

The symbol "$\subset$" is read "is contained in."

8-5.* Let A, B, C be arbitrary events.   Find expressions for the following:

(a) Only A occurs.   (b) Both A and B, but not C, occur.
(c) All three events occur.   (d) At least one occurs.
(e) At least two occur.   (f) One and no more occurs.
(g) Two and no more occur. (h) None occurs.
(i) Not more than two occur. ◆

8-6.   Derive the expansions of $P(A \cup B \cup C)$, $P(A \cup B \cup C \cup D)$, etc.   What mnemonic is suggested?

8-7.* The union $A \cup B$ of two events can be expressed as the union of the two mutually exclusive events, thus $A \cup B = A \cup (B - AB)$.   Express, in a similar way, the union of three events A, B, C.

8-8.   Prove the assertions:

(a) $\binom{n}{0} = \binom{n}{n} = 1$ (b) $\binom{n}{0} + \binom{n}{1} + \cdots + \binom{n}{n} = 2^n$

[4] Problems marked with an asterisk have been reprinted from [3].

(c) $\dbinom{n}{k} = \dbinom{n}{n-k}$ (d) $(1 + u)^n = 1 + \dbinom{n}{1} u + \dbinom{n}{2} u^2 + \cdots + \dbinom{n}{n} u^n$

8-9. Using the identity $(1 + u)^n (1 + u)^m \equiv (1 + u)^{n+m}$ and the binomial theorem, conclude that

$$\dbinom{n}{0}\dbinom{m}{i} + \dbinom{n}{1}\dbinom{m}{i-1} + \cdots + \dbinom{n}{i}\dbinom{m}{0} = \dbinom{n+m}{i}$$

for $i = 0, 1, \ldots, n + m$, where n and m are nonnegative integers.◆

8-10. Stirling's approximation formula is written

$$n! \simeq \sqrt{2\pi}\, n^{n+1/2}\, e^{-n}$$

It is a remarkably good approximation. For $n = 100$, the error is less than 0.1%. For $n = 10$, the error is less than 1%. What are the errors for $n = 1, 2,$ and 3?

8-11. Show that for any $m \geqslant 0$,

$$(x + y + z)^m = \sum \frac{m!}{i!\,j!\,k!}\, x^i\, y^j\, z^k$$

where $i, j,$ and k are nonnegative integers such that $i + j + k = m$ and the summation extends over all possible values of $i, j,$ and k.

8-12. Recall that the combination $\dbinom{n}{k}$ is defined by

$$\dbinom{n}{k} = \frac{(n)_k}{k!} = \frac{n(n-1)\,\cdots\,(n-k+1)}{k!}$$

for integer values of k and all nonnegative values of n and provided that $n \geqslant k$ and $k > 0$. Show that

$$\dbinom{-1}{k} = (-1)^k \qquad \dbinom{-2}{k} = (-1)^k (k + 1)$$

and, in general, for integer values of k,

$$\dbinom{-n}{k} = (-1)^k \dbinom{n+k-1}{k}$$

8-13. Use an $m \times n$ matrix to prove that with m elements of one type and n elements of the second type, there are exactly mn pairs consisting of an element of each type. Extend the proof to k types of elements.

8-14. Given that $P(X \geqslant a) = (1 + a/k)^{-k}$ for $k > 0$ and $0 \leqslant a < \infty$:
(a) Find $F(x)$, the cumulative distribution.
(b) Find $f(x)$, the density function.
(c) If three observations are taken at random and $k = 2$, what is the probability that all three will exceed 4?

8-15. Find the marginal law for Y and the conditional law for X, given Y, if X and Y are jointly governed by

$$f(x,y) = 4y(x - y)\,e^{-(x+y)} \qquad 0 \leqslant x < \infty; 0 \leqslant y \leqslant x$$

8-16. Prove that each of the probability laws in Sec. 8-4 properly sums to unity. The result in Prob. 8-9 is useful for the hypergeometric law.

8-17. Distinguish the sample spaces for the binomial and hypergeometric laws.

8-18. The random variable K is governed by the binomial law. Find the probability that K is even. If K is governed by the Poisson law, what is the probability that K is even?

8-19. In rolling six true dice, find the probability of obtaining (a) at least one ace, (b) exactly one ace, (c) exactly two aces. Compare with the Poisson approximations.

8-20. By writing $P\{\tau > t + t_0 | \tau > t_0\} = P\{\tau > t + t_0\}/P\{\tau > t_0\}$ and substituting, deduce Eq. (21) for the exponential law. [The uniqueness property follows from a theorem which asserts that if a function $f(t)$ satisfies the equation $f(t + s) = f(t)f(s)$, then either $f(t) = 0$ or $f(t) = e^{-\lambda t}$, where λ is a constant. A proof appears in Chap. XVII of [3].]

8-21. Prove the results in Eq. (30).

8-22. Show that the limits $\pm\sigma$, $\pm 2\sigma$, and $\pm 3\sigma$ about the mean include 68, 95, and 99% of the area under a normal curve.◆

8-23. For the normal density, prove that (a) it is symmetric about the mean, (b) the mean locates the mode and the median, and (c) the inflection points have the abscissa $\mu \pm \sigma/\sqrt{2}$.

    Note: The median is the value x_m which bisects the unit area under the probability function.

8-24. Obtain a Monte Carlo estimate of $\int_0^1 e^{-x} dx$.◆

8-25. Exactly K jobs are being offered for bid among K contractors. Suppose that bidding is random, in that any job is equally likely to be won by any contractor. What is the probability that no contractor will win more than one contract? The probability that a certain contractor will win h contracts?

8-26. Two urns, u_1 and u_2, contain white, black, and red balls in the following respective numbers: w_1, b_1, r_1 and w_2, b_2, r_2. An urn is selected at random, and a red ball and a white ball are drawn. What is the probability that the drawing took place in u_1?◆

8-27. Consider a population of N urns, each containing N red and N white balls; the urn numbered k contains k red and $N - k$ white balls $(k = 0, 1, \ldots, N)$. An urn is chosen at random, and n drawings are made from it, the ball being replaced each time. Suppose that all n balls turn out to be red (event A). Find the conditional probability that the next drawing will also yield a red ball (event B).

8-28. In a container where concrete cylinders of identical size are placed for curing purposes, C_1 cylinders are marked A (made of type A aggregates) and C_2 cylinders are marked B (made of type B aggregates). Unidentified cylinders are removed randomly for compression testing until K remain. One more cylinder is removed. Prove that the probability that it is marked A is $C_1/(C_1 + C_2)$ and that it is marked B is $C_2/(C_1 + C_2)$.

8-29. A designer can use any of 20 possible materials for the elements A and C in a proposed linkage. The connecting element B can be chosen from among five possibilities. How many designs are possible if:

    (a) A and C must be of the same material?

    (b) A and C may be of different materials?

8-30. Certain missile components are shipped in lots of 25. Three components are selected from each lot, and the lot is accepted if none of them is defective. What is the probability that a lot will be accepted if it contains five defectives?

8-31. A load is supported by two nominally identical cables, each designed to support the load. Let p denote the probability that a cable survives whether or not the other cable has failed. Find the probability that the load will be supported.

8-32. A box contains 90 good and 10 defective screws. If 10 screws are used at random, what is the probability that none is defective?

8-33. On the average, a certain type of steel member runs about 5% defective. From an inventory of 100 such members, 10 are selected at random. What is the probability that no more than 1 of the 10 will be defective?

8-34. In a particular type of concrete pouring, experience indicates that about 20% are defective. What is the probability (and under what assumption) that none of four specimens is defective? That at most two specimens are defective?

8-35. If the probability of hitting a target is 1/3 and eight shots are fired independently, what is the probability of the target's being hit at least twice? Find the conditional probability of the target's being hit at least twice, assuming that at least one hit is scored.

8-36. The strength of nominally identical steel tension specimens has been observed to be a random variable described by a (truncated) normal law. Let the mean and standard deviation be 151 lb and 15 lb, respectively. In a group of 500 (independent) specimens, how many can be expected to have strengths of between 120 and 155 lb? Of more than 185 lb?

8-37. A fuel reservoir is replenished at intervals of time T. Between replenishment intervals, a random volume X of fuel is required according to the law $f(x) = 5(1 - x)^4$, $0 < x < 1$. What should be the capacity of the reservoir so that the probability that its supply will be exhausted in a given period is 0.01?

8-38. The bending moment at a point y on a simply supported beam of unit length, due to a random load at position x and uniformly distributed weight W, is

$$M(y) = \frac{W}{2} y(1 - y) + yL(1 - x) - L(y - x)\, \mathcal{U}(y - x)$$

where $\mathcal{U}(y - x) = \begin{cases} 1 \text{ if } y \geqslant x \\ 0 \text{ if } y < x \end{cases}$. If the random variable P is described by an exponential law

with parameter λ, find the expected bending moment. Where is the expected moment a maximum?

8-39. Suppose that the number of airplanes arriving at a certain airport in any 20-min period obeys a Poisson probability law with mean 100. Use Chebyshev's inequality to determine a lower bound for the probability that the number of airplanes arriving in a given 20-min period will be between 80 and 120.

8-40. An inebriate begins to walk from a streetlamp. Imagine that each step is of unit length and is taken in one of the directions north, south, east, and west with equal probability. Considering the lamppost as origin, use a Monte Carlo to determine the average distance from the post after 10 steps.

8-41. Describe how the cut-and-fill quantities for a section of roadway could be obtained from the following topographic map, using a Monte Carlo approximation. Dotted lines indicate finished grade, and heavy lines show the boundaries of earthwork. (Additional considerations appear in M. Gates and A. Scarpa, Earthwork Quantities by Random Sampling, *J. Construct. Div. ASCE*, July, 1969.)

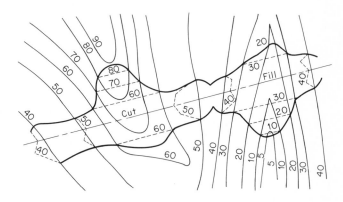

REFERENCES

1. Benjamin, J. R., and C. A. Cornell: "Probability, Statistics, and Decision for Civil Engineers," McGraw-Hill Book Company, New York, 1970.
2. Dubes, R. C.: "The Theory of Applied Probability," Prentice-Hall, Inc., Englewood Cliffs, N.J., 1968.
3. Feller, W. T.: "An Introduction to Probability Theory and Its Applications," 3d ed., vol. I, John Wiley & Sons, Inc., New York, 1968.
4. Fry, J.: "Probability and Its Engineering Uses," 2d ed., D. Van Nostrand Company, Inc., Princeton, N.J., 1965.
5. Hadley, G.: "Introduction to Probability and Statistical Decision Theory," Holden-Day, Inc., Publishers, San Francisco, 1967.
6. Hahn, G. J., and S. S. Shapiro: "Statistical Models in Engineering," John Wiley & Sons, Inc., New York, 1967.
7. Hammersley, J. M., and D. C. Handscomb: "Monte Carlo Methods," Methuen & Co., Ltd., London, 1964.
8. Olkin, I., and J. W. Pratt: A Multivariate Chebyshev Inequality, *Ann. Math. Stat.*, vol. 29, pp. 201–211, 1958.
9. Papoulis, A.: "Probability, Random Variables, and Stochastic Processes," McGraw-Hill Book Company, New York, 1965.
10. Parzen, E.: "Modern Probability Theory and Its Applications, John Wiley & Sons, Inc., New York, 1960.
11. RAND Corporation: "A Million Random Digits with 100,000 Normal Deviates," Glencoe Press, The Macmillan Company, New York, 1955.
12. Tribus, M.: "Rational Descriptions, Decisions, and Designs," Pergamon Press, New York, 1969.
13. Wadsworth, G. P., and J. G. Bryan: "Introduction to Probability and Random Variables," McGraw-Hill Book Company, New York, 1960.

9
Probability Functions from Random Models

A random model is a representation of reality which takes explicit account of randomness.   The primary hope in building a random model is to obtain the probability function for the process under study so that the probabilities of various outcomes and expectations of functions which may be of interest can be determined.   Unfortunately, it is not always easy to determine the probability function.

In this chapter we study some basic random models which arise frequently in applications and which serve as stepping stones to more difficult model building.   The chapter is divided into two parts to reflect differences in techniques.   Part I deals with fundamental probability functions derived from *recursive models.*   Part II derives probability functions for *symbolic models.*

PART I
Recursive Models

The binomial, Poisson, and exponential probability functions, introduced in Sec. 8-5 by formal arguments, are derived here as solutions to recursive random models. Each is of fundamental importance. The recursive approach seeks an *event relation*, using the ideas in Sec. 8-2. From this a probability statement is formed, usually in the form of a difference and/or differential equation. The solution is the desired probability function.

9-1 REPEATED EXPERIMENTS IN DISCRETE TIME: BINOMIAL LAW

Consider a sequence of independent experiments (trials) which can result in only one of two possible outcomes—referred to as "success" and "failure," "yes" and "no," "zero" and "one," etc. Suppose that the probabilities of the two outcomes are constant from experiment to experiment. For example, this is the model for the probability that $k(=0,1,\ldots,n)$ soil samples exceed a given unconfined compressive strength or that k out of n peak annual stream-flows exceed a given discharge rate.

We seek the probability function $P(k;n)$ for the event A defined by

$$\{A\} = \{\text{exactly } k \text{ of } n \text{ experiments result in "success"}\}$$

The essential step is to write a useful event relation. We identify the *joint* events:

$$\{A_1\} = \{\text{exactly } k \text{ of } n - 1 \text{ trials result in "success"}$$
$$\text{and the } n\text{th trial is a "failure"}\}$$
$$\{A_2\} = \{\text{exactly } k - 1 \text{ of } n - 1 \text{ trials result in "success"}$$
$$\text{and the } n\text{th trial is a "success"}\}$$

Clearly, events $\{A_1\}$ and $\{A_2\}$ are related to event $\{A\}$ by their union, that is,

$$\{A\} = \{A_1\} \cup \{A_2\}$$

Also,

$$P\{A\} = P\{A_1 \cup A_2\} = P\{A_1\} + P\{A_2\} \tag{1}$$

since $\{A_1\}$ and $\{A_2\}$ are mutually exclusive events. The joint events can be written

$$\{A_1\} = \{k \text{ of } n - 1 \text{ trials are "successful" and } n\text{th trial is a "failure"}\}$$
$$\{A_2\} = \{k - 1 \text{ of } n - 1 \text{ trials are "successful" and } n\text{th trial is a "success"}\}$$

Since the experiments are mutually independent, the component probabilities are multiplied. Therefore,

$$b(k;n) = (1 - p)\,b(k;n - 1) + pb(k - 1;n - 1) \qquad k = 0, 1, \ldots, n \qquad (2)$$

is simply another way of writing Eq. (1) under the assumptions.

Equation (2) is a partial difference equation of first order in the variables k and n whose solution is the desired probability function. The boundary conditions for Eq. (2) are easily established by requiring that $b(0;1) = 1 - p = q$ and $b(1;1) = p$. We also define

$$b(0;0) = 1 \qquad \text{and} \qquad b(-1;0) = b(1;0) = 0 \qquad (3)$$

The solution, using techniques in Appendix 5, is

$$b(k;n) = \binom{n}{k} p^k q^{n-k} \qquad k = 0, 1, \ldots, n$$

the binomial law. Tables for the binomial law are available. See Appendix 4 and [4].

One concludes that the binomial law arises from a recursive model with the following features:

1. A sequence of independent experiments
2. Constant probabilities from trial to trial
3. Only two possible outcomes for each experiment

Experiments of this kind are called *Bernoulli trials*. Sometimes it is useful to think of the trials as occurring at fixed time intervals. The reader might find it helpful to review the discussion of the binomial law in Sec. 8-5.

The binomial law is used to test for a suspected dependence between experiments. For example, suppose that the proportion of trucks to total traffic on a road is p. To test a hypothesis that the trucks tend to cluster, the number of trucks k among a sample of n consecutive vehicles is recorded. If the trucks travel independently of each other, measurements of k should agree with predictions of the binomial law. A lack of agreement, as defined by statistical procedures, suggests that the trucks tend to cluster.

The binomial law can also be used in situations where the usefulness of a certain procedure is questioned. For example, a claim is made that a certain coating will cause retarding of rusting of steel beams. To avoid the influence of varying environments, one-half of each beam is given the second treatment. First we assume that the new treatment is worthless, that is, $p = q = \frac{1}{2}$, where p is the probability that the treated half is better. In a group of n beams, k are noted in which the treated portion has better retarded rust formation. These numbers are compared with the predictions of the binomial law.   A lack of agreement suggests that the new treatment *is* better (we are assuming that it could not be worse).

The binomial law is also suited to dam design studies when it can be assumed that the maximum annual floods are sequentially independent and that the probability of a flood greater than the spillway capacity is constant over the dam life.

9-2   REPEATED EXPERIMENTS IN CONTINUOUS TIME: POISSON LAW

Consider the model of the preceding section when the experiment evolves continuously rather than at fixed (time) intervals.   Formally, the discrete parameter n is replaced by the continuous parameter t to form the probability function $p(k;t)$, $k = 0, 1, \ldots$ and $t \geqslant 0$.   For example, if a position on a highway is monitored continuously, $p(k;t)$ is the probability that k vehicles pass in time t.   The interval $\{0, t\}$ can be regarded as made up of a large number of subintervals of length Δt, each regarded as an independent experiment.   The probability that an event arises in any interval of duration Δt is assumed to be proportional to Δt, say $\lambda \Delta t$, $\lambda > 0$.   This probability is the analog of the discrete trial probability p of the last section.

Again, the essential task is to formulate an event relation.   In analogy to Eq. (2), we conclude that

$$p(k;t) = p(k-1;t-\Delta t)\lambda \Delta t + p(k;t-\Delta t)(1 - \lambda \Delta t) \qquad (4)$$

Rearranging, dividing by Δt, and passing to the limit $\Delta t \to 0$ yields the difference-differential equation

$$\frac{dp(k;t)}{dt} = \lim_{\Delta t \to 0} \frac{p(k;t) - p(k;t-\Delta t)}{\Delta t} = -\lambda p(k;t) + \lambda p(k-1;t) \qquad (5)$$

Readers familiar with such equations will note its elementary character (see Appendix 5).   It is adequate here to state the easily verified solution

$$p(k;t) = \frac{(\lambda t)^k}{k!} e^{-\lambda t}$$

which is the *Poisson law* with mean $v = \lambda t$.   Note that it satisfies the boundary condition $p(k;t) = 0$ for all $k < 0$ and $p(0;0) = 1$.

The Poisson law is one of the fundamental probability functions.   It arises repeatedly in theory and applications—as, for example, in [5], [6], and [12].   A plot of cumulative Poisson probabilities appears in Appendix 4. It is important to recognize the three assumptions underlying the model:

1.   The probability of a random arrival in any subinterval t is independent (in the probability sense) of previous arrivals.   This is called *independent increments*.

2. The probability of an arrival in an interval Δt is independent of absolute time. This is called *stationarity*.
3. The probability of an arrival in an interval Δt is $\lambda \, \Delta t$, where λ is a positive constant. The probability of no arrival is $1 - \lambda \, \Delta t$, that is, no more than one arrival is allowed in any single interval Δt. This is called a *unit jump*.

These assumptions define the *Poisson process.*

In a traffic context, the assumption of independent increments means that whether or not a vehicle passes in an interval Δt is not influenced by the number of vehicles previously recorded. If the recording site happens to be located just after a traffic signal, the assumption is not useful since a group of vehicles awaiting a signal change means that the first arrival is likely to be followed by others very shortly. The Poisson law arises repeatedly in traffic studies, but it should not be used indiscriminately. The stationarity assumption requires that the process which gives rise to the passing vehicles be time-independent, that is, that λ does not depend upon the arrival time of the vehicle. The assumption is not acceptable for certain traffic conditions [5]. For example, as the population of an area changes, traffic patterns also change, so that the random process which gives rise to the passing vehicles is not time-independent, that is, $v = \int_0^t \lambda(t') \, dt'$. The unit-jump assumption (3) implies that not more than one vehicle can arrive in an interval Δt. The assumption may not be useful for studies of, say, a four-lane highway. Models with less restrictive assumptions are considered in Chap. 12. Also, one can reread the discussion in Sec. 8-5.

The Poisson law is a one-parameter law, that is, $v = \lambda t$ equals both the mean and the variance. Although this limits the flexibility in fitting a Poisson probability function to data, we have noted the surprising frequency with which it arises. This is largely due to its versatile random model. Another reason is that the Poisson law is a good approximation to the normal law, which describes a wide range of phenomena by virtue of the central limit theorem. The assumptions we cite are necessary, but not sufficient, conditions. If the random model reasonably describes the phenomena under study, then the Poisson law follows, but the converse may not be true. That is, the fact that the functional form closely approximates data is not adequate grounds for concluding that the process is Poisson. The parameter λ can be interpreted as the *intensity* of the process, and v as the *mean arrival rate* per unit time. The continuous parameter t can have units other than time. For example, k may be the number of breaks encountered in spinning a roll of thread whose total length is t. In Example 9-3 we show that the sum of any number of Poisson variables is another Poisson variable with its parameter equal to the sum of the individual parameters.

9-3 THE WAITING TIME BETWEEN CONSECUTIVE ARRIVALS: EXPONENTIAL LAW

When the number of arrivals in a time t is described by a Poisson law with parameter λt, the *random time between consecutive arrivals is described by the exponential law with parameter* λ.   To prove this, consider the events

$$\{A\} = \{\text{no arrival occurs in the first } t \text{ sec since the last arrival}\}$$
$$\{B\} = \{\text{an arrival occurs in the interval } (t, t + \varDelta t)\} \tag{6}$$

If $e(t)$ denotes the desired probability function for the time of the first arrival, then the probability of the joint event $\{AB\}$ is written as $e(t)\, \varDelta t$.   Now, the events $\{A\}$ and $\{B\}$ of a Poisson process are independent, by assumption 1 of the last section.   Also, the probability of event $\{B\}$ is $\lambda\, \varDelta t$ according to assumptions 2 and 3.   The probability of event $\{A\}$ is obtained by setting $k = 0$ in the solution to Eq. (5).   Thus we have

$$e(t)\,\varDelta t = \lambda\, \varDelta t\, e^{-\lambda t} \qquad t > 0$$

which is the exponential law.   This is the probability law cited in Sec. 8-5 for its memoryless property.

The discrete analog to the exponential law is the *geometric law*.   Consider the binomial model of Sec. 9-1 and suppose that $\{A\}$ in event relations (6) is interpreted such that t is a nonnegative integer.   This means that if the experiments take place at fixed intervals, then t is the number of experiments which have resulted in no arrival since the last one.   Similarly, $\{B\}$ is interpreted to mean the probability, $1 - q$, that the $(t + 1)$st experiment resulted in an arrival.   With this interpretation, the probability $ge(t;q)$ of the joint event $\{AB\}$ is the geometric law

$$ge(t;q) = (1 - q)q^t \qquad t = 0, 1, 2, \ldots \tag{7}$$

It is often interpreted as the probability for the number of failures before the first success.

9-4 BROWNIAN MOTION: NORMAL LAW

The chaotic movement of microscopic particles in a colloidal suspension, resulting from the collisions of these particles with themselves and with the molecules of the fluid, is called *Brownian motion*.   Imagine that at time zero we tag a particle at the origin of a coordinate system.   A short time later its displacement from the origin is described by the vector components X_1, Y_1, Z_1.   At a subsequent time, its displacement from its previous position is described by a vector with components X_2, Y_2, Z_2, and so on.   At time t, the particle's displacement vector has the components

$$X = X_1 + X_2 + \cdots + X_n$$
$$Y = Y_1 + Y_2 + \cdots + Y_n$$
$$Z = Z_1 + Z_2 + \cdots + Z_n$$

The displacements X_i, Y_i, Z_i, $i = 1, \ldots, n$, are random variables. While we may lack knowledge of the probability functions, the central limit theorem assures us that the displacement components X, Y, Z will be closely described by the normal law. This is one of the outstanding applications of probability and is called the *Wiener process*. For Brownian motion, the mean displacement is zero and the mean square displacement, i.e., the variance, was shown by Einstein (1905) to be

$$\sigma^2 = \frac{4RT}{Na} t$$

where R = the universal gas constant
$\quad T$ = absolute temperature
$\quad N$ = the Avogadro number
$\quad a$ = a constant of the medium

Using this relation, Perrin (1916) performed his Nobel Prize–winning Brownian-motion experiments to determine the Avogadro number.

9-5 AN EXTREME-VALUE LAW

For design purposes, the random variable of interest is often the maximum of a sequence of random variables. For example, floor loads in a structure are random variables and the design strength may be based upon an assessment of their maximums. *Extreme-value probability functions*, as they are called, have appeared in the civil engineering literature for many years. There are several types of extreme-value laws.

Let $X_1, X_2, \ldots, X_n$ be a sequence of nonnegative continuous and independent variables governed by a common probability law, $f(x)$, and let X be their maximum, that is,

$$X = \max(X_1, X_2, \ldots, X_n) \tag{8}$$

For example, X_i is the random maximum streamflow in the ith year of a design life of n years, $i = 1, \ldots, n$. Then X is the maximum streamflow for the design life. To construct an event relation for this random model, let A_i be the event $x \leqslant X_i \leqslant x + \Delta x$. To express the event, $x \leqslant X \leqslant x + \Delta x$, use the event relation

$$\{x \leqslant X \leqslant x + \Delta x\} = \{A_1 A_2^* \cdots A_n^* \cup A_1^* A_2 A_3^* \cdots A_n^* \cup \cdots$$
$$\cup A_1^* A_2^* \cdots A_{n-1}^* A_n\} \tag{9}$$

where the asterisk denotes the event $X_i < x$, $i = 1, \ldots, n$.

Let $ev(x)$ be the probability function for X. The probability statement for the event relation (9) is

$$ev(x)\,\Delta x \simeq n[F(x)]^{n-1}f(x)\,\Delta x \tag{10}$$

where $F(x)$ is the common cumulative distribution of the X_i. The terms corresponding to events of the type "at least two of the X_i are in the interval $\{x, x + \Delta x\}$" are proportional to higher powers of Δx. They have been neglected, so an approximation sign is used in Eq. (10). It follows from Eq. (10) that

$$F_X(x) = [F(x)]^n \tag{11}$$

where $F_X(x)$ is the cumulative distribution for X. The functional relation

$$F(x) \simeq 1 - e^{-g(x)} \tag{12}$$

where $g(x)$ is an arbitrary nondecreasing function, so that $g(x) \to \infty$ as $x \to \infty$, is a reasonable choice. For example, if the X_i are described by the exponential law, then for $g(x) = \lambda x$, Eq. (12) is exact. The *characteristic value u* is defined by

$$F(u) = 1 - \frac{1}{n}$$

In words, u is the value of X_i for which the probability that X_i will exceed u is the reciprocal of the number of random variables in the sequence. It follows from Eq. (11) that

$$F_X(x) \simeq (1 - e^{-g(x)})^n = \left(1 - \frac{1}{n}e^{g(u)-g(x)}\right)^n$$

since $e^{g(u)} = n$. Using the property of the exponential function noted in Sec. 9-3, the right-hand side of the last expression can be approximated by

$$F_X(x) \simeq \exp\left(-e^{g(u)-g(x)}\right)$$

Suppose that the X_i are described by the exponential law as suggested. Then

$$F_X(x) = \exp\left(-e^{-\lambda(x-u)}\right)$$

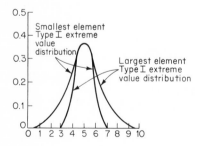

Fig. 9-1 Type I extreme-value law. (*Reprinted from G. J. Hahn and S. S. Shapiro, "Statistical Models in Engineering," John Wiley & Sons, Inc., New York, 1967.*)

Table 9-1 Standard type I extreme-value law[1]

Z	$ev(z)$	$F_Z(z)$
−2.0	0.0046	0.0006
−1.0	0.1794	0.0660
−0.5	0.3170	0.1923
0	0.3679	0.3679
+0.5	0.3307	0.5452
1.0	0.2546	0.6922
1.5	0.1785	0.8000
2.0	0.1182	0.8374
2.5	0.0756	0.9212
3.0	0.0474	0.9514
4.0		0.9818

[1] Reprinted from J. R. Benjamin and C. A. Cornell, "Probability, Statistics, and Decision for Civil Engineers, McGraw-Hill Book Company, New York, 1970.

whence

$$ev(x) = \lambda \exp\left[-\lambda(x - u) - e^{-\lambda(x-u)}\right] \qquad x > 0 \tag{13}$$

which is called the *type I extreme-value law* (see Fig. 9-1). Interestingly, the *mode*, i.e., the maximum value of $ev(x)$, is at $x = u$. The reader is asked to show this in Prob. 9-12.

A useful feature of this extreme-value law is that it can be tabulated in a standard form. Using the transformation

$$Z = \lambda(X - u) \tag{14}$$

we have a new variable, Z, whose associated values of u and λ are zero and unity, respectively. Table 9-1 indicates several values.

When one is interested in the smallest of a sequence of random variables, a similar argument is used to derive the desired probability function. The most comprehensive work on extreme-value laws is by Gumbel [8]. While the extreme-value model is useful, our knowledge of it is not complete. For example, independence of the random variables $X_i, i = 1, \ldots, n$, may not always be justified and answers to questions concerning the rapidity of convergence are not as well understood as for the central limit theorem. Still, it is an attractive model for many hydrologic [7] and wind [13] phenomena. Also, the extreme-value laws are useful in models of systems (or materials) where the strongest (or weakest) link describes the capacity. For example, the extreme-value law might be used to describe the (random) strength of brittle materials.   Consider an axially loaded cylindrical bar to be made up of a large number of short cylinders having the cross-sectional area of the bar. The bar is assumed to fail when the capacity of the weakest cylinder is exceeded [10].

PART II
Symbolic Models

Consider a function of a random variable X, say $Y = g(X)$.   The problem is to derive the probability function for Y from a knowledge of the probability function for X.   The probability function for Y is called a *derived distribution*, and the function $g(X)$ is the symbolic model.

9-6 LINEAR MODELS

The simplest linear model is $Y = aX + b$, where X is a continuous random variable with probability function $f(x)$ and a and b are constants.   The probability function for Y is

$$q(y) = \frac{1}{|a|} f\left(\frac{y-b}{a}\right) \tag{15}$$

While we prefer to avoid formal derivations, it is useful to provide the rationale for Eq. (15).   The probability that Y does not exceed some arbitrary value t is

$$P\{Y \leqslant t\} = P\{aX + b \leqslant t\} = P\left\{X \leqslant \frac{t-b}{a}\right\}$$

for $a > 0$.   Let $F_Y(y)$ and $F_X(x)$ be the respective distribution functions, so that the last expression can be written

$$F_Y(t) = F_X\left(\frac{t-b}{a}\right) \tag{16}$$

Since t is arbitrary, we can differentiate $F_Y(t)$ with respect to t.   This yields Eq. (15) with t replaced by y.   If $a < 0$, the probability statement is slightly different (see Prob. 9-2).

Example 9-1 Probability function for bending moment   The
bending moment M at the support of a cantilever beam having a random load P at a distance of 5 ft and a fixed load of 15 lb at 10 ft is given by

$$M = 5P + 150$$

If the probability function $f(p)$ for the load P is the exponential law $3e^{-3p}$, $p > 0$, it follows from Eq. (15) that the probability function $q(m)$ for the bending moment is

$$q(m) = (\tfrac{3}{5}e^{90})e^{-3m/5} \qquad m \geqslant 150$$

Now consider a linear function Y of two random variables X_1 and X_2 with given densities $f_1(x_1)$ and $f_2(x_2)$, that is,

$$Y = a_1 X_1 + a_2 X_2 \tag{17}$$

where a_1 and a_2 are arbitrary constants. To find the density function for Y, we temporarily "freeze" one of the random variables so that Eq. (17) is comparable to Eq. (15). We calculate the density for this transformation by Eq. (15). Next, we "thaw" the "frozen" variable and apply Eq. (15) once again. Specifically, we "freeze" X_2 to obtain the conditional density for Y given X_2, that is, $q_1(y|x_2)$. By Eq. (15),

$$q_1(y|x_2) = \frac{1}{|a_1|} f_1\left(\frac{y - a_2 x_2}{a_1}\right)$$

The joint density is then

$$q_2(y,x_2) = q_1(y|x_2) f_2(x_2) = \frac{1}{|a_1|} f_1\left(\frac{y - a_2 x_2}{a_1}\right) f_2(x_2)$$

For the marginal density $q_3(y)$, we integrate to obtain

$$q_3(y) = \int_{x_2} q_2(y,x_2)\,dx_2 = \frac{1}{|a_1|} \int_{x_2} f_1\left(\frac{y - a_2 x_2}{a_1}\right) f_2(x_2)\,dx_2$$

Example 9-2 Probability function for sum of two forces Assume that collinear forces P_1 and P_2 are random variables described by the rectangular law $f_i(p_i) = 1$, on $\{0,1\}$, $i = 1, 2$. To find the probability function

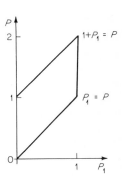

Fig. 9-2 Sample space for (P, P_1).

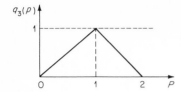

Fig. 9-3 "Triangular" density for $P = P_1 + P_2$.

for the total force $P = P_1 + P_2$, we first assume that P_1 is "frozen." Thus,

$$q_1(p|p_1) = f_2(p - p_1) = 1 \qquad 0 \leqslant p_1 \leqslant 1; p_1 \leqslant p \leqslant 1 + p_1$$

Note the care needed to specify the domain (sample space) of P. The joint density is

$$q_2(p,p_1) = q_1(p|p_1)f_1(p_1) = 1 \qquad 0 \leqslant p_1 \leqslant 1; p_1 \leqslant p \leqslant 1 + p_1$$

To find the marginal density, we integrate over the range of P_1. Figure 9-2 shows that integration limits depend upon the value of P. Therefore, the density $q_3(p)$ will exhibit a "split structure." Since the integration limits for P_1 are 0 to P for $0 \leqslant P \leqslant 1$ and $P - 1$ to 1 for $1 \leqslant P \leqslant 2$,

$$q_3(p) = \begin{cases} \int_0^P dp_1 = P & 0 \leqslant P \leqslant 1 \\ \int_{P-1}^1 dp_1 = 2 - P & 1 \leqslant P \leqslant 2 \end{cases}$$

This "triangular" density is illustrated in Fig. 9-3.

The same approach can be extended to a linear function of n variables,

$$Y = a_1 X_1 + \cdots + a_n X_n \tag{18}$$

by freezing all the variables except one. From the conditional density, the joint density of Y and the "frozen" variables is written. Finally, a multiple integration over the domain of the "frozen" variables yields the marginal density of Y.

Example 9-3 Sums of Poisson variables

Suppose that the probability of vehicles passing a freeway entrance in time T is Poisson with parameter $\lambda_1 T$. The entrance traffic joining the traffic stream is also Poisson, with parameter $\lambda_2 T$. What is the probability function for the number of vehicles passing a point on the freeway just after the entrance?

Let n_1 be the random number of vehicles on the freeway just before the entrance, and let n_2 be the number entering, so that the total is $n = n_1 + n_2$. Now

$$P\{n = k\} = P\{n_1 = 0, n_2 = k \cup n_1 = 1, n_2 = k - 1 \cup \cdots \cup n_1 = k, n_2 = 0\}$$

That is, the event $n = k$ is the union of the mutually exclusive events $n_1 = 0$ and $n_2 = k$, $n_1 = 1$ and $n_2 = k - 1$, etc.   Assuming that n_1 and n_2 are independent random variables, it follows that

$$P\{n = k\} = \sum_{i=0}^{k} P\{n_1 = i, n_2 = k - i\} = \sum_{i=0}^{k} P\{n_1 = i\}P\{n_2 = k - i\}$$

Substituting the Poisson law, we get

$$P\{n = k\} = \sum_{i=0}^{k} \frac{(\lambda_1 T)^i}{i!} e^{-\lambda_1 T} \frac{(\lambda_2 T)^{k-i}}{(k - i)!} e^{-\lambda_2 T} = \frac{[(\lambda_1 + \lambda_2) T]^k}{k!} e^{-(\lambda_1 + \lambda_2)T}$$

since

$$\sum_{i=0}^{k} \binom{k}{i} \left(\frac{\lambda_1 T}{\lambda_1 T + \lambda_2 T} \right)^i \left(\frac{\lambda_2 T}{\lambda_1 T + \lambda_2 T} \right)^{k-i} = 1$$

Thus, as noted, the sum of two independent Poisson variables is also a Poisson variable with the parameter equal to the sum of the individual parameters. The result is easily generalized (see Sec. 12-1).

9-7 NONLINEAR MODELS

Frequently we are interested in nonlinear functions of random variables. For example, the random kinetic energy of a particle is a nonlinear function of its random velocity.

Let $Y = \alpha(X)$ be the nonlinear function of a random variable X which is described by the density function $f(x)$, $(-\infty, \infty)$.   Assume that $\alpha(X)$ is monotonic increasing and differentiable (Fig. 9-4).   To seek the probability function for Y, $q(y)$, begin with the probability statement

$$P\{X \leqslant x\} = P\{Y \leqslant y = \alpha(x)\} \tag{19}$$

As before, rewrite Eq. (19) in terms of the integrals

$$F_X(x) = \int_{-\infty}^{x} f(x)\,dx = \int_{-\infty}^{y = \alpha(x)} q(y)\,dy = F_Y(\alpha(x))$$

where $F_X(x)$ and $F_Y(y)$, are respective distribution functions.

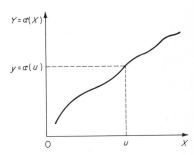

Fig. 9-4 Monotonic increasing function.

Differentiating with respect to x yields

$$\frac{dF_Y(\alpha(x))}{d\alpha(x)}\frac{d\alpha(x)}{dx}=\frac{dF_X(x)}{dx}$$

or, equivalently,

$$q(y)=\frac{dx}{dy}f(\alpha^{-1}(y)) \tag{20}$$

where $\alpha^{-1}(y)$ is the inverse of $\alpha(x)$, that is, $\alpha(\alpha^{-1}(y))=y$.

Example 9-4 Measurement errors Suppose that the speed of a particle is measured as v when the actual speed is V.   The measurement error is $\epsilon=V-v$, and the resulting error in the kinetic energy is

$$\mathscr{E}=\frac{m}{2}(V^2-v^2)=\frac{m}{2}(\epsilon^2+2\epsilon v)$$

For $-1/2\leqslant\epsilon\leqslant 1/2$, this equation is monotonic increasing for $|v|>1/2$. Figure 9-5 illustrates the relationship between the random errors $\mathscr{E}$ and ϵ in this region.   Assume that the density function for the random error in the velocity is rectangular:

$$r(\epsilon;-1/2,1/2)=1 \qquad -1/2\leqslant\epsilon\leqslant 1/2$$

Since

$$\frac{d\epsilon}{d\mathscr{E}}=\left[2m\left(\frac{m}{2}v^2+\mathscr{E}\right)\right]^{-1/2}$$

it follows from Eq. (19) that the density function $q(\mathscr{E})$ for the error in the kinetic energy is given by

$$q(\mathscr{E})=\left[2m\left(\frac{m}{2}v^2+\mathscr{E}\right)\right]^{-1/2} \qquad \frac{m}{2}\left(\frac{1}{4}-v\right)\leqslant\mathscr{E}\leqslant\frac{m}{2}\left(\frac{1}{4}+v\right)$$

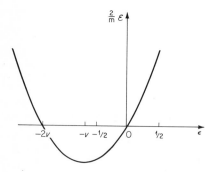

Fig. 9-5 $(2/m)\mathscr{E}$ vs. ϵ, $|v|>\frac{1}{2}$.

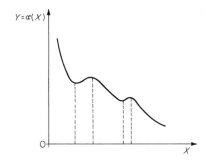

$Y = \alpha(X)$

Fig. 9-6 A nonmonotonic function.

Only minor modifications are needed if $\alpha(x)$ is monotonic decreasing. The probability relation (19) would be rewritten as

$$P\{X \leqslant x\} = P\{Y \geqslant y\}$$

and the integral relationship as

$$F_X(x) = \int_{-\infty}^{x} f(x)\, dx = \int_{y=\alpha(x)}^{\infty} q(y)\, dy = 1 - F_Y(\alpha(x))$$

Differentiating, we obtain

$$\frac{dF_X(x)}{dx} = -\frac{dF_Y(\alpha(x))}{d\alpha(x)}\left(-\left|\frac{d\alpha(x)}{dx}\right|\right)$$

since the derivative of the decreasing function $\alpha(x)$ is negative.   Equivalently,

$$q(y) = \left|\frac{dx}{dy}\right| f(\alpha^{-1}(y)) \qquad\qquad (20')$$

Thus, if the relation between X and Y, $\alpha(X)$, is monotonic, then Eq. (20) can be used to obtain the density function for Y (always remembering to use the absolute value of the derivative dx/dy).   If the function is not monotonic, as in Fig. 9-6, the interval is divided into domains in which $\alpha(x)$ is monotonic. The above techniques apply, but the resulting probability function is "split-structured."   A particularly useful treatment of symbolic models is given in Wadsworth and Bryan [15].

Example 9-5 Measurement errors (continued)   In the last example we assumed that $|v| > 1/2$ in order that $\mathscr{E}$ be a monotonic function of ϵ.   Now suppose that $|v| < 1/2$, so that $\mathscr{E}(\epsilon)$ is monotonic decreasing for $-1/2 \leqslant \epsilon \leqslant -v$ and monotonic increasing for $-v \leqslant \epsilon \leqslant 1/2$.   Again we assume that the measurement error is governed by a rectangular distribution on $[-1/2, 1/2]$.

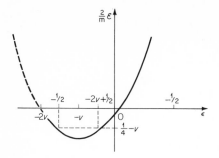

Fig. 9-7 $(2/m)\mathscr{E}$ vs. ϵ, $|v| < \frac{1}{2}$.

The density function $q_1(\mathscr{E})$ for the interval $-1/2 \leqslant \epsilon \leqslant -v$ and, consequently, $(m/2)(\frac{1}{4} + v) \leqslant \mathscr{E} \leqslant -(m/2)v^2$ is

$$q_1(\mathscr{E}) = \left[2m\left(\frac{m}{2}v^2 + \mathscr{E}\right)\right]^{-1/2}$$

For $-v \leqslant \epsilon \leqslant 1/2$ and, consequently, $-(m/2)v^2 \leqslant \mathscr{E} \leqslant (m/2)(\frac{1}{4} + v)$, the density function $q_2(\mathscr{E})$ is the same as $q_1(\mathscr{E})$. Now, for $\mathscr{E}$ values in the interval $-(m/2)v^2 \leqslant \mathscr{E} \leqslant (m/2)(\frac{1}{4} - v)$, there is a "double contribution," so that the density is

$$q(\mathscr{E}) = \begin{cases} 2\left[2m\left(\dfrac{m}{2}v^2 + \mathscr{E}\right)\right]^{-1/2} & -\dfrac{m}{2}v^2 \leqslant \mathscr{E} \leqslant \dfrac{m}{2}\left(\dfrac{1}{4} - v\right) \\[2ex] \left[2m\left(\dfrac{m}{2}v^2 + \mathscr{E}\right)\right]^{-1/2} & \dfrac{m}{2}\left(\dfrac{1}{4} - v\right) \leqslant \mathscr{E} \leqslant \dfrac{m}{2}\left(\dfrac{1}{4} + v\right) \end{cases}$$

(See Fig. 9-7.)

Example 9-6 An absolute-value model Let the distance a particle moves be a random variable d described by $f(d) = \frac{1}{4}$, $-2 \leqslant d \leqslant 2$. Find the probability function $q(D)$ for the displacement D of the particle, that is, $D = |d|$.

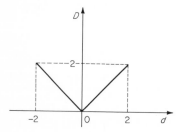

Fig. 9-8 Graph of $D = |d|$.

Figure 9-8 illustrates the relationship between distance and displacement. Since

$$D = \begin{cases} -d & -2 \leqslant d \leqslant 0 \\ d & 0 \leqslant d \leqslant 2 \end{cases}$$

it is clear that D is a "split-structured" function. Since D is linear in the intervals about the origin, we use the result in Eq. (15). Therefore,

$$q_-(D) = \tfrac{1}{4} \qquad -2 \leqslant d \leqslant 0$$
$$q_+(D) = \tfrac{1}{4} \qquad 0 \leqslant d \leqslant 2$$

so that

$$q(D) = \tfrac{1}{4} + \tfrac{1}{4} = \tfrac{1}{2} \qquad 0 \leqslant D \leqslant 2$$

Example 9-7 Fundamental diagram of road traffic   The object in the preceding symbolic models was to obtain the probability function for Y given the transformation $Y = g(X)$ and the probability function of X. An inverse problem is to estimate the transformation from statistical information. The *fundamental diagram of road traffic* provides an example. Our discussion follows Haight [9].

Consider the identity

$$\frac{\text{Cars}}{\text{Time}} \equiv \frac{\text{cars}}{\text{distance}} \frac{\text{distance}}{\text{time}}$$

Let λ denote the traffic flow or volume per unit time (cars/time), ρ the concentration or density (cars/distance), and m the mean speed of a collection of vehicles. The identity is written

$$\lambda(\rho) = \rho m(\rho) \tag{21}$$

using the functional notation to suggest that flow and mean speed depend upon the concentration. Clearly, ρ has an upper limit, ρ', corresponding to solidly packed cars. The boundary values of $\lambda(\rho)$ and $\lambda(0) = \lambda(\rho') = 0$. Between these limits one anticipates a maximum flow called the *capacity* of the road. The fundamental diagram of road traffic in Fig. 9-9, a plot of

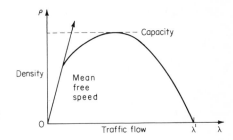

Fig. 9-9   The fundamental diagram of road traffic.

Eq. (21), illustrates these features.   Its determination is a central problem of traffic theory.   A knowledge of either $\lambda(\rho)$ or $m(\rho)$ determines the other by Eq. (21).   We next derive $m(\rho)$.

Let x be the free speed of each car.   This random variable is assumed to be time-independent as long as the vehicle is free of interaction with other vehicles (or road impediments).   Let m_0 and v_0 denote its mean and variance. Note that, because of interactions with other vehicles, the free speed is an upper bound.

Let $y(x,\rho)$ denote a (random) overall average speed.   To determine the transformation $y = y(x,\rho)$ between the random variables x and y, boundary conditions are useful.   For example, $y(x,0) = x$ expresses the constancy of the free speed in the absence of interference; $y(x,\rho') = y(0,\rho) = 0$ describe a traffic jam and a vehicle that chooses to stop, respectively.   Possible transformations might be

$$y = \ln \frac{\rho' e^x}{\rho e^x + \rho' - \rho}$$

or

$$y = \frac{\rho' - \rho}{\rho} \tan^{-1} \frac{\rho x}{\rho' - \rho}$$

since both satisfy the boundary conditions.

Note that while x can assume any nonnegative value, the overall average speed y will be bounded because of the dependence upon ρ.   Let $L(\rho) = (\infty,\rho)$ denote the upper bound on y.   In seeking a convenient probability density for y on the interval $\{0,L\}$, note that as $\rho \to 0$ we require that $L(\rho) \to \infty$ and, also, that as $\rho \to \rho'$, $L(\rho') \to 0$.   The *beta density* function described in Sec. 9-8 possesses these properties, that is,

$$\frac{y^{\alpha-1}(L - y)^{L\beta-1}}{L^{L\beta+\alpha-1} B(\alpha,L\beta)} \qquad 0 < y < L$$

where α and β are parameters.   The function $B(\alpha,L\beta)$ is given by

$$B(\alpha,L\beta) = \frac{\Gamma(\alpha)\,\Gamma(L\beta)}{\Gamma(\alpha + L\beta)}$$

where $\Gamma(\alpha)$ and $\Gamma(L\beta)$ are gamma functions defined in Sec. 9-8.

The desired mean $m(\rho)$ is given by

$$E(y) = m(\rho) = \frac{\alpha L}{\beta L + \alpha} \tag{22}$$

Letting $\rho \to 0$ so that $L \to \infty$, $y \to x$, and $m(\rho) \to m_0$, we have

$$m_0 = \frac{\alpha}{\beta}$$

Similarly, one can conclude the variance of the free speed

$$v_0 = \frac{\alpha}{\beta^2}$$

Note that in view of Eq. (22), the problem of determining $m(\rho)$ in order to deduce the fundamental diagram has reduced to finding $L(\rho)$. Two functions which have the requisite properties are

$$L = \ln \frac{\rho'}{\rho}$$

so that, from Eq. (22),

$$m(\rho) = \frac{\alpha \ln (\rho'/\rho)}{\beta \ln (\rho'/\rho) + \alpha}$$

and

$$L = \frac{\pi}{2} \frac{\rho' - \rho}{\rho}$$

whence

$$m(\rho) = \frac{\rho' - \rho}{A\rho' + B\rho}$$

where $A = m_0^{-1}$ and $B = 2/\pi - m_0^{-1}$.

9-8 ADDITIONAL PROBABILITY LAWS

THE BETA LAW

The beta law is defined by

$$be(x;\alpha,\beta) = \frac{1}{B(\alpha + 1, \beta + 1)} x^\alpha (1 - x)^\beta \qquad \alpha, \beta > -1; 0 \leqslant x \leqslant 1$$

where

$$B(m,n) = \frac{\Gamma(m)\,\Gamma(n)}{\Gamma(m + n)} \qquad m, n > 0$$

and the gamma function is defined in conjunction with Eq. (23) below. The beta law is used as a model for random fractions and percentages. Its popularity also stems from the variety of shapes available for various parameter values (Fig. 9-10). The domain of the beta variable is easily extended to any other finite interval besides $0 \leqslant x \leqslant 1$.

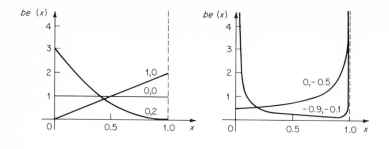

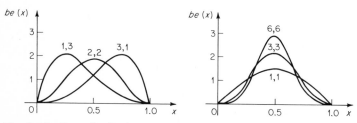

Fig. 9-10 Beta distributions with various selections of parameters α, β. The symbol *a, b* means $\alpha = a$, $\beta = b$. (*Reprinted from Wadsworth and Bryan* [15].)

THE GAMMA (ERLANG) LAW[1]

The gamma law is defined by

$$ga(x;\lambda,\alpha) = \frac{\lambda}{\Gamma(\alpha)}(\lambda x)^{\alpha-1} e^{-\lambda x} \qquad x, \lambda, \alpha > 0 \tag{23}$$

where $\Gamma(\alpha)$ is a constant called the *gamma function* and is defined by the integral

$$\Gamma(\alpha) = \int_0^\infty y^{\alpha-1} e^{-y} \, dy \qquad \alpha > 0$$

In the case where α is a positive integer, the last integral becomes

$$\Gamma(\alpha) = (\alpha - 1)! \qquad \alpha = 1, 2, \ldots$$

Note that the exponential law is the special case $\alpha = 1$. Actually, the gamma law describes the sum of α independent exponential variables with common mean $1/\lambda$ (Prob. 9-10). Since the time between consecutive arrivals in a Poisson process is described by the exponential law with mean $1/\lambda$, the total

---

[1] A. K. Erlang was a Danish telephone engineer early in this century. His observation of the Poisson nature of arriving telephone calls led to subsequent developments in random-service systems.

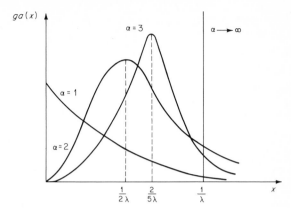

Fig. 9-11 Erlang law.

waiting time for α arrivals is described by the gamma law with mean α/λ. This assertion follows since

$$t = t_1 + \cdots + t_\alpha$$

where t_i is the time between the $(i-1)$st and ith arrivals, $i = 1, \ldots, \alpha$, and t is the total waiting time. The expected value of t is clearly α/λ since $1/\lambda$ is the common mean for the t_i. Similarly, the variance is α/λ^2.

Since the exponential law is a gamma law with $\alpha = 1$, and the sum of independent exponential variables with a common mean is a gamma law, one might speculate that the sum of independent gamma variables with a common parameter is also a gamma variable. This is the result of Prob. 9-11.

The gamma law is often used as an approximation to laws in which the standard deviation is less than the mean. Its popularity stems from the wide variety of shapes it can assume with only two parameters (see Fig. 9-11). The gamma laws have been used to describe streamflows and monthly precipitation [3] and the yield strength of reinforced concrete members [14].

The discrete analog of the gamma law is the *negative binomial law* (see Prob. 9-13 and Appendix 4).

THE CHI-SQUARE LAW

The quadratic model

$$\chi_n^2 = X_1^2 + X_2^2 + \cdots + X_n^2$$

where $X_1, X_2, \ldots, X_n$ are independent unit normal variables, defines the chi-square variable with n degrees of freedom. This variable is one of the most widely used by statisticians as a criterion to fit probability functions to observed data [11].

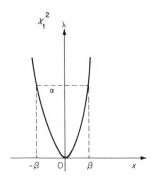

Fig. 9-12 Quadratic transformation.

Suppose that $n = 1$, and derive the probability function for χ_1^2.   Using Fig. 9-12, we write the probability relation

$$P\{\chi_1^2 \leqslant \alpha\} = P\{-\beta \leqslant X \leqslant \beta\} \tag{24}$$

Let chi (χ_1^2) be the required density, and let $n(x)$ be the unit normal law.   We can express Eq. (24) by

$$\int_0^\alpha \text{chi}\,(\chi_1^2)\,d\chi_1^2 = C(\alpha) = \int_{-\beta}^\beta n(x)\,dx = N(\beta) - N(-\beta)$$

where the capital letters denote the distribution functions.   Differentiating with respect to β and noting that $\alpha = \beta^2$, we have

$$\text{chi}\,(\alpha)\frac{d\alpha}{d\beta} = n(\beta) - n(-\beta)\frac{d(-\beta)}{d\beta}$$

whence we conclude that

$$\text{chi}\,(\chi_1^2) = \frac{1}{\sqrt{2\pi\chi_1^2}}e^{-\chi_1^2/2} \qquad \chi_1^2 \geqslant 0 \tag{25}$$

But this is precisely the gamma law with $\lambda = \alpha = \frac{1}{2}$ since $\Gamma(\frac{1}{2}) = \sqrt{\pi}$ (see a table of definite integrals [1]).   It follows that

$$\text{chi}\,(\chi_n^2;n) = \frac{1}{2^{n/2}\,\Gamma(n/2)}(\chi_n^2)^{(n/2)-1}\,e^{-\chi_n/2} \qquad \chi_n^2 > 0 \tag{26}$$

Statistics texts describe the use of the chi-square law [11].

THE LOG-NORMAL LAW

The log-normal law arises in multiplicative random models.   The log-normal density function is defined by

$$\lg n\,(x;\mu,\sigma) = \frac{1}{\sqrt{2\pi}\sigma x}e^{-\frac{(\ln x - \mu)^2}{2\sigma^2}} \qquad x > 0 \tag{27}$$

where $\mu = E(\ln X)$ and $\sigma^2 = E[(\ln X - \mu)^2]$ (see Fig. 9-13 and Appendix 4).

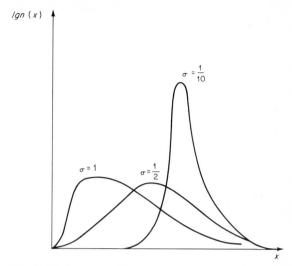

Fig. 9-13 Log-normal law.

Consider the sequence of independent random variables $Y_1, Y_2, \ldots, Y_n$ and their product Y,

$$Y = Y_1 Y_2 \cdots Y_n \tag{28}$$

Taking logarithms,

$$\ln Y = \ln Y_1 + \ln Y_2 + \cdots + \ln Y_n$$

Since Y_i is a random variable, so is $\ln Y_i$, $i = 1, \ldots, n$. As n increases, we expect $\ln Y$ to closely approximate the normal law. Suppose that $X = \ln Y$ is, in fact, described by a normal law with mean μ and variance σ^2. To find the probability function which describes Y, the procedure of the last section is applicable since $Y = e^X$ is a monotonic function. Using Eq. (20), the desired density is

$$\frac{1}{y} \frac{1}{\sqrt{2\pi}\sigma} e^{-\frac{(\ln y - \mu)^2}{2\sigma^2}}$$

the log-normal law of Eq. (27).

There are several reasons for the popularity of the log-normal law in civil engineering. First, phenomena involving random splittings may be reasonably described by the multiplicative model of Eq. (28). The breakage of large stones in mutual collisions [10], fatigue models, and certain hydrologic phenomena [2] are examples. Second, when the phenomenon under study is not understood well enough to suggest a more specific model, the variety of skew curves (Fig. 9-13) suggests the choice of a log-normal density. Also, the nonnegativity of the log-normal variable is often useful.   The log-normal law has an important regenerative property for products of random variables (Sec. 12-4).

SUMMARY

This chapter developed random models and indicated how some basic probability functions are a consequence of the model.   The chapter is divided into two parts: recursive models and symbolic models.

The recursive models of Part I resulted in the five basic probability functions of Secs. 9-1 to 9-5.   The symbolic models of Part II indicated how probability functions for desired processes can be derived from the given ones for linear and nonlinear relationships.

A final section defined some additional useful probability functions.

PROBLEMS

9-1.   Consider repeated experiments as in Sec. 9-1, except that each experiment may result in one of three possible outcomes.   Let the trial probabilities be p_1, p_2, and $p_3(=1 - p_1 + p_2)$. In a series of n experiments, what is the probability that the outcome with probability p_1 occurs k_1 times; with p_2, k_2 times; and with p_3, $k_3(=n - k_1 - k_2)$ times?   The resulting probability function is called the multinomial law, $m(k_1, \ldots, k_r; p_1, \ldots, p_r, n)$, with $r = 3$.

9-2.   Complete the discussion in Sec. 9-6 for the case $Y = aX + b$ with $a < 0$.   (The probability statement is easily written with the aid of a graph.)

9-3.   Let the probability function for X be the normal law with mean $\mu = 2$ and variance $\sigma^2 = 1$.   Find the probability function for $Y = 2X + 3$.   More generally, show that when X is normal with arbitrary mean and variance, then $Y = aX + b$ (a and b arbitrary) is also a normal variable.

9-4.   Let X_1 and X_2 be two observations of a random variable X which is described by the rectangular law $f(x) = 1$, $\{0,1\}$.   Find the probability function for $X = X_1 - X_2$.

9-5.   Let X_1 be described by $f_1(x_1) = \frac{1}{2}$, $\{1,3\}$, and X_2 by $f_2(x_2) = \frac{1}{3}$, $\{5,8\}$.   Find the probability function for $Y = X_1 + X_2$.

9-6.   Let the random variables X and Y be described by the joint density

$$f(x,y) = 6xy(2 - x - y) \qquad 0 \leqslant x, y \leqslant 1$$

Find the probability function for $Z = X + Y$. ◆

9-7.   The random variable X, with a given density $f(x)$, is related to another random variable Y by

$$\begin{aligned} Y &= b & X &\leqslant a \\ Y &= c > b & a &< X < b \\ Y &= a & X &\geqslant b \end{aligned}$$

Find the probability function for Y.   Incidentally, these relations define a square-wave correspondence between X and Y.

9-8.   Let X be a random variable described by $f(x) = e^{-x}$, $x > 0$.   Find the density of $Y = X^{1/3}$.

9-9.   In a group of steel beams, the probability, p, that any particular beam will not meet specifications is $0 \leqslant p \leqslant 1$.   The group is divided into two lots of n_1 and n_2 beams, and the number of rejects in each lot, X_1 and X_2, respectively, is counted.   Intuitively, it is clear that the probability law for the sum $X_1 + X_2$ is binomial.   Support your intuition with an analytic argument. ◆

9-10. Let X_1 and X_2 be independent exponential variables with common parameter λ. Prove that $Y = X_1 + X_2$ is an Erlang variable with mean $2/\lambda$.   Generalize for the sum of k variables.

9-11. Let X_1 and X_2 be independent gamma variables with parameters α_1, λ and α_2, λ, respectively.   Derive the probability law for $Y = X_1 + X_2$.

Generalize the result for the sum of 3, 4, . . . , n independent Erlang variables with respective parameters α_3, λ; α_4, λ; . . . , n.

9-12. Show that u is the mode of the extreme-value law.   Also, verify that the mean is approximately $u + \gamma/\lambda$ and the variance is $\pi^2/6\lambda^2$, where γ is Euler's number [1].

9-13. Let X_1 and X_2 be discrete random variables described by a common geometric law. Find the probability law for the sum $X_1 + X_2$.

Show that the sum of r discrete random variables, each described by a common geometric law, is described by the negative binomial law:

$$nb(k;q,r) = \binom{r + k - 1}{k} p^r q^k \qquad \begin{matrix} k = 0, 1, \ldots \\ r = 1, 2, \ldots \end{matrix}$$

9-14. Prove that the sum of two independent normal variables, with means μ_1 and μ_2 and standard deviations σ_1 and σ_2, is also a normal variable, with mean $\mu_1 + \mu_2$ and variance $\sigma_1^2 + \sigma_2^2$.   (The result can be generalized.   See Example 12-3.)

REFERENCES

1. "CRC Standard Mathematical Tables," Chemical Rubber Publishing Co.
2. Chow, V. T.: The Log-normal Law and Its Engineering Applications, *Proc. ASCE,* vol, 80, no. 536, September, 1954.
3. Chow, V. T.: "Handbook of Applied Hydrology," McGraw-Hill Book Company, New York, 1964.
4. Computation Laboratory, Harvard University: "Tables of the Cumulative Binomial Probability Distribution," Harvard University Press, Cambridge, Mass., 1955.
5. Drew, D. R.: "Traffic Flow Theory and Control," McGraw-Hill Book Company, New York, 1968.
6. Feller, W.: "An Introduction to Probability Theory and Its Applications," vol. I, John Wiley & Sons, Inc., New York, 1967.
7. Gumbel, E. J.: Statistical Theory of Droughts, *Proc. ASCE,* vol. 80, no. 439, September, 1954.
8. Gumbel, E. J.: "Statistics of Extremes," Columbia University Press, New York, 1958.
9. Haight, F.: "Mathematical Theories of Traffic Flow," Academic Press, Inc., New York, 1963.
10. Johnson, A. I.: Strength, Safety, and Economical Dimensions of Structures, *Div. Bldg. Statistics Struct. Eng. Bull.* 12, Royal Institute of Technology, Stockholm, 1953.
11. Mood, A. R., and F. A. Graybill: "Introduction to the Theory of Statistics," McGraw-Hill Book Company, New York, 1963.
12. Saaty, T. R.: "Elements of Queueing Theory," McGraw-Hill Book Company, New York, 1961.
13. Thom, H. C. S.: Distribution of Extreme Winds in the United States, *Proc. ASCE,* vol. 86, no. ST4, April, 1960.
14. Tichy, M., and M. Vorlicek: Safety of Reinforced Concrete Framed Structures, *Proc. Int. Symp. Flexural Mech. Reinforced Concrete, ASCE-ACI Publ.,* 1965.
15. Wadsworth, G. P., and J. G. Bryan: "Introduction to Probability and Random Variables," McGraw-Hill Book Company, New York, 1960.

10
Mathematical Expectation

Mathematical expectation is an important concept in the theory and application of probability. In Sec. 8-6, the expected value of a function $g(X)$ of the continuous random variable X with probability function $f(x)$ was defined as

$$E(g(X)) = \int_{\substack{\text{all} \\ x}} g(x)f(x)\,dx$$

The term "mathematical expectation" derives from outcomes of a chance game and poses questions of long-term, or expected, value. The use of

332

expectation in decision making is an extension of this notion, and applications span many subjects. When the measure of performance is a function of random variables, it cannot be an optimization criterion. The most common procedure is to use the expected value of the random performance. Carrying out the optimization yields the *decision rule*, i.e., values of the decision variables. Note that the use of an expected-value criterion implies a long-run process (in order to provide statistical stability).

The first three sections of this chapter illustrate applications to decision making. Section 10-1 exhibits a variety of examples, and Secs. 10-2 and 10-3 apply similar ideas to the subjects of contract bidding and equipment replacement and maintenance. Expected values are also widely used to describe random processes in applications other than decision making. A derivation of the probability functions to describe a random process is often impractical. Such processes are described less completely, but usefully, using expectations. Section 10-4 briefly illustrates applications to random vibrations.

10-1 EXAMPLES WITH AN EXPECTED-VALUE CRITERION

The examples in this section illustrate a variety of applications of an expected-value criterion. The first five examples can be classed as problems in *inventory theory*, a recent branch of applied mathematics ([1], [25], and [26]). For our purpose, regard inventory as a resource in storage subject to control to meet demands on a system. Usually, the resource in question is replenishable, although it need not be. When the resource is replenishable, an *operational decision* is desired, such as a decision about the amount of water to release from a dam for irrigation, hydroelectric, or flood-control purposes or perhaps about the number of spare parts to stock for a truck fleet. When the resource is not readily replenishable, a *design decision* is desired, e.g., regarding the sizing of a dam and its outlet works or the sizing of oil storage capacity at a refinery.

Example 10-1   The newsboy problem   To illustrate the main ideas in a fundamental stochastic optimization, let us consider the problem of stocking a resource to meet random demand. The resource may be fuel, machine parts, water in a reservoir, etc., and the operational decision is to determine the optimum resource level. In an ideal operation, the supply exactly matches demand. No costs are incurred for having either too much or too little in supply. Suppose that the unit resource cost is c, so that a resource level Y costs cY. Let the return on each resource unit which fulfils a unit of demand be $r(>c)$. The expected-value criterion is a convenient means for determining the optimal resource level Y_0.

There are two cases to distinguish since the resource level either does or

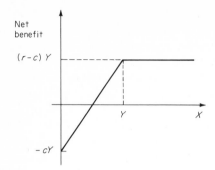

Fig. 10-1 Random net-benefit function.

does not exceed the demand X.   The random returns for this cost situation
corresponding to a resource level Y are (Fig. 10-1)

$$\text{Net benefit} = \begin{cases} rX - cY & X \leqslant Y \\ (r-c)\,Y & X \geqslant Y \end{cases}$$

The total expected net benefit is

$$E(Y) = \int_0^Y (rx - cY)f(x)\,dx + \int_Y^\infty (r-c)\,Yf(x)\,dx \tag{1}$$

where $f(x)$ is the probability density for X.   To determine the optimal resource
level, we equate to zero the derivative of the previous equation with respect
to the parameter Y.   A useful formula for differentiating an integral with
respect to a parameter is *Leibnitz' rule*.   Consider the integral

$$I(v) = \int_{a(v)}^{b(v)} f(u,v)\,du$$

where $f(x,y)$ is a function of two variables, one of which is the integration
variable.   The integration limits $a(y)$ and $b(y)$ may be functions of y.   Its
derivative with respect to y is

$$\frac{dI(v)}{dv} = \int_{a(v)}^{b(v)} \frac{\partial f(u,v)}{\partial v}\,du + \frac{db(v)}{dv}f(b(v),v) - \frac{da(v)}{dv}f(a(v),v)$$

A proof appears in most advanced calculus texts [21].
    Applying Leibnitz' rule to Eq. (1) yields the optimizing condition

$$\frac{c}{r} = \int_{Y_0}^\infty f(x)\,dx = 1 - F(Y_0)$$

where Y_0 is the optimizing value of Y and $F(x)$ is the cumulative distribution.
Figure 10-2 shows a graphical interpretation of this condition and a means
of estimating solutions when only partial information is available.   Note
that only the ratio c/r is required and not the values c and r.

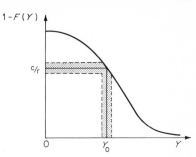

Fig. 10-2 Optimizing condition.

The discussion has implied a continuous random variable, but the analysis is similar for the discrete case. In examples of this section the reader will find situations fundamentally the same as the above. In inventory theory this problem is widely referred to as the *newsboy problem*. Problem 10-1 asks the reader to derive the optimizing condition for arbitrary return and cost functions. Also see Beckenbach [3].

Example 10-2 Diversion capacity for constructing a dam

A timber flume is needed for the first-stage diversion of water during the construction of a dam. The first stage requires $2\frac{1}{2}$ years for its completion. Larger flume capacities are more costly to build, and since streamflow is random, the problem is to determine a flume size for minimum total expected cost.

Figures 10-3 and 10-4 give the estimated cost of flood damage during the first-stage diversion and the estimated construction cost as a function of flume size, respectively. Assume that flooding occurs whenever streamflows exceed 1.5 times the flume capacity, due to the storage-discharge characteristics of the reservoir and flume. A more refined analysis would include the modified Puls or other method for flood routing through a reservoir.

The total expected cost $K(q)$ consists of the construction cost $c_s(q)$ for a flume of size q and the flooding cost $c_f(t)$, which depends upon the time t

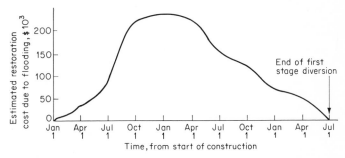

Fig. 10-3 Restoration cost due to flooding during first-stage diversion.

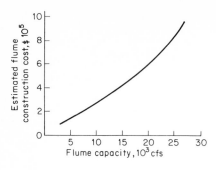

Fig. 10-4 Flume construction cost vs. capacity.

at which the flood occurs (Fig. 10-3). The streamflow record (Fig. 10-5) may be used to estimate the probability of flooding in each 3-month interval, $p(t)$, during the 30-month life of the flume. The expected cost of flooding over the life of the flume is

$$c_f = \sum_{t=1}^{10} c_f(t)p(t)$$

Values of $p(t)$ calculated from the data in Fig. 10-5 are shown in Table 10-1.

Table 10-2 illustrates the calculation of expected flooding costs for the three flume sizes $q = 6{,}670$, $10{,}000$, and $16{,}670$ cfs.

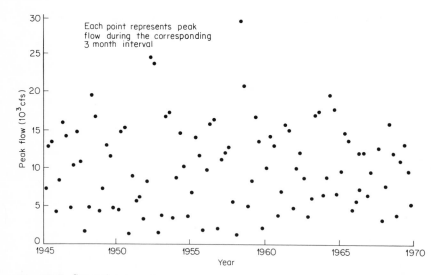

Fig. 10-5 Streamflow record.

Table 10-1 Runoff probabilities

Peak runoff, 10^3 cfs	Jan.–Mar. n	N	April–June n	N	July–Sept. n	N	Oct.–Dec. n	N
0–5	4	21	0	25	0	25	20	5
5–10	17	4	1	24	3	22	5	0
10–15	4	0	13	11	14	8	0	0
15–20	0	0	9	2	6	2	0	0
20–25	0	0	1	1	2	0	0	0
25–30	0	0	1	0	0	0	0	0

n = number of occurrences over 25-year record; N = number of excedances.

Calculating the costs for additional flume sizes enables one to construct the cost curves shown in Fig. 10-6. A flume size of about 12,000 cfs corresponds to minimum total expected cost.

Example 10-3 Storage capacity between machines A common problem is to size a storage tank or hopper between two machines when the output of one is the input to the other. Storage reduces the idle time of the second machine whenever the first machine is being repaired. The optimal storage capacity depends upon the relative costs of idle time and of the storage facility. We shall determine optimal storage capacity, assuming that the

Table 10-2 Expected flooding cost

Period $t =$	Avg. flood-damage cost (from Fig. 10-3) $c_f(t)$	6,670-cfs flume (10,000-cfs flow) Flood prob. $p(t)$	Risk cost $c_f(t)$	10,000-cfs flume (15,000-cfs flow) Flood prob. $p(t)$	Risk cost $c_f(t)$	16,670-cfs flume (25,000-cfs flow) Flood prob. $p(t)$	Risk cost $c_f(t)$
1. J–M	$ 15,000	4/25	$ 2,400	0	$ 0	0	$ 0
2. A–J	55,000	24/25	52,800	11/25	24,200	2/25	4,400
3. J–S	185,000	22/25	163,000	8/25	59,100	2/25	14,800
4. O–D	237,000	0	0	0	0	0	0
5. J–M	240,000	4/25	38,400	0	0	0	0
6. A–J	190,000	24/25	182,500	11/25	83,600	2/25	15,200
7. J–S	140,000	22/25	123,000	8/25	44,800	2/25	11,200
8. O–D	100,000	0	0	0	0	0	0
9. J–M	63,000	4/25	10,000	0	0	0	0
10. A–J	33,000	24/25	31,700	11/15	15,400	2/25	2,800
$c_f =$			$603,800		$227,100		$48,400

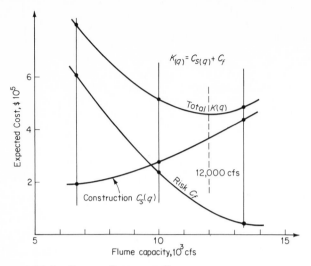

Fig. 10-6   Costs vs. flume capacity.

first machine has greater production capacity than the second and that the
storage facility is filled except during breakdowns.   Let

> S = storage capacity
> μ = mean time interval between breakdowns of the first machine
> τ = duration of breakdown
> $g(\tau)$ = probability density of τ
> p = production rate of the second machine
> c = cost per unit idle time of the second machine
> r = cost per unit time of one unit of storage capacity

The idle time of the second machine due to breakdown of the first is

$$
t = \begin{cases} \tau - \dfrac{S}{p} & S < p\tau \\ 0 & S \geqslant p\tau \end{cases}
$$

Therefore, the expected cost of idle time per breakdown of the first machine is

$$
c \int_{S/p}^{\infty} \left(\tau - \frac{S}{p} \right) g(\tau)\, d\tau
$$

With an average of $1/\mu$ breakdowns per unit time, total cost per unit time,
$K(S)$, is

$$
K(S) = rS + \frac{c}{\mu} \int_{S/p}^{\infty} \left(\tau - \frac{S}{p} \right) g(\tau)\, d\tau
$$

Using Leibnitz' rule,

$$\frac{dK(S)}{dS} = r - \frac{c}{p\mu}\left[1 - G\left(\frac{S}{p}\right)\right]$$

where $G(\tau)$ is the cumulative function of $g(\tau)$. Setting the derivative to zero to obtain optimum storage capacity,

$$G\left(\frac{S_0}{p}\right) = 1 - p\mu\frac{r}{c}$$

If $p\mu r > c$, no storage should be used because one unit of idle time of the second machine costs less than storing p units of product between breakdowns. Note that the cost function r can be made nonlinear with no computational difficulty. This solution was outlined by Hanssmann [18]. Problem 10-4 provides an exercise.

Example 10-4 Random demand with lead time The newsboy problem (Example 10-1) illustrates a basic model for stocking against a random demand. This example deals with the same situation except that a *lead time*, during which demand continues to act, has been included between order and delivery dates. The illustration is adapted from [29].

Orders for fuel are placed each month for delivery a month hence. The random demand X, assumed to arise uniformly during the month, is independent from month to month and is described by the density function $f(x)$. The cost of storing the fuel is c_h dollars per gal-month and the penalty cost is c_s dollars per gal-month for fuel not available upon demand. A monthly overhead cost of cS is incurred for a storage facility of capacity S. The problem is to choose the storage capacity S and the monthly ordering policy which minimize total expected costs. Assume that if the storage facility cannot hold the entire delivery, the excess is diverted to alternate storage at an added cost of c_w dollars per gal.

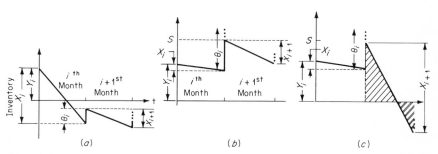

Fig. 10-7 Inventory vs. time. $s_i = Y_i + \theta_i$; $Y_i = $ stock on hand, $\theta_i = $ order quantity.
(a) Backlog $(s_i - X_i < 0)$; (b) no second-month shortage $(s_i - X_i \geqslant S$ and $X_{i+1} \leqslant S)$; (c) second-month shortage $(s_i - X_i \geqslant S$ and $X_{i+1} > S)$.

Let s be the amount on hand plus the amount ordered at the beginning of any month. Thus s is the operating decision variable, and its choice will affect costs only during the second month after ordering. At the end of the ith month, $i = 1, 2, \ldots$, the inventory will either be negative (i.e., a shortage or backlog) or nonnegative. For negative inventory, that is, $s_i - X_i < 0$, the cost during the $(i + 1)$st month is

$$c_s(X_i - s_i + \tfrac{1}{2}X_{i+1})$$

where the expression within parentheses represents the time-average shortage during the $(i + 1)$st month (see Fig. 10-7a).

For nonnegative inventory, two cases arise, depending on whether or not storage capacity is adequate for the incoming order. The two cases corresponding to positive inventory, but less than capacity, are:

1. For the case in which the $(i + 1)$st month begins with full storage S, that is, $s_i - X_i \geqslant S$, the costs are

$$c_h(S - \tfrac{1}{2}X_{i+1}) + c_w(s_i - X_i - S) \qquad \text{if } X_{i+1} \leqslant S$$

and

$$\frac{c_h S^2}{2X_{i+1}} + \frac{c_s(X_{i+1} - S)^2}{2X_{i+1}} + c_w(s_i - X_i - S) \qquad \text{if } X_{i+1} > S$$

respectively. In the first instance, $X_{i+1} \leqslant S$ (Fig. 10-7b), no shortages develop, and since demand is uniform during the month, the average inventory is $\tfrac{1}{2}[S + (S - X_{i+1})] = S - \tfrac{1}{2}X_{i+1}$. If $X_{i+1} > S$ (Fig. 10-7c), shortages do develop during the month. Holding costs arise until time t, and shortage accumulates thereafter. The average inventory (positive or negative) equals the area of the shaded triangles. The area of the upper triangle is $S^2/2X_{i+1}$, while the area of the lower triangle is $(X_{i+1} - S)^2/2X_{i+1}$. Also, the quantity $(s_i - X_i - S)$ is the amount that could not be accommodated in the shortage facility.

2. When the $(i + 1)$st month begins with a nonnegative inventory which is less than capacity, the costs are

$$c_h\left(s_i - X_i - \frac{X_{i+1}}{2}\right) \qquad \text{if } X_{i+1} \leqslant s_i - X_i$$

and

$$c_h\frac{(s_i - X_i)^2}{2X_{i+1}} + c_s\frac{(X_i + X_{i+1} - s_i)^2}{2X_{i+1}} \qquad \text{if } X_{i+1} \geqslant s_i - X_i$$

The total expected cost, $K(s,S)$, is obtained by summing the component costs, each weighted by its probability of occurrence (per month), that is,

$$K(s,S) = \int_{x_{i+1}=0}^{\infty} \int_{x_i=s}^{\infty} [c_s(x_i - s) + \tfrac{1}{2}x_{i+1}]f(x_i)f(x_{i+1})\, dx_i\, dx_{i+1}$$

$$+ \int_{x_{i+1}=0}^{S} \int_{x_i=0}^{s-S} [c_h(S - \tfrac{1}{2}x_{i+1}) + c_w(s - x_i - S)]f(x_i)f(x_{i+1})\\ dx_i\, dx_{i+1}$$

$$+ \int_{x_{i+1}=S}^{\infty} \int_{x_i=0}^{s-S} \left[\frac{c_h S^2}{2x_{i+1}} + \frac{c_s(x_{i+1} - S)^2}{2x_{i+1}} + c_w(s - x_i - S) \right]\\ f(x_i)f(x_{i+1})\, dx_i\, dx_{i+1}$$

$$+ \int_{x_{i+1}=0}^{s-x_i} \int_{x_i=s-S}^{s} [c_h(s - x_i - \tfrac{1}{2}x_{i+1})]f(x_i)f(x_{i+1})\, dx_i\, dx_{i+1}$$

$$+ \int_{x_{i+1}=s-x_i}^{\infty} \int_{x_i=s-S}^{s} \left[c_h \frac{(s - x_i)^2}{2x_{i+1}} + c_s \frac{(x_i + x_{i+1} - s)^2}{2x_{i+1}} \right]\\ f(x_i)f(x_{i+1})\, dx_i\, dx_{i+1}$$

$$+ cS$$

The subscripts on s have been dropped because of the equivalence from month to month. To obtain the derivatives $\partial K/\partial s$ and $\partial K/\partial S$, one uses Leibnitz' rule (Sec. 10-1). A solution for s and S can be obtained using numerical methods.

Example 10-5 Sizing of parallel reservoirs Water is required to operate the locks of a navigation canal to be built across an isthmus. Two nearby streams are likely sources of supply. To utilize them requires reservoirs to store and release water as needed. The mean monthly reservoir delivery capacities as functions of the annual costs of the dams and reservoirs for each stream, C_1 and C_2, are indicated in Fig. 10-8. The annual costs include

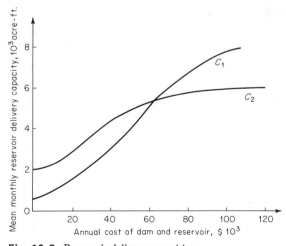

Fig. 10-8 Reservoir delivery capacities.

amortization of the construction and operating costs. The asymptotic character of the curves suggests reservoir capacities large enough to be capable of supplying nearly the mean streamflow. The problem is to determine the optimum investment level in each reservoir.

Assume that the monthly delivery capacity for each reservoir is an independent normal random variable. The mean depends upon reservoir size and is given by Fig. 10-8. The standard deviation is approximately 1,000 acre-ft per month regardless of reservoir capacity. Since shipping on the canal is anticipated to be random, the monthly water requirement is also random and assumed to be an independent normal variable with a mean of 4,000 acre-ft per month and a standard deviation of 1,000 acre-ft per month. An expected revenue loss of $60,000 is estimated due to delayed or rerouted shipping for each month that an inadequate supply of water results from insufficient reservoir capacity.

We choose a total monthly expected cost criterion. The annual expected cost K is the sum of the nonrandom annual operating and amortization costs C_s and the cost of a water shortage C_d multiplied by the associated probability p, that is,

$$K = C_s + 12pC_d$$

The factor 12 multiplies the monthly expected cost of water shortage.

The total delivery capacity S is the sum of the random delivery capacities from each reservoir. The total mean delivery capacity is $\mu_s = \mu_1 + \mu_2$, and the standard deviation is $\sigma_s = \sqrt{\sigma_1^2 + \sigma_2^2}$, where the subscripts refer to corresponding reservoirs. Letting the random demand for water be D, the difference $S - D$ is the random excess (or deficiency) of supply over demand, The difference between two normal variables is also a normal variable, with mean $\mu_s - \mu_d$ and variance $\sigma_s^2 + \sigma_d^2$, according to Prob. 9-14. Therefore, the probability of a deficiency in water supply is

$$p = \frac{1}{\sqrt{2\pi}} \int_{-\infty}^{-L} e^{-z^2/2} \, dz$$

where the limit L is

$$L = \frac{\mu_s - \mu_d}{\sqrt{\sigma_s^2 + \sigma_d^2}} = \frac{\mu_1 + \mu_2 - \mu_d}{\sqrt{\sigma_1^2 + \sigma_2^2 + \sigma_d^2}} = \frac{\mu_1 + \mu_2 - 4,000}{1,734}$$

since $\sigma_1 = \sigma_2 = \sigma_d = 1,000$ and $\mu_d = 4,000$ acre-ft per month.

Table 10-3 enumerates the total expected annual cost K for various combinations of reservoir costs C_1 and C_2. Values of p are obtained using the normal table in Appendix 4. Figure 10-9 illustrates the family of total annual expected costs, and interpolation provides the optimal solution (point A), $C_1 = \$75,000$ per year and $C_2 = 0$. Hence we build only one dam.

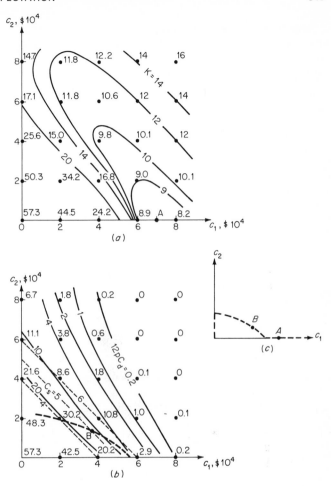

Fig. 10-9 (a) K contours; (b) $12pC_d$ contours; (c) optimal-investment trajectory.

Assume that an initial fund equivalent to amortized construction and operating costs of only $50,000 is available. Since this is less than the unconstrained minimum of $75,000, what reservoir capacities should be built? Fiscal constraints are common in industry and government. We now wish to minimize $C_s + 12pC_d$ subject to the constraint $C_s \leqslant \$50,000$. By inspection of Fig. 10-9b, the optimal solution is point B ($C_1 = \$37,000$, $C_2 = \$13,000$). It occurs at the point of tangency of a $12pC_d$ contour and the constraint $C_s = \$50,000$. The locus of points of tangency for various values of the constraint is the heavily dashed curve in Fig. 10-9b. It establishes the *optimal-*

Table 10-3 Total expected annual cost

Annual cost, 10^4 \$/yr Reservoir		Total	Mean capacity, 10^3 acre-ft/mo			Probability of shortage		Annual shortage cost, 10^4 \$/yr	Total expected annual cost, 10^4 \$/yr
C_1	C_2	C_s	μ_1	μ_2	μ_s $(=\mu_1+\mu_2)$	L	p	$12c_d p$	K
0	0	0	0.5	2.0	2.5	−0.866	0.81	57.3	57.3
	2	2		2.8	3.3	−0.405	0.67	48.3	50.3
	4	4		4.4	4.9	0.520	0.30	21.6	25.6
	6	6		5.2	5.7	0.980	0.16	11.5	17.1
	8	8		5.8	6.3	1.32	0.093	6.7	14.7
2	0	2	1.6	2.0	3.6	−0.231	0.59	42.5	44.5
	2	4		2.8	4.4	0.230	0.42	30.2	34.2
	4	6		4.4	6.0	1.15	0.12	8.6	14.6
	6	8		5.2	6.8	1.62	0.053	3.8	11.8
	8	0		5.8	7.4	1.96	0.025	1.8	11.8
4	0	4	3.0	2.0	5.0	0.575	0.28	20.2	24.2
	2	6		2.8	5.8	1.04	0.15	10.8	16.8
	4	8		4.4	7.4	1.96	0.025	1.8	9.8
	6	10		5.2	8.2	2.42	0.008	0.6	10.6
	8	12		5.8	8.8	2.77	0.003	0.2	12.2
6	0	6	5.0	2.0	7.0	1.73	0.041	3.0	9.0
	2	8		2.8	7.8	2.19	0.014	1.0	9.0
	4	10		4.4	9.4	3.11	0.001	0.1	10.1
	6	12		5.2	10.2	3.58	0	0	12
	8	14		5.8	10.8	3.92	0	0	14
8	0	8	6.8	2.0	8.8	2.77	0.003	0.2	8.2
	2	10		2.8	9.6	3.23	0.001	0.1	10.1
	4	12		4.4	11.2	4.15	0	0	12
	6	14		5.2	12.0	4.61	0	0	14
	8	16		5.8	12.6	4.97	0	0	16

investment trajectory when funds are limited. The technique also applies when the constraint, as well as the objective function, is nonlinear.

Hence, with unlimited resources we build one dam but with limited resources we build two. This apparent paradox arises because the curves in Fig. 10-8 intersect. In fact, without further computation, we would expect from the information in Fig. 10-8 that the shape of the complete optimal-investment trajectory will be approximately as shown in Fig. 10-9c.

From inspection of Fig. 10-8 one might incorrectly conclude that an optimal-investment trajectory should indicate building only reservoir 1 for $C_s > \$62{,}000$ and only reservoir 2 for $C_s < \$62{,}000$, the cost at which the two lines cross. The fallacy lies in a relationship which we shall encounter again in the reliability of parallel components (Sec. 11-1) and in the mean service rate of parallel servers for a queue (Sec. 11-5). The random-service function (reliability, delivery capacity, service rate) of two or more items (components, storage units, servers) used in parallel is greater than the sum of their individual random-service functions. This means that over a cost range where the mean monthly delivery capacities are approximately equal, it is cheaper to have two reservoirs than one.

Example 10-6   Sensitivity to traffic volume   In Example 1-4, an average daily traffic of 5,000 vehicles was assumed. Daily traffic is, however, a notoriously difficult quantity to predict. Suppose that an average daily traffic of between 3,000 and 6,000 vehicles is anticipated. Will this lack of precision in estimated traffic affect our choice of route?

We solve for the average daily traffic v, for which BCR_{m-r} is unity. Since

$$AUC_r = 365v\left[\frac{20}{50}(1 + 1.6) + 20(0.05 + 0.048)\right] = 1{,}095v$$

$$AUC_m = 365v\left[\frac{15}{50}(1 + 1.6) + 15(0.05 + 0.048)\right] = 901v$$

and

$$BCR_{m-r} = 1 = \frac{(1{,}095 - 901)v}{671{,}600 - 475{,}300} = \frac{194v}{196{,}300}$$

it follows that $v = 1{,}012$ vehicles per day. Since the lower bound of our estimate was 3,000 vehicles per day, the mountain route is chosen.

If noncommercial users' time value is also uncertain, we must consider a *multivariable analysis* [23]. We repeat the computations for two additional

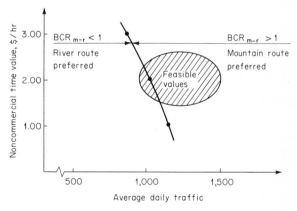

Fig. 10-10 BCR_{m-r} related to feasible values of time cost and daily traffic.

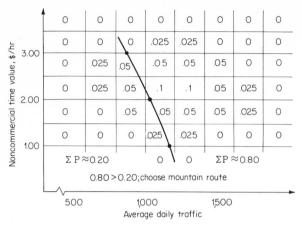

Fig. 10-11 Probability map.

values of noncommercial time cost, $1 and $3 per hour. Figure 10-10 illustrates the results.

If the ranges of feasible values for daily traffic and noncommercial time cost (shaded) lie largely in the "mountain route preferred" region, its choice seems sound. If approximately equal portions of the feasible region lie on each side of the BCR = 1 line, a more refined effort is suggested. The expected-value decision criterion seems appropriate if an a priori joint density distribution, such as that shown in Fig. 10-11, can be established. The probabilities may be assigned on the basis of previous records from similar installations, collective judgment, or other sources as appropriate. The sum of the conditional probabilities over all cells must be unity.

The technique clearly can be extended to more than two alternatives. For three routes, we would have two BCR = 1 lines and three regions in Fig. 10-11, and so on. The BCR = 1 lines divide the probability map into areas of alternative superiorities. Although we have applied sensitivity analysis to a BCR comparison, its application is also pertinent to other comparison methods.

Example 10-7   Minimizing expected cost of testing   Soil sampling and testing and tests on structural components require decisions regarding the number of tests to perform. Increasing the number of tests increases the cost of testing but reduces costs in design or construction due to mis-estimation. The problem is to determine the test size which minimizes total expected cost.

Let μ be the mean value of a random property, say the failure strength of a beam. A series of n tests results in values $x_1, x_2, \ldots, x_n$, and their average $x = (x_1 + \cdots + x_n)/n$ is used as the estimate of μ. Assume that the cost of misestimation is proportional to its magnitude but differs according to whether the estimate is high or low. Let C_h and C_l be the unit costs of high and low estimates, respectively, so that the total cost of misestimation is

$$C_h(\bar{x} - \mu) \, \mathcal{U} \, (\bar{x} - \mu) + C_l(\mu - \bar{x}) \, \mathcal{U} \, (\mu - \bar{x})$$

where $\mathcal{U}(a - b)$ is the step function of Sec. 5-6. The sampling cost C_s is assumed to be proportional to the test size plus a fixed setup cost C_f and might be described by

$$C_s = C_f + C_u n$$

where C_u is the unit cost of testing.

In many engineering applications, the random property being measured can be described by a normal law with mean μ and variance σ^2. It follows that the random variable $\bar{x}$ is also described by a normal law, $n(\bar{x})$, with mean μ and variance σ^2/n. The total expected cost associated with a sample of size n, $K(n)$, is

$$K(n) = C_f + C_u n + C_l \int_{-\infty}^{\mu} (\mu - \bar{x}) \, n(\bar{x}) \, d\bar{x} + C_h \int_{\mu}^{\infty} (\bar{x} - \mu) \, n(\bar{x}) \, d\bar{x}$$

$$= C_f + C_u n + \frac{(C_l + C_h) \sigma}{\sqrt{2\pi n}}$$

By integrating, and differentiating with respect to n, one concludes that the sample size for minimum expected cost is

$$n_0 = \left(\frac{C_l + C_h}{2} \frac{\sigma}{\sqrt{2\pi C_u}} \right)^{2/3}$$

The appearance of the average unit cost of misestimation, $(C_l + C_h)/2$, is due to the symmetry of the normal law about its mean and is not a general result. Although the costs of misestimation cannot usually be precisely identified, the example indicates how one might improve upon simply guessing at an appropriate test size. Of course, the differentiation with respect to a discrete variable is only suggestive.

Example 10-8 Optimal test sequence Sometimes economies are achieved by a judicious choice of the sequence in which required tests of hardness, dimensional tolerance, conductivity, etc., are performed. Suppose that there are three tests a, b, and c. Let C_a, C_b, C_c and p_a, p_b, p_c be the associated costs of performing the ith test and the probabilities that the component fails the test, respectively. The sequence of tests continues until the first rejection, after which no further tests are performed on that component. In what sequence should the tests be performed so that the total expected cost of testing is a minimum?

For convenience, assume that the tests are identified so that $C_a/p_a < C_b/p_b < C_c/p_c$. Let $K(a,b,c)$ be the expected cost of performing the tests in the sequence a, b, c. Clearly,

$$K(a,b,c) = C_a + C_b(1 - p_a) + C_c(1 - p_a)(1 - p_b)$$

since the tests can be performed in any order and the costs and probabilities are independent of each other. Now suppose that the order of tests a and b is transposed. The expected cost $K(b,a,c)$ is

$$K(b,a,c) = C_b + C_a(1 - p_b) + C_c(1 - p_a)(1 - p_b)$$

Consider the ratio

$$\frac{K(b,a,c)}{K(a,b,c)} = \frac{C_b + C_a(1 - p_b) + C_c(1 - p_a)(1 - p_b)}{C_a + C_b(1 - p_a) + C_c(1 - p_a)(1 - p_b)} = \frac{\alpha - C_a/p_a}{\alpha - C_b/p_b}$$

where $\alpha = [(C_a + C_b) + C_c(1 - p_a)(1 - p_b)] \div p_a p_b$. Since $C_a/p_a < C_b/p_b$, the numerator exceeds the denominator, so that the expected cost of testing in the sequence b, a, c exceeds the expected cost of testing in the sequence a, b, c. Next, the expected cost of the order a, b, c can be compared with that for the order a, c, b. Since $C_b/p_b < C_c/p_c$, the order a, b, c has the lower expected cost.

For more than three tests, a similar logic is applied. By a series of transpositions of adjacent pairs of tests, each yielding a lower expected cost, an optimal sequence is reached. One concludes that tests should be performed in the sequence determined by the increasing order of the cost-to-probability ratios [24].

Example 10-9   Direct probabilistic design[1]   This example reprints a portion of a recent paper by Benjamin [5].

> Structural design can be based directly on probabilistic concepts. All such procedures depend on the quantity and quality of the available information. If adequate data on maximum loads are not available, design can be accomplished using a deterministic loading and a probabilistic response. For example, assume that actual strength data are available for reinforced concrete beams of a particular type under service conditions and that the strength can be satisfactorily modeled by Fig. 5. If a 3 % chance of failure is acceptable at or prior to attaining a total load of 9.5 kips, design follows directly. The designer sets the allowable acceptable chance of failure in the range of well defined probabilities, and finds the ultimate load capacity of the beam. If this

[1] The figure numbers and reference numbers in this example correspond to the paper from which the material is reprinted, not to the other portions of this text.

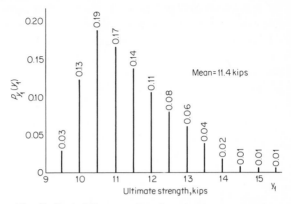

Fig. 5 Probability mass function of ultimate strength.

load level is inadequate, a similar set of data for a larger beam can be used or a theoretical strength relationship can be used to revise the design, assuming that the basic random variable shown in Fig. 3 applies to the new beam.

An alternate and more promising procedure has been suggested. In this approach, analysis and design remain deterministic as to detail but both loading and strengths are described probabilistically. For example, with conventional buildings it can be shown that it is only necessary to estimate the chances of exceeding the dead load plus live load, and of the acceptable ultimate load to obtain a sufficient probabilistic model of the real loading. Similarly, owing to the particular

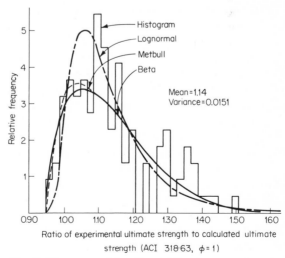

Fig. 3 Histogram of data for 109 beams.

nature of strength data for concrete beams, a sufficient description of the strength of concrete beams can be made by estimates of two probability measures. The great advantage of such a development is that the underlying basis of analysis and design is admitted to be probabilistic in nature. The development of more complex rational probability-based code formats can then proceed within well established rules. Furthermore, existing deterministic procedures can be modified on a rational step-by-step basis to improve consistency with known reliability once this fundamental step is taken.

DYNAMIC LOADINGS

The two most important sources of dynamic loadings are wind and seismic activity. The observed vibration of some tall flexible buildings under wind loading dictates that the design of such structures for a static wind loading is no longer acceptable. Actual wind loadings are probabilistic and dynamic in character, requiring a solution based on the theory of random vibrations (4, 5). Deterministic code wind pressures may lead to improper design with these structures. The real design problem may not even be recognized.

Earthquake loadings have long been recognized as probabilistic in nature (2, 3, 16). The response of the structure to the loading is a problem in probabilistic structural dynamics (6, 15). Furthermore, the structural designer must consider more than possible damage to the structural system. Architectural, mechanical, and electrical damage must be considered as well as damage to the building contents. In design for normal live loadings, it is always possible to be so conservative that the probability of damage under any legal loading approaches zero. In contrast, it is impossible to design an earthquake-proof building system even if unlimited funds were available. This means that the responsible structural engineer can either use the unrealistic static loads recommended by building codes, or attempt to make a rational design under the most difficult of conditions.

The selection of the optimum building system under conditions of uncertainty about possible damage by seismic loadings requires an acceptance of the probabilistic nature of reality. Well developed techniques for making decisions under uncertainty exist in the business world (11), and these concepts can be adapted to the earthquake engineering problem. The probabilistic model is illustrated by the decision tree (2) of Fig. 11. The model is a good representation of reality in which the engineer must make a decision under conditions of uncertainty about the future.

In Fig. 11, the decision maker is shown faced with taking one of

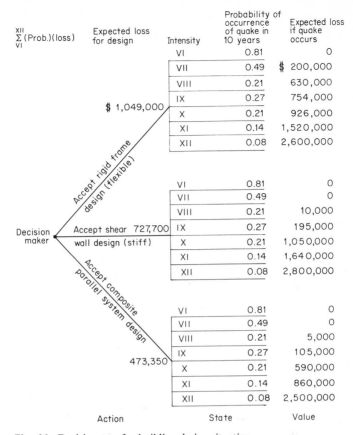

$\sum_{VI}^{XII}$ (Prob.)(loss)	Expected loss for design	Intensity	Probability of occurrence of quake in 10 years	Expected loss if quake occurs
		VI	0.81	0
		VII	0.49	$ 200,000
		VIII	0.21	630,000
		IX	0.27	754,000
	$ 1,049,000	X	0.21	926,000
		XI	0.14	1,520,000
		XII	0.08	2,600,000
		VI	0.81	0
		VII	0.49	0
		VIII	0.21	10,000
Decision maker	Accept shear 727,700 wall design (stiff)	IX	0.27	195,000
		X	0.21	1,050,000
		XI	0.14	1,640,000
		XII	0.08	2,800,000
		VI	0.81	0
		VII	0.49	0
		VIII	0.21	5,000
		IX	0.27	105,000
	473,350	X	0.21	590,000
		XI	0.14	860,000
		XII	0.08	2,500,000
Action		State		Value

Fig. 11 Decision tree for building design situation.

three possible actions. If he uses a rigid frame structural system and an earthquake of Modified Mercalli intensity VI occurs, he estimates his likely loss to be $0. The probability of occurrence of one such event in the 10-yr time interval of interest is 0.81. If an intensity of VII is found, the expected damage is $200,000. The chance of one such event in 10 yr is 0.21. The decision tree shown assumes that only one occurrence need be considered and nonoccurrence does not involve a loss so that these branches can be omitted. The occurrences of the intensity levels are independent, so that the sum of the probabilities of occurrence of all the intensity levels is not necessarily unity, as with mutually-exclusive collectively-exhaustive states.

The decision situation is analyzed by computing the expected values of the losses for each action. Thus, for the rigid frame, $1,049,000 is equal to the sum of the products of the probability of occurrence by

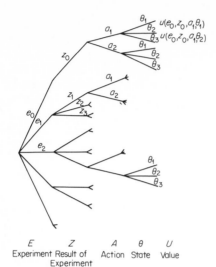

E	Z	A	θ	U
Experiment	Result of Experiment	Action	State	Value

Fig. 12 Decision tree including information branches.

the loss, given an occurrence.   The optimum decision has the smallest expected loss.   The general model shown in Fig. 12 includes the possibility of making an information decision before taking an action. This is a probabilistic mathematical model of reality superior to all possible deterministic concepts.

  2. Benjamin, J. R., "Probabilistic Models for Seismic Force Design," ASCE Design Seminar: Buildings in Earthquake and Wind and Analysis of Their Lateral Resistance, May, 1967, Seattle, Wash.
  3. Cornell, C. A., "Stochastic Process Models in Structural Engineering," *Technical Report No. 34*, Department of Civil Engineering, Stanford University, Calif., 1964.
  6. Freudenthal, A. M., and Shinozuka, M., "On Upper and Lower Bounds of the Probability of Structural Failure Under Earthquake Acceleration," *Transactions*, Japan Society of Civil Engineers, Tokyo, Japan, June, 1965.
 11. Raiffa, H., and Schlaifer, H., "Applied Statistical Decision Theory," Graduate School of Business Administration, Harvard University, 1961.
 15. Rosenblueth, E., and Bustamante, J. I., "Distribution of Structural Response to Earthquakes," *Journal of the Engineering Mechanics Division*, Vol. 88, No. EM3, ASCE, Proc. Paper No. 3177, June, 1962.
 16. Rosenblueth, E., "Probabilistic Design to Resist Earthquakes," *Journal of the Engineering Mechanics Division*, ASCE, Vol. 90, No. EM5, Proc. Paper 4090, Oct., 1964, pp. 189–220.

Example 10-10 Stochastic and chance-constrained linear programming

In the mathematical programming formulations in Chaps. 2 to 6, we usually assumed that parameters were known constants.   When the parameters are random variables, the formulation is called *stochastic programming*.   The theoretical development of stochastic programming is quite limited, and most of the results are for linear problems.   Much of the discussion here is based upon Hillier and Lieberman [19].

Consider the case in which the random parameters are defined on a finite sample space.   If any of the objective coefficients are random, we replace the random objective function by its expected value.   If constraint coefficients or the resource constants are random-valued, then some clarification is needed as to what constitutes a feasible solution.   The assumption here is that the solution must satisfy all the constraints for all values of the random parameters. One procedure for solving the stochastic linear-programming problem is simply to augment the constraint set to include all possibilities.

A trivial numerical example illustrates the idea.   Consider a two-variable linear-programming problem with two constraints.   The three possible combinations of random parameters are:

	c_1	c_2	b_1	b_2	a_{11}	a_{12}	a_{21}	a_{22}
1	3	2	5	4	1	3	2	2
2	1.5	2	5	3.5	1	2	1	2
3	4	2	5	8	1	2	5	2

and the associated probabilities are 0.5, 0.2, and 0.3, respectively.   Note that c_1, b_2, a_{12}, and a_{21} are random parameters while c_2, b_1, a_{11}, and a_{22} are fixed.

The objective function, $z = c_1 x_1 + c_2 x_2$, is replaced by its expected value since c_1 is a random parameter.   Thus,

Min: $E(z) = [(3)(0.5) + (1.5)(0.2) + (4)(0.3)] x_1 + 2x_2 = 3x_1 + 2x_2$

The constraint set

$$a_{11} x_1 + a_{12} x_2 \leqslant b_1$$
$$a_{21} x_1 + a_{22} x_2 \leqslant b_2$$

becomes

$$x_1 + 3x_2 \leqslant 5$$
$$2x_1 + 2x_2 \leqslant 4$$
$$x_1 + 2x_2 \leqslant 5$$
$$x_1 + 2x_2 \leqslant 3.5$$
$$x_1 + 2x_2 \leqslant 5$$
$$5x_1 + 2x_2 \leqslant 8$$

And, of course, the nonnegativity conditions are unchanged.   Note the tendency of the constraint set to become large even for relatively small problems.   In this instance, the first, second, and sixth constraints dominate and

the others can be ignored.   Thus, the stochastic linear-programming problem
is written

Min: $E(z) = 3x_1 + 2x_2$

Subject to: $x_1 + 3x_2 \leqslant 5$
$2x_1 + 2x_2 \leqslant 4$
$5x_1 + 2x_2 \leqslant 8$
$x_1, x_2 \geqslant 0$

Techniques for somewhat more general cases have been developed
([16], [19] and [34]).   Another case arises when it is not essential that every
constraint be satisfied.   Instead, preferences (or probabilities) on a unit
scale are assigned to indicate the relative desirability that a constraint be
satisfied.   This approach has been called *chance-constrained programming*
by its authors, Charnes and Cooper ([7] and [8]).

In chance-constrained programming, a constraint with random param-
eters is replaced by a probability statement.   For example, if $\sum a_{ij}x_j \leqslant b_i$
is a random constraint, it is replaced by

$$P\{\sum a_{ij}x_j \leqslant b_i\} \geqslant p_i$$

where p_i is the given probability that the constraint be satisfied.   For the
stochastic linear-programming problem, the probabilities are unity.   A
feasible solution in the chance-constrained problem need not satisfy every
constraint.

To simplify the discussion, suppose that the b_i are random and the
a_{ij} have fixed values.   Let β_i be the value of $\sum a_{ij}x_j$ for which the probability
statement is a strict equality, that is,

$$P\{b_i \geqslant \beta_i\} = p_i$$

Chance-constrained programming replaces the random constraint and its
probability statement by the nonrandom linear constraint

$$\sum a_{ij}x_j \leqslant \beta_i$$

Note that the β_i are known when the probability functions for the b_i are
known (see Fig. 10-12).   For the special case in which the b_i are normal variables with means μ_i and variances σ_i, one can write

$$P\{b_i \geqslant \sum a_{ij}x_j\} = P\left\{\frac{b_i - \mu_i}{\sigma_i} \geqslant \frac{\sum a_{ij}x_j - \mu_i}{\sigma_i}\right\} \geqslant p_i$$

Letting β_i be the value of

$$\frac{\sum a_{ij}x_j - \mu_i}{\sigma_i}$$

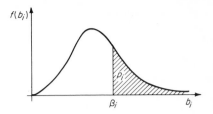

Fig. 10-12 Forming a chance constraint.

for which the probability is p_i, one forms the linear constraints

$$\sum a_{ij} x_j \leqslant \mu_i + \sigma_i \beta_i$$

No mention has been made of the objective function for the chance-constrained case when the cost coefficients are random. A variety of choices is possible, including the expected value. Summarizing, a chance-constrained version of the linear-programming problem is

Min: $E(z) = E(c_1) x_1 + \cdots + E(c_n) x_n$

Subject to: $\sum_{j} a_{ij} x_j \leqslant \mu_i + \sigma_i \beta_i$ $i = 1, \ldots, n$

$x_j \geqslant 0$ $j = 1, \ldots, m$

for random cost coefficients and normally distributed resource variables.

An extension of this example appears in Example 11-9 as Markov decision programming. Also, see [34].

10-2 CLOSED COMPETITIVE BIDDING

Bidding is fundamental to the construction industry and to much of our economic system. The subject has recently attracted interest in several industries. This section describes models for closed competitive bidding, i.e., bidding by sealed tenders, and probes other aspects of the decision process.

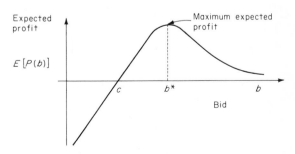

Fig. 10-13 Expected profit vs. amount bid.

A bidder may have a number of objectives, and they may vary in time. We assume an expected-profit criterion. The expected profit $E[P(b)]$ with a bid b is

$$E[P(b)] = (b - c)\,\alpha(b) \tag{2}$$

where c is the expected (estimated) cost of executing the job and $\alpha(b)$ is the probability of winning with bid b. Figure 10-13 illustrates an expected-profit function.

For a given probability-of-winning function, the optimum bid b^* might be obtained by setting the derivative of Eq. (2) to zero. The common difficulty is to determine the function $\alpha(b)$. Consider some possibilities.

PROBABILITY OF WINNING

Bids are often a matter of public record. Insights to a competitor's strategy may be obtained by studying the ratios of his cost estimates to ours for past contracts on which we both had bid. Let r be this ratio, and suppose that a density function $f(r)$ is formed. Our chance of winning with a bid b, $\alpha(b)$, is the chance that our competitor's bid is greater than b, that is,

$$\alpha(b) = \int_{b/c}^{\infty} f(r)\,dr \tag{3}$$

Usually, one bids against k known competitors, and Eq. (3) generalizes as

$$\alpha(b;k) = \int_{b/c}^{\infty} \cdots \int_{b/c}^{\infty} f(r_1, \ldots, r_k)\,dr_1 \cdots dr_k$$

where $f(r_1, \ldots, r_k)$ is the joint density for the entire competition [30]. Sometimes a competitor is not known, or perhaps available data are inadequate. Then one might study the ratios of the winning bids to our cost estimates for past contracts.

Another approach is to approximate the last integral by the sum

$$1 - \sum_{j=0}^{n-1} [F(r_j + \Delta r_j) - F(r_j)]$$

where the interval $\{0, b/c\}$ has been divided into n subintervals of length Δr_j, $j = 0, 1, \ldots, n - 1$, and $F(r)$ is the cumulative distribution. The approximation improves as n increases while each $\Delta r_j \to 0$.

SIMULTANEOUS BIDDING OF SEVERAL CONTRACTS

Consider simultaneous bidding of several contracts. Generalizing Eq. (2) and assuming independent situations, one has

$$E[P(b_1, \ldots, b_m)] = \sum_{i=1}^{m} (b_i - c_i)\,\alpha_i(b_i)$$

for the total expected profit from bidding m contracts at levels $b_1, \ldots, b_m$. Suppose that there is a bid limit B, that is,

$$b_1 + \cdots + b_m \leqslant B$$

We seek to derive the optimum bid mix.

Solution by Lagrange multiplier   If the total of the unconstrained optimal bids exceeds B, the inequality in the bid constraint is replaced by an equality.   This assumes that the total expected profit function is strictly increasing for bids below the unconstrained optimal values.   As in Sec. 5-2, we form the Lagrangian:

$$L = \sum_{i=1}^{m} (b_i - c_i)\, \alpha_i(b_i) + \lambda \left(\sum_{i=1}^{m} b_i - B \right)$$

where λ is the Lagrange multiplier.   The optimization proceeds as usual.

Solution by this technique requires the simultaneous solution of non-linear equations and is convenient only when the number of contracts is small. There is also an implicit assumption that all m contracts must be bid.   If it is permissible to refrain from bidding a contract(s), the total expected profit may be increased.   There are exactly $2^m - 1$ combinations of $1, 2, \ldots, m$ contracts, and in principle, the optimum bids for each contract combination must be determined—an unattractive prospect even for moderate numbers of contracts.

Solution by graphical technique   One can plot the expected profits for various bids on each of the m contracts.   Points of positive slope (Fig. 10-13) are located so that the total bid constraint is satisfied.   Using the technique of Example 5-19, the optimal solution occurs where the expected-profit-to-bid ratios for each contract are equal.   As in Example 5-19, various combinations of the available bid curves must be evaluated to ensure a global optimum.

Solution by dynamic programming   The m individual contracts are regarded as stages of a dynamic-programming formulation.   Let $\pi_i(b_i, s)$ be the expected profit from an allocation of s dollars among (the last) i contracts using an optimal policy with a bid b_i for the ith contract.

The recursion relation, as suggested in Chap. 6, is written

$$\pi_i^*(s) \equiv \max_{0 \leqslant b_i \leqslant s} [\pi_i(b_i, s)] = \max_{0 \leqslant b_i \leqslant s} [(b_i - c_i)\, \alpha_i(b_i, k_i)(1 - \delta_0^{b_i})$$

$$+ \pi_{i-1}^*(s - b_i)]$$

for $i = 1, 2, \ldots, m$, where $\delta_0^{b_i} \equiv \delta(b_i)$ is the Kronecker delta and the center member defines $\pi_i^*(s)$.   One can set the initial value $\pi_0^*(s) = 0$, although other choices are possible.

$$\begin{array}{ccc} & \xrightarrow{\quad} \Delta_{ij} \xleftarrow{\quad} & \\ \hline 0 & \gamma_i = \beta_{i,0}\,\beta_{i,j-1}\,\beta_{i,j} & \gamma_i' = \beta_{i,n} \quad \overset{\longrightarrow}{\text{Bid}} \text{ for contract } i \end{array}$$

Fig. 10-14 Division of the bid range into intervals.

Note how the dynamic-programming formulation avoids bidding less profitable contracts while satisfying the total bid constraint.

Solution by integer linear programming Using the approximate (subjective) probabilities of Eq. (3), one can devise a formulation from which solutions can be derived by the integer linear-programming techniques of Sec. 4-6.

For each contract, identify a range $[\gamma_i, \gamma_i']$ which seems certain to include the optimal bid. In a competitive industry, this is not likely to be an unreasonable identification. Next, divide the range into n_i appropriate intervals. Let Δ_{ij} be the length of the jth interval and $\beta_{i,j-1}$ and $\beta_{i,j}$ its end points, $j = 0, 1, \ldots, n$ (see Fig. 10-14).

The expected profit ϵ_{ij} for a bid $b = \beta_{ij}$ on the ith contract is written

$$\epsilon_{ij} = (\beta_{ij} - c_i)\left[1 - F\left(\frac{\beta_{ij}}{c_i}\right)\right]$$

Let x_{ij} be a zero-one variable such that

$$\sum_{j=0}^{n_i} x_{ij} \leqslant 1 \qquad \text{all } i$$

In other words, no more than one of the $n_i + 1$ variables x_{ij} for a given i can be unity.

The total expected profit for a single contract is

$$\sum_{j=0}^{n} x_j(\beta_j - c)\left[1 - F\left(\frac{\beta_j}{c}\right)\right] = \sum_{j=0}^{n} \epsilon_j x_j$$

This is to be maximized subject to the constraints

$$\sum_{j=0}^{n} x_j \leqslant 1 \qquad x_j = 0 \text{ or } 1; j = 0, 1, \ldots, n$$

For m contracts, the total expected profit is

$$E[P(b)] = \sum_{i=1}^{m} \sum_{j=0}^{n} \epsilon_{ij} x_{ij}$$

This is to be maximized subject to

$$\sum_{j=0}^{n} x_{ij} \leqslant 1 \qquad i = 1, 2, \ldots, m$$

and

$$\sum_{i=1}^{m} \sum_{j=0}^{n} \beta_{ij} x_{ij} \leqslant B$$

for $x_{ij} = 0$ or 1, all i and j.

For each i, the presence of an index $j = l$ such that $x_{il} = 1$ is the signal to bid the ith contract, and the optimum bid is $b_i = \beta_{il}$. The absence of an index j such that $x_{ij} = 1$ is a signal to not bid the ith contract.

These four formulations describe the same decision model. Each formulation has been suggested by an optimization technique: Lagrange multiplier, graphical, dynamic programming, and integer programming. Some techniques are better suited to certain situations than to others.

A disadvantage of the Lagrange multiplier and graphical optimizations has been mentioned, i.e., they do not determine the optimal bid mix directly. An advantage of the dynamic and integer linear programming and graphical techniques is their ability to use numerical information and, also, to use qualitative or partially reliable information when it is the best available. The dynamic-programming formulation has the advantage of routinely handling later contracts when (and if) desirable. Also, the two programming formulations can handle multiconstraint situations, e.g., limitations of men and machines, besides money. The ability to perform a sensitivity analysis may also give one formulation a preference over another.

The discussion illustrates how the knowledgeable analyst can "shape" models consistent with the data (or lack of it). References [13], [14], and [30] provide additional information. Consider a numerical example adapted from [30].

Example 10-11   Lagrange multiplier and dynamic-programming techniques   A contractor is invited to bid on three independent contracts. A prebid survey reveals the following cost estimates: $c_1 = \$4,000$, $c_2 = \$5,000$, $c_3 = \$6,000$. A single competitor is assumed, and his bidding behavior is judged to follow a rectangular distribution with respect to the contractor's cost estimates, namely,

$$\alpha_i(b_i) = \begin{cases} 0 & \beta c_i < b_i \\ \displaystyle\int_{b_i/c_i}^{\beta} \frac{1}{\beta - \alpha} \, dr & \alpha c_i \leqslant b_i \leqslant \beta c_i; \; i = 1, 2, 3 \\ 1 & b_i < \alpha c_i \end{cases}$$

The parameters, α and β, equal 1 and 2, respectively.

It is assumed that the contractor desires to maximize his total expected profits. Because of the independence assumption, the expected-profit function is

$$E[P(b_1,b_2,b_3)] = \sum_{i=1}^{3} (b_i - c_i)\,\alpha_i(b_i)$$

$$= \sum_{i=1}^{3} (b_i - c_i)\left(2 - \frac{b_i}{c_i}\right) \tag{4}$$

A maximization of Eq. (4) would result in bids of $6,000, $7,500, and $9,000, respectively. The total expected profit corresponding to these bids is $3,750.

The Lagrange multiplier   Suppose that a bonding company has limited the contractor's total bid-sum to $15,000. The required optimization is subject to the bid constraint

$$b_1 + b_2 + b_3 \leqslant \$15,000$$

The unconstrained optimal bids clearly violate this constraint.

If the decision is to bid the three contracts, the Lagrange formulation is appropriate:

$$L = \sum_{i=1}^{3} (b_i - c_i)\left(2 - \frac{b_i}{c_i}\right) + \lambda(b_1 + b_2 + b_3 - 15,000)$$

Optimization yields the bids $4,000, $5,000, and $6,000. The corresponding expected profit is zero.

Had the contractor bid contracts 1 and 3 at the optimal unconstrained-bid prices, his expected profit would have been $2,500. Had he bid only contracts 2 and 3, the given strategy would have resulted in an expected profit of $2,550. This strategy—do not bid 1, $b_2 = \$6,820$, $b_3 = \$8,180$—is the maximum of the 2^{m-1} possible bid-combination optima.

The limitation of the Lagrangian formulation is the implicit assumption that all three contracts be bid. This is not an adverse situation if the profit function is monotonic in the (bid) region of interest. Unfortunately, the profit function becomes multivalued when it is permissible to bid less than all m contracts.

Dynamic programming   Let $\pi^*(s) = $ maximum expected profit obtained from an optimal policy when s dollars are to be allocated among the last i contracts and let $\pi_0^*(s) = 0$ (because other investment opportunities are to be neglected).

The solution proceeds:

$$\pi_i^*(s) = \max_{0 \leqslant b_1 \leqslant s} \left\{ (b_1 - 4,000)\left(2 - \frac{b_1}{4,000}\right)[1 - \delta(b_1)] \right\}$$

Table 10-4 reveals the optimal policy for contract 1.

Table 10-4 Optimal policy for contract 1

s ($\$$)	Policy	Max. $E(P) = \pi_1^*(s)$ ($\$$)
$0 \leqslant s < 4,000$	Do not bid	0
$4,000 \leqslant s < 6,000$	Bid, $b_1 = \$s$	$3s - s^2/4,000 - 8,000$
$6,000 \leqslant s$	Bid, $b_1 = \$6,000$	1,000

Similarly,

$$\pi_2^*(s) = \max_{0 \leqslant b_2 \leqslant s} \left\{ (b_2 - 5,000)\left(2 - \frac{b_2}{5,000}\right)[1 - \delta(b_2)] + \pi_1^*(s - b_2) \right\}$$

Table 10-5 gives the optimal policy for the first two contracts.

Finally,

$$\pi_3^*(\$15,000) = \max_{0 \leqslant b_3 \leqslant 15,100} \left\{ (b_3 - 6,000)\left(2 - \frac{b_3}{6,000}\right)[1 - \delta(b_3)] \right.$$
$$\left. + \pi_2^*(s - b_3) \right\}$$

The optimal strategy for all three contracts is to bid only contracts 2 and 3—at \$6,820 and \$8,180, respectively. The expected profit for such a policy is \$2,550.

Figure 10-15 illustrates the character of the profit function for the two-contract situation. The figure reveals $2^m - 1 = 3$ local maximums corresponding to bidding either contract and bidding both contracts simultaneously.

Table 10-5 Optimal policy for contracts 1 and 2

s ($\$$)	Policy Contract 1	Contract 2	Max. $E(P) = \pi_2^*(s)$ ($\$$)
$0 \leqslant s < 4,000$	Do not bid	Do not bid	0
$4,000 \leqslant s < 6,000$	Bid, $b_1 = \$s$	Do not bid	$3s - s^2/4,000$ $-8,000$
$6,000 \leqslant s < 6,380$	Bid, $b_1 = \$6,000$	Do not bid	1,000
$6,380 \leqslant s < 7,500$	Do not bid	Bid, $b_2 = \$s$	$3s - s^2/5,000$ $-10,000$
$7,500 \leqslant s < 10,500$	Do not bid	Bid, $b_2 = \$7,500$	1,250
$10,500 \leqslant s < 13,500$	Bid, $b_1 = \$4/9s$	Bid, $b_2 = \$5/9s$	$3s - s^2/9,000$ $-18,000$
$13,500 \leqslant s$	Bid, $b_1 = \$6,000$	Bid, $b_2 = \$7,500$	2,250

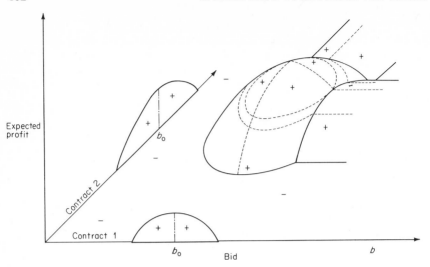

Fig. 10-15 Expected-profit function for a two-contract situation.

The shape of the expected-profit function in Fig. 10-15 arises because quadratic profit functions were assumed for each contract, rather than an asymptotic function (as shown in Fig. 10-13).

10-3 REPLACEMENT AND MAINTENANCE

The economics of equipment selection, maintenance, and replacement is of traditional interest because engineers depend upon machines and equipment to execute their designs.   Policies for equipment maintenance and replacement are inseparably related to aspects of management decision making.   For example, equipment stoppages for repair usually require rescheduling of operations.   The rescheduling depends upon available equipment reserves.   The reserves depend upon replacement policies, which, in turn, are linked to capital-investment decisions.   A useful principle is that investments for maintenance and replacement of equipment should compete with other investment opportunities available to the firm [11].

The theory of replacement is loosely divided into two parts according to whether the particular equipment tends to wear out or to fail suddenly. These cases are not mutually exclusive, of course.   Heavy equipment tends to deteriorate with use and undergoes maintenance before it is eventually salvaged.   Much inexpensive equipment, e.g., light bulbs, tends to fail suddenly, with little loss in efficiency during its service, and is discarded.   In this section we consider some general models for deteriorative replacement. References [10], [12], [29], and [33] provide additional details and considerations.

DETERIORATIVE REPLACEMENT

In deteriorative replacement, the question is one of continuing with incumbent equipment or switching to a challenger. Consider an example.

Example 10-12 Replacing a dump truck A new 15-ton type A bottom dump truck costs $17,000. From previous experience, annual operating costs are estimated at $8,000 for the first year, with an increase of $1,500 in each subsequent year. At what age should the truck be replaced?

Using average yearly cost $L(n)$ as the measure of performance, let $C(n)$ be the operating cost in the nth year and A the purchase price. We have

$$L(n) = \frac{A + \sum C(k)}{n} \qquad n = 1, 2, \ldots$$

where the summation extends from $k = 1$ to $k = n$. The results are given in Table 10-6. The minimum average yearly cost (column 4) is $14,400, corresponding to a 5-year replacement interval. Note that the minimum average yearly cost is approximately the same as the operating cost in that year.

A continuous model is sometimes more convenient than its discrete representation. Let $C(u)$ be the operating cost per unit time at time u. The average cost per unit time is written

$$L(t) = \frac{A + \int_0^t C(u)\,du}{t}$$

Differentiating with respect to t we find that the time, t_0, at which $L(t)$ is minimum satisfies

$$C(t_0) = L(t_0)$$

Table 10-6 Costs for type A trucks

(1) End of year	(2) Yearly operating cost, $	(3) Total cost, $	(4) Average yearly cost, $
		17,000 (investment)	
1	8,000	25,000	25,000
2	9,500	34,500	17,250
3	11,000	45,500	15,166
4	12,500	58,000	14,500
5	14,000	72,000	14,400
6	15,500	87,500	14,583
7	17,000	106,000	15,157

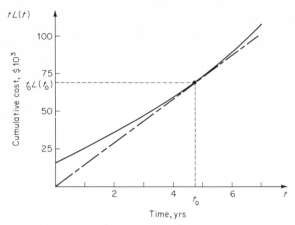

Fig. 10-16 Illustrating a tangent rule.

That is, t_0 is the time at which the average cost per unit time equals the operating cost per unit time. Adopting the data in the example, $A = \$17,000$ and $C(t) \simeq 7,250 + 1,500t$ gives $t_0 = 4.78$ years and $L(t_0) = \$14,390$, which corresponds approximately with the discrete representation.

There is another interesting aspect. In Fig. 10-16 the cumulative cost $tL(t)$ is plotted as a function of time. A line drawn from the origin and tangent to the cumulative-cost curve has a point of tangency corresponding to an abscissa of 4.78 years, the value of t_0. This is the so-called "tangent rule," which is widely used for replacement decisions (see Prob. 10-17). Note that formulas for $L(t)$ are not necessary; one needs only to plot cumulative costs until a straight edge, with one point at the origin, is tangent to the curve.

Suppose a type B truck costs $19,000 and its performance is equivalent to a type A truck. The operating cost in the first year is also $8,000, but the cost increases by only $600 per year. Presently, a contractor has a fleet of type A trucks that are 1 year old and he wants to determine if, and when, they should be replaced with type B trucks. In Fig. 10-17, we plot the cumulative costs for both truck types. Note that the replacement interval for type B trucks is about 8 years, with an average yearly cost of $\simeq \$12,500$. Therefore, he should replace with type B trucks, but when?

Replacement should be made when the operating costs of type A trucks exceed the optimum average annual cost of type B trucks. The graph furnishes the answer: replace when the slope of the curve for type A exceeds the slope of the "tangent line" for type B. Type A trucks should be replaced when they are $3\frac{1}{2}$ years old, corresponding to point P in Fig. 10-17.

The above model neglects several factors which require consideration in replacement decisions. For example, technologic obsolescence is crucial

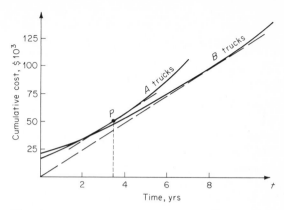

Fig. 10-17 Replacement with improved trucks.

in replacing a computer; equipment usually has a salvage value which depends on both its model year (vintage) and its cumulative operating time, and money values should be discounted with time.

For a more detailed model, we distinguish between equipment vintage τ and operating time t. Let

$A(\tau) =$ acquisition cost for new equipment of vintage τ
$C(t,\tau) =$ operating cost per unit time of equipment of vintage τ and operating time t
$S(t,\tau) =$ salvage value of equipment of vintage τ which has been operating for t years
$i =$ interest rate
$tL(t,\tau) =$ total discounted cost to time t for equipment of vintage τ

The total discounted cost is

$$tL(t,\tau) = A(\tau) + \int_0^t e^{-iu} C(u,\tau) \, du - e^{-it} S(t,\tau)$$

where the exponential arises from continuous discounting (Sec. 1-5).

If the equipment vintage is irrelevant for the decision period, the total-cost expression simplifies, that is,

$$tL(t) = A + \int_0^t e^{-iu} C(u) \, du - e^{-it} S(t)$$

For a suitably long decision period, the discounted cost per unit time for a series of identical replacements is

$$L(t) + e^{-it} L(t) + e^{-2it} L(t) + \cdots = \frac{L(t)}{1 - e^{-it}}$$

since the series is geometric with a term ratio equal to the discount factor. Minimizing the last expression yields the condition

$$iS(t_0) + C(t_0) - S'(t)|_{t_0} = \frac{iL(t_0)}{1 - e^{-it_0}} \sim \frac{L(t_0)}{t_0}$$

where the prime indicates differentiation with respect to t and the evaluation is at t_0. This equation is the generalization of the tangent rule for equipment having salvage value. Terborgh, in 1949, apparently was the first to develop a replacement model of this type by assuming a linear operating-cost function. Terborgh's book [33] is recommended for background reading. Much of the deteriorative-replacement literature appears to center about the preceding model. An exception is the following dynamic-programming model of Bellman [4].

Example 10-13   Keep or replace?   Replacement can be viewed as a sequential process, in the sense that we periodically decide whether to "keep" for another period or to "replace." Let $K(n)$ be the present worth of all future costs using an optimal policy for equipment now of age n. If we keep the equipment for another period, the present value of all future costs will be

     Keep: $C(n + 1) + \rho K(n + 1)$ $n = 0, 1, \ldots$

while if we replace now,

     Replace: $-S(n) + A + C(1) + \rho K(1)$ $n = 1, 2, \ldots$

where ρ is the discount factor $(1 + i)^{-1}$ and $C(n)$, $S(n)$, and A are defined in the previous example. Clearly,

$$K(n) = \min\,[C(n + 1) + \rho K(n + 1);\; A - S(n) + (C1) + \rho K(1)]$$

In Prob. 10-20 the reader is asked to prove that the minimum present worth of all future costs is given by

$$K(0) = \min_n \left\{ \frac{[A - S(n)]\rho^n + \sum_{k=1}^{n} \rho^{k-1} C(k)}{1 - \rho^n} \right\}$$

and the optimal replacement interval is the minimizing value of n.

MAINTENANCE

Replacement decisions are frequently influenced by maintenance policies, and vice versa. Maintenance may be either corrective, i.e., to restore equipment to operation, or preventive, i.e., to service the equipment in order to reduce operating costs or unanticipated failures. A limitation in replacement models is the individuality of types and brands of equipment and the environment

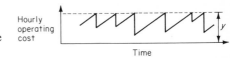

Fig. 10-18 Cableway repairs made when hourly operating cost reaches y.

in which they function. In addition, maintenance models require knowledge of equipment behavior as a consequence of previous maintenance. Maintenance studies are common, but they usually appear in a specific context. General considerations are available in [2] and [20]. We illustrate with an example adapted from reference [4] of Chap. 7.

Example 10-14 Cableway maintenance Throughout much of the construction period of a concrete dam, cableway operation is the rate-limiting step in the production and placement of concrete. Two critical factors in maintaining maximum cableway efficiency are operator skill and periodic adjustment of the electrically operated cable brake drums.

During a period when no adjustment is made, the operating cost (in terms of reduced efficiency) is estimated to increase linearly with time at the rate of \$0.01 per hr per hr of operation. Previous cost records suggest that the hourly operating cost after repair is a random variable X with a density function

$$f(x) = \begin{cases} 30 - (x - 35)^2 & 29.5 \leqslant x \leqslant 40.5 \\ 0 & \text{otherwise} \end{cases}$$

If adjustments cost \$800 each, how frequently should they be made to minimize expected cost per unit time?

We might minimize expected costs, for example, for one of the following policies:

1. Repair whenever the hourly operating cost reaches y dollars per hr (see Fig. 10-18).
2. Repair at fixed time intervals T (see Fig. 10-19).

We outline the solution for the second policy. The difference in hourly cost between successive repairs is $y - x$. Since the hourly cost increases at the rate of \$0.01 per hr, the time between repairs is $100(y - x)$, as indicated in

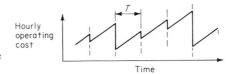

Fig. 10-19 Cableway repair at time interval T.

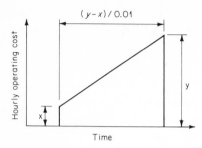

Fig. 10-20 A cycle of cableway repairs.

Fig. 10-20. Since the fixed cost per cycle is $800, the fixed cost per unit time is $8/(y - x)$. The operating cost per unit time is simply the average operating cost over the cycle, $1/2\,(y + x)$, that is, the mean height of the trapezoid in Fig. 10-20. Thus the (random) total cost per unit time is the sum

$$\frac{8}{y - x} + \frac{1}{2}(y + x)$$

and its expected value (as a function of y) is

$$E(y) = \int_{29.5}^{40.5} \left[\frac{8}{y - x} + \frac{1}{2}(y + x) \right] f(x)\,dx$$

To minimize, we differentiate with respect to y to obtain

$$\frac{dE}{dy} = \int_{29.5}^{40.5} [30 - (x - 35)^2] \left[\frac{1}{2} - \frac{8}{(y - x)^2} \right] dx$$

$$= \frac{1}{2} + 8 \int_{29.5}^{40.5} \frac{x^2 - 70x + 1,195}{(y - x)^2}\,dx = 0$$

Carrying out the integration by partial fractions, the equation can be solved for y_0, the maximum allowable operating cost.

Example 10-15   Maintenance of carriage drills   A stone-quarry owner operates 10 identical carriage drills for which the probabilities of breakdown are:

Months since maintenance	Probability of breakdown in preceding month
1	0.1
2	0.2
3	0.3
4	0.4

The cost of repair after failure, i.e., corrective maintenance, is \$90 per drill, and the cost of preventive maintenance is \$40 per drill. What should be the maintenance policy?

For a monthly preventive-maintenance policy, the expected cost per month c_1 is 40(10) plus 90 for each failure in the first month after maintenance, that is,

$$c_1 = 40(10) + 90 \times 10(0.1) = \$490$$

For bimonthly preventive maintenance, the expected number of drills to fail during the first month is $0.1 \times 10 = 1$ and the expected number to fail during the second month is 0.2×10 plus the expected number repaired during the first month which fail again, or $0.1 \times 0.1 \times 10$. The total expected cost is

$$c_2 = 40(10) + 90 \times 10[P_1 + P_2] = 400 + 900[0.1 + (0.2 + 0.1 \times 0.1)]$$

$$= 400 + 900(0.1 + 0.21) = \$679$$

where P_1 and P_2 are the probabilities of failure during the first and second months, respectively. The expected cost per month is $679/2 = \$339.50$.

For a trimonthly preventive-maintenance policy, we find

$$c_3 = 400 + 900(P_1 + P_2 + P_3) = 400 + 900[P_1 + P_2 + (0.3 + 0.2$$
$$\times 0.1 + 0.1 \times 0.2)]$$

$$= 400 + 900(0.1 + 0.21 + 0.34) = \$985$$

The expected monthly cost is \$328.33.

For a 4-month preventive-maintenance interval,

$$c_4 = 400 + 900[P_1 + P_2 + P_3 + (0.4 + 0.3 \times 0.1 + 0.2 \times 0.2 + 0.1 \times 0.3)]$$

$$= \$1,435$$

The expected monthly cost is \$358.75. Table 10-7 summarizes the results.

Table 10-7 Expected cost of preventive-maintenance policies

Preventive-maintenance period, months	Failure probabilities				Total failures $10 \sum_{k=1}^{i} P_k$	Costs, \$			
	P_1	P_2	P_3	P_4		Repair	Maint.	Total	Monthly
1	0.1				1.0	90	400	490	490
2	0.1	0.21			3.1	279	400	679	339.50
3	0.1	0.21	0.34		6.5	585	400	985	328.33←
4	0.1	0.21	0.34	0.50	11.5	1,035	400	1,435	358.75

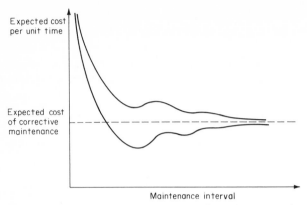

Fig. 10-21 Typical expected-cost functions for preventive maintenance of multicomponent systems.

If drills were repaired only upon failure (no preventive maintenance), the proportion of failures each month would be the reciprocal of the average operating life. This assertion is discussed further in Sec. 11-3. The average operating life is $0.5(0.1) + 1.5(0.2) + 2.5(0.3) + 3.5(0.4) = 2.5$ months. Thus, the expected number of failures each month is $10/2.5 = 4$, and the policy of repairing only upon failure would cost $4(90) = \$360$ per month. Since $328.33 < 360$, trimonthly preventive maintenance is the preferred policy.

We have assumed that a trimonthly policy is the global minimum. If Table 10-7 were continued, the average monthly cost might oscillate. Typical expected-cost functions are shown in Fig. 10-21. The dashed horizontal line represents the expected cost per unit time for a policy of repair only upon failure, i.e., for a strict corrective-maintenance policy, corresponding to an infinite preventive-maintenance interval. For preventive maintenance, two situations can arise [1]:

1. The first relative minimum is greater than the expected cost of a policy of strict corrective maintenance. Successive minimums asymptotically approach the expected cost of strict corrective maintenance (upper curve in Fig. 10-21).
2. The first relative minimum is less than the expected cost of strict corrective maintenance and is global (lower curve in Fig. 10-21).

This example corresponds to case 2 since the expected monthly cost is less than the expected cost of corrective maintenance. We assumed preventive maintenance for all drills, no matter how recently they had been repaired. Additional savings might be realized by skipping preventive maintenance for drills which were repaired in the previous month, or the previous 2 months, etc. Problem 10-28 shows that performing preventive maintenance only for those drills which were not repaired in the preceding month is superior to the policy just evaluated. Figure 10-21 remains valid.

Example 10-16 Replacing a conveyor belt
A conveyer is used to transport rock from a receiving hopper to the primary crusher of an aggregate processing plant. If the belt breaks during working hours, the total cost of replacement, including idle time, is $600. If the belt is replaced during preventive maintenance on off-shift hours, the cost is only $250. What is the optimum replacement policy? The belt failure probabilities are:

	Belt failure probabilities					
Days in operation	5	10	15	20	25	30
Failure probability during preceding 5 days	0.02	0.03	0.04	0.19	0.46	0.26

We compare three maintenance policies:

1. Corrective maintenance only
2. Preventive maintenance with belt replacement at prescribed intervals independent of failures
3. Preventive maintenance with belt replacement at prescribed intervals since the previous replacement

For policy 1, average belt life is $[2.5(0.02) + 7.5(0.03) + 12.5(0.04) + 17.5(0.19) + 22.5(0.46) + 27.5(0.26)] = 21.6$ days and the expected cost is $600/21.6 = \$27.80$ per day.

Table 10-8 Expected daily costs for policy 2

Preventive maintenance period, days	Failure probabilities, %						Total failure prob., % $\sum_{i=1}^{6} P_i$	Costs, $			
	P_1	P_2	P_3	P_4	P_5	P_6		Repair	Maint.	Total	Daily
5	0.0200						0.0200	12.00	250	262	52.40
10		+0.0304					0.0504	30.24	250	280	28.00
15			+0.0412				0.0916	54.96	250	305	20.33←
20				+0.1925			0.2841	170.46	250	420	21.00
25					+0.4700		0.7541	452.46	250	702	28.08
30						+0.2914	1.0455	627.30	250	877	29.57

Table 10-9   Expected daily costs for policy 3

Ave. age at failure, days	Cumulative failure probability P_x	Expected cost of replacing failures	$1 - P_x$	Expected cost of replacing nonfailures	C_x	Cost/day
$2\frac{1}{2}$	0.02	12.00	0.98	245.00	257.00	103.00
$7\frac{1}{2}$	0.05	30.00	0.95	237.50	267.50	35.40
$12\frac{1}{2}$	0.09	54.00	0.91	227.50	281.50	22.50
$17\frac{1}{2}$	0.28	168.00	0.72	180.00	348.00	19.90←
$22\frac{1}{2}$	0.74	444.00	0.26	65.00	509.00	22.60
$27\frac{1}{2}$	1.00	600.00	0	0	600.00	21.80

Expected costs for policy 2 are calculated by adding the fixed cost of the known number of replacements in a given time to the cost of an average number of failures in that period, as in the previous example. The results in Table 10-8 show a minimum expected daily cost of $20.33 for a maintenance interval of 15 days.

For policy 3, the results are shown in Table 10-9. Hence, use policy 3 with a replacement interval of 20 days and an expected cost of $19.90 per day.

Finally, we illustrate a recursion technique for maintenance and replacement problems.

Example 10-17   Group vs. individual replacement   This example is based upon a problem in [29].

A system is made up of N components whose lives cannot exceed 2 months. The components are observed each month, and items are regarded as having lives of either 1 or 2 months with probabilities p and $q(=1 - p)$, respectively. When an item fails, it is replaced by a new item at a cost C_r. Group replacement costs C_g per unit, with $C_g < C_r$. We study conditions under which:

1. A monthly group-replacement policy minimizes monthly expected cost.
2. A bimonthly group-replacement policy minimizes monthly expected cost.

Let X_n be the random number of failures in month $n = 1, 2, \ldots$. The total cost of a group-replacement policy every k months is

$$NC_g + C_r \sum_{n=1}^{k-1} X_n$$

and the monthly expected cost $K(k)$ is

$$K(k) = \frac{NC_g}{k} + \frac{C_r}{k} \sum_{n=1}^{k-1} E(X_n)$$

To obtain $E(X_n)$, we begin with the recursion relation

$$X_n = \alpha X_{n-1} + (1 - \alpha) X_{n-2} \qquad n = 2, 3, \ldots$$

where α is a random number for the chance that a component will fail after a month's service. The relation follows from the observation that the failures in month n must derive from the replacements made within the past 2 months. Taking the expectation, assuming independent random variables, yields the difference equation

$$E(X_n) = pE(X_{n-1}) + qE(X_{n-2}) \qquad n = 2, 3, \ldots$$

where $p = E(\alpha)$. The initial condition is $E(X_0) = N$ since all items are new at month zero. Using techniques in Appendix 5, one can derive the solution

$$E(X_n) = \frac{N}{1+q}[1 - (-q)^{n+1}]$$

so that

$$K(k) = \frac{NC_g}{k} + \frac{NC_r}{k(1+q)} \sum_{n=1}^{k-1} [1 - (-q)^{n+1}]$$

$$= \frac{NC_g}{k} + \frac{NC_r}{k(1+q)} \left\{ (k-1) - \frac{q^2}{1+q}[1 - (-q)^{k-1}] \right\} \tag{5}$$

Note the sum of a finite geometric series. A monthly group-replacement policy, corresponding to policy 1, has an expected cost obtained by setting $k = 1$ in Eq. (5), that is,

$$K(1) = NC_g$$

A bimonthly policy has a monthly expected cost

$$K(2) = \frac{NC_g}{2} + \frac{NC_r}{2}p$$

Now, $K(2) > K(1)$ implies

$$\frac{NC_g}{2} + \frac{NC_r}{2}p > NC_g$$

or

$$p > \frac{C_g}{C_r}$$

Clearly, for $p > C_g/C_r$, a policy of monthly group replacement is preferable to a bimonthly policy. The comparison can be generalized for longer group-replacement intervals, although the expressions become inconvenient in the absence of specific values of C_g and C_r.

10-4 RANDOM PROCESSES

Consider a family of random variables $X(t_1), X(t_2), \ldots$ which represent a random process at fixed times $t_1, t_2, \ldots$, with $t_2 > t_1$, etc. Figure 10-22 illustrates a sample record of the process, which is called an *ensemble*.

A complete specification of a random process at times $t_1, t_2, \ldots, t_n$ is given by the joint density

$$f(x(t_1), x(t_2), \ldots, x(t_n)) \qquad \text{all } n; \ t_1 < t_2 < \cdots < t_n$$

As noted, these joint and marginal densities are not available in many instances. An analysis is often based upon the expectations

$$E[X(t)] = \int_{\substack{\text{all} \\ x}} x f_{X(t)}(x) \, dx$$

$$E\{[X(t)]^2\} = \int_{\substack{\text{all} \\ x}} x^2 f_{X(t)}(x) \, dx$$

$$E\{[X(t_1) - \mu_1][X(t_2) - \mu_2]\}$$
$$= \iint_{\substack{\text{all} \\ x_1, x_2}} (x_1 - \mu_1)(x_2 - \mu_2) f_{X(t_1), X(t_2)}(x_1, x_2) \, dx_1 \, dx_2$$

and

$$E[X(t_1) X(t_2)] = \iint_{\substack{\text{all} \\ x_1, x_2}} x_1 x_2 f_{x(t_1), x(t_2)}(x_1, x_2) \, dx_1 \, dx_2$$

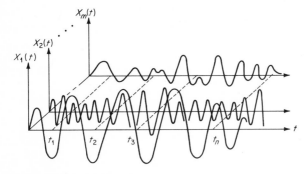

Fig. 10-22 An ensemble of $X(t)$.

where, for convenience, the subscript i on x_i implies t_i, that is, $x_i \rightarrow x(t_2)$. The last expectation is called the *autocorrelation*. A conditional expectation [27] is defined by

$$E(X | Y = y) = \int_{-\infty}^{\infty} x f_{X|Y}(x|y) \, dx$$

where $f_{X|Y}(x|y)$ is the conditional density defined by

$$f_{X|Y}(x|y) = \frac{f(x,y)}{f_1(y)}$$

where $f(x,y)$ and $f_1(y)$ are the respective joint and marginal densities. More precise definitions and further details appear in Lin [22].

STATIONARY PROCESSES

Stationary, or *homogeneous*, random processes provide the important special case

$$f(x(t_1),x(t_2), \ldots, x(t_n)) = f(x(t_1 + T),x(t_2 + T), \ldots, x(t_n + T))$$

for all $T \geqslant 0$. That is, the probability function is invariant under a time shift. As a consequence, the expectations do not depend upon the absolute time but upon the time interval. For example,

$$E[X(t_1)X(t_2)] = E[X(0)X(t_2 - t_1)] = E[X(0)X(\tau)] = R(\tau)$$

where $\tau = t_2 - t_1$ and $R(\tau)$ is the stationary autocorrelation function.

SPECTRAL DENSITY

A convenient means of studying periodic excitations is by a Fourier decomposition of $R(\tau)$, that is,

$$R(\tau) = \int_{-\infty}^{\infty} S(\omega) e^{i\omega\tau} \, d\omega$$

where ω is the transform variable and is interpreted as a frequency of the vibration. The function $S(\omega)$ is called the *spectral density* and is defined by the Fourier transform pair

$$S(\omega) = \frac{1}{2\pi} \int_{-\infty}^{\infty} R(\tau) e^{-i\omega\tau} \, d\tau$$

The spectral density can be interpreted as the contribution of various frequencies to the autocorrelation.

When the random process under consideration can be regarded as the sum of a number of other random processes, the central limit theorem suggests the aptness of the normal law. The normal, or gaussian, law is therefore a frequent choice in the study of random vibrations. A useful property of

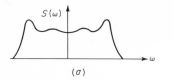 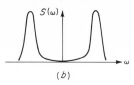

(a)   (b)

Fig. 10-23 Random processes. (a) Wide-band process; (b) narrow-band process.

the gaussian process is that it is completely described by its mean and the spectral density.

Random processes are commonly categorized as *wide-band* or *narrow-band* processes, according to whether or not the spectral density is well distributed over the frequency spectrum. Naturally, the designation is somewhat arbitrary (see Fig. 10-23). Pressure fluctuations on the surface of a rocket due to the supersonic boundary-layer turbulence is an example of a wide-band process. Jet noise and some fatigue problems have also been represented as wide-band processes [9]. Narrow-band processes typically arise in resonant systems.

Figure 10-24 illustrates an extreme example of a wide-band process in which the vibration contains all frequencies uniformly. This is called *white noise*. Although white noise may be physically unrealizable, that is, $E(X^2) \to \infty$, it has computational advantages as an approximation [27].

Example 10-18   Random vibration   Let $X(t)$ and $\dot{X}(t)$ be the response and response velocity, respectively, of a stationary random process for a vibrating system. Let the event "failure" be defined as the first passage through the response level a, that is, $X(t) \geqslant a > 0$. An assumption usually made is that the time t between successive crossings with positive slope $X(t)$ is described by an exponential law (see Sec. 9-3) with mean $1/v_a^+$, that is,

$$f_T(t) = v_a^+ \, e^{-v_a^+ t} \qquad t > 0$$

To determine the mean crossing rate v_a^+, consider the joint event

$$\{X(t) < a \text{ and } X(t + \Delta t) \geqslant a > 0\}$$

which is equivalent to the intersection of the events

$$\{X(t) < a\}$$

(a)   (b)

Fig. 10-24 White noise. (a) Spectral density; (b) autocorrelation.

and

$$\left\{ \dot{X}(t) \geqslant \frac{a - X(t)}{\Delta t} \right\}$$

We assume that $\dot{X}(t)$ is essentially constant in the small interval $\{t, t + \Delta t\}$. The probability of the joint event is

$$\int_0^\infty \int_{a - \dot{x}(t)\Delta t}^a f(x, \dot{x}) \, dx \, d\dot{x}$$

where $f(x, \dot{x})$ is the joint density.   Now

$$v_a{}^+ = \lim_{\Delta t \to 0} \frac{\int_0^\infty \int_{a - \dot{x}\Delta t}^a f(x, \dot{x}) \, dx \, d\dot{x}}{\Delta t} = \int_0^\infty \dot{x} f(a, \dot{x}) \, d\dot{x}$$

after evaluating the inner integral over the infinitesimal range.   Note that the time-dependence of $X(t)$ has been discarded because of the stationarity assumption.

Another assumption usually made is that $X(t)$ and $\dot{X}(t)$ are stationary independent gaussian processes with zero mean.   That is,

$$f(x, \dot{x}) = \frac{1}{2\pi \sigma_x \sigma_{\dot{x}}} \exp\left[-\frac{1}{2}\left(\frac{x^2}{\sigma_x{}^2} + \frac{\dot{x}^2}{\sigma_{\dot{x}}{}^2} \right) \right]$$

Calculating $v_a{}^+$ yields

$$v_a{}^+ = \frac{1}{2\pi} \frac{\sigma_{\dot{x}}}{\sigma_x} \exp\left(-\frac{1}{2} \frac{a^2}{\sigma_x{}^2} \right)$$

A knowledge of $v_a{}^+$ can be used to derive the density function for the amplitude.   The difference

$$v_a{}^+ - v_{a + \Delta a}^+$$

represents the number of peaks per unit time between the levels a and $a + \Delta a$. The total number of peaks in unit time is $v_0{}^+$.   Therefore, the amplitude density is

$$f_p(a) \Delta a = \lim_{\Delta a \to 0} \frac{v_a{}^+ - v_{a + \Delta a}^+}{v_0{}^+} = \frac{1}{v_0{}^+} \frac{dv_a{}^+}{da} \Delta a$$

If the process is gaussian with zero mean, one finds

$$f_p(a) = \frac{a}{\sigma_x{}^2} \exp\left(-\frac{1}{2} \frac{a^2}{\sigma_x{}^2} \right)$$

which is known as the *Rayleigh law* (see Appendix 4).   The Rayleigh law arises again in Sec. 11-1.   Another brief consideration of random vibrations arises in Chap. 12.   In addition to [6] and [22], a paper by Swanson [32] provides an excellent bibliography.

SUMMARY

This chapter contains many examples illustrating the use of expectation in design decisions.   The criterion of performance is an expectation, e.g., expected cost, and the desired decision minimizes it.

In Sec. 10-2, competitive bidding models were developed not only to illustrate an expected-value criterion but also to illustrate how the optimization techniques studied in the earlier chapters can be fashioned to utilize the available information.   Section 10-3 provided an introduction to the theory of replacement and maintenance of equipment and again illustrated the use of an expected-value criterion in making operating and design decisions.

Section 10-4 briefly introduced random processes based upon expected values and their use in structural dynamics.

PROBLEMS

10-1.   The newsboy in Example 10-1 buys newspapers for $0.07 and sells them at $0.10 each.   If demand per day, X, is described by a uniform law on the interval $\{26,50\}$, how many papers, y, should he order each day?   Each unsold paper can be returned for a $0.02 credit.

10-2.   Study the newsboy problem for arbitrary (analytic) return and cost functions $g(y)$ and $c(y)$, respectively.

10-3.   Community demand X for water (in thousands of gallons) is described by a rectangular law on the interval $\{2,000, 3,000\}$.   Water pumped and stored in advance in a local reservoir costs $0.04 per 1,000 gal.   If the supply is inadequate to meet the demand, water is brought from other reservoirs at a cost of $0.06 per 1,000 gal.   What quantity should be stored at the local reservoir?

10-4.   Find the optimum capacity for a surge bin between a primary jaw crusher and secondary hammer-mill crusher of a Portland cement plant using an expected value criterion. The normal operating rate of the secondary crusher is 50 tons of limestone per hr, and the profit loss due to interruption is $100 per hr.   The primary crusher requires occasional maintenance and repair.   The mean repair interval and downtime of the primary crusher are anticipated to be 45 days and 8 hr (exponentially distributed), respectively.   Capital and maintenance costs for the bin are estimated at $1 per ton capacity per month.

10-5.   Supplies are ordered every Monday for delivery a week hence.   The weekly random demand X is described by the probability function $f(x)$ and is independent from week to week.   A cost of C_h dollars is assessed for each item in stock at the end of the week.   A cost of C_s dollars is assessed for each item short.   All demand is eventually filled.   Show that the ordering policy for least expected cost is given by

$$\frac{C_s}{C_h + C_s} = \int_0^{S_0} F(S_0 - x) f(x) \, dx$$

where S_0 is the optimal amount to have on hand immediately after delivery plus the optimal order quantity.   The cumulative probability function is denoted by $F(x)$.◆

10-6.   Show that the expected value of the fluctuation $(X - a)$ is zero when a is the mean and that the expected value of the absolute deviation $|X - b|$ is minimized when b is the median.   The random variable X has a density $f(x)$.

10-7. A player is to be paid the value of X, which he chooses according to the following mechanism: He takes a random draw from a population with density

$$f(x) = \begin{cases} 1 & 0 < x < 1 \\ 0 & \text{elsewhere} \end{cases}$$

He can keep this value of X or discard it permanently and draw again. A total of four draws is permitted. What policy should be used?

10-8. Expansion of a rail heading and port facility are required, and construction starts April 1. If a crash schedule is adopted, the project can be completed by October 1. Slower construction is less expensive, with the possible exception of added costs due to severe weather in the fall. It is estimated that the total additional cost in ship waiting time, tie-up of port facilities, etc., before the new construction is completed would be $8,000 in October, $12,000 in November, and $20,000 in December.

Given the following weather estimates and corresponding construction costs, choose the construction schedule which minimizes total expected cost.

Target date	Fair-weather construction cost, $	Probability of bad construction weather	Bad-weather construction cost, $
Oct. 1	600,000	0	– – –
Nov. 1	550,000	0.1	560,000
Dec. 1	520,000	0.3	580,000
Jan. 1	500,000	0.7	600,000

10-9. Consider

Max.: $z = 10x_1 + 15x_2 + 18x_3$
Subject to: $x_1 + x_2 + x_3 \leq b_1$
$x_1 + 2x_2 + 3x_3 \leq b_2$
$4x_2 + 3x_3 \leq b_3$
$x_1, x_2, x_3 \geq 0$

where b_1, b_2, and b_3 are random variables described by the gamma law, with means 1.5, 2, and 3 and with variances 0.75, 1, and 3, respectively. The constraints are to hold with probabilities 0.92, 0.855, and 0.96, respectively.

Compare the result with the dual solution, in which the b_i become the cost coefficients and the minimization becomes an expected value.

10-10. Consider the linear-programming problem

Max.: $z = \sum_{j=1}^{n} c_j x_j$

Subject to: $\sum_{j=1}^{n} a_{ij} x_j \leq b_i \qquad i = 1, \ldots, m$
$x_j \geq 0 \qquad j = 1, \ldots, n$

For $m = 3$ and $n = 2$, solve the problem for the following sets of possible parameters such that every solution is feasible.

	c_1	c_2	a_{11}	a_{12}	a_{21}	a_{22}	a_{31}	a_{32}	b_1	b_2	b_3
1	5	6	2	3	1	1	5	3	9	5	12
2	5	5	2	3	1	1	5	3	8	4	14
3	5	4	3	5	1	1	5	2	16	8	14
4	3	5	6	6	3	3	4	2	18	9	10

The data in rows 1 to 3 occur with equal probabilities of $1/6$, while the fourth-row data occur with probability $1/2$. Maximize the expected value of z.

10-11. A contractor can bid on any one of these three contracts:

Contract	Cost estimate, $\times 10^4$	Competitors' low-bid-cost density
A	$4.5	Exponential: mean $1.125, $1 < r < \infty$
B	6	Normal: mean $1.15, variance $0.5
C	5.5	Gamma: $\lambda = 1.75$, $\alpha = 3$

Neglecting completion times and alternative investments, what contract bid maximizes total expected profit?

10-12. Past histories of three competitors indicate that their markups over cost are exponentially distributed with mean 0.15. Using extreme-value techniques (Chap. 9), determine the density function for the low markup. What markup should a contractor use in order to maximize profits while bidding against these three opponents?

Determine the low-bid density for n identical bidders whose bid markups are uniformly distributed on the interval $\{0,1\}$. From the sponsor's point of view, what is the expected markup of the low bid? From a contractor's viewpoint, what is the optimal bid markup against the remaining $n - 1$ bidders? Assume $n = 2, 3, \ldots$.

10-13. Bids are to be formed for two contracts. The cost estimates are $Ce_1 = \$200,000$ and $Ce_2 = \$100,000$. A single opponent is anticipated in each situation. Suppose that the density functions which describe the past behavior of these competitors in ratio to our cost estimate are gamma laws with parameters $\lambda_1 = 2$, $\alpha_1 = 3$ and $\lambda_2 = 1$, $\alpha_2 = 2$.

(a) Maximize the total expected profit.

(b) Suppose that the firm is restricted to a bid total of $500,000. The required optimization must include the linear constraint $x_1 + x_2 = \$500,000$. Using the Lagrange multiplier technique, obtain the optimal bids.

10-14. Bids are to be formed for two jobs, and cost estimates have been prepared for each job separately. If the firm is successful with both bids, substantial economies can be achieved. These economies often arise, for example, from bulk buying of materials and from a more efficient utilization of labor, management, and equipment. The table lists the estimated costs:

	Separately	Jointly
Job 1	$200,000	$150,000
Job 2	100,000	75,000

Indications are that competitor 1 is likely to bid job 1. His past bidding behavior relative to our cost estimate can be described by the gamma law:

$$f_1(\gamma_1) = 4\gamma_1 e^{-2\gamma_1} \qquad \gamma_1 > 0$$

where γ_1 is the ratio of his bid to our cost estimate. Competitor 2 is likely to bid job 2, and his past bidding behavior is described by the uniform law:

$$f_2(\gamma_2) = \tfrac{1}{2} \qquad 1 \leqslant \gamma_2 \leqslant 3$$

where γ_2 is the ratio of competitor 2's bid to our cost estimate. What bids maximize expected profit? ◆

10-15. The probability that k competitors submit bids follows a Poisson law with mean ν. The probability density function of an average bidder's bid to our cost estimate can be approximated by a gamma law with parameters λ and α. Assuming each of the k (unknown) bidders to act as independent "average" bidders, derive the expected-profit function for a contract with cost estimate C_e. Determine an optimal bid for the case $\nu = 2$, $\lambda = \alpha = 2$, and $C_e = \$10,000$.

10-16. A contractor has three contracts which he can bid. The respective cost estimates and competitor's low-bid-to-cost densities are:

    (a) $10,000; gamma, $\lambda = 2$, $\alpha = 2$
    (b) $15,000; gamma, $\lambda = 1.25$, $\alpha = 2$
    (c) $20,000; gamma, $\lambda = 1.5$, $\alpha = 2$

Neglecting constraints, what are the optimal bids? Assuming that the total bid sum is restricted to $35,000, which contracts should be bid? Suppose the limit is $25,000?

10-17. Prove that the abscissa of the line passing through the origin and tangent to the curve $L(t)$ is the optimum replacement interval discussed in Example 10-12. Conclude also that the "rule" is to replace when the operating cost per unit time equals the total cost per unit time. Finally, study the effect of interest and salvage values upon the adequacy of the "rule."

10-18. A population consists of items which are replaced at age T or at failure, whichever occurs first. The probability density for the life t is $f(t)$. The costs of replacement are c_f at failure and c_r for preventive replacement. Write the expected cost per item per unit time in the steady state.

10-19. A structural member is subject to repeated identical loads and eventually undergoes fatigue failure. When the member fails, it is replaced at a cost c_f before operation can continue. If the member is replaced prior to failure (while in service), the replacement cost c_r is less than c_f. The probability p_k of failure of the member depends upon the number of loadings k it has survived ($k = 1, 2, \ldots$). What criterion should be adopted for replacing the fatigued member so that long-run expected costs are a minimum?

10-20. Prove the assertion for $K^*(0)$ in the dynamic-programming replacement model in Example 10-13. *Hint:* Assume that the optimal replacement interval is r periods, and enumerate the $K(n)$, $n = 0, 1, 2, \ldots, r$.

10-21. The purchase price of a machine is $12,000. Its operating cost is $1,250 for the first year and increases linearly in subsequent years at the rate of $1,500 per year. Neglecting salvage value and the discounted value of money, find the economic age at which the machine is to be replaced with a new one of the same type.

10-22. A contractor finds that the annual running and resale prices of an air-operated type A wagon drill whose purchase price is $1,500 are:

Type A drill

Year	1	2	3	4	5	6	7	8
Running cost	$250	300	350	450	575	700	850	1,000
Resale price	$750	375	190	95	50	50	50	50

He now owns six type A wagon drills. Four of them are 2 years old, and two are a year old. He is considering type B wagon drills, which have 50% greater drilling speed at a unit price of $2,000. He estimates annual running costs and resale prices for a type B drill as:

Type B drill

Year	1	2	3	4	5	6	7	8
Running cost	$ 300	375	450	600	760	1,000	1,250	1,500
Resale price	$1,000	500	250	125	75	75	75	75

The volume of work is adequate for six type A drills or four type B drills. If a change in drills is made, the transition is completed at one time. When should type A drills be replaced by type B drills?

10-23. A machine requires an initial investment of $15,000. Its operating costs are:

Year	1	2	3	4	5	6	7
Operating cost, 10^3	6	7	9	12	16	20.5	26

Determine the economic life for these situations:

(a) The machine has no salvage value, and the interest rate is negligible.
(b) The machine has no salvage value, and the interest rate is 10%.
(c) The interest rate is negligible, and the salvage values are:

Year	1	2	3	4	5	6	7
Salvage value, 10^3	11	7.5	4.5	2	1.5	1	0.5

(d) The salvage values are as in part c, and the interest rate is 10%.

10-24. A firm is presently using a machine which has a market value of $6,000 and a maximum useful life of 8 years. The operating costs and salvage values are:

Year	1	2	3	4	5	6	7	8
Operating cost, 10^3	1.8	2.2	2.4	2.8	3.2	3.6	4.0	4.5
Salvage value, 10^3	4.5	4.0	3.5	3.0	2.5	2.0	1.0	0.0

A new machine has been developed which can be purchased for $10,000 and which has the following costs and values:

Year	1	2	3	4	5	6	7	8
Operating cost, 10^3	1.0	1.2	1.6	2.0	2.2	2.6	3.0	3.4
Salvage value, 10^3	9.6	9.2	8.8	8.4	8.0	7.6	7.2	6.8

(*a*) If interest is neglected, when should the new machine be purchased?

(*b*) If interest is 5%, when should the new machine be purchased? ◆

10-25. Failure in service of tires on ready-mix concrete trucks can cause expensive delays. New tires cost $120 each, and the average cost of failures in service is $300. If tires have the mortality rates shown below, determine a replacement policy (to replace tires after a fixed mileage or upon failure, whichever occurs first) which minimizes average tire cost per mile.

Tire mortality

Miles at failure, $\times 10^3$	Percent of tires
5–6	0.010
6–7	0.015
7–8	0.020
8–9	0.025
9–10	0.035
10–11	0.060
11–12	0.120
12–13	0.180
13–14	0.240
14–15	0.150
15–16	0.085
16–17	0.060
	1.000

10-26. An architectural engineering firm requires additional office space. It can either rent a nearby building (building A) for $8,000 per year on a 5-year lease or buy a smaller building (building B) for $60,000. The firm estimates that the probability of its work load being high over the first 5 years is 0.4. If there is a high work load in the first 5 years, the chance that it will continue at that level for the next 5 years is estimated to be 0.8. If the work load is low for the first 5 years, then the chance that it will continue at that level for the next 5 years is estimated as 0.6. The following annual savings in work performance, exclusive of rental or purchase costs, are anticipated for the two circumstances:

Future state	Annual savings Bldg. A	Bldg. B
High work load	$16,000	$6,000
Low work load	10,000	4,000

After 5 years, the lease of building A could be terminated and building B purchased for $65,000, or building B could be sold at that time for $65,000 and building A leased for 5 years at $8,500 per year.

Using a study period of 10 years and an interest rate of 10%, determine whether the firm should initially rent building A or purchase building B. The resale value of building B in 10 years would be $68,000.

10-27. Thirty-foot sections of galvanized corrugated steel pipes are coated with bitumen in the bottom for hydraulic efficiency. The pipe diameter, the density of exposed areas, and the bitumen thickness are subject to certain tolerances and require inspection. From the following information, determine a test sequence which minimizes the total expected time:

(a) The pipe diameter is a normal random variable with a mean of 60 in. and a standard deviation of $\frac{1}{2}$ in. Acceptable pipes have diameters of between 59.5 and 61 in. Inspection time is 5 min.

(b) The number of exposed areas per linear foot of galvanized surface is a Poisson variable with a mean of 0.15 bare spot per lin ft. No more than 1 exposure per lin ft is acceptable. Inspection time is 8 min.

(c) Bitumen thickness at the root of the corrugation is a normal random variable with a mean of 2.0 in. and a standard deviation of 0.15 in. For an acceptable pipe, no more than 1 of 5 measurements on it can be less than 1.8 in. Inspection time is 2 min.

10-28. Solve Example 10-15 for the case where preventive maintenance is performed only for those drills which were not repaired due to breakdown within the preceding 1 month.

10-29. Wagon drills are operated from an 800-cfm mobile compressor. Efficiency of the drills drops sharply when they must operate at pressures below 90 psi, the rated pressure of the compressor. Records show that the most critical factor in maintaining pressure is the interval at which the compressor valves are replaced. Valve replacement costs $200. The contractor estimates an operating cost immediately after replacement of $15 per hr, increasing at the rate of $0.01 per hr as compressor efficiency decreases. At what hourly operating cost should valves be replaced? How many operating hours should elapse between successive valve replacements?

REFERENCES

1. Ackoff, R. L., and M. Sasieni: "Fundamentals of Operations Research," John Wiley & Sons, Inc., New York, 1968.
2. Barlow, R. E., and F. Proschan: "Mathematical Theory of Reliability," John Wiley & Sons, Inc., New York, 1965.

3. Beckenbach, E. F.: "Modern Mathematics for the Engineer," 2d ser., McGraw-Hill Book Company, New York, 1961.
4. Bellman, R.: Equipment Replacement Policy, *J. SIAM*, vol. 3, p. 133, 1955.
5. Benjamin, J. R.: Probabilistic Structural Analysis and Design, *J. Struct. Div. ASCE*, vol. 94, no. ST7, July, 1968.
6. Bogdanoff, J. L., and F. Kozin: "Proceedings of First Symposium on Engineering Application of Random Function Theory and Probability," John Wiley & Sons, Inc., New York, 1963.
7. Charnes, A., and W. W. Cooper: Chance Constrained Programming, *Management Sci.*, vol. 6, pp. 73–80, 1959.
8. Charnes, A., and W. W. Cooper: Deterministic Equivalents for Optimizing and Satisficing under Chance Constraints, *Operations Res.*, vol. 11, pp. 18–39, 1963.
9. Crandall, S. H., and W. D. Mark: "Random Vibration in Mechanical Systems," Academic Press, Inc., New York, 1963.
10. Dean, B. V.: Replacement Theory, in R. L. Ackoff (ed.), "Progress in O.R.," vol. I, John Wiley & Sons, Inc., New York, 1961.
11. Dean, J.: "Capital Budgeting," Columbia University Press, New York, 1951.
12. Douglas, J.: Optimum Life of Equipment for Maximum Profit, *Proc. ASCE*, vol. 94, no. CO1, pp. 41–54, January, 1968.
13. Friedman, L.: A Competitive Bidding Strategy, *Operations Res.*, vol. 4, pp. 104–112, 1956.
14. Gates, M.: Bidding Strategies and Probabilities, *J. Construct. Div. ASCE*, vol. 93, March, 1967.
15. Graves, R. L., and P. Wolfe: "Recent Advances in Mathematical Programming," McGraw-Hill Book Company, New York, 1963.
16. Hadley, G.: "Non-linear and Dynamic Programming," Addison-Wesley Publishing pany, Inc., Reading, Mass., 1964.
17. Hahn, G. J., and S. S. Shapiro: "Statistical Models in Engineering," John Wiley & Sons, Inc., New York, 1967.
18. Hanssmann, F.: "Operations Research in Production and Inventory Control," John Wiley & Sons, Inc., New York, 1962.
19. Hillier, F. S., and G. J. Lieberman: "Introduction to Operations Research," Holden-Day, Inc., Publishers, San Francisco, 1967.
20. Jorgenson, D. W., J. J. McCall, and R. Radner: "Optimal Replacement Policy," Rand McNally & Company, Chicago, 1967.
21. Kaplan, W.: "Advanced Calculus," Addison-Wesley Publishing Company, Inc., Reading, Mass., 1952.
22. Lin, Y. K.: "Probabilistic Theory of Structural Dynamics," McGraw-Hill Book Company, New York, 1967.
23. Manheim, M. L.: Data Accuracy in Route Location, *Traffic Quart.*, pp. 153–178, January, 1961.
24. Mitten, L. G.: An Analytic Solution to the Least Cost Testing Sequence Problem, *J. Ind. Eng.*, vol. 11, January–February, 1960.
25. Morse, P. M.: "Queues, Inventories, and Maintenance," John Wiley & Sons, Inc., New York, 1958.
26. Naddor, E.: "Inventory Systems," John Wiley & Sons, Inc., New York, 1966.
27. Parzen, E.: "Stochastic Processes," Holden-Day, Inc., Publishers, San Francisco, 1962.
28. Peurifoy, R. L.: "Construction Planning, Equipment, and Methods," McGraw-Hill Book Company, New York, 1956.
29. Sasieni, M., A. Yaspan, and L. Friedman: "Operations Research—Methods and Problems," John Wiley & Sons, Inc., New York, 1955.

30. Stark, R. M., and R. H. Mayer, Jr.: Static Models and Other Aspects of Closed Competitive Bidding, *Dept. Civil Eng. Tech. Rep.*, University of Delaware, January, 1969.

31. Stark, R. M., and R. H. Mayer, Jr.: Discussion, *J. Construct. Div. ASCE*, vol. 95, pp. 131–133, July, 1969.

32. Swanson, S. R.: Load Fatigue Testing: State of the Art Survey, *Mater. Res. Std.*, vol. 8, no. 4, 1968.

33. Terborgh, G.: "Dynamic Equipment Policy," McGraw-Hill Book Company, New York, 1949.

34. Wagner, H. A.: "Principles of Operations Research," Prentice-Hall, Inc., Englewood Cliffs, N.J., 1969.

11
Random Models and Queues

In a sense, this chapter is a continuation of Chap. 9 with the random models organized into subject areas. The first three sections provide brief introductions to reliability, random walk, and Markov chains. The bulk of the chapter deals with queueing. Section 11-4 considers the single-server queue in some detail and provides a number of applications. Section 11-5 deals with multiserver queues. A large literature is available for each of the subjects in the chapter, as reflected by the extensive references.

11-1   RELIABILITY

Reliability is the probability that a system (or one of its components) will function acceptably for a specified time.   That is, reliability is a probability of survival for a given period.

Systems are composed of components whose performance is random. For given performance specifications, the reliability of a system can be improved, basically, in three ways: by using more reliable components, by using the system in a lower stress environment, or with additional components in parallel and redundant arrangements.   The additional components may either reduce the load of other components or serve as standbys in case of component failures.   Additional components increase the cost, weight, size, etc., so that their use is constrained.   The object of reliability theory is to maximize the reliability of a design subject to constraints or, alternatively, to minimize some system property subject to reliability constraints.

Reliability theory has developed largely in the context of electronic systems ([5],[6],[36],[40],[47],[53]).   Electronic components tend to fail suddenly; i.e., there is little loss of efficiency prior to failure.   Mechanical and structural components, however, tend to wear, and criteria for failure or unserviceability are not well defined.   Also, there may be several failure modes for such components.   Reliability studies have recently attracted the attention of civil engineers.   In structures with random loads and response, one seeks to size, arrange, and duplicate components to achieve more effective designs.   The choice and sizing of redundancies in water-supply systems for municipal, irrigation, or hydroelectric uses are examples.   Also, the sizing of cofferdams and diversion works for dam construction can be studied in a reliability framework.

HAZARD FUNCTION AND RELIABILITY

Let the random life T of a new item be described by the probability density $f(t)$, $t > 0$.   What is the conditional probability $h(t)$ that an item which has survived to time t will fail in the next instant, $\{t, t + \Delta t\}$?   The probability of the joint event "a new item lives until t and fails in $\{t, t + \Delta t\}$" is $f(t) \Delta t$, by definition.   The probability of the given event "a new item survives to time t" is the reliability

$$R(t) = 1 - \int_0^t f(t)\, dt$$

Therefore, the required conditional probability, $h(t) \Delta t$, is the ratio

$$h(t)\, \Delta t = \frac{f(t)\, \Delta t}{1 - \int_0^t f(t)\, dt}$$

or

$$h(t) = \frac{f(t)}{R(t)} \tag{1}$$

The probability density function $h(t)$ is called the *hazard function*. It is also referred to as the *hazard* or *failure rate*. Besides a conditional density, the hazard function can also be interpreted as the ratio of the expected number of failures in $\{t, t + \Delta t\}$ to the expected number of survivors at time t.

Consider some simple cases. Let $h(t) = \lambda$; that is, assume a constant conditional density or failure rate, independent of the age t. To determine the life density $f(t)$, we differentiate the expression $R(t) = f(t)/h(t)$ and solve the resulting differential equation. Thus,

$$R'(t) = f(t) = \frac{f'(t)h(t) - f(t)h'(t)}{[h(t)]^2} = \frac{f'(t)}{\lambda}$$

where the prime denotes differentiation with respect to t. Solving, one gets $f(t) = \lambda e^{-\lambda t}$, an exponential law (see Sec. 9-3).

For $h(t) = \lambda t$, that is, for a failure rate proportional to age, one finds the life density

$$f(t) = \lambda t e^{-\lambda t^2/2} \qquad t > 0 \tag{2}$$

This probability density is the Rayleigh law (Fig. 11-1a; $k = 1$), which was encountered in Sec. 10-4. The reason for its occurrence in random vibrations is now apparent. The probability that a vibrating system "peaks" in the next instant, $h(t)$, is assumed to be directly proportional to the time since it last was at equilibrium.

In some instances, a decreasing hazard rate is appropriate. For example, the strength of concrete improves with age and the life expectancy of an airplane engine increases shortly after it has survived initial testing. Problem 11-1 asks the reader to derive the life density for a linearly decreasing hazard rate. A famous hazard rate $h(t) = \lambda t^k$ for $k > -1$ is called the *Weibull* model. The associated density

$$wy(t;\lambda,k) = \lambda t^k e^{-\lambda t^{k+1}/(k+1)} \tag{3}$$

and the reliability

$$R(t) = e^{-\lambda t^{k+1}/(k+1)}$$

are well known to reliability engineers (see Fig. 11-1a and Appendix 4). Note that $k = 0$ and $k = 1$ correspond to the exponential and Rayleigh laws, respectively.

The human mortality curve (Fig. 11-1b) is apt for some equipment, e.g., aircraft engines. The high "infant" (initial) mortality is followed by a

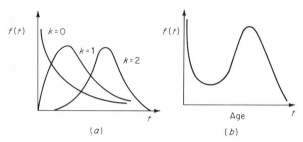

Fig. 11-1 Life densities. (*a*) Weibull law; (*b*) human mortality.

period of relatively constant chance, or accidental, mortality, and eventually, "old age" (wear-out) mortality prevails.

The hazard function has been used for such diverse models as the lives of mechanical equipment and business enterprises ([37] and [58]). Its use in the design of water-resource systems can be found in [33].

RELIABILITY OF SERIES AND PARALLEL COMBINATIONS

Consider a system of n series components (Fig. 11-2*a*) with respective reliabilities $r_1, r_2, \ldots, r_n$. Since the components are assumed independent, the reliability of the combination is

$$R_s(n) = \prod_{i=1}^{n} r_i \qquad (4)$$

The corresponding expression for a parallel combination of n components (Fig. 11-2*b*) is

$$R_p(n) = 1 = \prod_{i=1}^{n} (1 - r_i) \qquad (5)$$

To see this, let f_i be the event "the ith element fails." Then the event $\{f_1, f_2, \ldots, f_n\}$ describes the failure of the combination, and its negation describes its success.

Observe that a series combination is never more reliable than its least reliable component and that a parallel combination is at least as reliable as its most reliable component (see Prob. 11-4). For example, the reliability

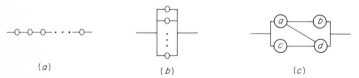

Fig. 11-2 Combinations of components. (*a*) Series combination; (*b*) parallel combination; (*c*) mixed combination.

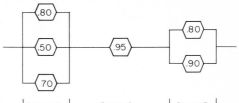

Fig. 11-3   Three-stage series system. | Stage 1 |← — Stage 2 — →| Stage 3 |

R of a three-stage series system (Fig. 11-3) with stage reliabilities R_1, R_2, R_3 is

$$R = R_1 R_2 R_3$$

using Eq. (4).   The stage reliabilities, using Eq. (5), are

$$R_1 = 1 - (1 - 0.8)(1 - 0.5)(1 - 0.7) = 0.97$$
$$R_2 = 0.95$$
$$R_3 = 1 - (1 - 0.8)(1 - 0.9) = 0.98$$

so that $R = 0.90$.

Not all combinations can be separated into distinct series and parallel combinations for which Eqs. (4) and (5) apply directly.   The reliability of a combination such as that shown in Fig. 11-2c is obtained by writing the

Table 11-1   Status of components

	a	b	c	d
(1)	x	x	x	x
(2)	0	x	x	x
(3)	x	0	x	x
(4)	x	x	0	x
(5)	x	x	x	0
(6)	0	0	x	x
(7)	0	x	0	x
(8)	0	x	x	0
(9)	x	0	0	x
(10)	x	0	x	0
(11)	x	x	0	0
(12)	x	0	0	0
(13)	0	x	0	0
(14)	0	0	x	0
(15)	0	0	0	x
(16)	0	0	0	0

appropriate event relation and seeking its probability. Let "x" indicate
that a component is "alive" or operative and "0" that it is not. Since there
are four components, there are $16(=2^4)$ possible configurations. The possible
system states can be conveniently enumerated, as in Table 11-1.

In order for the combination in Fig. 11-2c to survive, at least two components must be operative. Thus, configurations (12) to (16) do not apply.
In addition, component pairs a and d, a and c, and b and d cannot be "dead"
since there would be no complete load path. Thus configurations (7), (8),
and (10) are not possible. The union of the eight configurations (1) to (6),
(9), and (11) makes up the event that the system operates. The reliability is
the probability of that union of mutually exclusive configurations.

There are two basic ways to increase the reliability of a system with
additional components. First, we could parallel m identical systems, each
with reliability R; this is called *system standby* (Fig. 11-4a). The associated
reliability is

$$R_{ss}(n,m) = 1 - (1 - R)^m \tag{6}$$

where R_{ss} is the reliability of the entire system. This is simply Eq. (5) applied
to nominally identical parallel components. A second way is to include
redundant components in parallel; this is called *component standby* (Fig.
11-4b). The associated reliability for nominally identical elements in series is

$$R_{cs}(n,m) = [1 - (1 - r)^m]^n \tag{7}$$

RELIABILITY OPTIMIZATION

Consider obtaining a minimum-cost design subject to a reliability constraint.
Let c_i be the cost of the ith component in a component-standby system. An
m_i-fold redundancy has a reliability $1 - (1 - r_i)^{m_i}$. The problem is to determine the redundancies m_i for minimum cost. That is,

$$\text{Min:} \quad z = \sum_{i=1}^{n} m_i c_i \tag{8}$$

$$\text{Subject to:} \quad \prod_{i=1}^{n} [1 - (1 - r_i)^{m_i}] \geqslant P \tag{9}$$

$$0 \leqslant r_i \leqslant 1 \quad \text{all } i \tag{10}$$

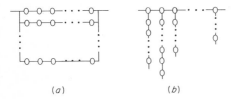

(a)   (b)

Fig. 11-4 System and component
standby. (a) System standby; (b) component standby.

where P is the minimum tolerable reliability for the system. The required optimization is suggested in the next example.

Example 11-1 Minimum-cost design Suppose that the above component-standby system has three components in series with reliabilities 0.80, 0.90, and 0.85 and respective costs of $400, $300, and $200. An overall system reliability of 0.97 is required. Redundant components are to be added, and a minimum-cost system is desired.

Each stage must have a reliability of at least 0.97, according to Eq. (4). Using this value in Eq. (5) and solving, we get $n = \log(1 - 0.97)/\log(1 - r)$. From this we obtain 2.18, 1.52, and 1.85 redundancies for the components having reliabilities 0.80, 0.90, and 0.85, respectively. We choose the next larger integer values, e.g., 3, 2, and 2, respectively. Using a recursive technique suggested by Bellman and Dreyfus [7], the stages of the system are first grouped into pairs. Since there are only three stages, let stages 1 and 2 constitute the first group and stage 3 the second. For each group we develop a sequence of more reliable combinations which are the least expensive for each level of reliability. These preferred sequences for pairs of stages are then combined to give a preferred sequence for 4, 8, 16, ... stages until a single preferred sequence is obtained for all stages. The final result indicates the lowest-cost redundancy assignment for any desired level of reliability.

We form a matrix (Table 11-2), with the numbers of components in stages 1 and 2 entered in rows and columns. The two numbered elements are the *reliability*, i.e., success probability for the corresponding combination of redundant components, and the cost. For example, element (43) represents

Table 11-2 Matrix and optimal redundancy investment sequence, stages 1 and 2

		Stage 2			
		2 0.99 $ 600	3 0.999 $ 900	4 0.9999 $1,200	...
	3	0.992 $1,200	0.982 $1,800	0.991 $2,100	0.9919 $2,400
Stage 1	4	0.9984 $1,600	0.9884 $2,200	0.9974 $2,500	0.9983 $2,800
	5	0.9997 $2,000	0.9897 $2,600	0.9987 $2,900	0.9996 $3,200

**Investment sequence
(in order of increasing
cost)**

Stage 1	Stage 2
3	2
3	3
3	4
4	3
4	4
5	3
5	4

4 components in stage 1 and 3 components in stage 2 with a total cost of $4(400) + 3(300) = \$2,500$. The corresponding reliability is

$$[1 - (1 - 0.8)^4][1 - (1 - 0.9)^3] = 0.9984 \times 0.999 = 0.9974$$

One examines the elements in order of increasing cost. Elements having higher cost and lower reliability than another element are deleted. We delete (42) by comparison with (33), and (52) by comparison with (43) (shaded elements in Table 11-2). The resulting suboptimal investment sequence, considering stages 1 and 2 only, is indicated above.

**Table 11-3 Optimal redundancy investment sequence, stages
1, 2, and 3**

			Stage 3			
			2 0.9775 \$ 400	3 0.9966 \$ 600	4 0.9995 \$ 800	...
	(3-2)	0.982 \$1,800	0.9595 \$2,200	0.9786 \$2,400	0.9815 \$2,600	
Stages 1 and 2	(3-3)	0.991 \$2,100	0.9685 \$2,500	0.9876 \$2,700	0.9905 \$2,900	
(combined)	(3-4)	0.9919 \$2,400	0.9694 \$2,800	0.9885 \$3,000	0.9915 \$3,200	
	(4-3)	0.9974 \$2,500	0.9749 \$2,900	0.994 \$3,100	0.9969 \$3,300	

Investment sequence (in order of increasing cost)			System reliability	Total cost
Stage 1	Stage 2	Stage 3		
3	2	2	0.9595	$2,200
3	2	3	0.9786	2,400
3	2	4	0.9815	2,600
3	3	3	0.9876	2,700
3	3	4	0.9905	2,900
4	3	3	0.9940	3,100
4	3	4	0.9969	3,300

We repeat the process, combining these results with stage 3 (Table 11-3). Shaded entries are deleted from further consideration. They indicate combinations which have higher costs and lower reliabilities than an alternative. The final tabulation indicates investment sequences and the associated system reliability. The optimum combination—3, 2, 3 at $2,400—has the lowest cost while satisfying the reliability constraint of 0.97.

Now consider the reverse situation, in which the reliability is to be maximized subject to constraints.

Example 11-2 Maximum-reliability design Two types of underwater craft are available for exploring three potential submarine mining areas. The problem is to deploy the craft so as to maximize the probability of striking a mineral deposit subject to resource constraints on the numbers of craft types and a fuel supply of 20,000 gal.

Craft type	Site 1		Site 2		Site 3		No. available
	Fuel reqt.	Strike prob.	Fuel reqt.	Strike prob.	Fuel reqt.	Strike prob.	
1	200	0.10	235	0.15	260	0.18	20
2	180	0.08	210	0.10	235	0.15	12

The probability of at least one strike is the complement of the probability of no strike. Thus, maximizing the reliability is the same as minimizing the unreliability. The unreliability is

$$\text{Min:} \quad (1 - 0.10)^{x_{11}} (1 - 0.15)^{x_{12}} (1 - 0.18)^{x_{13}} (1 - 0.08)^{x_{21}}$$
$$(1 - 0.10)^{x_{22}} (1 - 0.15)^{x_{23}}$$

where x_{ij} is the number of type i craft to be deployed to site j, $i = 1, 2, j = 1, 2, 3$.

The constraints are

Fuel: $200x_{11} + 235x_{12} + 260x_{13} + 180x_{21} + 210x_{22} + 235x_{23} \leqslant 20{,}000$

Craft: $x_{11} + x_{12} + x_{13} \leqslant 20$

$x_{21} + x_{22} + x_{13} \leqslant 12$

Here the constraints are linear but the objective is not. Since the logarithm is an increasing function, minimizing the objective function is equivalent to minimizing its logarithm. The logarithm of the objective is linear, so the required optimization can be accomplished by linear programming.

STRUCTURAL RELIABILITY

Some structures are designed for more predictable environments than others. Environments characterized by earthquakes and floods or by wind gusts on aircraft wings or guyed towers tend to be less predictable. Similarly, the strength of some materials is reliably predicted, e.g., steels, or is less predictable, as the strength of a stabilized soil base course. To briefly illustrate a facet of structural reliability, consider a structural member whose strength is a random variable and which is subjected to a random load. Suppose that there are only two independent and mutually exclusive failure modes: failure in compression and failure in tension.

From compressive tests, the compressive strength S_c is described by the density function $f_c(s_c)$; similarly, S_t is the tensile strength, and $f_t(s_t)$ is its associated density. Observations on the structural environment are used to establish load patterns. Suppose that the environment is such that loads causing compression, L_c, are described by the density function $q_c(l_c)$ and loads causing tension, L_t, are described by $q_t(l_t)$. Actually, these are conditional densities for the load magnitudes *given* that the element is in the particular mode, say compression. Let p_c and $p_t = 1 - p_c$ be the probabilities for the element compression and tension, respectively.

The conditional event "compression failure" is the probability that a compressive load exceeds the compressive strength, or

$$C_f = \int_0^\infty \int_{s_c}^\infty f_c(s_c) q_c(l_c)\, dl_c\, ds_c = \int_0^\infty \int_0^{l_c} f_c(s_c) q_c(l_c)\, ds_c\, dl_c \qquad (11a)$$

and for the conditional "tension failure"

$$T_f = \int_0^\infty \int_0^{l_c} f_t(s_t) q_t(l_t)\, ds_t\, dl_t \qquad (11b)$$

The reliability of the structural element is the complement of its unreliability, which is the probability of the union {(failure in compression mode) $\cup$ (failure in tension mode)}. Each of these events is a joint event, which can be written {compressive failure|compression mode}{compression mode}, etc. Since the modes are mutually exclusive, we have for the un-reliability

$$1 - R = p_c C_f + p_t T_f \tag{12}$$

where R is the structure's reliability and C_f and T_f are given by Eqs. (11). When the structure can be decomposed into independent elements, its re-liability can be derived by combining expressions such as Eq. (12). Unfortu-nately, the independence assumption seldom seems justified for structures. A few recent references to the structural-reliability literature include Ang and Amin [3], Moses and Kinser [44], and Freudenthal et al. [20]. Consider also the following examples.

Example 11-3 Reliability of a structure subjected to repeated loads A structure is to be designed to withstand repeated earthquake forces. To derive the probability that it survives a sequence of N disturbances over the design life, we assume independent disturbances with a common prob-ability distribution. Also, for simplicity, we assume random structural resistances that are both load- and time-invariant.

Let $f(l_1, l_2, \ldots, l_N, s_c, s_t)$ be a joint density for the loads and resistances. Disturbances give rise to both tensile and compressive forces. The prob-ability that the structure survives exactly n compressive loads and $N - n$ tensile loads is

$$P_S(n,N) = \binom{N}{n} \int_0^\infty \int_0^\infty \left[\int_0^{s_c} p_c g(l) \, dl \right]^n \left[\int_0^{s_t} p_t g(l) \, dl \right]^{N-n} f(s_c, s_t) \, ds_c \, ds_t$$

where $g(l)$ is the common load density and $f(s_c, s_t)$ the joint strength density and where independence of loads and resistances is assumed. Since there may be $n = 0, 1, \ldots, N$ compressive loads, the required survival probability is the sum

$$P_S(N) = \sum_{n=0}^N P_S(n,N) = \int_0^\infty \int_0^\infty \left[\int_0^{s_c} p_c g(l) \, dl + \int_0^{s_t} p_t g(l) \, dl \right]^N f(s_c, s_t) \, ds_c \, ds_t$$

where we have used the binomial expansion. The probability that the structure fails at the Nth load application, $h(N)$, is found from

$$P_S(N) = P_S(N - 1) [1 - h(N)]$$

Example 11-4 Reliability of a determinate structure Consider a determinate structure composed of n elements. A determinate structure corresponds to a series system in that if any element fails, the structure fails.

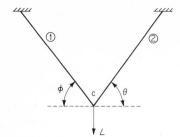

Fig. 11-5   Two-element truss.

The formulas derived earlier in this section do not apply here because all the elements do not act independently.   The probability of survival is

$$P_S = P\{S_1, S_2, \ldots, S_m\} = P\{S_m | S_{m-1}, \ldots, S_1\} P\{S_{m-1} | S_{m-2}, \ldots, S_1\}$$
$$\ldots P\{S_1\}$$

where $S_1, \ldots, S_m$ denotes the respective events "survival of member 1," "survival of member 2," etc.

The two-member determinate truss (Fig. 11-5) is assumed to bear a random load L with probability function

$$P\{L\} = \begin{cases} 0.9 & L = 50 \text{ kips} \\ 0.1 & L = 60 \text{ kips} \end{cases}$$

The cross-sectional areas of the two bars are chosen such that the tensile resistances have the common probability function

$$P\{S_i < c_i L\} = \begin{cases} 0.1 & L = 50 \text{ kips} \\ 0.9 & L = 60 \text{ kips} \end{cases}$$

where S_i is the strength of bar i and c_i is the load factor for the ith member, that is, the force in bar i resulting from a unit load applied at c, $i = 1,2$.

Using the previous expression for the survival probability, we have

$$P_S = (1 - P\{S_2' | S_1\})(1 - P\{S_1'\})$$

where the prime denotes negation, i.e., failure.   Now,

$$P\{S_1' | S_1\} = \frac{P\{S_2', S_1\}}{P\{S_1\}}$$

and

$$P\{S_2', S_1\} = P\{s_2 < c_2 L, s_1 \geqslant c_1 L\}$$

$$= \sum_{i=1}^{2} P\{s_2 < c_2 L_i, s_1 \geqslant c_1 L_i | L = L_i\} P\{L = L_i\}$$

$$= (0.1)(0.9)(0.9) + (0.9)(0.1)(0.1) = 0.09$$

where $L_1 = 50$ kips and $L_2 = 60$ kips. Also,

$$P\{S_1\} = \sum_{i=1}^{2} P\{s_1 \geqslant c_1 L_i\} P\{L = L_i\} = (0.9)(0.9) + (0.1)(0.1) = 0.82$$

Therefore, the survival probability is

$$P_S = (1 - 0.18)\frac{1 - 0.09}{0.82} = 0.73$$

Note that this survival probability is greater than the product $P\{S_1\}P\{S_2\}$ $= (0.82)(0.82) = 0.67$. The reason is that the certainty of survival of one member under a random load increases the chances of survival of the remaining members. This is the effect of a lack of independence.

The development of reliability in structural engineering is recent. Further research is needed to effectively generalize the time invariance of loads and resistances which we have assumed. Loads and resistances may change in time and use. Indeed, the character of the structure may change as a result of cumulative damage or fatigue. These considerations suggest time-dependent reliability functions.

11-2 RANDOM WALK

The repeated experiments in the discrete time model of Sec. 9-1, which led to the binomial law, can be modified in a minor but useful way. Imagine a particle which moves along the X axis at discrete times, moving a unit step to the right with probability p and a unit step to the left with probability q. The probability of no movement is $r(=1 - p - q)$. If X_n is the particle's position at the nth step, then the recursion relation is

$$X_n = X_{n-1} + Z_n \qquad n = 1, 2, \ldots$$

where Z_n is a random variable taking values $+1$, 0, -1 with respective probabilities p, r, q. The trials are assumed to be independent, as in Sec. 9-1. This typical case is called a *simple random walk*. The special case $q = X_0 = 0$ corresponds to the occurrence of X_n successes in n Bernoulli trials with success probability p. In more general random walks, the movement takes place in space rather than on a line. Also, the trial variable Z_n can be regarded as a continuous random variable.

First we restrict the random walk to the interval $\{a,b\}$ on the X axis. That is, *barriers* are assumed at $x = a$ and $x = b$. An *absorbing barrier* terminates the particle's walk whenever it is reached. A *reflecting barrier* returns the particle to the interior of the interval. For example, it might return the particle to a previous or otherwise specified position. An *elastic barrier* combines these features. It acts as an absorbing barrier with a specified probability and as a reflecting barrier with the complementary probability.

Consider a random walk with $r = 0$ and with absorbing barriers at $x = 0$ and $x = b$. Let $v(x,t)$ be the probability that the particle is at x, $(0 \leqslant x \leqslant b)$, at trial (or time) t; x and t are integers. In the manner of Sec. 9-1, we identify the events:

{The particle is at x at time t}
{The particle is at $x - 1$ at time $t - 1$ and moves to the right}
{The particle is at $x + 1$ at time $t - 1$ and moves to the left}

The first event is the union of the other two mutually exclusive events (neglecting boundaries for the moment). Equating probabilities:

$$v(x,t) = pv(x - 1, t - 1) + qv(x + 1, t - 1) \tag{13}$$

To establish the boundary conditions, suppose that the particle began at the origin at $t = 0$, that is, $v(0,0) = 1$. For $x = 0$, the second event is not possible, and zero probability is associated with $v(-1, t - 1)$ for all t. Similarly, $v(b + 1, t - 1) = 0$ for all t since a barrier exists at $x = b$. Equation (13) is a partial difference equation. Techniques for solution are suggested in Appendix 5.

The probabilities of ultimate absorption are useful. Let $\Omega(x)$ be the probability that the particle at x will eventually be absorbed at the origin. Reasoning as before, one forms the recursion relation

$$\Omega(x) = p\Omega(x + 1) + q\Omega(x - 1) \tag{14}$$

with the boundary conditions $\Omega(0) = 1$ and $\Omega(b) = 0$. The indicial equations yield the roots $\Omega(x) = 1$ and $\Omega(x) = (q/p)^x$. Using techniques of Appendix 5 (and the boundary conditions), we find the solution

$$\Omega(x) = \begin{cases} \dfrac{(q/p)^b - (q/p)^x}{(q/p)^b - 1} & q \neq p \\[2mm] 1 - \dfrac{x}{b} & q = p = 1/2 \end{cases} \tag{15}$$

Equation (15) is the solution to a well-known gambling problem (see Probs. 11-11 to 11-13); an excellent discussion appears in Feller [18]. It can be shown that the probability of absorption at b is simply $1 - \Omega(x)$, and the limiting case $b \to \infty$ yields $\Omega(x) = 1$ for $p \leqslant q$ and $(q/p)^x$ for $p > q$.

In a two-dimensional random walk, the particle moves in a plane in unit steps parallel to the coordinate axes. At each point there are four possible positions to which the particle can move with given probabilities. Let $p_{1,0}$, $p_{0,1}$, $p_{-1,0}$, and $p_{0,-1}$ be the probabilities that the particle moves one step either to the right, up, to the left, or down, respectively. Let $v(x,y,t)$

be the probability that the particle is at (x,y) at time t. In a manner similar to that used to derive Eq. (14), one can conclude

$$v(x,y,t) = p_{-1,0}\, v(x+1, y, t-1) + p_{0,-1}\, v(x, y+1, t-1)$$
$$+ p_{1,0}\, v(x-1, y, t-1) + p_{0,1}\, v(x, y-1, t-1) \qquad (16)$$

with boundary conditions as appropriate. In analogy to the absorbing barriers, the boundary of the "walk region" is divided into two classes, B and B', so that they make up the entire absorbing boundary. Let $\Omega(x,y)$ be the probability that a particle at (x,y) will eventually be absorbed into class B. In analogy to Eq. (14), we write

$$\Omega(x,y) = p_{-1,0}\, \Omega(x+1, y) + p_{0,-1}\, \Omega(x, y+1)$$
$$+ p_{1,0}\, \Omega(x-1, y) + p_{0,1}\, \Omega(x, y-1) \qquad (17)$$

The boundary conditions are expressed as $\Omega(x_B, y_B) = 1$ and $\Omega(x'_B, y'_B) = 0$, where (x_B, y_B) and (x'_B, y'_B) denote boundary points in classes B and B', respectively. For the symmetric case, $p_{-1,0} = p_{0,-1} = p_{1,0} = p_{0,1} = 1/4$, Eq. (17) is used as an approximation to the second-order derivatives (laplacian operator) in classical problems. We shall consider this point shortly, but first it is useful to pass to the limiting case where the position and time variables are continuous rather than discrete. This limiting procedure leads to the Fokker-Planck partial differential equation, which plays an important role in diffusion theory and structural dynamics, among other subjects.

Begin by letting x and t in Eq. (13) be continuous variables, and make the respective step sizes Δx and Δt. This yields

$$v(x,t) = pv(x - \Delta x, t - \Delta t) + qv(x + \Delta x, t - \Delta t)$$

Expanding both sides of this equation in Taylor series about position x at time t yields, to second-order terms,

$$\Delta t \frac{\partial v}{\partial t} - \frac{(\Delta t)^2}{2} \frac{\partial^2 v}{\partial t^2} + \cdots = (1 - 2p)\Delta x \frac{\partial v}{\partial x} + \frac{(\Delta x)^2}{2} \frac{\partial^2 v}{\partial x^2} + \cdots \qquad (18)$$

Before letting Δx and Δt approach zero, it is prudent to require that the mean and variance of the displacement remain bounded. The total random displacement δ is the sum of the individual random displacements: δ_1 at time Δt, δ_2 at time $2\Delta t, \ldots, \delta_n$ at time $t = n\Delta t$ (where n is an integer). Since $\delta = \delta_1 + \delta_2 + \cdots + \delta_n$, the first two moments are $E(\delta) = E(\delta_1) + \cdots + E(\delta_n)$ and $E(\delta^2) = E(\delta_1^2) + \cdots + E(\delta_n^2)$. Since we are dealing with identical independent repeated trials, these can be written $E(\delta) = nE(\delta_1)$ and $E(\delta^2) = nE(\delta_1^2)$.

The random variable δ_1 takes two values, $+\Delta x$ and $-\Delta x$, with probabilities p and q, respectively. Clearly, $E(\delta_1) = (+\Delta x)p + (-\Delta x)q = (p - q)\Delta x$ and $E(\delta_1^2) = (+\Delta x)^2 p + (-\Delta x)^2 q = (\Delta x)^2$. We conclude that

$$E(\delta) = t(p - q)\frac{\Delta x}{\Delta t}$$

and

$$\text{Var}(\delta) = E(\delta^2) - [E(\delta)]^2 = \frac{t(\Delta x)^2}{\Delta t}[1 - (p - q)^2]$$

$$= \frac{4t(\Delta x)^2}{\Delta t}p(1 - p)$$

Letting $D = \lim\limits_{\substack{\Delta x \to 0 \\ \Delta t \to 0}} \dfrac{\text{var}(\delta)}{4tp(1 - p)}$ and $c = \lim\limits_{\substack{\Delta x \to 0 \\ \Delta t \to 0}} \dfrac{E(\delta)}{t}$, Eq. (18) is written in the limit as

$$\frac{\partial v}{\partial t} = -c\frac{\partial v}{\partial x} + \frac{D}{2}\frac{\partial^2 v}{\partial x^2} \tag{19}$$

Equation (19) is the *Fokker-Planck* or *diffusion equation*, with c as the *drift coefficient* and D the *diffusion coefficient*. When $p = 1/2$, we have $c = 0$, and the process is said to be without drift. Equation (19) is a special case of more general processes, and the subject has been well studied (see, e.g., [8] and [61]). Brownian motion has been explained as the random movement of particles in a suspension undergoing many mutual collisions (Sec. 9-4). Each collision initiates a random step, and in the limit the Fokker-Planck equation gives a reasonable description (see Wang and Uhlenbeck's paper reprinted in [61]). Feller [18, p. 356] explains it as follows:

Essentially the same consideration applies to many other phenomena in physics, economics, learning theory, evolution theory, etc., when slow fluctuations of the state of a system are interpreted as the result of a huge number of successive small changes due to random impacts. The simple random-walk model does not appear realistic in any particular case, but fortunately the situation is similar to that in the central limit theorem. Under surprisingly mild conditions the nature of the individual changes is not important, because the observable effect depends only on their expectation and variance. In such circumstances it is natural to take the simple random-walk model as a universal prototype.

A random-walk model can also be useful in the study of differential equations arising in problems which have no apparent random aspects. The essential idea is to (1) interpret the equation as a random walk and (2) to simulate the random walk by a Monte Carlo (see Sec. 8-7). We illustrate with two examples.

Example 11-5 Laplace's equation The steady-state two-dimensional flow of fluid through a homogeneous porous medium is described by

$$k_x \frac{\partial^2 h}{\partial x^2} + k_y \frac{\partial^2 h}{\partial y^2} = 0 \tag{20}$$

where $h(x,y)$ is the fluid head and k_x and k_y are coefficients of permeability of the medium in the x and y directions. One seeks the solution $h(x,y)$ of Eq. (20) at points of the flow region in Fig. 11-6 subject to the boundary conditions. For simplicity, the upstream boundary is assumed to be at a pressure head of $h(x_B, y_B) = 100$ while the downstream boundary is at $h(x'_B, y'_B) = 0$.

The numerical solution begins by dividing the region into a grid whose mesh size is Δx and Δy along the respective axes. The computation is simplified if a grid can be chosen which matches the boundaries and which also has nodes located approximately at points where $h(x,y)$ is desired, such as point A in Fig. 11-6. The partial differential equation (20) is approximated by a central difference equation. The derivative $\partial h/\partial x$ is replaced by

$$\frac{h(x + \Delta x, y) - h(x - \Delta x, y)}{2\Delta x}$$

and the second derivative $(\partial/\partial x)(\partial h/\partial x)$ is obtained by using the preceding expression in place of $\partial h/\partial x$, that is,

$$\frac{h(x + \Delta x, y) - 2h(x,y) + h(x - \Delta x, y)}{(\Delta x)^2}$$

Similar expressions hold for the derivatives with respect to y. Replacing $h(x,y)$ by $\Omega(x,y)$ and setting $\Delta x = \Delta y = 1$, Eq. (17) is the partial difference equation which approximates the partial differential equation (20). Note that

$$\frac{k_x}{2(k_x + k_y)} = p_{-1,0} = p_{1,0} \quad \text{and} \quad \frac{k_y}{2(k_x + k_y)} = p_{0,-1} = p_{0,1}$$

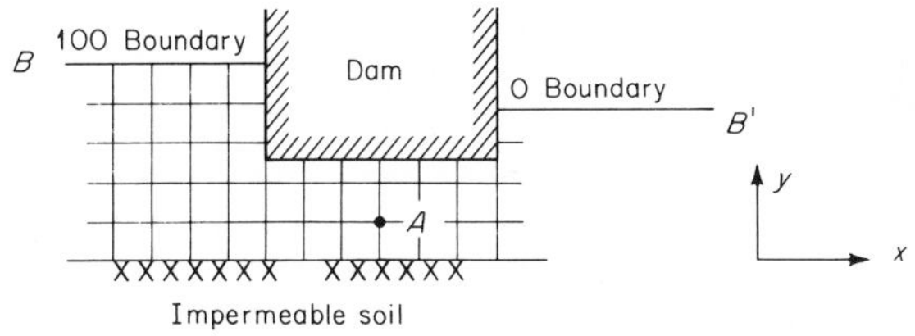

Fig. 11-6 Flow through a porous medium.

which account for the anisotropy of the medium. Thus, a random-walk model is provided whose governing equation is the same as that for the fluid-flow problem. A Monte Carlo technique can be employed considering the boundaries B and B' as absorbing barriers, the dam and impermeable soil surfaces as reflecting barriers, and infinite barriers to the left and right. The head at (x,y), $h(x,y)$, is determined by starting at that position and moving to one of four adjacent points, chosen with the appropriate probability. The choice $p_{ij} = 1/4$, all i, j, is used. One continues until a boundary, B or B', is reached. The experiment is repeated many times, starting from (x,y). The ratio of the number of times the boundary at head = 100 is reached to the total number of experiments (walks), multiplied by 100, is an estimate of $h(x,y)$. A more detailed description can be found in Scott [55].

Although inefficient compared with other solution methods, the random walk is useful for determining the potential (hydrostatic, temperature, electro-static, etc.) at a few specific points in a flow region governed by the Laplace equation.

Example 11-6 A random-walk model in random vibration
Toland and Yang [64], and others, have studied random-walk models for a general second-order dynamic system excited by a random forcing function, that is,

$$\frac{\partial^2 y}{\partial t^2} + H(y,\dot{y}) = f(t)$$

where y is the displacement at time t and $f(t)$ is the random forcing function per unit mass. For example, in elementary dynamics one studies the harmonic oscillator with the restoring force $H(y,\dot{y}) = ky$ or the damped oscillator $H(y,\dot{y}) = (ky + 2c\dot{y})/M$, where k is a spring constant, c a damping coefficient, and M the mass. Also, $f(t)$ is assumed to be governed by a normal law (gaussian white noise) with zero mean (Sec. 10-4), that is, $E[f(t)] = 0$, and autocorrelation

$$E[f(t_1)f(t_2)] = \alpha\delta(t_2 - t_1)] = \begin{cases} \alpha & t_2 = t_1 \\ 0 & t_2 \neq t_1 \end{cases}$$

Here α is a positive constant and $\delta(t_2 - t_1)$ is the Dirac delta function. For the damped oscillator, the Fokker-Planck equation for the probabilities $v(y,\dot{y},t)$ that the system will be at the random position y with random velocity $\dot{y}$ at time t turns out to be

$$\frac{\partial v}{\partial t} = 2cv - \dot{y}\frac{\partial v}{\partial y} + (2c\dot{y} + ky)\frac{\partial v}{\partial \dot{y}} + \frac{\alpha}{2}\frac{\partial^2 v}{\partial \dot{y}^2}$$

The difference equation for the corresponding random walk having step sizes Δy, $\Delta \dot{y}$, and Δt for y, $\dot{y}$, and t, respectively, is

$$v(m,n,s) = \left[\frac{1}{2} - \frac{m-1}{K} + L(n-m+1)\right]v(m-1,n-m+1,s-1)$$

$$+ \left[\frac{1}{2} + \frac{m+1}{K} + L(n-m-1)\right]v(m+1,n-m-1,s-1)$$

where $m = \dot{y}/\Delta\dot{y}$, $n = y/\Delta y$, $s = t/\Delta t$, and the constants

$$K = (c\,\Delta t)^{-1} \qquad \text{and} \qquad L = k\,\Delta t\,(2\Delta\dot{y})^{-1}$$

For example, suppose $\Delta t = 0.05$, $\Delta\dot{y} = 0.224$, $N = 1$, $c = 1$, $k = 1$, and $y = \Delta t\,\Delta\dot{y}$ $= 0.0112$. The random-walk model is

$$v(m,n,s) = \left[\frac{1}{2} - \frac{m-1}{20} - (0.112)(n-m+1)\right]v(m-1,n-m+1,s-1)$$

$$+ \left[\frac{1}{2} + \frac{m+1}{20} + (0.112)(n-m-1)\right]v(m+1,n-m-1,s-1)$$

with the initial condition $v(0,0,0) = 1$. The result of the numerical procedure is illustrated for the first three time increments (steps) in Fig. 11-7. The indicated probabilities are the (approximate) values of $v(y,\dot{y},t)$ for successive instants corresponding to $s = 0, 1, 2$, etc., as indicated in Fig. 11-7a, b, and c, respectively.

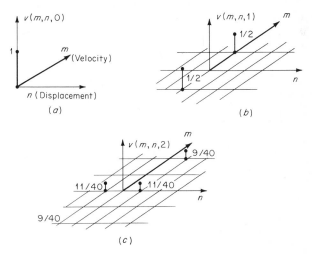

Fig. 11-7 Random-walk model. (a) Initial condition, $s = 0$; (b) first step, $s = 1$; (c) second step, $s = 2$.

11-3 MARKOV CHAINS

Much of probability theory deals with random variables which evolve in time, the so-called *stochastic processes*. The models of Secs. 9-1 and 9-2, for example, could be called stochastic models. The symbol $X(t)$ describes the random state at time (parameter) t. Stochastic processes are divided into four cases, corresponding to whether a discrete or a continuous state variable is combined with a discrete or a continuous time parameter. Sections 11-4 and 11-5 deal with queues, which are stochastic processes with a discrete state (number in the queue) and continuous parameter (time). Random-walk models usually have a discrete state (integer positions) and a discrete parameter (number of trials). Brownian motion is described by a continuous state variable (displacement) and a continuous time parameter. Finally, maximum monthly streamflow might be a continuous state variable in discrete time. While the analysis differs for each case, the main ideas are similar. The central problem of stochastic processes is to determine the probabilities associated with the variables $X(t)$ describing the random state at time t for all states and times. In general, these probabilities depend upon the history of the process. For a discrete time parameter $t = 0, 1, 2, \ldots$, we can write the conditional probabilities as

$$P\{X(t + 1) | X(t), X(t - 1), \ldots, X(1), X(0)\}$$

The simplest random processes are described by the probabilities

$$P\{X(t + 1) | X(t), \ldots, X(0)\} = P\{X(t + 1)\}$$

That is, the probability of the next state (at time $t + 1$) is entirely independent of the history of the process. The Bernoulli trials of Chaps. 8 and 9 are of this type. The next generalization is to processes of the type

$$P\{X(t + 1) | X(t), \ldots, X(0)\} = P\{X(t + 1) | X(t)\}$$

That is, the conditional probabilities at time $t + 1$ depend only upon the state at time t and not upon previous history. Stochastic processes which can be described with such information are called *Markovian*. Most applications of stochastic processes to date use the Markov property. A *Markov chain* is a Markov process in which the state space and the time parameter are both discrete-valued. There is a vast literature on Markov chains, but only a few steady-state results are illustrated here.

The conditional probabilities $P\{X(t + 1) = j | X(t) = i\}$, $t = 0, 1, 2, \ldots$, all i, j, are called one-step *transition probabilities* from state i to state j at time t. We consider the *stationary case*, for which $P\{X(t + 1) | X(t)\}$ is independent of t. That is,

$$P\{X(t + 1) | X(t)\} = p_{ij} \tag{21}$$

for all $t = 0, 1, 2, \ldots$. In a similar way, one describes the stationary n-step transition probabilities by

$$P\{X(t+n)|X(t)\} = p_{ij}{}^{(n)} \qquad n = 1, 2, \ldots; \text{ all } t > 0 \tag{22}$$

where the superscript denotes the number of steps. For $n = 1$, corresponding to a single step, we drop the superscript, that is, $p_{ij}{}^{(1)} = p_{ij}$.

It is convenient to collect one-step transition probabilities in a matrix:

$$\mathbf{P} = \begin{bmatrix} p_{00} & p_{01} & \cdots & p_{0m} \\ p_{10} & p_{11} & \cdots & p_{1m} \\ \hdotsfor{4} \\ p_{m0} & p_{m1} & \cdots & p_{mm} \end{bmatrix}$$

The element p_{ij} of $\mathbf{P}$ is the one-step transition probability from state i to state j in a space composed of $m + 1$ states $0, 1, \ldots, m$. For example, consider structural specimens subjected to random loads of $0, 1, \ldots, m$ kips at successive intervals. The element p_{ij} is the probability that the load will change from level i to level j in the next interval. Another example is a three-state description of a structure where "state 0" corresponds to a "new" condition and states 1 and 2 correspond to damaged and unserviceable states, respectively. The one-step transition matrix can be written

$$\begin{bmatrix} p_{00} & p_{01} & p_{02} \\ 0 & p_{11} & p_{12} \\ 1 & 0 & 0 \end{bmatrix}$$

The element $p_{20} = 1$ indicates that an unserviceable condition must be restored to new condition. The row sums in a transition matrix must be unity.

The n-step transition probabilities of a Markov chain, $p_{ij}{}^{(n)}$, satisfy the following fundamental transition law:

$$p_{ij}{}^{(n)} = \sum_k p_{ik}{}^{(r)} p_{kj}{}^{(n-r)} \tag{23}$$

for all states i and j and for all times n and t, $0 < r < n$; and the summation extends over all intermediate states k. The term $p_{ik}{}^{(r)} p_{kj}{}^{(n-r)}$ is the conditional probability that, starting from state i, the process moves to state k in r steps and then to step j in $n - r$ steps. This is called the *Chapman-Kolmogorov equation* (or Chapman equation) and holds for all Markov chains and some non-Markovian processes as well. The importance of Eq. (23) is that it enables us to calculate the chance of transitions between states during extended periods. If one can estimate the one-step transition probabilities, the Chapman equation provides the multistep transition probabilities. To illustrate, set $n = 2$ and $r = 1$ in Eq. (23). This enables us to calculate the two-step transition probabilities. Having the two-step probabilities, we could set $n = 4$ and $r = 2$ to obtain the four-step probabilities or, perhaps, set $n = 3$

and $r = 1$ or 2 to calculate the three-step probabilities, and so on. For the preceding 3×3 structural matrix, the nine possible two-step probabilities are calculated, using the Chapman equation, as

$$p_{00}^{(2)} = p_{00}p_{00} + p_{01}p_{10} + p_{02}p_{20} = p_{00}^2 + p_{02}$$
$$p_{01}^{(2)} = p_{00}p_{01} + p_{01}p_{11} + p_{02}p_{21} = p_{00}p_{01} + p_{01}p_{11}$$
$$p_{02}^{(2)} =$$
$$p_{10}^{(2)} =$$
$$p_{11}^{(2)} = \qquad \vdots$$
$$p_{12}^{(2)} =$$
$$p_{20}^{(2)} =$$
$$p_{21}^{(2)} =$$
$$p_{22}^{(2)} = p_{20}p_{02} + p_{21}p_{12} + p_{22}p_{22} = p_{02}$$

Since we required that the unserviceable condition be restored to new condition, $p_{20} = 1$ and $p_{10} = p_{21} = p_{22} = 0$.

There is a very convenient observation regarding the Chapman equation. Equation (23) describes the rule for matrix multiplication. For example, the last calculation of transition probabilities could have been represented by

$$\mathbf{P}^{(2)} = \mathbf{P}\mathbf{P} = \mathbf{P}^2 = \begin{bmatrix} p_{00} & p_{01} & p_{02} \\ 0 & p_{11} & p_{12} \\ 1 & 0 & 0 \end{bmatrix} \begin{bmatrix} p_{00} & p_{01} & p_{02} \\ 0 & p_{11} & p_{12} \\ 1 & 0 & 0 \end{bmatrix}$$

$$= \begin{bmatrix} p_{00}^2 + p_{02} & p_{00}p_{01} + p_{01}p_{11} & p_{00}p_{02} + p_{01}p_{12} \\ p_{12} & p_{11}^2 & p_{11}p_{12} \\ p_{00} & p_{01} & p_{02} \end{bmatrix}$$

where $\mathbf{P}^{(2)}$ represents a two-step transition matrix. More generally, we can calculate n-step matrices since

$$\mathbf{P}^{(n)} = \mathbf{P} \cdots \mathbf{P} = \mathbf{P}\,\mathbf{P}^{n-1} = \mathbf{P}^{n-1}\,\mathbf{P} = \mathbf{P}^n \qquad \text{all } n \tag{24}$$

Note that the Chapman equation implies that transition matrices commute in multiplication.

Often one seeks the probabilities associated with being in the various states at various times. These are the *absolute*, or *unconditioned*, *probabilities* $P\{X(t)\}$. Besides transition probabilities, one must know the *initial-state* probabilities $P\{X(0)\}$. If a process always begins at state 0, as a new structure, then the initial probabilities are

$$P\{X(0) = 0\} = 1 \qquad \text{and} \qquad P\{X(0) = k\} = 0 \qquad k = 1, \ldots, m$$

The initial probabilities $P\{X(0)\}$ and the transition-probability matrix $\mathbf{P}$ completely determine the behavior of a stationary Markov chain. That is,

$$P\{X(t)\} = \mathbf{P}^t\, P\{X(0)\} \tag{25}$$

As an example, let α_0, α_1, α_2 $(=1 - \alpha_0 - \alpha_1)$ be the initial probabilities for the three-state structure. The probability that the structure is in state 2 after two steps is

$$P\{X(2) = 2\} = \alpha_0(p_{00}p_{02} + p_{01}p_{12})$$
$$+ \alpha_1(p_{11}p_{12})$$
$$+ \alpha_2(p_{02})$$
$$\vdots$$

and so on. These observations are more important than they at first appear. A knowledge of $P\{X(0)\}$ and $\mathbf{P}$ enables one to calculate so-called *first-passage probabilities*, i.e., probabilities for when a particular state, say failure, is reached for the first time. For example, let $f_{jk}^{(n)}$ be the probability that a process beginning in state j enters state k for the first time at the nth step. For $n = 1$, naturally,

$$f_{jk}^{(1)} = p_{jk}$$

For $n = 2$, $p_{jk}^{(2)}$ is the two-step transition probability from state j to state k. This can occur in two mutually exclusive ways, namely, {a transition from j to k on the first step and the process remains there for step 2} or {first passage to state k occurs at the second step}. In symbols,

$$p_{jk}^{(2)} = f_{jk}^{(1)}p_{kk} + f_{jk}^{(2)} = p_{jk}p_{kk} + f_{jk}^{(2)}$$

which can easily be solved for $f_{jk}^{(2)}$ once $p_{jk}^{(2)}$ is known.

Similar reasoning leads to the general formula

$$p_{jk}^{(n)} = \sum_{r=1}^{n} f_{jk}^{(r)}p_{kk}^{(n-r)} \qquad n = 1, 2, \ldots \qquad (26)$$

If the $p_{jk}^{(n)}$ are known for the desired time period N (all $n \leqslant N$), the first-passage probabilities can be derived recursively, beginning at $f_{jk}^{(1)}, f_{jk}^{(2)}, \ldots$. The converse also holds; i.e., if the $f_{jk}^{(n)}$ are known for all $n \leqslant N$, then the $p_{jk}^{(n)}$ can be calculated. For the three-state structure example, assume that $\alpha_0 = 1$ and $j = 0$, that is, that the process begins with a structure in new condition. The first-passage probabilities to state 2, i.e., unserviceability, are

$$f_{02}^{(1)} = p_{02}$$
$$f_{02}^{(2)} = p_{00}p_{02} + p_{01}p_{12}$$
$$f_{02}^{(3)} = p_{00}^2 p_{02} + p_{00}p_{01}p_{12} + p_{01}p_{11}p_{12}$$
$$\ldots\ldots\ldots\ldots\ldots\ldots\ldots\ldots\ldots\ldots\ldots\ldots$$

and so on. For a particular design life N, the first-passage probabilities can be added to give the probability $f_{jk}(N)$ that a certain state k is reached, that is,

$$f_{jk}^{(N)} = \sum_{n=1}^{N} f_{jk}^{(n)} \qquad (27)$$

Consider next *steady-state transition probabilities*, defined by

$$\lim_{n \to \infty} p^{(n)} = \pi_j \qquad \text{all } j \tag{28}$$

These limits exist for Markov chains in which transitions are possible from any state to any other state. The situation corresponds to one in which the effect of the initial state has "worn off." An analogous situation arises in queueing (Secs. 11-4 and 11-5). Using the Chapman equation (23) with $r = 1$, one writes for the steady state,

$$\pi_j = \sum_i \pi_i p_{ij} \qquad \text{all } j \tag{29}$$

where the summation extends over all states i and, clearly,

$$\sum_j \pi_j = 1 \qquad \text{and} \qquad \pi_j > 0 \qquad \text{all } j \tag{30}$$

The steady-state probabilities π_j have a useful interpretation as reciprocals of the average time of return to state j (all j). For example, for the three-state structure

$$\pi_0 = \pi_0 p_{00} + \pi_1 p_{10} + \pi_2 p_{20}$$
$$\pi_1 = \pi_0 p_{01} + \pi_1 p_{11} + \pi_2 p_{21}$$
$$\pi_2 = \pi_0 p_{02} + \pi_1 p_{12} + \pi_2 p_{22}$$
$$1 = \pi_0 + \pi_1 + \pi_2$$

where $p_{20} = 1$ and $p_{10} = p_{21} = p_{22} = 0$. Although four equations have been written, only three are independent since the fourth is the sum of the first three. Solving the last three equations simultaneously gives

$$\pi_0 = \frac{1 - p_{11}}{\beta}$$

$$\pi_1 = \frac{p_{01}}{\beta}$$

$$\pi_2 = \frac{p_{12} p_{01} + p_{02} - p_{02} p_{11}}{\beta} = \frac{p_{12} p_{01} + p_{02}(1 - p_{11})}{\beta}$$

where $\beta = p_{01}(1 + p_{12}) + (1 + p_{02})(1 - p_{11})$. The average time before a recently "replaced" structure fails (unserviceable) is $1/\pi_2 = \beta/[p_{12} p_{01} + p_{02}(1 - p_{11})]$.

Consider two simple examples to further illustrate these ideas.

Example 11-7 Rainfall in Tel Aviv Gabriel and Neumann [21] used a two-state Markov chain to describe wet and dry days during Tel Aviv's rainy season from December through January. For a 77-year history, the following numbers were found

"Today'

		Dry	Wet	Totals
"Yesterday"	Dry	1,049	350	1,399
	Wet	351	687	1,038
				2,437

The relative frequencies are taken to be the one-step transition probabilities

$P\{$today is wet|yesterday was dry$\} = 350/1,399 \backsim 0.250$
$P\{$today is dry|yesterday was wet$\} = 351/1,038 \backsim 0.338$

For convenience, let "state 0" be the event "dry day" and "state 1" the event "wet day." The single-step transition matrix is

$$\mathbf{P} = \begin{bmatrix} 0.750 & 0.250 \\ 0.338 & 0.662 \end{bmatrix}$$

The n-step transition matrices are easily calculated using Eq. (24). For example, the five-step matrix is

$$\mathbf{P}^{(5)} = \begin{bmatrix} 0.580 & 0.420 \\ 0.568 & 0.432 \end{bmatrix}$$

This implies that if January 1 is a wet day, then the probability that January 6 is also wet is 0.432; if January 1 is dry, then January 6 is dry with probability 0.580, etc., assuming that the model is adequate.

Since every state can be reached from every other state, the steady-state limits, Eq. (28), exist and lead to the simultaneous equations (29) and (30):

$\pi_0 = \pi_0 p_{00} + \pi_1 p_{10}$
$\pi_1 = \pi_0 p_{01} + \pi_1 p_{11}$
$1 = \pi_0 + \pi_1$

The solution is $\pi_0 = 0.575$ and $\pi_1 = 0.425$. Actually, to three decimal places

$$\mathbf{P}^{(10)} = \mathbf{P}^{(5)}\mathbf{P}^{(5)} = \begin{bmatrix} 0.575 & 0.425 \\ 0.575 & 0.245 \end{bmatrix}$$

For most practical purposes, the steady state is reached in about 10 steps (days). Thus, independent of the weather on New Year's Day, the probability is 0.575 that January 11 is dry and 0.425 that it is wet.

The distribution of wet and dry days is also of interest. Let W be the consecutive number of wet days before the next dry day, that is, W is a first-passage time for state 0. Clearly,

$$P\{W = k\} = P\{X(2) = 1, \ldots, X(k) = 1, X(k + 1) = 0 \mid X(1) = 1\}$$
$$= (p_{11})^{k-1} p_{10} = (0.662)^{k-1} (0.338)$$

a geometric law. The expected duration of wet weather is

$$E(W) = \sum_{k=1}^{\infty} k(1 - p)^{k-1} p = p^{-1} = 2.96 \text{ days}$$

where $p = p_{10} = 0.338$. The expected duration of dry weather, D, is similarly found to be about 4 days. A weather cycle is the expectation $E(D + W) = E(D) + E(W) \sim 7$ days. The example is continued in Cox and Miller [13].

Example 11-8   Operating a dam   This example, adapted from Hillier and Lieberman [30], concerns a dam used for power generation and flood control. The monthly inflow W is assumed to be independent of time (month) and takes values $W = 0, 1, 2, 3$ million acre-ft with respective probabilities 1/6, 1/3, 1/3, and 1/6. If the available amount exceeds the dam capacity of 3 million acre-ft, the excess is released through spillways. Power generation requires 2 million acre-ft to be released at the end of each month. If less than 2 million acre-ft is available, the entire amount is released.

Let $X(t)$ be the inventory at month t immediately after water is released. The inventory a month hence, $X(t + 1)$, is clearly $X(t) + W - 2$, provided this is a positive quantity. Otherwise, we assign $X(t + 1)$ a value of zero because there is no water behind the dam. At the other extreme, if $X(t) + W - 2$ exceeds unity, we assign the value 1 since 2 million acre-ft would have been released through the spillway during the month. In symbols,

$$X(t + 1) = \min\{1, [X(t) + W - 2] \, \mathcal{U}[(X(t) + W - 2]\}$$

where, again, $\mathcal{U}[X(t) + W - 2]$ denotes the step function defined by

$$\mathcal{U}(x - a) = \begin{cases} 0 & x < a \\ 1 & x \geqslant a \end{cases}$$

To form the transition matrix, we note that there are only two possible states: the dam can have either 1 million acre-ft of water or no water. Therefore, the one-step transition matrix is made up of four probabilities—p_{00}, p_{01}, p_{10}, and p_{11}. To evaluate p_{00}, we note that since the dam is empty at the moment, any input value less than 3 million acre-ft would result in a zero state for the next period since the entire input would be released for power generation. Clearly, $p_{00} = 1/6 + 1/3 + 1/3 = 5/6$. In a similar way, one concludes that

$$\mathbf{P} = \begin{bmatrix} 5/6 & 1/6 \\ 1/2 & 1/2 \end{bmatrix}$$

We assume for convenience that the dam is empty at the start. This furnishes the initial condition $P\{X(0) = 0\} = 1$. Since every state of this Markov chain can be reached from every other state, the steady-state equations (29) and (30) can be applied to yield

$$\pi_0 = 5/6\pi_0 + 1/2\pi_1$$
$$\pi_1 = 1/6\pi_0 + 1/2\pi_1$$
$$1 = \pi_0 + \pi_1$$

The solution is $\pi_0 = 3/4$ and $\pi_1 = 1/4$. As mentioned earlier, the reciprocals $1/\pi_0 = 4/3$ and $1/\pi_1 = 4$ are the expected number of months between returns to state 0 and state 1, respectively.

Now consider steady-state expected costs. When less than 2 million acre-ft is available for power generation, the balance is purchased at a cost of \$200,000 per million acre-ft per month. Let $C(X(t))$ be the cost associated with the process $X(t)$. Since we are considering the steady state, this is the same for all t. Enumerating, for $x = 0$ (that is, there is no water in the dam from the previous month), we can associate possible inflows of $I = 0$, 1, 2, or 3. The cost function $C(0)$ is

$I = 0$, 2 million acre-ft are purchased: $\quad C(0) = \$400,000$
$I = 1$, 1 million acre-ft are purchased: $\quad C(0) = \$200,000$
$I = 2$, no water is purchased: $\quad C(0) = 0$
$I = 3$, no water is purchased: $\quad C(0) = 0$

$E[C(0)] = (400,000)\, 1/6 + (200,000)\, 1/3 = \$133,000$

Similar calculations when the month begins with 1 million acre-ft in the dam yield $E[C(1)] = \$33,333$.

To calculate the total expected cost per unit time in the steady state, we write

$$\pi_0\, E[C(0)] + \pi_1\, E[C(1)] = 3/4(133,000) + 1/4(33,333) = \$108,083.50$$

These calculations could be repeated for other release policies, say 1 million or 3 million acre-ft per month, to determine an optimal operating policy for the dam.

Example 11-9 Markov decision programming Here we extend the ideas in Example 10-10 on stochastic and chance-constrained programming. Consider a finite state space to be associated with a discrete time parameter

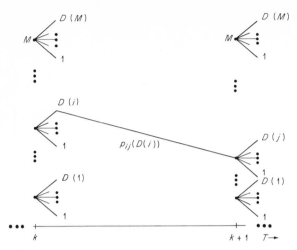

Fig. 11-8 State-parameter space.

T on an infinite planning horizon.   Figure 11-8 illustrates the period $T = k$ to $k + 1$.   There are M possible states, and alternatives or required decisions are associated with each.   At $T = k$, there are $D(i)$ alternatives associated with the ith state, etc.   Suppose that we are in the ith state and a decision is made to select alternative $d(i)$, where $d(i) = 1$ or 2 or ... or $D(i)$.   The chance event resulting from the selection $d(i)$ causes the system to move to state j at time $T = k + 1$ with probability $p_{ij}(d(i))$.   This transition from state i to state j yields a reward $r_{ij}(d(i))$.   Both the transition probabilities $p_{ij}(d(i))$ and the reward functions $r_{ij}(d_i)$ are assumed to be stationary and Markovian.

Let $R(i)$ be the maximum discounted expected reward for the indefinite future starting from state i.   The problem of *Markov decision programming* is to select a vector of decisions $d(i)$ (for $T = 1, 2, ...$) such that the objective $R(i)$ is achieved.   In symbols,

$$R(i) = \max_{s} R_s(i) = \max_{s} \left[\max_{d(i)} R'_s(i) \right]$$

where $R'_s(i) = \sum_{j=1}^{M} p_{ij}(d(i)) \{ r_{ij}(d(i)) + \rho R'_s(j) \}$, $i = 1, 2, ..., M$, and where ρ is the discount factor and $s(=0, 1, 2, ...)$ is an iterative index.   Initially, the $R'_0(i)$ are obtained for each state by simultaneously solving the above linear recursive equations for an arbitrary policy $d(i)$.   Using the values $R'_1(j) = R'_0(j)$, the $R'_1(i)$ are evaluated for each alternative $d(i)$.   The largest of these, that is, $\max_{d(i)} [R'_1(i)]$ $(i = 1, ..., M)$, constitute the decision policy for the next iteration.

Table 11-4 State space and alternatives for equipment decision

State	Alternatives
1. Efficient	*a.* (Minor) repair
	b. Replace
2. Inefficient	*c.* (Major) repair
	d. Replace

The iterative procedure continues until there is no additional improvement. A more general discussion, including convergence considerations, appears in Hadley's text on "Non-Linear and Dynamic Programming." We illustrate the technique with a simple numerical example.

Each year a contractor is to decide whether to keep or replace his equipment. He judges whether the equipment is operating efficiently (state 1) or not (state 2). Table 11-4 illustrates the state space and alternatives in the kth year.

The rewards $r_{ij}(d(i))$ are

$$r_{11}(a) = 14 \qquad r_{12}(a) = 1 \qquad r_{21}(c) = 12 \qquad r_{22}(c) = 0$$
$$r_{11}(b) = 10 \qquad r_{12}(b) = -2 \qquad r_{21}(d) = 9 \qquad r_{22}(d) = -4$$

and the associated transition probabilities are

$$p_{11}(a) = 0.5 \qquad p_{12}(a) = 0.5 \qquad p_{21}(c) = 0.3 \qquad p_{22}(c) = 0.7$$
$$p_{11}(b) = 0.6 \qquad p_{12}(b) = 0.4 \qquad p_{21}(d) = 0.6 \qquad p_{22}(d) = 0.4$$

To begin the iterative procedure, we arbitrarily select an alternative $d(i)$ for each state, say repair for both states, that is, a and c. We calculate the $R'_0(1)$ and $R'_0(2)$ using

$$R'_0(1) = p_{11}(a) \{r_{11}(a) + \rho R'_0(1)\} + p_{12}(a) \{r_{12}(a) + \rho R'_0(2)\}$$
$$= 0.5\{14 + 0.9R'_0(1)\} + 0.5\{1 + 0.9R'_0(2)\}$$

and

$$R'_0(2) = p_{21}(c)\{r_{21}(c) + \rho R'_0(1)\} + p_{22}(c)\{r_{22}(c) + \rho R'_0(2)\}$$
$$= 0.3\{12 + 0.9R'_0(1)\} + 0.7\{0 + 0.9R'_0(2)\}$$

to yield $R'_0(1) = 53.7$ and $R'_0(2) = 49.0$. Note that a discount factor of 0.9 has been assumed.

Using these values of $R'_0(1)$ and $R'_0(2)$, we calculate $R'_1(1)$ for each alternative. Thus $R'_1(1)$ for alternative a is

$$p_{11}(a)\{r_{11}(a) + 48.4\} + p_{12}(a)\{r_{12}(a) + 44.1\} = 53.7$$

and $R_1'(1)$ for alternative b is

$$p_{11}(b)\{r_{11}(b) + 48.4\} + p_{12}(b)\{r_{12}(b) + 44.1\} = 51.9$$

so that $R_1(1) = \max_{d(1)} R'(1) = 53.7$.   Similarly, $R_1'(2)$ for alternative c is

$$p_{21}(c)\{r_{21}(c) + 48.4\} + p_{22}(c)\{r_{22}(c) + 44.1\} = 49.0$$

and $R_1'(2)$ for alternative d is

$$p_{21}(d)\{r_{21}(d) + 48.4\} + p_{22}(d)\{r_{22}(d) + 44.1\} = 50.5$$

so that $R_1(2) = \max_{d(2)} R_1'(2) = 50.5$.   Therefore, a preferred policy is to choose alternative a when in the first state and alternative d when in the second state.

Using the recursion relation and the new decision policy, we next form the simultaneous equations for $R_2'(1)$ and $R_2'(2)$:

$$R_2'(1) = 0.5\{14 + 0.9R_2'(1)\} + 0.5\{1 + 0.9R_2'(2)\}$$
$$R_2'(2) = 0.6\{9 + 0.9R_2'(1)\} + 0.4\{-4 + 0.9R_2'(2)\}$$

to yield $R_2'(1) = 58$ and $R_2'(2) = 55.3$.   The next iteration yields the same choice of alternatives and, hence, the same values of discounted reward for succeeding iterations.   Therefore, we conclude that $R(1) = 58$ and $R(2) = 55.3$, using the optimal policy of choosing alternative a when in state 1 and alternative d in state 2.

11-4 SINGLE-SERVER QUEUES

Waiting lines, or queues, occur in many contexts.   Airplanes waiting in the "stack," trucks or ships waiting to load or unload, vehicles waiting at tollbooths or signalized intersections, the flow of paper work, customers being served at a computing center, equipment utilization in construction operations —all are examples of queues.

The mathematical study of waiting lines is usually dated from Erlang's work for the telephone industry early in the century.   The theory has developed rapidly since World War II.   Queueing theory has been used for the sizing and layout of ticket counters, baggage facilities, runways, and air-traffic holding patterns; for the sizing of navigation locks and canals, truck-terminal loading docks, rail classification yards; for the sizing of reservoirs, pumps, storage tanks, and other components of water storage and transmission systems.   Other applications of interest to civil engineers include the timing of traffic signals, the metering of vehicles onto freeways, the scheduling of public transportation, and the setting of speed limits.

Waiting time depends upon the capacity of the system to provide service. Larger service capacities tend to increase operating costs, but they also reduce waiting time and associated costs.   One studies queueing to design and operate better facilities.

There are three fundamental characteristics of queues. First, the characterization of arrivals to the facility: how often they come, how patient they are in waiting for service, and so on. Second, the service operation: how many servers should be provided, what quality of service is needed, and where the servers should be located. Third, the rules for selecting members of the queue for service, i.e., the *queue discipline*.

These queue characteristics vary in many ways. Arrivals may join the queue at constant rate, as parts delivered from an assembly line, or at random times, as vehicles arriving at a tollbooth. Arriving customers may leave if the queue is too large, i.e., they *balk*, or a member of the queue may become impatient and leave, i.e., he *reneges*. When queuers can be served at one of several facilities, the service arrangement is said to be in *parallel*, as in a barbershop. Sometimes queues form before each server, such as before bank tellers, and when some queues become shorter than others, the customers *jockey* between them. In *series* (*tandem*) queues, the output of one server is the input to another. Sometimes, the capacity of a waiting facility is reached and the immediately preceding server cannot discharge his customer until a waiting space for the next server becomes available; i.e., *blocking* occurs. The most common queue discipline is *first come, first served*. However, priority disciplines are common in hospital emergency rooms, airplane "stacks," and so on. In some systems, the customer whose service requires the least time is selected first.

This section considers the single-server queue, and Sec. 11-5 deals with multiserver queues. The quantity of principal interest to the queueing theorist is the *state probability function* $P_n(t)$. This function describes the probability that *there are n units in the system at time t*. The "units" may be people, machines requiring repair, etc., and the "system" refers to the queuers and those being served. The determination of $P_n(t)$ depends upon two other functions: an arrival rate function $\lambda_n(t)$ and a service rate function $\mu_n(t)$ per unit time. These functions are proportional to the chance of a change in the system, an arrival or a service, in the next instant when there are n people in the system at time t. Our use of the notation $\lambda_n(t)$ instead of the usual functional notation $\lambda(n,t)$ provides consistency with the queueing literature.

The determination of $P_n(t)$ also depends upon the *initial state*, i.e., the number in the system at time zero. However, one expects that eventually the influence of the initial state should become negligible, i.e., when a *steady state* is reached and the state probabilities no longer depend upon time. The analysis of steady-state queues is appreciably easier than for *transient queues*. This is fortunate for design purposes since interest tends to be upon long-term rather than transient fluctuations in the operation of a system.

Consider a single server and the queue that forms seeking his services. To obtain the probability function $P_n(t)$ for $n = 0, 1, \ldots$ and $t \geqslant 0$, a recursive approach is used, similar to that in Sec. 9-2 for the derivation of the Poisson

Table 11-5 Changes during $\{t, t + \Delta t\}$

State at time t, $n = 1, 2, \ldots$	Change in $\{t, t + \Delta t\}$	Associated probability
$n + 1$ in system	No arrivals and one departure	$[1 - \lambda_{n+1}(t)\Delta t][\mu_{n+1}(t)\Delta t]P_{n+1}(t)$
n in system	No change	$[1 - \mu_n(t)\Delta t][1 - \lambda_n(t)\Delta t]P_n(t)$
$n - 1$ in system	One arrival and no departures	$[\lambda_{n-1}(t)\Delta t][1 - \mu_{n-1}(t)\Delta t]P_{n-1}(t)$
All other possibilities	—	Zero

law.   The analysis leads to a difference-differential equation whose solution yields $P_n(t)$.

Arrivals are characterized by the probability $\lambda_n(t)\Delta t$ for a new arrival in $\{t, t + \Delta t\}$ when there are n in the system at time t.   The event of no arrival in $\{t, t + \Delta t\}$ is assigned the probability $1 - \lambda_n(t)\Delta t$.   Therefore, a negligible probability is being assigned to the event that two or more arrivals arise in the interval $\{t, t + \Delta t\}$.   Actually this is not as restrictive as it appears since we will soon set $\Delta t \to 0$.   In Chap. 12 we show how the generalized Poisson process overcomes this unit-jump restriction, whose main purpose is to simplify the event enumeration below.

The service operation is characterized in the same way; that is, $\mu_n(t)\Delta t$ is the probability that a unit being served at time t when there are n in the system will be discharged from service in $\{t, t + \Delta t\}$.   The probability of no completed service in $\{t, t + \Delta t\}$ is $1 - \mu_n(t)\Delta t$, and again, multiple services have zero probability. Table 11-5 and Fig. 11-9 illustrate the changes during the interval $\{t, t + \Delta t\}$ which result in having n units in the system at time $t + \Delta t$.

The probabilities in Table 11-5 assume that the events are independent and that a first-come–first-served discipline is used.   The event "n in the system at $t + \Delta t$" is the union of the joint events in Table 11-5.   Therefore, the probability $P_n(t + \Delta t)$ is the sum of the corresponding probabilities, that is,

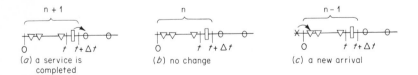

Fig. 11-9   Changes during $\{t, t + \Delta t\}$.

$$P_n(t + \Delta t) = [1 - \lambda_{n+1}(t)\,\Delta t]\,[\mu_{n+1}(t)\,\Delta t]\,P_{n+1}(t)$$
$$+ [1 - \mu_n(t)\,\Delta t]\,[1 - \lambda_n(t)\,\Delta t]\,P_n(t)$$
$$+ [\lambda_{n-1}(t)\,\Delta t]\,[1 - \mu_{n-1}(t)\,\Delta t]\,P_{n-1}(t) \qquad n = 1, 2, \ldots$$

Note that this equation applies for $n = 1, 2, \ldots$. The case $n = 0$ is not included because the fourth state listed in Table 11-5 is not sensible and should be omitted. This amounts to setting $n = 0$ in the above equation and ignoring the last term, that is,

$$P_0(t + \Delta t) = [1 - \lambda_1(t)\,\Delta t]\,[\mu_1(t)\,\Delta t]\,P_1(t) + [1 - \lambda_0(t)\,\Delta t]\,P_0(t)$$

where we have assumed that $\mu_0(t) = 0$. Rearranging these equations leads to

$$\frac{P_n(t + \Delta t) - P_n(t)}{\Delta t} = -[\lambda_n(t) + \mu_n(t)]\,P_n(t) + \mu_{n+1}(t)\,P_{n+1}(t)$$

$$+ \lambda_{n-1}(t)\,P_{n-1}(t)$$

and

$$\frac{P_0(t + \Delta t) - P_0(t)}{\Delta t} = -\lambda_0(t)\,P_0(t) + \mu_1(t)\,P_1(t)$$

where the remaining terms involving Δt have been neglected. This neglect is justified because in passing to the limit we obtain, for $n \geqslant 1$,

$$P_n'(t) = -[\lambda_n(t) + \mu_n(t)]\,P_n(t) + \mu_{n+1}(t)\,P_{n+1}(t) + \lambda_{n-1}(t)\,P_{n-1}(t) \tag{31}$$

and

$$P_0'(t) = -\lambda_0(t)\,P_0(t) + \mu_1(t)\,P_1(t)$$

where the prime denotes differentiation with respect to time. These *difference-differential equations* are fundamental in queueing theory. Note their generality, since the nature of the functions $\lambda_n(t)$ and $\mu_n(t)$ have not been specified. Next we consider the steady-state solutions, and later, time-dependent (transient) solutions will be noted.

THE STEADY STATE

The steady-state assumption is that the functions $\lambda_n(t)$, $\mu_n(t)$, and $P_n(t)$ do not depend upon the absolute time t. Formally,

$$\lim_{t \to \infty} \lambda_n(t) = \lambda_n \qquad \lim_{t \to \infty} \mu_n(t) = \mu_n \qquad \lim_{t \to \infty} P_n(t) = P_n \tag{32}$$

where λ_n, μ_n, and P_n are independent of t but may depend upon the state n of the system. As a consequence, the derivative $P_n'(t)$ vanishes as $t \to \infty$, and Eq. (31) becomes

$$-(\lambda_n + \mu_n)\,P_n + \mu_{n+1}\,P_{n+1} + \lambda_{n-1}\,P_{n-1} = 0 \qquad n \geqslant 1$$

and

$$-\lambda_0 P_0 + \mu_1 P_1 = 0 \qquad n = 0$$

The first of these equations can be further simplified as

$$-\lambda_{n-1} P_{n-1} + \mu_n P_n = 0 \qquad n \geqslant 1 \tag{33}$$

To see this, successively set $n = 1, 2, \ldots,$ using the "starting equation" $-\lambda_0 P_0 + \mu_1 P_1 = 0$. A simple induction (Appendix 2) establishes Eq. (33). These are first-order difference equations, the differential equation having been destroyed by the steady-state assumption, whose solution depends upon the functions λ_n and μ_n.

In the simplest case, these functions are assumed constant, that is,

$$\lambda_n = \lambda \quad \text{and} \quad \mu_n = \begin{cases} \mu & n = 1, 2, \ldots \\ 0 & n = 0 \end{cases} \tag{34}$$

This choice corresponds to the discussion in Sec. 9-2. Indeed, with $\mu_n(t) = 0$ and $\lambda_n(t) = \lambda$, Eq. (31) is Eq. (5) of Sec. 9-2.

Substituting in Eq. (33), we have

$$P_n = \rho P_{n-1} \qquad n = 1, 2, \ldots \tag{35}$$

where $\rho = \lambda/\mu$. The ratio $\rho = \lambda/\mu$, called the *utilization factor* or *traffic density*, is fundamental in queueing. Only for $\rho < 1$ will steady-state queues be stable. The solution of Eq. (5) of Sec. 9-2 is easily verified to be

$$P_n = \rho^n(1 - \rho) \qquad n = 0, 1, 2, \ldots \tag{36}$$

(see Appendix 5). The steady-state probabilities for the number in the system define the geometric law and are widely used. Again, note that these results hold only if $\rho < 1$. Note also that the probability of k arrivals in an interval $\{0,1\}$ is governed by the Poisson law, as described in Sec. 9-2. Similarly, the time between consecutive arrivals for the single-server queue with $\lambda_n(t) = \lambda$ is the situation considered in Sec. 9-3 which led to an exponential law. Since the number of services completed in a time $\{0,t\}$ is also Poisson, provided that service is going on continuously, the time between consecutive services follows an exponential law.

The waiting time in the queue and the service time are random variables of obvious interest. The waiting time in the queue is a continuous random variable except for the "spike" at $n = 0$. There is a nonzero probability that an arrival will not need to wait if he is fortunate enough to arrive when the system is empty. The probability that the waiting time W is zero, that is, $P\{W = 0\}$, follows from Eq. (36) with $n = 0$:

$$P\{W = 0\} = P_0 = 1 - \rho$$

For nonzero waiting times, we construct the waiting-time density function $\psi(w)$ as follows: Consider the event {the waiting time in the queue is in the interval $\{w, w + \Delta w\}$} whose probability we denote by $\psi(w)\Delta w$. This event is equal to the union of the mutually exclusive events {there are n in the system when a unit arrives, $n - 1$ are served in the interval $\{0,w\}$, and the immediately preceding unit is served in the interval $\{w, w + \Delta w\}$} for $n = 1, 2, \ldots$. These joint events are composed of independent events (by assumption), so that the associated probabilities are the products

$$\rho^n(1 - \rho)\left[\frac{(\mu w)^{n-1}}{(n - 1)!}e^{-\mu w}\right][\mu\,\Delta w] \qquad n = 1, 2, \ldots$$

The probability of the union is the sum of these probabilities:

$$\psi(w)\,\Delta w = \sum_{n=1}^{\infty} [\rho^n(1 - \rho)]\left[\frac{(\mu w)^{n-1}}{(n - 1)!}e^{-\mu w}\right][\mu\,\Delta w]$$

$$= \lambda(1 - \rho)\,e^{(\lambda-\mu)w}\,\Delta w$$

Therefore, the probability function for the waiting time in the queue is the mixed function

$$P\{W = 0\} = 1 - \frac{\lambda}{\mu}$$

$$\psi(w) = \lambda\left(1 - \frac{\lambda}{\mu}\right)e^{(\lambda-\mu)w} \qquad w \geqslant 0 \tag{37}$$

In Prob. 11-28, the reader is asked to derive an analogous result for the total time in the system V.

Equations (38a) to (38f) below summarize some expected values for the single-server queue with Poisson arrivals and exponential service times. The average number in the system (queue and service facility):

$$L = E(n) = \rho(1 - \rho)^{-1} \qquad \text{var}\,(n) = \rho(1 - \rho)^{-1}\,[1 + \rho(1 - \rho)^{-1}] \tag{38a}$$

The average queue length:

$$L_q = E(n - 1) = \rho^2(1 - \rho)^{-1} \qquad n > 0 \tag{38b}$$

The average length of nonempty systems:

$$L_{q'} = E(n|n > 0) = (1 - \rho)^{-1} \tag{38c}$$

The average time in the queue:

$$W_q = E(W) = \rho(1 - \rho)^{-1}\,\mu^{-1} = \frac{L_q}{\lambda} \tag{38d}$$

The average time in the queue for those who wait:

$$W_{q'} = E(W \mid W > 0) = \mu^{-1}(1 - \rho)^{-1} \tag{38e}$$

The average time in the system:

$$V_s = E(V) = (\mu - \lambda)^{-1} = \frac{L}{\lambda} \tag{38f}$$

Thus far, we have studied the steady-state case in which $\lambda_n(t) = \lambda$ and $\mu_n(t) = \mu$, the so-called "Poisson arrivals and exponential service." Generalizations can be made with respect to time t and the state n of the system. When $\lambda_n(t) = \lambda_n$ and $\mu_n(t) = \mu_n$, that is, when the arrival and service rates are functions of the state n, Eq. (33) still applies and yields P_n. When $\lambda_n(t)$ and $\mu_n(t)$ are functions of time, the steady-state limits, Eqs. (32), may not exist and Eq. (31) is required. The following examples illustrate generalizations.

Example 11-10   A queue-sensitive server   Consider a server whose "working rate" increases with the number in the system. This is common with human servers, e.g., tollbooth collectors. The service time is still a random variable, but its mean is no longer constant. Specifically, let $\mu_n = n\mu$. Substituting into Eq. (33) yields

$$P_n = \frac{\rho}{n} P_{n-1} \qquad n = 1, 2, \ldots$$

The solution to this difference equation is

$$P_n = \frac{(\rho)^n}{n!} e^{-\rho} \tag{39}$$

which, coincidentally, is a Poisson law. A further generalization is the non-linear service rate

$$\mu_n = n^c \mu \qquad n = 0, 1, \ldots \tag{40}$$

where c is a *pressure coefficient*. The above example is the case $c = 1$, while the result in Eq. (36) is the case $c = 0$. Conway and Maxwell [10] have shown that the state probabilities obtained in the solution of Eq. (33) using the service rate (40) are

$$P_n = \frac{\rho^n}{(n!)^c} \left[\sum_{i=0}^{\infty} \frac{\rho^i}{(i!)^c} \right]^{-1} \qquad n = 0, 1, \ldots \tag{41}$$

Example 11-11   A cyclic queue   In a well-known industrial application described by Feller [18], a group of m identical machines operate independently. The machines are assumed to break down at random, and the repair time is a random variable.   Thus the population from which the queue is formed is fixed, and units can recycle; i.e., it is a *cyclic queue*.   Let Eqs. (34) describe the situation for each machine.   A single repairman services the machines. The state n at time t is the number of machines not working.   This is a *birth-and-death process*, i.e., arrivals and services, described by Eq. (31) with

$$\lambda_n(t) = (m - n)\lambda \qquad \text{and} \qquad \mu_n(t) = \mu - \delta_0^n \mu \tag{42}$$

for all $n = 0, 1, \ldots, m$.   The Kronecker delta, δ_0^n, is unity for $n = 0$ and zero otherwise.   The recursive equation analogous to Eq. (33) is

$$(m - n)\lambda P_n = \mu P_{n+1} \tag{43}$$

for $n = 0, 1, \ldots, m - 1$.   The solution is

$$P_n = \frac{m!}{(m - n)!}\rho^n P_0 \qquad n = 1, \ldots, m \tag{44}$$

with

$$P_0^{-1} = \sum_{n=0}^{m} \rho^n \frac{m!}{(m - n)!}$$

Equation (44) is known as *Erlang's loss formula*.   The numerical values in Table 11-6 are taken from [18].

The probability P_0 is the probability that the repairman is idle.   For the case in Table 11-6, he is idle nearly half the time.   The average number of machines waiting for repair is

$$L_q = E(n - 1) = \sum_{n=1}^{\infty} (n - 1)P_n = \sum_{n=1}^{\infty} nP_n - (1 - P_0)$$

To evaluate the summation, use Eq. (43) by summing from $n = 0$ to $n = m$:

$$m\lambda \sum_{n=0}^{m} P_n - \lambda \sum_{n=0}^{m} nP_n = \mu \sum_{n=0}^{m} P_{n+1}$$

Table 11-6 Probabilities P_n for $\rho = 0.1$ and $m = 6$

n	No. in waiting line	P_n
0	0	0.4845
1	0	0.2907
2	1	0.1454
3	2	0.0582
4	3	0.0175
5	4	0.0035
6	5	0.0003

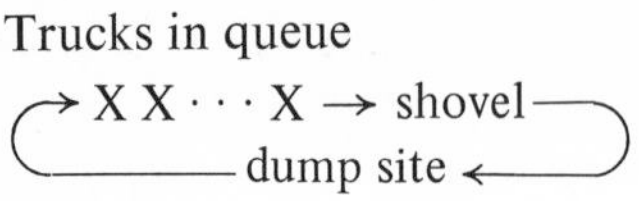

Trucks in queue

Fig. 11-10 A shovel loading operation.

or

$$m\lambda - \lambda[L_q + (1 - P_0)] = \mu(1 - P_0)$$

which yields

$$L_q = m - \frac{\lambda + \mu}{\lambda}(1 - P_0)$$

In the example, $L_q = 6 - 5.6705 = 0.3295$ machine. Whether or not this is a tolerable number depends upon the relative costs of idle machines and additional repairmen. To evaluate the effect of additional repairmen, one needs to alter $\mu_n(t)$ in Eq. (42). We postpone this to the next section since it is a multiserver queue.

The next situation is analogous to an earth-excavation operation studied by Spaugh [59]. A single shovel excavates and loads m incoming trucks. The loaded trucks haul the material to the dumping site (Fig. 11-10). Spaugh assumes Poisson arrivals, with an arrival rate proportional to the number of trucks not waiting and an exponential service time to load trucks at rate μ. The above equations for the machines apply. The Poisson arrival and exponential service assumptions may be questionable in some cases. However, O'Shea, Slutkin, and Shaffer [45] found that the model provided a reliable production measure in a case where the assumptions did not strictly apply.

Example 11-12 Arrivals who balk The reasoning which leads to Eq. (31) is the starting point for variations in the queue characteristics. For

Table 11-7 Event statements for balking

Number in system at time t	An arrival in $\{t, t + \Delta t\}$?	Balk?	A service in $\{t, t + \Delta t\}$?
n	Yes	Yes	No
$n - 1$	Yes	No	No
$n + 1$	No	—	Yes
n	No	—	No

example, for the system described by Eqs. (31) to (36), let us suppose that an arrival's decision to join the queue is based upon its length. Suppose that

$$b_n = \begin{cases} 1 - \dfrac{\beta}{n} & n = 1, 2, \ldots \\ 0 & n = 0 \end{cases}$$

defines a balking-probability function, i.e., the probability that an arrival leaves the queue when there are n in the system.   The constant $\beta \leqslant 1$ is a measure of his willingness to join.   The events which yield n units in the system at time $t + \Delta t$ are summarized in Table 11-7.

Again, events are omitted whose probabilities involve higher orders of Δt and, hence, will vanish in the limit as $\Delta t \to 0$.   The analog to Eq. (31) is

$$P_n(t + \Delta t) = \lambda_n(t)\,\Delta t \left(1 - \frac{\beta}{n}\right)[1 - \mu_n(t)\,\Delta t]\,P_n(t)$$

$$+ \lambda_{n-1}(t)\,\Delta t \frac{\beta}{n-1}[1 - \mu_{n-1}(t)\,\Delta t]\,P_{n-1}(t)$$

$$+ [1 - \lambda_{n+1}(t)\,\Delta t][\mu_{n+1}(t)\,\Delta t]\,P_{n+1}(t)$$

$$+ [1 - \lambda_n(t)\,\Delta t][1 - \mu_n(t)\,\Delta t]\,P_n(t)$$

Collecting terms and passing to the limit, we find, for $n > 1$,

$$P_n'(t) = -[\lambda_n(t)\frac{\beta}{n} + \mu_n(t)]\,P_n(t) + \lambda_{n-1}(t)\frac{\beta}{n-1}P_{n-1}(t) + \mu_{n+1}(t)\,P_{n+1}(t)$$

In the steady state, we have

$$-\lambda_0 P_0 + \mu_1 P_1 = 0 \qquad\qquad\qquad n = 0$$

$$-(\mu_1 + \lambda_1 \beta)P_1 + \lambda_0 P_0 + \mu_2 P_2 = 0 \qquad\qquad n = 1$$

$$-\left(\mu_n + \lambda_n\frac{\beta}{n}\right)P_n + \frac{\beta\lambda_{n-1}}{n-1}P_{n-1} + \mu_{n+1}P_{n+1} = 0 \qquad n \geqslant 2$$

from which we conclude

$$P_{n+1} = \frac{\beta\rho}{n}P_n \qquad n = 0, 1, 2, \ldots$$

The solution is

$$P_n = \rho^n \frac{\beta^{n-1}}{(n-1)!}(1 + \rho e^{\rho\beta})^{-1}$$

A similar situation concerns reneging, as suggested in Prob. 11-33. Saaty [52] treats some additional aspects of impatient customers.

While the assumption of Poisson arrivals is often adequate, the exponential service assumption often is not. It is possible to derive relations for the mean queue length and mean waiting time for an arbitrary service-time distribution and Poisson arrivals. Let n' and n'' be the steady-state numbers in the system between two consecutive departures from service. Let s' be the time between these services, and let m be the number of arrivals during the service time. Clearly, $n'' = n' + m - 1$ if $n' \neq 0$ and $n'' = m$ when $n' = 0$, or

$$n'' = n' + m - 1 + \delta_0^{n'} \tag{45}$$

where $\delta_0^{n'}$ is the Kronecker delta. The expectation yields

$$E(m) + E(\delta_0^{n'}) = 1$$

since, in the steady state, $E(n') = E(n'')$. $E(m)$ is the expected number of arrivals in the expected service time $E(s)$, and

$$E(m) = \lambda E(s) = \rho$$

where $E(s)$ is defined for an arbitrary service-time distribution as $1/\mu$. Thus,

$$E(\delta_0^{n'}) = 1 - E(m) = 1 - \rho$$

Now, square Eq. (45) and take the expectation of both members, remembering that in the steady state $E[(n')^2] = E[(n'')^2]$:

$$0 = E[(m-1)^2] + E[(\delta_0^{n'})^2] + 2E[n'(m-1)] + 2E[\delta_0^{n'}(m-1)]$$
$$= E[m^2] - 2\rho + 1 + (1-\rho) + 2E(n')E(m-1) + 2E(\delta_0^{n'})E(m-1)$$

where $E(n'\delta_0^{n'}) = 0$, $E[n'(m-1)] = E(n')E(m-1)$, and $E[\delta_0^{n'}(m-1)] = E(\delta_0^{n'})E(m-1)$ since m is dependent on the random variables n' and $\delta_0^{n'}$. Using the expectations for m and $\delta_0^{n'}$ just derived, one concludes

$$E(n) = \rho + \frac{E(m^2) - \rho}{2(1 - \rho)}$$

The superscript on n has been dropped because the expression applies to the average queue length in the steady state.

To make the expression more useful, we evaluate $E(m^2)$, the mean square of the number of arrivals during a service time. The probability of m arrivals in a time s is Poisson with parameter λs since the arrival distribution is Poisson. The conditional expectation for fixed s, $E(m^2|s)$, is $(\lambda s) + (\lambda s)^2$. Here, the second-moment properties of the Poisson law have been used (Sec. 8-6). The unconditioned expectation of m^2 is

$$E(m^2) = \int_0^\infty E(m^2|s)f(s)\,ds$$

where $f(s)$ is the density function for the service time. Integrating the last expression gives

$$E(m^2) = \int_0^\infty [(\lambda s) + (\lambda s)^2] f(s)\, ds = \lambda \frac{1}{\mu} + \lambda^2 \left[\sigma_s^2 + \left(\frac{1}{\mu}\right)^2 \right]$$

$$= \rho + \rho^2 + \lambda^2 \sigma_s^2$$

where σ_s^2 is the variance of the service time and, again, the mean is $1/\mu$. Substituting,

$$E(n) = \rho + \frac{\rho^2 + \lambda^2 \sigma_s^2}{2(1 - \rho)} \tag{46}$$

This is the famous *Pollaczek-Khintchine formula.* It has important implications for steady-state design since it applies to all single-server queues with Poisson input and requires knowledge only of the mean and variance of the service-time distribution. Furthermore, it is easy to derive the average waiting time since $E(n) = \lambda E(S + W)$, where W is the waiting time in the queue. Clearly,

$$\lambda E(W) = E(n) - \rho = \frac{\rho^2 + \lambda^2 \sigma_s^2}{2(1 - \rho)} \tag{47}$$

The ratio of the average waiting time in the queue to the average service time,

$$\frac{E(W)}{E(S)} = \frac{\rho}{2(1 - \rho)}(1 + \mu^2 \sigma_s^2) \tag{48}$$

can be used as a measure of the *inefficiency* of a system. By inefficiency, we mean long periods in the queue compared with time in service. To illustrate Eq. (48), note that the ratio is minimum, for a fixed ρ, when $\sigma_s^2 = 0$. That is, the service requires a fixed time and

$$\frac{E(W)}{E(S)} = \frac{\rho}{2(1 - \rho)}$$

For exponential service times with mean $1/\mu$, $\sigma_s^2 = (1/\mu)^2$ and

$$\frac{E(W)}{E(S)} = \frac{\rho}{1 - \rho}$$

Hence, an exponential-service-time queue has an inefficiency of twice that for the case of a fixed service time.

The main purpose for studying queueing theory is to provide information needed in the formulation of decision models. Chapter 6 of [24] discusses the use of queueing in design. The next several examples illustrate the use of queueing results for decision making.

Example 11-13   A speeding auto (optimization with respect to a parameter)   An auto is to travel a fixed distance D in the least expected time.   So long as the speed does not exceed the legal limit v_l, the auto is not stopped.   However, at excessive speeds there is a possibility of being stopped and held for a fixed (service) time $1/\mu$.   The probability of being stopped increases with increasing speed.   Let $\lambda(v)\Delta t$ be the probability of being stopped in $\{t, t + \Delta t\}$ when the auto moves with speed v.   Clearly, $\lambda(v)$ is an increasing function of v and is independent of the state, the number of stops n, and the stopped time t.   Successive stops for speeding correspond to "arrivals" into a single-server (policeman) queue.   The problem is to determine the speed which minimizes expected travel time.

The total travel time consists of the fixed time to travel a distance D, namely, D/v, plus the random stopping time n/μ:

$$\text{Travel time} = \frac{D}{v} + \frac{n}{\mu}$$

The probabilities for the number of stops are the same as those for the number of arrivals in a time D/v for a Poisson process with arrival parameter $\lambda(v)$ The mean of n is $\lambda(v)\,D/v$, so that the expected travel time is

$$\frac{D}{v}[1 + \rho(v)]$$

where $\rho(v) = \lambda(v)/\mu$.

So far, we have not mentioned the character of the function $\lambda(v)$.   The fact that the coefficient of the last expression vanishes as $v \to \infty$ suggests that we define a "suicidal velocity," v_s, above which stops for speeding are certain.   The probability of a stoppage in the interval $\{t, t + \Delta t\}$ is

$$P\{\text{stop in } \{t, t + \Delta t\}\} = \begin{cases} 0 & v \leqslant v_l \\ \lambda(v)\,\Delta t & v_l < v < v_s \\ 1 & v \geqslant v_s \end{cases}$$

For a minimum in the range $v_l < v < v_s$, we set the derivative of the expected travel-time expression to zero and rewrite the resulting expression in differential form as

$$\frac{d[1 + \rho(v)]}{dv} = \frac{1 + \rho(v)}{v}$$

This optimizing condition indicates that the optimum speed is the abscissa for which the slope of $\rho(v)$ equals the slope of a tangent line from the origin (see Fig. 11-11).   The sketch of $\rho(v)$ in Fig. 11-11, showing $1 + \rho(v)$ as convex, is a typical representation.   This can be seen by studying the second derivative of the expected travel time and noting that it is positive for minimizing values

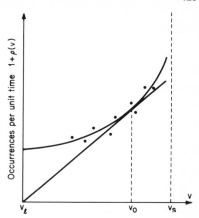

Fig. 11-11 Optimum speed.

of v. The point of tangency has abscissa v_0. It is interesting to observe the effect of inadequate data. The constants μ and v_l are likely to be known, but adequate data to form the function $\lambda(v)$ could be elusive. Without fitting a curve, one might simply plot the several available points (Fig. 11-11) and estimate the range of speeds that includes v_0. The example suggests turnpike driving and might be a kind of model that law-enforcement officers or traffic engineers would construct to determine policing levels and legal speeds in order to keep the "optimum speed" (from the driver's point of view) within acceptable bounds.

Example 11-14   Optimum service rate   Let $C_s(\mu)$ be the cost per unit time of using a server with rate μ, and let C_w be a constant cost per unit time of waiting.   The total expected cost per unit time, $K(\mu)$, is

$$K(\mu) = C_s(\mu) + LC_w$$

where, again, L is the average number in the system.   We illustrate with the simple case $C_s(\mu) = \mu C_s$, where C_s is a constant and L is assumed to be given by Eq. (38a).   Thus the cost per unit time of a server is assumed proportional to his service rate:

$$K(\mu) = \mu C_s + \frac{\lambda C_w}{\mu - \lambda}$$

as shown in Fig. 11-12.

Differentiating with respect to μ and equating to zero yields the optimum service rate, μ_0:

$$\mu_0 = \lambda + \sqrt{\frac{C_w \lambda}{C_s}}$$

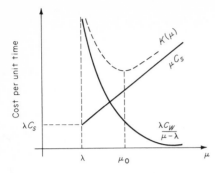

Fig. 11-12 Optimum service rate.

In a sense, designs are based upon incomplete information because the gathering of information can be expensive and system operation usually cannot be precisely forecast.   Specifying the ratio C_w/C_s requires less information than specifying both C_w and C_s.   To study the sensitivity of the design to imperfect information, let inaccurate values C_s', C_w', and λ' be used in place of the true values C_s, C_w, and λ.   Consequently, a value μ' is calculated from the last expression instead of μ_0.   It is convenient to express μ' as $\alpha\mu_0$, where α is a positive constant.   For $\alpha = 1$, $\mu' = \mu_0$.   Evaluating $K(\mu)$ for $\mu = \mu_0$ and for $\mu = \mu'$, we obtain

$$K(\mu_0) = \lambda C_s + 2\sqrt{C_w\, C_s\, \lambda}$$

and

$$K(\mu') = \alpha\mu_0\, C_s + \frac{\lambda C_w}{\alpha\mu_0 - \lambda}$$

Therefore,

$$\frac{K(\mu')}{K(\mu_0)} = \frac{\alpha^2 - \alpha\rho + \gamma^2(1-\rho)}{(\alpha - \rho)(1 + \gamma^2)}$$

where $\rho = \lambda/\mu_0$ and

$$\gamma^2 = \frac{(C_w/C_s)\,\rho^2}{\lambda(1-\rho)}$$

A plot of the cost per unit time ratio is shown in Fig. 11-13.   Note that only the interval $[\rho,\infty]$ is indicated.   For $\alpha < \rho = \lambda/\mu_0$, the arrival rate exceeds the service rate, that is, $\mu' = \alpha\mu_0 < \lambda$.   This would contradict the steady-state assumption.   This cost per unit time ratio measures the effect of nonoptimal operation upon the design criterion.   Note the relative insensitivity of the cost ratio in the neighborhood of $\alpha = 1$ (Fig. 11-13).   Other models of this type appear in Morse [43] and Hillier and Lieberman [30].   A paper by Hillier [29] describes several travel-time models which appear to have promise in

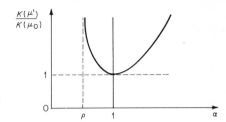

Fig. 11-13 Ratio of actual to minimum cost per unit time.

layout and design of service facilities, such as counters at an air terminal and supply depots to serve nearby construction sites.

Example 11-15 Travel time to the service facility Consider a single server located at the origin of coordinates in the center of a square area with dimension $2e$ (Fig. 11-14a). Arrivals to the center arise uniformly from any point in the area, and they proceed directly to the service center with speed v. We calculate the expected travel time to and/or from the server. The probability that an arrival arises in the differential element whose sides are of length Δx and Δy and which lies at (x,y) is

$$f(x,y)\,\Delta x\,\Delta y = \frac{1}{4e^2}\,\Delta x\,\Delta y \qquad -e \leqslant x,y \leqslant e$$

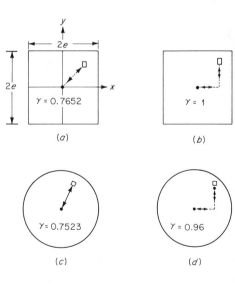

Fig. 11-14 Expected travel times, $\tau = \gamma\sqrt{\bar{A}}/v$. (a) Direct travel; (b) orthogonal travel; (c) direct travel; (d) orthogonal travel; (e) orthogonal travel.

since arrivals are assumed to come from any position with equal likelihood. Other probability functions can also be used to describe arrivals. For example, if the area is a factory floor, workers performing operations at different locations might require supplies at different rates. In the present case, the distance from the center to (x,y) is the radius vector r in polar coordinates. Thus the travel distance is $2r$, and the element of area in polar coordinates is $rdrd\phi$. The expected travel time to and from the server, τ, is

$$\tau = 2E(T) = 8 \int_0^{\pi/4} \int_0^{e \cdot \sec\phi} \frac{2r}{v} \frac{1}{4e^2} rdrd\phi = 0.7652 \frac{\sqrt{A}}{v}$$

where A is the area $4e^2$, ϕ the polar angle, and T the random travel time in either direction. Note that the integration region has been conveniently chosen as a half quadrant and that this accounts for the factor 8. Calculations of τ for other configurations and modes of travel, illustrated in Fig. 11-14, show that the coefficients γ of $\sqrt{A}/v$ are similar. This suggests that the total travel time may not be very sensitive to the geometry of the service area, but sensitive to the geometry of the route.

RANDOM ORDER OF SERVICE
Our analysis has assumed that arrivals are served in the order of arrival, i.e., first come, first served. Other queue disciplines are also of interest. We derive the appropriate differential-difference equation for random-order service to illustrate the generality of our approach to queueing.

Let $w_n(t)$ be the conditional probability that an arrival (we) waits at least a time t before being served, given that n others are also waiting. Again, form a recursion relation from the mutually exclusive events with nonvanishing probabilities: (1) an arrival occurs in $\{0,\Delta t\}$, and hence there are $n + 1$ others now in the queue, and he waits at least an additional time t; or (2) a service (not us) is completed in $\{0,\Delta t\}$, and $n - 1$ others are now in the queue at time Δt; or (3) no arrival or service occurs in $\{0,\Delta t\}$, so there are still n others in the queue who "compete" with us for the next service. In symbols,

$$w_n(t + \Delta t) = \lambda \Delta t w_{n+1}(t) + \mu \Delta t \frac{n}{n+1} w_{n-1}(t) + (1 - \lambda\Delta t)(1 - \mu\Delta t) w_n(t)$$

The factor $n/(n + 1)$ is the probability that, since a service has just been completed, we are not the arrival selected for service. Note that among the $n + 1$ units in the system, any of the n besides us can be selected to go into service (other probability functions for the random selection for service could also be used). The usual rearrangement of the last expression and passage to the limit yields

$$w_n'(t) = -(\lambda + \mu) w_n(t) + \frac{n}{n+1} \mu w_{n-1}(t) + \lambda w_{n+1}(t)$$

Discussions of service priorities usually require more sophisticated analysis than we have assumed here. An excellent treatment of the effect of random arrivals and priorities upon sequencing and scheduling of jobs can be found in Chaps. 8 and 9 of Conway et al. [11], but a knowledge of generating and characteristic functions (Chap. 12) is a prerequisite. Some discussion of priorities is given by Morse [43].

Fortunately, the steady state considered here is useful for design purposes. Transient queues, i.e., solutions to Eq. (31), are usually much more difficult. For example, for the simple case of Eq. (34) where λ and μ are constants, the solution to Eq. (31) is

$$P_n(t) = e^{-(\lambda+\mu)t} \left[\rho^{n/2} I_n(2\sqrt{\lambda\mu}t) + \rho^{n-1/2} I_{n+1}(2\sqrt{\lambda\mu}t) \right.$$
$$\left. + (1-\rho)\rho^n \sum_{k=n+2}^{\infty} \sqrt{\rho^{-k}} I_k(2\sqrt{\lambda\mu}t) \right]$$

where $I_n(x) = i^{-n}J_n(ix)$ is the modified Bessel function of order n (for example, see Wylie [63]). The reader familiar with Bessel functions may wish to show that as $t \to \infty$, the last equation reduces to Eq. (36).

11-5 MULTISERVER QUEUES

In this section we consider queuers ($\triangledown$) at service stations ($\square$) arranged in parallel or series (Fig. 11-15). We use the terms "channel" and "phase" to indicate parallel and series arrangements of servers, respectively.

We begin with the infinite-server queue. Imagine a large telephone switchboard or other facility with adequate capacity so that arrivals can always go into service immediately. Consider the problem of determining the probabilities that exactly n channels are busy. We conclude that

$$\lambda_n = \lambda \qquad \text{and} \qquad \mu_n = n\mu$$

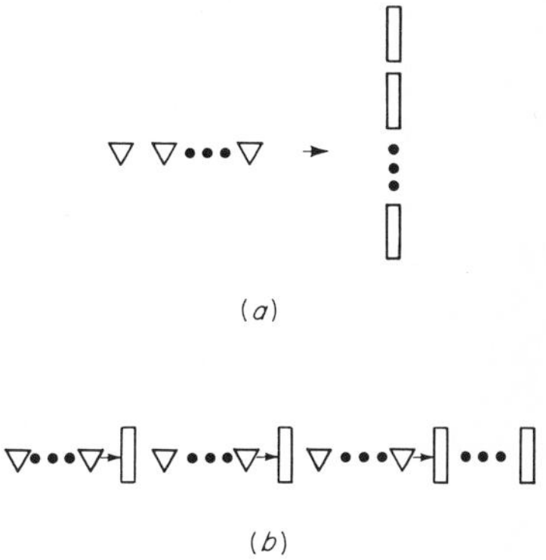

(a)

Fig. 11-15 Arrangements of servers. (a) Parallel servers; (b) series (tandem) servers.

(b)

for Poisson arrivals and exponential service at rate μ for each busy channel. This, however, is precisely the situation for the queue-sensitive server (Example 11-10), and the solution applies here.

Consider next a finite server queue.

Example 11-16 Finite-parallel-server queue Consider a queue which forms before k nominally identical servers who serve according to an exponential law at mean rate μ. The first step is to deduce the functions λ_n and μ_n. For Poisson arrivals, $\lambda_n = \lambda$. The service is complicated because of the finite number of servers. If there are $n \leqslant k$ in the system, the probability of a service in the next time increment is $n\mu \Delta t$. Otherwise, a queue exists and the probability of a service in the next time increment is $k\mu \Delta t$. Summarizing,

$$\lambda_n = \lambda \quad \text{and} \quad \mu_n = \min(n\mu, k\mu) \quad n = 0, 1, 2, \ldots$$

The steady-state equations are easily derived as

$$
\begin{aligned}
&\lambda P_0 = \mu P_1 \\
&(\lambda + n\mu) P_n = \lambda P_{n-1} + (n+1) \mu P_{n+1} \quad && 1 \leqslant n < k \\
&(\lambda + k\mu) P_n = \lambda P_{n-1} + k\mu P_{n+1} \quad && n \geqslant k
\end{aligned}
\tag{49}
$$

The solution is

$$
P_n = \begin{cases}
\dfrac{\rho^n}{n!} P_0 & n < k; \dfrac{\rho}{k} < 1 \\[2ex]
\dfrac{\rho^n}{k! \, k^{n-k}} P_0 & n \geqslant k
\end{cases}
\tag{50}
$$

where

$$
P_0^{-1} = \sum_{n=0}^{k-1} \frac{\rho^n}{n!} + \frac{\rho^k}{k!} \frac{k}{k - \rho}
\tag{51}
$$

The expectations are summarized in Prob. 11-41.

Example 11-17 Parallel servers with cyclic queue The situation is the same as in Example 11-11 except that the m machines are served by $k(\leqslant m)$ repairmen. Our discussion follows closely Feller's description of Palm's work [18]. The proper representations for λ_n and μ_n are

$$
\begin{aligned}
&\lambda_n = (m - n) \lambda \\
&\mu_n = \min(n\mu, k\mu) \quad n = 0, 1, \ldots, m
\end{aligned}
$$

Table 11-8 Probabilities P_n for $\rho = 0.1$, $m = 20$, $k = 3$[1]

n	Machines served	Machines waiting	Repairmen idle	P_n
0	0	0	3	0.13625
1	1	0	2	0.27250
2	2	0	1	0.25888
3	3	0	0	0.15533
4	3	1	0	0.08802
5	3	2	0	0.04694
6	3	3	0	0.02347
7	3	4	0	0.01095
8	3	5	0	0.00475
9	3	6	0	0.00190
10	3	7	0	0.00070
11	3	8	0	0.00023
12	3	9	0	0.00007

[1] Reprinted from Feller [18].

since the arrival rate is proportional to the number of operating machines. The steady-state equations for the state probabilities are

$$m\lambda P_0 = \mu P_1$$
$$[(m - n)\lambda + n\mu]P_n = (m - n + 1)\lambda P_{n-1} + (n + 1)\mu P_{n+1} \qquad 1 \leqslant n < k$$
$$[(m - n)\lambda + k\mu]P_n = (m - n + 1)\lambda P_{n-1} + k\mu P_{n+1} \qquad k \leqslant n \leqslant m$$

These reduce to

$$(n + 1)\mu P_{n+1} = (m - n)\lambda P_n \qquad n < k$$
$$k\mu P_{n+1} = (m - n)\lambda P_n \qquad n \geqslant k$$

Table 11-9 Effects of additional repairmen[1]

	Example 11-11	Example 11-17
Machines	6	20
Repairmen	1	3
Machines per repairman	6	$6\frac{2}{3}$
Idle repairmen per repairman	0.4845	0.4042
Waiting machines per machine	0.0549	0.01694

[1] Reprinted from Feller [18].

Numerical results for arbitrarily chosen values of ρ, m, and k appear in Table 11-8.   Tables 11-6 and 11-8 represent similar machines and repairmen since $\rho = 0.1$.   Table 11-9 compares the two cases.   Note that although the number of machines per repairman increases, the average number of waiting machines per machine decreases.   Also, the average number of idle repairmen per repairman decreases substantially.   This is one manifestation of increased efficiency with increase of plant size.   Palm [46] provides graphs and tables for the most economical number of repairmen.

Next consider arrangements of servers.

Example 11-18   Servers in parallel   Consider two channels fed by a single queue.   The solutions in Example 11-16 lack two details which are considered here.   First, the conditional probabilities $q_i(t)$ that the ith ($i = 1, 2$) channel is occupied when there is exactly one unit in the system is derived, and second, channel priorities ϵ_i ($i = 1, 2$) are assigned, that is, ϵ_i is the probability that a newcomer selects the ith channel.   For $n = 0$, we have

$$P_0(t + \Delta t) = (1 - \lambda \Delta t)P_0(t) + (1 - \lambda \Delta t)[\mu_1' q_1(t)\Delta t + \mu_2' q_2(t)\Delta t]P_1(t)$$

since the one unit in the system, corresponding to the second term, may be in either channel.   Arrivals are assumed to be Poisson with rate λ, and μ_1' and μ_2' are the exponential service rates at the respective channels, independent of n.   The usual limiting process gives

$$P_0'(t) = -\lambda P_0(t) + \{\mu_1' q_1(t) + \mu_2'[1 - q_1(t)]\}P_1(t)$$

since $q_1(t) + q_2(t) = 1$.   The primes on the service rates indicate that the subscript refers to the channel and not the number in the system, as previously.

For $n = 1$, the situation is complicated by the possibilities that the departing unit can leave from either channel and that an arriving unit may enter either channel.   From the event statements, one can write for the probability that there is one unit in the system and that it is in channel 1,

$$q_1(t + \Delta t)P_1(t + \Delta t) = \epsilon_1 \lambda \Delta t P_0(t) + (1 - \lambda \Delta t)(1 - \mu_1' \Delta t)q_1(t)P_1(t)$$
$$+ \mu_2' \Delta t P_2(t)$$

The usual limiting process yields

$$\{q_1(t)P_1(t)\}' = -(\lambda + \mu_1')q_1(t)P_1(t) + \lambda \epsilon_1 P_0(t) + \mu_2' P_2(t)$$

From symmetry, the corresponding equation for the second channel is

$$\{q_2(t)P_1(t)\}' = -(\lambda + \mu_2')q_2(t)P_1(t) + \lambda \epsilon_2 P_0(t) + \mu_1' P_2(t)$$

Adding, and recalling that $q_1(t) + q_2(t) = 1$, we get

$$P_1'(t) = -[\lambda + q_1(t)\mu_1' + q_2(t)\mu_2']P_1(t) + \lambda P_0(t) + (\mu_1' + \mu_2')P_2(t)$$

For $n \geqslant 2$, the considerations involving individual channels are not pertinent since both channels are busy when arrivals enter the queue. The only difference from the earlier situation is that since the channels are not assumed to be identical, the service rate is $\mu_1' + \mu_2'$. Thus,

$$P_n'(t) = -[\lambda + (\mu_1' + \mu_2')]P_n(t) + (\mu_1' + \mu_2')P_{n+1}(t) + \lambda P_{n-1}(t)$$

For steady-state probabilities,

$$q_1 = \frac{\mu_2'}{\mu_1' + \mu_2'} \frac{\lambda + \epsilon_1(\mu_1' + \mu_2')}{\lambda + \epsilon_1 \mu_2' + (1 - \epsilon_1)\mu_1'}$$

$$q_2 = \frac{\mu_1'}{\mu_1' + \mu_2'} \frac{\lambda + (1 - \epsilon_1)(\mu_1' + \mu_2')}{\lambda + \epsilon_1 \mu_2' + (1 - \epsilon_1)\mu_1'} \tag{52}$$

where $q_i = \lim_{t \to \infty} q_i(t)$, $i = 1, 2$. The reader may derive these results and also the steady-state probabilities, as given in Prob. 11-43.

Example 11-19 Servers in series In a series service arrangement, the output of one server is the input to the next. Consider two servers S_1 and S_2 in series, with exponential service rates μ_1' and μ_2'. Arrivals to the first server, S_1, are Poisson with rate λ. Let $P(n_1, n_2, t)$ be the probability that there are n_1 units at S_1 and n_2 units at S_2 at time t.

The state (n_1, n_2) at time $t + \Delta t$ is equal to the union of the four events:

1. State (n_1, n_2) at t, no arrivals and no services in $\{t, t + \Delta t\}$
2. State $(n_1 + 1, n_2 - 1)$ at t, a service leaves S_1 and enters S_2 in $\{t, t + \Delta t\}$
3. State $(n_1, n_2 + 1)$ at t, a departure from S_2 in $\{t, t + \Delta t\}$
4. State $(n_1 - 1, n_2)$ at t, an arrival at S_1 in $\{t, t + \Delta t\}$

Note, again, that the enumeration of events is not exhaustive and that only contributions with nonvanishing probabilities have been mentioned.

Using these events, one can derive the equations

$$P'(n_1, n_2, t) = -(\lambda + \mu_1' + \mu_2')P(n_1, n_2, t) + \mu_2' P(n_1, n_2 + 1, t)$$
$$+ \mu_1' P(n_1 + 1, n_2 - 1, t) + \lambda P(n_1 - 1, n_2, t) \quad n_1, n_2 \geqslant 1 \tag{53a}$$

with the starting equations

$$P'(n_1, 0, t) = \lambda P(n_1 - 1, 0, t) + \mu_2' P(n_1, 1, t) - (\lambda + \mu_1')P(n_1, 0, t)$$
$$P'(0, n_2, t) = \mu_1' P(1, n_2 - 1, t) + \mu_2' P(0, n_2 + 1, t) - (\lambda + \mu_2')P(0, n_2, t)$$
$$P'(0, 0, t) = -\lambda P(0, 0, t) + \mu_2' P(0, 1, t) \tag{53b}$$

The steady-state solution is [52]

$$P(n_1, n_2) = \rho_1^{n_1} \rho_2^{n_2}(1 - \rho_1)(1 - \rho_2) \tag{54a}$$

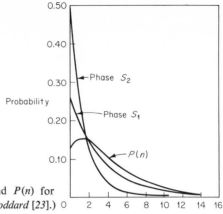

Fig. 11-16 Probabilities $P(n_1)$, $P(n_2)$, and $P(n)$ for $\rho_1 = 3/4$ and $\rho_2 = 1/2$. (*Reprinted from Goddard* [23].)

where $\rho_1 = \lambda/\mu_1'$ and $\rho_2 = \lambda/\mu_2'$. It is easy to verify this solution, although the derivation is elusive. The marginal probability $P(n_2)$ for the number in the second phase is

$$P(n_2) = \rho_2^{n_2}(1 - \rho_2) \tag{54b}$$

while the probability for the total number in both phases, $P(n)$, is

$$P(n) = \sum_{n=n_1+n_2} P(n_1,n_2) = \frac{(1 - \rho_1)(1 - \rho_2)(\rho_2^{n+1} - \rho_1^{n+1})}{\rho_2 - \rho_1} \tag{54c}$$

These results are plotted in Fig. 11-16.

The expected numbers in the system are given in Prob. 11-44. Notice that the two phases appear to act independently. Actually, this is a special case. To illustrate some of the pitfalls in using queueing results indiscriminately, we further describe the situation. Most work in tandem queues has been for Poisson arrivals and exponential service times in the steady state. Clearly, we should seek the probability functions to describe the output from one phase which becomes the input to the next. In the steady state, the output of a phase is independent of the service priority used for entry into that phase. However, only for Poisson input and exponential service in the steady state can the input to the next phase be assumed to be Poisson. This was an implicit assumption in this example, but it is not necessarily the case for other input probability distributions. Further, the Poisson assumption for inputs to the next phase is strictly true only if there is no limitation on the size of the queue that can build between phases (*blocking*). Before considering the effect of blocking, we mention that the above analysis can be extended to several queues in series. It is not difficult, but it is beyond our scope, to study combined systems of parallel and series queues. It is also interesting to study cases in which the arrivals to a later phase come from both previous phases and from outside the system. The reader is referred to Saaty [52].

Example 11-20 Series queues with blocking In many series queues, the "waiting room" in successive phases is limited—e.g., production lines, cars at intersections. When the queue length in a given phase is limited, the effective service rate of the preceding phase is the product of its service rate and the fraction of time during which the phase in question is unblocked.

Consider a two-phase queue in which the first phase may have an unlimited queue while the second phase may not have any queuers. Let n be the number of units in S_1 (including the unit in service). To describe the system adequately, we introduce three state probabilities corresponding to the three possible ways of having n units in S_1 at time t:

$P(n,0,t) = P\{n$ units are in S_1, and S_2 is empty$\}$

$P(n,1,t) = P\{n$ units are in S_1, and a unit is in service in $S_2\}$

$P(n_b,1,t) = P\{n$ units are in S_1, and a unit has completed service in S_1 and is blocked by a service in S_2, that is, no service is being performed in $S_1\}$

One concludes the system of equations for $n \geqslant 1$,

$$P'(n,0,t) = -(\lambda + \mu_1')P(n,0,t) + \lambda P(n-1,0,t) + \mu_2'P(n,1,t)$$
$$P'(n,1,t) = -(\lambda + \mu_1' + \mu_2')P(n,1,t) + \lambda P(n-1,1,t) + \mu_1'P(n+1,0,t)$$
$$+ \mu_2'P(n+1_b,1,t) \qquad (55a)$$
$$P'(n_b,1,t) = -(\lambda + \mu_2')P(n_b,1,t) + \lambda P(n-1_b,1,t) + \mu_1'P(n,1,t)$$

with the starting equations

$$P'(0,0,t) = -P(0,0,t) + \mu_2'P(0,1,t)$$
$$P'(0,1,t) = -(\lambda + \mu_2')P(0,1,t) + \mu_1'P(1,0,t) + \mu_2'P(1_b,1,t) \qquad (55b)$$
$$P'(1_b,1,t) = -(\lambda + \mu_2')P(1_b,1,t) + \mu_1'P(1,1,t)$$

Passing to the steady state, and assuming $\mu_1' = \mu_2' = \mu'$, gives

$$-(1+\rho)P(n,0) + \rho P(n-1,0) + P(n,1) = 0$$
$$-(2+\rho)P(n,1) + \rho P(n-1,1) + P(n+1,0) + P(n+1_b,1) = 0 \qquad (56)$$
$$-(1+\rho)P(n_b,1) + \rho P(n-1_b,1) + P(n,1) = 0$$

and the appropriate starting equations Here $\rho = \lambda/\mu'$, as before. Since these are difference equations with constant coefficients, they suggest solutions of the form

$$P(n,0) = c_1 r^n \qquad P(n,1) = c_2 r^n \qquad \text{and} \qquad P(n_b,1) = c_3 r^n$$

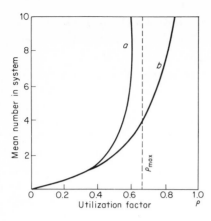

Fig. 11-17 Two-phase queues. (*a*) Complete blocking in second phase; (*b*) no blocking. (*Adapted from Goddard [23].*)

where c_1, c_2, and c_3 are constants to be determined by the initial conditions and r is to be determined by the indicial equation. Substituting these and using the initial conditions leads to four roots of the indicial equation:

$$r_1 = 1 \qquad r_2 = \frac{\rho}{\rho + 1} \qquad r_3, r_4 = \frac{\rho}{4}[(\rho + 3) \pm \sqrt{\rho^2 + 6\rho + 1}]$$

Since the state probabilities are linear combinations of powers of these roots, we discard any which exceed unity. It may be verified that $\rho_{max} = 2/3$ is the maximum value of ρ for which the roots do not exceed unity.

The maximum tolerable arrival rate for the first phase such that steady-state conditions are satisfied is μ'_1 times the fraction of time the phase is unblocked, that is, $\mu'_1 \rho_{max}$. For a three-phase queue, $\rho_{max} = 0.5641$; and for four phases, $\rho_{max} = 0.5115$. The effect of complete blocking in the second phase for the two-phase queue is shown in Fig. 11-17. The mean number in the system can be calculated from

$$L = \sum_{n=0}^{\infty} [nP(n,0) + (n + 1)P(n,1) + (n + 2)P(n + 1_b, 1)]$$

The left-hand curve in Fig. 11-17 describes L for the complete blocking case, and the right-hand curve is for the unblocked case.

The result for ρ_{max} when $\mu'_1 \neq \mu'_2$ is

$$\rho_{max} = \frac{\mu'_2(\mu'_1 + \mu'_2)}{(\mu'_1)^2 + \mu'_1 \mu'_2 + (\mu'_2)^2}$$

This and additional results for partial blocking are given in Chap. 12 of Saaty [52]. Now consider some applications of multiserver queues.

Example 11-21   Optimum number of parallel servers (unknown k)
In Example 11-14 we studied the effect of increasing service rate. Now suppose
that the service rate is fixed but that the number of servers, k, can be varied.
The total cost per unit time is

$$kC_s + LC_w \tag{57}$$

where C_s and C_w are the costs per unit time of service and waiting, respectively.
The optimization is carried out with respect to k using the expressions for
L and P_0 given in Prob. 11-41 and Eq. (51), respectively.   The calculation is
cumbersome but not prohibitive in specific instances.   Mangelsdorf [38]
has summarized solutions graphically.

A related example deals with a facility which has limited waiting room
and houses up to k servers (for example, a port facility).   Without the limited
waiting room, arrivals are Poisson at rate λ.   The actual arrival rate is

$$\lambda_n = \begin{cases} \lambda & n < N + k \\ 0 & n \geqslant N + k \end{cases}$$

where N is the number of storage spaces.   The number of arrivals per unit
time is a random variable α whose expectation is

$$\bar{\lambda} = E(\alpha) = \lambda P_0 + \lambda P_1 + \cdots + \lambda P_{N+k-1} = \bar{\lambda}(1 - P_{N+k}) \tag{58}$$

since $\lambda_n = 0$ for $n \geqslant N + k$ and since

$$\sum_{n=0}^{N+k} P_n = 1$$

In the case of a port facility, one can associate a constant revenue r with each
customer admitted, so that the revenue per unit time is $r\alpha$.   Associating a
fixed cost C_s with each server, the expected profit function is

$$r\bar{\lambda} - kC_s$$

The problem is to determine the number of servers, k, which maximizes this
function.   In order to proceed, one needs $E(\alpha)$.   In turn, this expectation
depends upon the probabilities P_n.   One is tempted to use Eqs. (50) and (51)
for these probabilities, but these are not quite applicable since not all arrivals
can be accommodated.   The probabilities are given by

$$P_n = \begin{cases} \dfrac{\rho^n}{n!} P_0 & n = 1, 2, \ldots, k - 1 \\[2mm] \dfrac{\rho^n}{k!\, k^{n-k}} P_0 & n = k, k+1, \ldots, k + N \\[2mm] 0 & n > k + N \end{cases} \tag{59}$$

where

$$P_0^{-1} = \sum_{n=0}^{N} \frac{\rho^n}{n!} + \frac{\rho^k}{k!} \sum_{n=k+1}^{N} \left(\frac{\rho}{k}\right)^{n-k} \tag{60}$$

Note the resemblance to Eqs. (50) and (51). Problem 11-45 suggests deriving Eqs. (59) and (60).

Example 11-22 Optimum number and size of parallel servers (unknown k and μ)

A petroleum company plans construction of an offshore mooring facility to serve a new refinery. A decision is to be made regarding the number of unloading berths and the type of pumps and hose-handling equipment. A maximum of three berths will be built, and the same type of pumping and hose-handling equipment will be used for each. From the data below, determine how many berths should be built and which type of pumping equipment should be used.

Pump type	Fixed cost/day	Operating cost/day	Capacity, avg. bbl unloaded/pump/day
A	$140	$ 980	150,000
B	260	1,500	300,000

Tankers carry 360,000 bbl each and arrive in Poisson fashion at a mean rate of three per week. Unloading times vary exponentially about the mean rates shown in the table. Ship time (waiting and unloading) costs $1,800 per ship per day.

We have six possible combinations of pump types (A or B) and numbers of berths (1, 2, or 3). However, pump type A with one berth is not feasible because the mean arrival rate of $3/7 = 0.4286$ ship per day is greater than the mean service rate of $150,000/360,000 = 0.4167$ ship per day. Five combinations remain, and from among these we wish to find the one having minimum total daily cost (fixed cost + operating cost + ship holding cost).

Fixed cost per day:

Pump type	No. of berths		
	1	2	3
A	—	$280	$420
B	$260	520	780

Operating cost per day $= \rho C_0$, where C_0 is the operating cost per berth per day and $\rho = \lambda/\mu$. Note that ρ may be greater than 1 so long as $k\mu > \lambda$. For pump A, $\rho_A = 1.0286$, and for pump B, $\rho_B = 0.5143$. The operating costs are therefore:

Pump type	No. of berths		
	1	2	3
A	—	$1,008	$1,008
B	$771.5	771.5	771.5

Another way to calculate daily operating costs is to use the percentages of time 0, 1, . . . pumps are actually in use. The probabilities $P_0 = 0.321$, $P_1 = 0.330$, and $\sum_{n=2}^{\infty} P_n = 0.349$ are the fraction of a day that zero, one, or more pumps are in use under policy A2; these are calculated from Eqs. (50) and (51). The expected operating cost of this policy, i.e., using two type A pumps, is

$$C_0(A2) = \$980 \times (0 \times 0.321 + 1 \times 0.330 + 2 \times 0.349) = 1,008$$

Ship holding cost per day $= 1,800L$, where L is the average number of ships waiting for and in service. For parallel servers, Poisson arrivals, and exponential services, L can be calculated using the expectations in Prob. 11-41 to yield

Pump type	No. of berths		
	1	2	3
A	—	1.398	1.079
B	1.056	0.551	0.518

The ship holding costs are:

Pump type	No. of berths		
	1	2	3
A	—	$2,516	$1.942
B	$1,901	992	932

Adding the previous three results, total costs per day are:

Pump type	No. of berths		
	1	2	3
A	—	$3,804	$3,370
B	$2,932.5	2,283.5	2,483.5

We choose two berths with pump B.

This example is adapted from Sasieni et al. [54].

Example 11-23   Optimum service population (unknown k and λ)

A number N of identical facilities, each staffed with k servers, are to service identical segments of a large population seeking service at a daily rate λ_p (for example, N tool cribs on a large factory floor, each having k clerks). There are costs associated with waiting for service and the number of servers. How should N and k be chosen to minimize total expected costs?

Let C_w be the waiting cost per unit time and C_s the cost per server per day, as in Example 11-14. Also, let τ be the expected round-trip travel time, as in Example 11-15, and W the expected waiting time. The total daily expected cost of operating the N facilities is

$$N[C_f + kC_s + \lambda(W + \tau) C_w]$$

where C_f is the fixed cost per day of operating a facility independent of the number of servers and $\lambda = \lambda_p/N$ is the daily arrival rate at any of the facilities. Note that for simplicity the same cost rate, C_w, is used for travel time and waiting time. Dividing by the average number of arrivals per day, $N\lambda$, one obtains

$$K(\lambda,k) = \frac{C_f + kC_s}{\lambda} + (W + \tau) C_w$$

the daily expected cost per service. The expected waiting and travel times, W and τ, are functions of λ and k. One obtains τ using the analysis in Example 11-15 or Fig. 11-14. The expected waiting time for a parallel-server queue is given in Prob. 11-41. These expressions enable one to carry out the optimization.

Variants of this model can be used in interesting ways. For example, in a hospital emergency unit the waiting cost per unit time might be an increasing function of W rather than a constant and the pertinent expected travel time might be $\tau/2$ rather than τ. Other examples appear in Hillier [29], Hillier and Lieberman [30], and Morse [43]. Also see Probs. 11-46 to 11-48. Table 11-10 summarizes some queueing formulas.

Table 11-10 Some queueing formulas: Poisson arrivals, first-come–first-served discipline, $\rho = \lambda/\mu$

	Arrival rate (Poisson)	Service rate	P_0^{-1}	P_n	L_q	L	W_q	V_s
Single-server queue — Open	$\lambda_n = \lambda$ all n	$\mu_n = \mu$ $n \geq 1$ (exponential)	$\dfrac{1}{1-\rho}$	$(1-\rho)\rho^n$	$\dfrac{\rho^2}{1-\rho}$	$\dfrac{\rho}{1-\rho}$	$\dfrac{\rho}{\mu-\lambda}$	$\dfrac{1}{\mu-\lambda}$
	$\lambda_n = \lambda$ all n	Mean $= 1/\mu$ Variance $= \sigma^2$ (arbitrary)	$\dfrac{1}{1-\rho}$		$\dfrac{\lambda^2\sigma^2 + \rho^2}{2(1-\rho)}$	$\rho + L_q$		
	$\lambda_n = \begin{cases} \lambda & n < m \\ 0 & n \geq m \end{cases}$	$\mu_n = \mu$ $n \geq 1$ (exponential)	$\dfrac{1-\rho^{m+1}}{1-\rho}$	$\dfrac{1-\rho}{1-\rho^{m+1}}\,\rho^n$	$L - (1 - P_0)$	$\dfrac{\rho}{1-\rho}[1 - (m+1)\rho^m P_0]$	$\dfrac{L_q}{\lambda}$	$W_q + \dfrac{1}{\mu}$
Single-server queue — Cyclic	$\lambda_n = \begin{cases} (m-n)\lambda & n = 0, \ldots, m \\ 0 & n > m \end{cases}$	$\mu_n = \mu$ $n \geq 1$ (exponential)	$\displaystyle\sum_{n=0}^{m} \dfrac{m!}{(m-n)!}\,\rho^n$	$\dfrac{m!}{(m-n)!}\,\rho^n P_0$ $n \leq m$	$m - \dfrac{\lambda + \mu}{\lambda}(1 - P_0)$	$m - (1 - P_0)\rho^{-1}$		
Multiserver queue — Parallel, open, k server	$\lambda_n = \lambda$ all n	$\mu_n = \begin{cases} n\mu & 0 \leq n < k \\ k\mu & n \geq k \end{cases}$ (exponential)	$\displaystyle\sum_{n=0}^{k} \dfrac{\rho^n}{n!} + \dfrac{\rho^k}{k!}\,\dfrac{\rho}{k-\rho}$	$\begin{cases} \dfrac{\rho^n P_0}{n!} & 0 \leq n < k \\[2mm] \dfrac{\rho^n}{k!\,k^{n-k}}\,P_0 & n > k \end{cases}$	$\dfrac{\lambda\mu\rho^k}{(k-1)!\,(k\mu - \lambda)^2}\,P_0$	$L_q + \rho$	$\dfrac{L_q}{\lambda}$	$W_q + \dfrac{1}{\mu}$
Multiserver queue — Parallel, open, k server	$\lambda_n = \begin{cases} \lambda & 0 \leq n < m \\ 0 & n \geq m \end{cases}$	$\mu_n = \begin{cases} n\mu & 0 \leq n < k \\ k\mu & n \geq k \end{cases}$ (exponential)	$\displaystyle\sum_{n=0}^{k} \dfrac{\rho^n}{n!} + \dfrac{\rho^k}{k!} \sum_{n=k+1}^{m} \left(\dfrac{\rho}{k}\right)^{n-k}$	$\begin{cases} \dfrac{\rho^n P_0}{n!} & n \leq k \\[2mm] \dfrac{\rho^n}{k!\,k^{n-k}}\,P_0 & k \leq n \leq m \\[2mm] 0 & n > m \end{cases}$				
Multiserver queue — Tandem, open, two-phase	$\lambda_n = \lambda$ all n	$\left.\begin{aligned}\mu_1' &= \mu_1 \\ \mu_2' &= \mu_2\end{aligned}\right\}$ all n (exponential)		$\begin{aligned} P(n_2) &= \rho_2^{n_2}(1-\rho_2) \\ P(n_1,n_2) &= \rho_1^{n_1}\rho_2^{n_2}(1-\rho_1)(1-\rho_2) \\ P_n &= (1-\rho_1)(1-\rho_2)\dfrac{\rho_2^{n+1} - \rho_1^{n+1}}{\rho_2 - \rho_1} \end{aligned}$	$\dfrac{\rho_1^2}{1-\rho_1} + \dfrac{\rho_2^2}{1-\rho_2}$	$\dfrac{\rho_1}{1-\rho_1} + \dfrac{\rho_2}{1-\rho_2}$		

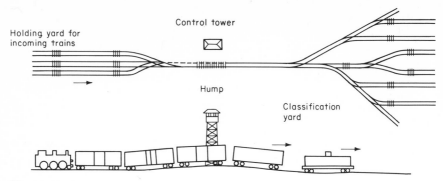

Fig. 11-18 Hump classification layout.

The Monte Carlo technique (see Chap. 8) is widely used in queueing situations.   The next example is a simple illustration.

Example 11-24 Consolidating freight yards (Monte Carlo)

A railroad plans to consolidate several of its freight-classification yards.   A new yard is proposed to classify trains by the humping process illustrated in Fig. 11-18.   Given the data in Tables 11-11 to 11-13 and Fig. 11-19, determine the capacity for which the yard should be designed.   Also, estimate the mean time a car spends in the holding yard.

Holding-yard cost—including initial cost, track and switch maintenance

**Table   11-11
Schedule of
incoming trains**

A.M.	P.M.
12:17	1:20
12:49	4:34
1:28	5:00
1:36	5:49
1:51	6:38
2:20	7:10
2:35	7:59
2:48	8:22
3:19	9:15
3:49	9:55
4:30	10:34
5:57	10:49
9:11	11:03
	11:42
	11:51

Table 11-12 Sample data on deviations
from scheduled arrival times

+2	+13	+2	+6	+9
+8	+11	+4	+5	+13
+12	+8	+6	+2	+21
−6	+5	+5	+15	+17
0	+1	+9	−7	+9
+4	+14	+10	+10	+3
+6	−3	+12	+8	+5
−2	+6	+17	+12	−4
+1	+2	+6	+5	+8
+3	+11	+3	+2	+6
+10	+5	−1	+7	+19
+22	+1	−8	+6	+10
+4	−16	+3	+7	−2
−1	+4	+5	+11	+9
+2	+2	+11	+5	+2
+5	−3	+20	+8	+5
+9	0	+7	+1	+20

and operation, property tax, etc.—is $0.005 per hr per car of holding capacity. The cost of switching to an unlimited secondary holding area when the proposed capacity is reached is $0.15 per car.   Tables 11-11 and 11-12 provide arrival-time information, and Table 11-13 and Fig. 11-19 provide service times.   Since service time is a random function of a random property (lengths of the arriving trains), a Monte Carlo solution is suggested (Sec. 8-7).   The random data in Tables 11-12 and 11-13 and Fig. 11-19 can be stored in several ways, e.g., storage in computer memory with random recall or by using a plot of the cumulative distribution to provide sample values.

Table 11-13 Sample data on single-channel
hump classification times

No. of cars in train	Minutes to classify	No. of cars in train	Minutes to classify
122	36.8	110	32.8
118	34.2	128	37.9
129	37.7	113	35.4
118	36.0	135	38.6
135	41.0	121	34.4
124	35.8	110	29.7
132	39.8	127	39.1
111	33.5	112	33.8

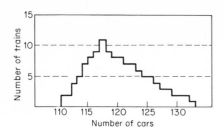

Fig. 11-19 Sample data on train sizes (frequency histogram) for 120 trains.

Table 11-14 provides a diary for incoming trains beginning at 12:17 A.M. From the sample data in Table 11-12 and Fig. 11-19 and a random-number table, one generates sample values of time-schedule deviations and the number of cars (column 5); for example, for train 1 the values are 4 min and 115 cars. The number of cars in the holding yard upon arrival (column 3) is the number that were in the yard when the previous train arrived plus the number of cars in the preceding train minus the number of cars classified between its arrival and the present train's arrival. The classification starting time in column 4 is the later of two times, the actual arrival time (column 2) and the finish time of the preceding train (column 7). Classification time Y depends upon the random number of cars, X, to be classified. Assuming a linear relationship, the sample data in Table 11-13 were used to obtain the least-square line (Appendix 1).

$$Y = 0.3X - 0.59$$

Substituting 115 (train 1) for X yields the 34-min classification time in column 6, so that classification is finished at 12:55 (column 7). The holding time for an average car is the waiting time until classification begins plus one-half of the classification time, that is, $0 + \frac{1}{2}(34) = 17$ min (column 8). Simulation

Table 11-14   Diary of events

Train No.	(1) Scheduled arrival time	(2) Actual arrival time	(3) Cars in holding yards at arrival time	(4) Classification starting time	(5) No. of cars	(6) Estimated classification time, min	(7) Finish time	(8) Average holding time per car, min
1	12:17	12:21	0	12:21	115	34	12:55	17
2	12:49	12:49	22	12:55	124	37	1:32	24
3	1:28	1:36	0	1:36	117	35	2:11	18
4	1:36	1:38	110	2:11	120	35	2:46	50
5	1:51	2:04	143	2:46	130	38	3:24	61
6	2:20	2:19	223	3:24	111	33	3:57	82

is continued until the desired convergence to steady state is observed.   Convergence is accomplished with a smaller sample if simulation is begun with units already in storage, although we have not done so here.

The mean car holding time for the six-train sample is

$$\frac{\sum\limits_{i=1}^{N} n_i h_i}{\sum\limits_{i=1}^{N} n_i} = \frac{115(17) + \cdots + 111(82)}{115 + \cdots + 111} = 42 \text{ min}$$

where N is the number of trains sampled, n is the number of cars (column 5), and h is the average holding time per car (column 8).   Total cost per hour, C, includes the fixed yard cost and the expected switching cost:

$$C = 0.005H + 0.15S$$

and

$$S = \frac{1 \text{ hr}}{t} \sum_{i=0}^{N} [(c_i + n_i) - H]$$

where H is the holding-yard car capacity, S the expected number per hour to be switched to the secondary holding area, c_i the number in holding yards at arrival, and t the simulation period in hours (see Fig. 11-20).   The minimum cost is approximated by choosing trial values of H and solving for the corresponding values of S.   This example is adapted from Krick [32].

Applications of queueing to civil engineering problems are quite recent. The analogy between the storage of runoff and queueing has given rise to a theory of storage ([31], [41], and [42]) for regulating variable streamflow [33] and for maximizing benefits from water-resource projects with variable streamflow [19].   One of the earliest applications was by Little [34] in connection with the design of facilities for hydroelectric power generation.   A useful discussion and bibliography appear in Chow [9].

Applications to road traffic are extensive.   Remarkable improvements in the effective capacity of a traffic artery can sometimes be achieved with minor perturbations in design and operation.   One of the earliest applications

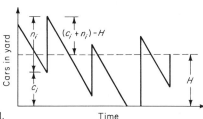

Fig. 11-20 Cars in yard.

In the Lincoln Tunnel, which carries traffic under the Hudson River between Manhattan and New Jersey, traffic control devices are in use which materially reduce traffic congestion, Alan Gonseth of the Port of New York Authority told a recent meeting of the ASCE Metropolitan Section.

Traffic can be controlled in three ways, depending on the seriousness of congestion. For light congestion, a lighted sign at the tunnel entrance is turned on; it reads "Pause here then go." If stricter control is called for, vertical rubber tubes pop up from the pavement at the entrance, narrowing the driving lane at the entrance and thus slowing the entering vehicles. The third stage is lights in the pavement inside the entrance.

Simply by controlling the number of vehicles per hour entering the controlled lane, traffic flow through it can be increased by 6 to 7 percent during peak hours. This increase seems modest; but as the accompanying graph shows, it sharply reduces the number of hours of bumper-to-bumper traffic during the daily rush hour. The two curves indicate backup when per-lane capacity is 1,200 and 1,250 cars per hour.

Another benefit of the traffic-control devices is in reducing congestion due to breakdowns in the tunnel. In 1967 the Lincoln Tunnel was the scene of 3,000 breakdowns. Because the one controlled lane (of six in the tunnel's three tubes) had less stop-and-go driving, the frequency of overheated, stalled and vapor-locked vehicles was reduced by 60 percent, Mr. Gonseth reported.

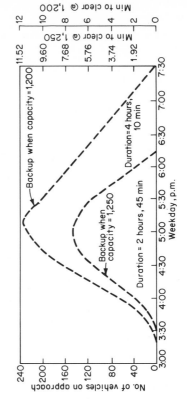

Fig. 11-21 Lincoln Tunnel traffic control. (*Reprint from Civil Eng., January, 1969.*)

was the prizewinning work of Edie for The Port of New York Authority [16]. A news item in *Civil Engineering* illustrates the point and is reprinted in Fig. 11-21.

The Erlang loss formula [Eq. (44)] has been used to estimate percentages of vehicles unable to "pass" and to estimate the improvement which can be obtained by adding an extra lane [4]. The vehicles on a road, it is assumed, form the queueing process, and the results of queueing are used to study delays, gap theories (in time and distance), and so on. The applications are numerous, and an extensive literature is available. Ashton [4], Haight [27], and Edie, Herman, and Rothery [17] tend to be more advanced and theoretical works. A well-written consideration of queues in traffic theory and control appears in Drew [15]. A very readable monograph is edited by Gerlough and Capelle [22]. There is also the application-oriented work of Wohl and Martin [62].

Applications to other areas are less developed but are actively sought. In construction, see Shaffer and Brooks [56], O'Shea, Slutkin, and Shaffer [45], and Spaugh [59]. A discussion of applications to the design of engineering systems appears in Gosling [24]. Chapter 10 of Conway, Maxwell, and Miller [11] deals with priorities in multiserver queues.

SUMMARY

This chapter resumed the emphasis upon models which began in Chap. 9.

The subject of reliability, well developed in an electronic context, has begun to be developed for mechanical systems, e.g., structures. Because the work to date is still fragmentary and because it is not clear that the development in an electrical context will be very useful for mechanical systems, only basic ideas were presented.

Section 11-2 briefly described random-walk models, and Sec. 11-3 provided the rudiments of Markov chains. An ample literature exists for both subjects, and the intent here was to provide the reader with an appreciation of their existence.

Sections 11-4 and 11-5 developed steady-state random queueing models in some detail. Queueing has the promise of contributing to better decisions in the design of many kinds of facilities which involve people or items in queues. A number of examples indicated how queueing models can be formulated and used for design.

PROBLEMS

11-1. Derive the life density corresponding to the linearly decreasing hazard function

$$h(t) = \lambda_0 - \lambda t \qquad 0 < t \leqslant \frac{\lambda_0}{\lambda} \; \blacklozenge$$

11-2. For certain retail businesses, Lomax [37] found the hazard function to be well represented by

$$h(t) = \frac{b}{t+a} \qquad a, b > 0$$

Find the failure time density.

11-3. Show that an exponential hazard, $h(t) = \lambda e^{at}$, leads to the extreme-value failure density

$$ev(t) = \lambda e^{at} e^{-(\lambda/a)(e^{at}-1)}$$

11-4. Prove that a series combination is never more reliable than its least reliable component and that a parallel system is at least as reliable as its most reliable component.

11-5. The mechanism used to bring a standby system or component into operation in the event of a failure is called a *sensing switch*. Derive expressions for $R_{ss}(n,m)$ and $R_{cs}(n,m)$ when a sensing switch of reliability r_s is used.

11-6. For the circuit in the figure, it is equally likely that any of the switches A, B, C, or D are open or closed, that is, $p = q = 1/2$. What is the probability that the bulb is lit?

   Given that the bulb is lit, calculate the probability that both switches A and B are closed.

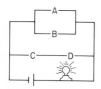

11-7. Consider the redundant system shown in the figure, in which C_1 and C_2 are used to convert an input I into an output z. Converters C_1 and C_2 each work successfully with probability p_c. To monitor failures, a device M is attached to converter C_1, and it "decides" whether or not C_1 has interpreted the data correctly. The probability that the monitor detects an error when C_1 is in error equals the probability that the monitor agrees with C_1's outcome when I is correct ($=p_m$).

   The input originally enters C_1. If the monitor detects a mistake in C_1's output (whether correctly or not), it sends a signal to the switch S to transfer the input to C_2. The switch operates correctly with probability p_s.

   Determine the probability that the entire system produces the desired output from a given input I. Is it possible that a system consisting of the single converter C_1 could be more reliable than the component system?

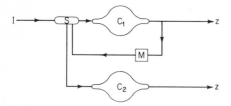

11-8. Develop a recursion relation (dynamic programming) for minimizing the weight of an m-member structure such that an overall probability of failure, $P_{f(max)}$, is not exceeded. Assume that the system can be represented by a series combination and that the individual success probabilities are functions of the member's cross-sectional area, $p_i(A_i)$. Let L_i and ρ_i be the respective length and unit volumetric weight of member i, $i = 1, \ldots, m$.

11-9. Assume that the individual survival probabilities of Prob. 11-8 can be approximated by $\ln p_i(A_i) \simeq D_i \ln A_i$ for the range of probabilities to be considered, $0 < A_i < 1$, and D_i a nonnegative parameter. Using the Lagrange multiplier technique, show that the minimum-weight solution is achieved by

$$\frac{\rho_i L_i}{D_i} A_i = \text{const} \qquad \text{all } i$$

11-10. In many engineering systems, the success of the system depends upon several parts which are influenced differently by a single variable. Consider a rocket that is subject to failure from two independent conditions:

(a) The power plant generates insufficient power.

(b) The radiation passed through the shielding exceeds equipment tolerance.

Suppose that $P_1 = \displaystyle\int_{L(w)}^{\infty} f(p)\,dp$ is the probability of sufficient power, where $L(w)$ is the minimum required power as a function of the weight w of radiation shielding. Suppose, also, that the probability of the shielding being adequate is

$$P_2 = \int_0^{R(w)} g(r)\,dr$$

where $R(w)$ is the maximum tolerable radiation level.

In a particular case it was found that $P_1 = e^{-aw}$ and $P_2 = 1 - e^{-bw}$, where a and b are positive constants. Find the weight w^* which maximizes the probability of system success.

11-11. A gambler begins with a capital x and plays against an opponent with $b - x$ dollars (i.e., there is a total of b dollars in the game). At each trial, the gambler receives \$1 if he wins, with probability p, and forfeits \$1 if he loses, with probability $q = 1 - p$. The probability that a gambler with capital x will eventually be ruined is $\Omega(x)$. The difference equation, Eq. (14), describes this "gambler's ruin" problem. Show that the gambler's expected gain, when he has x dollars, is $b[1 - \Omega(x)] - x$. Under what conditions is the expected gain zero?

11-12. What is the effect of changing the stakes in Prob. 11-11? Imagine that each player initially trades his dollar chips for twice as many half-dollar chips. Conclude that the probability of ultimate ruin with the new stakes, $\Omega'(x)$, is

$$\Omega'(x) = \Omega(x)\frac{(q/b)^b + (q/p)^x}{(q/p)^b + 1} \qquad q \neq p$$

and, hence, that if a game is unfavorable (that is, $p < q$), a gambler should play for the highest stakes his opponent is willing to accept. ◆

11-13. For the random walk of Prob. 11-11, let $d(x)$ be the random time for absorption (at the origin) when the particle is at x. Verify the recursion relation

$$E[d(x)] = pE[d(x + 1)] + qE[d(x - 1)] + 1$$

for $0 < x < b$ with the boundary conditions $d(0) = d(b) = 0$. Notice the similarity of this difference equation to Eq. (14). The solution is

$$E[d(x)] = \begin{cases} \dfrac{x}{q - p} - \dfrac{b}{q - p}\dfrac{1 - (q/p)^x}{1 - (q/p)^b} & p \neq q \\ x(b - x) & p = q \end{cases}$$

11-14. In a two-dimensional symmetric random walk, let $D_n^2 = x^2 + y^2$ be the square of the distance from the origin after n steps. By calculating the expected value of $D_{n+1}^2 - D_n^2$

prove that $E(D_n{}^2) = n$ [18].   Compare this result with the Monte Carlo for the perambulating drunk (Prob. 8-40).

11-15. Carry out the Monte Carlo suggested in Example 11-5 to estimate the head at point A. Assume that the permeability coefficients are equal, $k_x = k_y$, for all positions ($p_{ij} = 1/4$) with the exception of points coinciding with the dam's boundary and the impermeable soil surface which act as reflecting barriers.

11-16. Consider the thin homogeneous rectangular plate of the next figure. The insulated faces of the plate are bounded by the coordinate axes and the line $x = a$, $y = b$. For simplicity, assume that three of the axes are kept at $0°$ temperature while the edge corresponding to the x axis is maintained at $10°$.

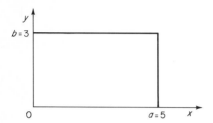

It has been shown that the temperature $t(x,y)$ of any point within the boundaries of the plate is governed by the second-order partial differential equation

$$\nabla^2 t = \frac{\partial^2 t}{\partial x^2} + \frac{\partial^2 t}{\partial y^2} = 0$$

where ∇^2 is the laplacian operator (see Wylie [63]).   Develop a Monte Carlo procedure to approximate the temperature of the plate at the position $(2,1)$.

11-17. For an arbitrary two-step transition matrix in which the steady-state equations (28) apply, derive the probabilities π_0 and π_1 in terms of the transition probabilities.

11-18. Consider a two-step transition matrix to describe a structure:

$$\begin{bmatrix} p_s & p_f \\ 0 & 1 \end{bmatrix}$$

where p_s and p_f are the probabilities of survival and failure, respectively ($p_s + p_f = 1$). Calculate the probabilities of the structural condition after 2, 3, etc., steps and deduce the result for n steps.

11-19. Consider a doubly stochastic transition matrix $\mathbf{P}$, that is, $\sum_{i=0}^{K} p_{ij} = 1$ for all i, where $K + 1$ is the number of states in the finite chain.   Assuming that all the states belong to the same class, derive the steady-state probabilities

$$\pi_j = \frac{1}{K + 1} \qquad j = 0, 1, \ldots, K$$

11-20. Arrivals are Poisson at a signalized intersection (in the east-west direction) with a mean rate of one car per green phase and two cars per red phase. If the green phase can handle up to four cars per cycle, determine the probability that n cars are waiting when the light changes to green. For simplicity, assume a maximum queue length of four cars; i.e., if more than four cars are waiting at a light, arrivals turn off to a side street.

11-21. A contractor has two power shovels, only one of which is used at a time.   On any day, a shovel has probability q of requiring maintenance, which takes 2 days.   Assume that breakdowns occur at the end of the day and that the replacement is ready for service 2 days later. Select an appropriate state space, develop the two-step transition matrix, and determine the steady-state probability of work postponement, i.e., with both shovels under repair.

11-22. Consider the three-unit-capacity dam of Example 11-8. The probability distribution for the quantity of water which flows into the dam is unchanged; that is, $I = 0, 1, 2, 3$ with probabilities $1/6, 1/3, 1/3$, and $1/6$, respectively.

The water is used both for generating electric power and for recreational purposes. The demand per month is random, with the following probabilities: $p_D(1) = 1/2, p_D(2) = 1/2$.

All demand must be satisfied, and in the event of insufficient water supply, additional water is purchased at \$2,000 per unit. Using Markov chain procedures, determine the average monthly cost of outside purchases.

11-23. An air compressor, which costs \$9,000, is assumed to operate from year to year in one of two states: efficient e or inefficient i. It is estimated that efficient operation costs \$1,000 per year and inefficient operation costs \$3,000 per year. Once each year, management decides whether to repair or replace the existing compressor. The alternatives and transition probabilities for each state (e and i) are as follows:

(a) Neither repair nor replace; cost = \$0:

$P_{ee} = 0.6 \quad P_{ie} = 0$
$P_{ei} = 0.4 \quad P_{ii} = 1$

(b) Perform minor repair; cost = \$1,500:

$P_{ee} = 0.7 \quad P_{ie} = 0.4$
$P_{ei} = 0.3 \quad P_{ii} = 0.6$

(c) Purchase a used compressor; cost = \$4,000:

$P_{ee} = 0.5 \quad P_{ie} = 0.5$
$P_{ei} = 0.5 \quad P_{ii} = 0.5$

(d) Purchase a new compressor; cost = \$9,000:

$P_{ee} = 0.7 \quad P_{ie} = 0.7$
$P_{ei} = 0.3 \quad P_{ii} = 0.3$

Neglecting obsolescence and assuming a discount factor of 0.9, what policy should management assume over an infinite horizon?

11-24. Demand for a product is Poisson with a mean of two units per week. At the end of each week, an order is placed for additional units. Delivery is immediate. Due to limited storage facilities, no more than five units can be handled in any week and demand not met is lost. If the sale of an item results in a profit of \$50 above acquisition costs, and storage costs for unsold items are \$18 per item per week, what is the optimal quantity to have available at the beginning of each week?

11-25. A certain product is bought once a week in constant amounts by consumers. Company A, which is one of the manufacturers of this product, has tested a marketing program which it believes will produce the following customer-purchase transition probabilities whenever it is used:

$$
\begin{array}{cc}
 & \textit{This week} \\
 & \text{Co. A} \quad \text{Other} \\
\textit{Last week} \quad \begin{array}{c} \text{Co. A} \\ \text{Other} \end{array} & \begin{bmatrix} 0.9 & 0.1 \\ 0.02 & 0.98 \end{bmatrix}
\end{array}
$$

The cost of the program increases with the number of customers, u, in the city in which it is used:

Cost $= 0.03u + \$500$/year

The company's incremental profit (exclusive of the above cost) is 30% of the selling price of the product.   Company A's current share of total product sales is 10%.   Total product sales are $2 per customer-year and are not expected to be affected by the program.

(a) What is company A's anticipated share of total product sales after the market reaches steady state?

(b) What minimum number of customers should there be in a city for it to be given the program?

11-26.   Derive the expectations in Eqs. (38a) to (38f) of Sec. 11-4 for the single-server steady-state queue.

11-27.   Using the nonlinear service rule in Eq. (40) of Sec. 11-4, derive the steady-state probabilities of Eq. (41).

11-28.   Derive the density function $q(v)$ for the total time in the system V in the steady-state queue.   Since the total time in the system is the waiting time in the queue, W, plus the service time S, check your result by deriving the density for $V = W + S$ using the techniques of Chap. 9.

11-29.   Ships arrive at a single dock facility in Poisson fashion with mean λ ships per day. Also, whenever ships are being serviced, they appear to depart in accord with a Poisson process with a mean of μ ships per day.   Unfortunately, tidal changes, shift changeovers, and facility maintenance close the port for an average of 4 hr each day.   What is the expected number of ships, L_q, waiting for service?

Hint: See Example 11-20.   A Poisson process with intensity μ is characterized by the fact that the time between arrivals is exponential with mean $1/\mu$.

11-30.   Pedestrians arrive at an intersection as a Poisson process with mean rate λ.   They remain in the queue until a suitable gap occurs in the traffic stream, and they then cross as a group.   Suppose "adequate gaps" occur in Poisson fashion also, with mean rate μ.   Use recursion relations to derive the steady-state probabilities for the number of waiting pedestrians.

11-31.   Units arrive at a queue in pairs but are served singly.   The arrival rate is Poisson with mean λ pairs per hr, while service is exponential with rate μ units per hr ($\mu > 2\lambda$).

(a) Derive the steady-state probabilities for the number n in the system.

(b) Find $L = E(n)$.

(c) Find the optimum service rate μ_0 if the expected cost per unit time of a server who works at rate μ is μC_s and the cost per unit time for each person of the queue is C_w, where C_s and C_w are constants.

11-32.   Along the lines of Example 11-12 for a single-server system with balking, let $p_n = 1 - \epsilon_n$ be the balking probability for one who encounters n people in the system upon arrival.   Conclude that the steady-state solution to the appropriate difference equation is

$$P_n = \left(\frac{\lambda}{\mu}\right)^n P_0 \prod_{i=0}^{n-1} \epsilon_i$$

Study the case

$$\epsilon_i = \frac{N - i}{N(1 + i)} \qquad i = 0, 1, \ldots, N$$

where N is a constant integer.   Other aspects of balking appear in an article by Haight [26].

11-33.   When a queuer leaves before he is served, he is said to have reneged.   Let $r_n \Delta t$ be the probability that reneging takes place $\{t, t + \Delta t\}$ when there are n units in the system. Derive the appropriate difference-differential equations for the single-server queue with Poisson input and exponential service.   Solve the steady-state equations for P_n, the steady-state probabilities.

Determine the optimal service rate μ_0 if the cost per unit time of service is $C_s\mu$ and the cost of waiting per unit time for each member of the queue is C_w. (Assume $r_i = r$ for all i.)

11-34. Trucks at a small warehouse use a single dock for loading, each crew loading its own truck. When the dock is in use, waiting crews assist in loading the truck in service. Loading time for one crew varies exponentially with a mean of 18 per 24-hr day, and the average loading time is inversely proportional to the number of crews loading a truck. Trucks arrive in Poisson fashion at an average rate of one per hour. What is the average time a crew spends at the warehouse? ◆

11-35. Using the Pollaczek-Khintchine and related formulas [Eqs. (46) and (47)], derive these expectations for the single-server queue with Erlang service distributions (see Sec. 9-8):

$$L_q = \frac{m+1}{2m} \frac{\lambda^2}{\mu(\mu - \lambda)}$$

$$L = \frac{m+1}{2m} \frac{\lambda^2}{\mu(\mu - \lambda)} + \frac{\lambda}{\mu} = L_q + \frac{\lambda}{\mu}$$

$$W_q = \frac{m+1}{2m} \frac{\lambda}{\mu(\mu - \lambda)} = \frac{L_q}{\lambda}$$

$$V_s = \frac{m+1}{2m} \frac{\lambda}{\mu(\mu - \lambda)} + \frac{1}{\mu} = W_q + \frac{1}{\mu}$$

where m denotes the specific member of the Erlang family.

11-36. How long can a pilot expect to wait in a holding pattern if planes arrive in Poisson fashion at an average rate of 20 per hr and if it takes 2 min to land an airplane once clearance to land is received? What if the time-to-land distribution is gamma with a common mean and variance of 2?

11-37. Dump trucks transport aggregate from an original source to stockpiles at the concrete plant for a dam. The piles are fed by dumping from timber trestles, which the trucks must back onto because the canyon walls do not allow room for forward turnarounds. Arrivals at the dump site are Poisson, with a mean frequency of 7 min. The time for dumping and turnaround is approximately gamma with a mean of 3 min and variance of 2 min². What is the average waiting time? The contractor would install a second dumping trestle if arrivals wait an average of 3 min or more before dumping. What average arrival rate would justify the second trestle?

11-38. A sea lab expedition is equipped with a redundant number ($m > 1$) of a particular instrument. Only one instrument is used at a time, and its time to failure is exponential with mean of 6 hr. A single repairman maintains the instruments, and his repair time is exponential with mean of 4 hr ($\mu_n = 4$; $n = 1, \ldots, m$). If stock-out (all m instruments inoperable) costs about \$50 per hr and if deterioration of unused instruments is estimated at \$1 per hr per unit, how many of the instruments, m, should be carried?

11-39. Consider customers arriving at a service station in Poisson fashion with mean $\lambda = 1$. Their service times follow a gamma law. Let X_n be the number of customers in the queue immediately following the nth service. Derive a recursion relation in terms of Z_{n+1}, the number of arrivals during the $(n + 1)$st service.

(a) Determine the probability function for Z_n.

(b) Form the transition matrix for the X_n (Sec. 11-3).

(c) For the case of the finite queue $N = 5$, solve for the steady-state probabilities. Assume the service time distribution to have a mean and variance of 2.

11-40. Customers arrive at a service station in Poisson fashion with mean arrival rate of $\lambda = 10$ per hr. Service time is assumed to be exponential with mean rate $\mu = 15$ per hr. Assuming that the process begins at time $t = 0$ with no one in the system, i.e., $n = 0$, formulate a Monte Carlo to determine the average waiting time of the Nth customer.

Simulate a single trial for the first 11 customers, and compare the transient average waiting time of the second through the eleventh customer with steady-state solutions.

11-41. For the finite-parallel-server queue of Sec. 11-5, deduce the following expectations:

$$L_q = \frac{\lambda\mu(\lambda/\mu)^k}{(k-1)!(k\mu-\lambda)^2} P_0$$

$$L = L_q + \frac{\lambda}{\mu}$$

$$W_q = \frac{\mu(\lambda/\mu)^k}{(k-1)!(k\mu-\lambda)^2} P_0$$

$$V_s = W_q + \frac{1}{\mu}$$

11-42. An electric circuit supplies m welders. The probability that a welder not using current will demand current in $\{t, t + \Delta t\}$ is $\lambda\Delta t$. Similarly, the probability that a welder using current will relinquish service in the next instant is $\mu\Delta t$. The parameters λ and μ are the same for each welder. Deduce the functions λ_n and μ_n. Derive the steady-state equations for the probabilities, and conclude that

$$P_n = \binom{m}{n}\left(\frac{\lambda}{\lambda+\mu}\right)^n \left(\frac{\mu}{\lambda+\mu}\right)^{m-n} \qquad n = 0, 1, \ldots, m$$

(This problem is adapted from [1] and [18].)

11-43. For the case of two parallel channels, derive the equations for q_1 and q_2 given in Example 11-18. For the case $\epsilon_1 = \epsilon_2 = 1/2$, derive the steady-state probabilities

$$P_n = \left(\frac{\lambda}{\mu_1+\mu_2}\right)^n \frac{(\mu_1+\mu_2)^2}{\mu_1\mu_2} P_0 \qquad n = 1, 2, \ldots$$

with

$$P_0 = \frac{2(\mu_1+\mu_2-\lambda)\mu_1\mu_2}{(\mu_1+\mu_2)^3} \qquad \lambda < \mu_1 + \mu_2$$

11-44. Deduce the probabilities for two channels in series, as given by Eqs. (54a) to (54c). Using them, conclude that the average number in the system is

$$E(n_1 + n_2) = \frac{\rho_1}{1-\rho_1} + \frac{\rho_2}{1-\rho_2}$$

and that

$$E(n_1 - 1) = \frac{\rho_1^2}{1-\rho_1}$$

11-45. In a parking lot with N spaces, the incoming traffic is Poisson with intensity λ, but only so long as empty spaces are available. The length of stay is exponential with mean μ. Find the appropriate differential equations for the probabilities $P_n(t)$ of finding exactly n spaces occupied. What are the steady-state probabilities for the number of cars in the lot [18]?

11-46. The number of vehicles arriving at a toll station follows a Poisson law with mean six vehicles per minute. Given that the average cost of customer delay, C_w, is \$2 per hr per vehicle and the cost of tollbooth operation, C_s, is \$4 per hr per booth, how many booths should be provided? Identical exponential service rates with mean three vehicles per minute are assumed.

If nighttime driving reduces the arrival rate to two vehicles per minute and if $C_w = \$1.50$ per hr per vehicle and $C_s = \$4$ per hr per booth, what is the optimal number of booths?

11-47. A company has in its factory N separate facilities to which workmen come for service. The arrival rates at each are $\lambda_1, \lambda_2, \ldots, \lambda_N$. A total service rate μ is available and can be arbitrarily divided so that $\mu = \sum_{i=1}^{N} \mu_i$. What division of μ into $\mu_1, \mu_2, \ldots, \mu_N$ will minimize the total waiting time in the system when $N = 3$?

11-48. Two single-server facilities operate with Poisson arrivals and exponential service with respective means of $\lambda_1' = 2$ per min, $\lambda_2' = 3$ per min, and $\mu_i', i = 1, 2$. The total expected cost per hour at each facility is

$$K_i = A_i + C_s \mu_i' + C_w L_i \qquad i = 1, 2$$

where the total cost consists of the fixed costs $A_1 = \$10$ per hr and $A_2 = \$15$ per hr, the service costs $C_s = 30\cancel{c}$ per service, and the delay costs $C_w = \$4$ per hr per queuer.

(a) Find the service rates μ_{10}' and μ_{20}' for minimum expected cost of operating both facilities.

(b) Calculate the savings from combining the two facilities into a single parallel-service queue operated with optimal service rates $\mu' = \mu_{11}' = \mu_{21}'$, an arrival rate of $\lambda = \lambda_1 + \lambda_2$, the same unit cost as before for service and delay, and a fixed cost of $A = \$25$ per hr.

(c) When is it preferable to operate a single-server queue with rate $\mu = 2\mu'$ and the same parameters (λ, A, C_s, C_w) instead of the parallel arrangement?

11-49. For the job shop of Prob. 11-48, assume the service area to be rectangular as shown in the figure. Include travel costs $C_T = \$4$ per hr per arrival in the preceding cost equation, and rework parts a and b for comparison. Assume an average arrival's velocity to be 2.5 ft per sec, travel to be orthogonal, and $f_i(x, y) = \dfrac{\lambda_i}{A} (i = 1, 2)$. Travel time $t = 2T$.

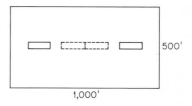

11-50. An open-pit mine operation is to be expanded through the lease of ten 30-ton dump trucks and a matching shovel capacity. Trucks will be assumed to arrive for loading in a Poisson fashion at mean rate $3m$ per hr, where m is the number of trucks in transit. The total hourly cost (operating and rental) of a truck is \$25.

The two available alternatives for leasing shovels are illustrated in the table. Which alternative minimizes total expected cost?

	Option A	Option B
Number of shovels	1	2
Est. hourly cost	\$140	\$80 each
Avg. loading rate (exponential)	30 trucks/hr	15 trucks/hr (each)

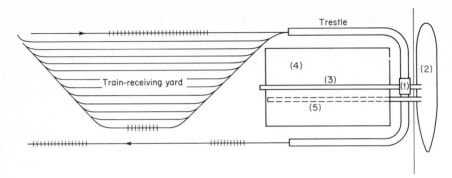

Fig. 11-22   Ore-loading post components.

11-51. A port facility transfers iron ore from trains to ships (Fig. 11-22). Rotary car dumper (1) empties the railcars into ship (2). When no ship is in dock, ore can be stock-piled by bridge conveyor (3) for subsequent transfer to the ship by reclaiming belt (5), located in a tunnel under the stockpile (4). A ship may be loaded simultaneously from the car dumper and the reclaiming belt.

     For the given data, outline a Monte Carlo simulation to determine the optimal reclaiming-belt capacity (tons per hour) and whether a single or double car dumper should be used. Assume 8% interest is required on investment.

Trains: Forty 90-ton carloads arrive every 6 hr. Assume that $6\frac{2}{3}$ cars arrive per hour. There is no demurrage charge for cars in the receiving yard.

Ships: 43,200-ton-capacity ships arrive in Poisson fashion at a mean rate of one ship per 72 hr. Cost of ship time during loading and waiting is $150 per hr.

	Car dumper	
	Single	*Double*
Capacity	15 cars/hr	30 cars/hr
Initial cost	$130,000	$230,000
Oper. and maint.	$25/operating hr	$40/operating hr
Salvage after 30 yr	0	0

Reclaiming Belt:
     Initial cost—$100 per ton per hr capacity
     Operation and maintenance—$0.015 per ton per hr used
     Salvage—$0 at 30 years

REFERENCES

1. Adler, H. A., and K. W. Miller: A New Approach to Problems in Electrical Engineering, *AIEE Trans.*, vol. 65, pp. 630–632, 1946.
2. Ancker, U. C., Jr., and A. V. Gafarian: Some Queueing Problems with Balking and Reneging—I and II, *Operations Res.*, vol. 11, pp. 88–100 and 929–937, 1963.

3. Ang, A., and M. Amin: Reliability of Structures and Structural Systems, *Proc. ASCE*, vol. 94, no. EM9, April, 1968.

4. Ashton, W. D.: "The Theory of Road Traffic Flow," John Wiley & Sons, Inc., New York, 1966.

5. Barlow, R., and F. Proschan: "Mathematical Theory of Reliability," John Wiley & Sons, Inc., New York, 1965.

6. Bazovsky, I.: "Reliability Theory and Practice," Prentice-Hall, Inc., Englewood Cliffs, N.J., 1961.

7. Bellman, R., and S. Dreyfus: Dynamic Programming and the Reliability of Multi-component Devices, *Operations Res.*, vol. 6, no. 2, March–April, 1958.

8. Caughey, T.: Derivation and Application of the Fokker Planck Equation to Discrete Nonlinear Dynamic Systems Subjected to White Random Excitation, *J. Acoustical Soc. Amer.*, vol. 35, no. 11, November, 1963.

9. Chow, V. T.: "Handbook of Applied Hydrology," McGraw-Hill Book Company, New York, 1964.

10. Conway, R. W., and W. L. Maxwell: A Queueing Model with State Dependent Service Rate, *J. Ind. Eng.*, vol. 12, pp. 132–136, 1961.

11. Conway, R. W., W. L. Maxwell, and L. W. Miller: "Theory of Scheduling," John Wiley & Sons, Inc., New York, 1968.

12. Cornell, C. A.: Bounds on the Reliability of Structural Systems, *Proc. ASCE*, vol. 93, no. ST1, February, 1967.

13. Cox, D. R., and Miller, H. D.: "The Theory of Stochastic Processes," John Wiley & Sons, Inc., New York, 1965.

14. Dawson, R. F., and H. W. Michael: Analysis of On-ramp Capacities by Monte Carlo Simulation, *Highway Res. Record* 118, pp. 1–20, 1966.

15. Drew, D. R.: "Traffic Flow Theory and Control," McGraw-Hill Book Company, New York, 1968.

16. Edie, L. C.: Traffic Delay at Toll Booths, reprinted in C. W. Churchman, R. L. Ackoff, and E. L. Arnoff, "Introduction to Operations Research," John Wiley & Sons, Inc., New York, 1957.

17. Edie, L. C., R. Herman, and R. Rothery: "Vehicular Traffic Science," Elsevier Publishing Company, Amsterdam, 1967.

18. Feller, W.: "Introduction to Probability Theory and Its Applications," 3d ed., vol. I, John Wiley & Sons, Inc., New York, 1968.

19. Fiering, M. B.: Queueing Theory and Simulation in Reservoir Design, *Proc. ASCE*, vol. 87, no. HY6, pp. 39–86, November, 1961.

20. Freudenthal, A. M., J. M. Garrelts, and M. Shinozuka: The Analysis of Structural Safety, *Proc. ASCE*, vol. 92, no. ST1, pp. 267–325, February, 1966.

21. Gabriel, K. R., and J. Neumann: A Markov Chain Model for Daily Rainfall Occurrence at Tel Aviv, *Quart. J. Roy. Meteorol. Soc.*, vol. 88, pp. 90–95, 1962.

22. Gerlough, D. L., and D. G. Capelle (eds.): An Introduction to Traffic Flow Theory, *Highway Res. Board Spec. Rep.* 79, 1964.

23. Goddard, L. S.: "Mathematical Techniques of Operational Research," Addison-Wesley Publishing Company, Inc., Reading, Mass., 1963.

24. Gosling, W.: "The Design of Engineering Systems," John Wiley & Sons, Inc., New York, 1962.

25. Hahn, G. J., and S. S. Shapiro: "Statistical Models in Engineering," John Wiley & Sons, Inc., New York, 1967.

26. Haight, F.: Queueing with Balking, *Biometrica*, pp. 360–369, 1957.

27. Haight, T.: "Mathematical Theories of Traffic Flow," Academic Press, Inc., New York, 1963.

28. Haugen, E. B.: "Probabilistic Approaches to Design," John Wiley & Sons, Inc., New York, 1968.
29. Hillier, F. S.: Economic Models for Industrial Waiting Line Problems, *Management Sci.*, vol. 10, pp. 119–130, 1963.
30. Hillier, F. S., and G. Lieberman: "Introduction to Operations Research," Holden-Day, Inc., Publishers, San Francisco, 1967.
31. Kendall, D. G.: Some Problems in the Theory of Dams, *J. Roy. Statist. Soc.*, ser. B, vol. 19, pp. 297–312, 1957.
32. Krick, E. V.: "An Introduction to Engineering and Engineering Design," John Wiley & Sons, Inc., New York, 1965.
33. Langbein, W. B.: Queueing Theory and Water Storage, *Proc. ASCE*, vol. 84, no. HY, pp. 1811–1824, October, 1958.
34. Little, J. D. C.: A Proof for the Queueing Formula $L = \lambda W$, *Operations Res.*, vol. 9, pp. 383–387, May, 1961.
35. Little, J. D., B. V. Martin, and J. T. Morgan: Synchronizing Traffic Signals for Maximal Bandwidth, *Highway Res. Record* 118, pp. 21–47, 1966.
36. Lloyd, D. K., and M. Lipow: "Reliability: Management, Methods, and Mathematics," Prentice-Hall, Inc., Englewood Cliffs, N.J., 1962.
37. Lomax, K. S.: Business Failures: Another Example of Failure Data, *J. Am. Statist. Ass.*, vol. 49, pp. 847–852, December, 1954.
38. Mangelsdorf, T. M.: Waiting Line Theory Applied to Manufacturing Problems, in E. H. Bowman and R. B. Fetter, "Analyses of Industrial Operations," Richard D. Irwin, Inc., Homewood, Il., 1959.
39. Montgomery, M. M., and W. R. Lynn: Analysis of Sewage Treatment Systems by Simulation, *Proc. ASCE*, vol. 90, no. SA1, pp. 73–97, February, 1964.
40. Moore, E. F., and C. E. Shannon: Reliable Circuits Using Less Reliable Relays, *J. Franklin Inst.*, vol. 262, September, 1956.
41. Moran, P. A. P.: A Probability Theory of Dams and Storage Systems, *Australian J. Appl. Sci.*, vol. 5, pp. 116–124, 1954.
42. Moran, P. A. P.: "The Theory of Storage," John Wiley & Sons, Inc., New York, 1959.
43. Morse, P. M.: "Queues, Inventories and Maintenance," John Wiley & Sons, Inc., New York, 1958.
44. Moses, F., and D. E. Kinser: Optimum Structural Design with Failure Probability Constraints, *AIAA J.*, vol. 5, June, 1967.
45. O'Shea, J. B., G. N. Slutkin, and L. R. Shaffer: An Application of the Theory of Queues to the Forecasting of Shovel-Truck Fleet Productions, *Construct. Res. Ser. Rep.* 3, Department of Civil Engineering, University of Illinois, 1964.
46. Palm, C.: The Distribution of Repairmen in Servicing Automatic Machines, *Industri-tidning en Norden*, vol. 75, pp. 75–80, 90–94, and 119–123, 1947.
47. Pieruschka, E.: "Principles of Reliability," Prentice-Hall, Inc., Englewood Cliffs, N.J., 1963.
48. Prabhu, N. U.: "Queues and Inventories," John Wiley & Sons, Inc., New York, 1965.
49. Rosenblueth, E.: Probabilistic Design to Resist Earthquakes, *Proc. ASCE*, vol. 90, no. EM5, pp. 189–220, October, 1964.
50. Ruiz-Pala, E., C. Avila-Beloso, and W. Hines: "Waiting-line Models," Reinhold Publishing Corporation, New York, 1967.
51. Saaty, T. L.: "Mathematical Methods of Operations Research," McGraw-Hill Book Company, New York, 1959.
52. Saaty, T. L.: "Elements of Queueing Theory," McGraw-Hill Book Company, New York, 1961.

53. Sandler, G. H.: "System Reliability Engineering," Prentice-Hall, Inc., Englewood Cliffs, N.J., 1963.
54. Sasieni, M., A. Yaspan, and L. Friedman: "Operations Research—Methods and Problems," John Wiley & Sons, Inc., New York, 1959.
55. Scott, R. F.: "Principles of Soil Mechanics," Addison-Wesley Publishing Company, Inc., Reading, Mass., 1963.
56. Shaffer, L. R., and A. Brooks: Queueing Models for Production Forecasts of Construction Operations, *Dept. Civil Eng. Tech. Rep.*, University of Illinois, 1969.
57. Shinozuka, M.: Probability of Structural Failure under Random Loading, *Proc. ASCE*, vol. 90, no. EM5, pp. 147–170, October, 1964.
58. Shooman, M. L.: "Probabilistic Reliability—An Engineering Approach," McGraw-Hill Book Company, New York, 1968.
59. Spaugh, J. M.: The Use of the Theory of Queues in the Optimal Design of Certain Construction Operations, *Natl. Sci. Found. Grant Tech. Rep.*, NSF G 15933, Department of Civil Engineering, University of Illinois, 1962.
60. Von Neumann, J.: Probabilistic Logics and Synthesis of Reliable Organisms from Unreliable Components, *Ann. Math. Studies*, no. 34, Princeton University Press, Princeton, N.J., 1956.
61. Wax, N.: "Selected Papers on Noise and Stochastic Processes," Dover Publications, Inc., New York, 1954.
62. Wohl, M., and B. V. Martin: "Traffic Systems Analysis for Engineers and Planners," McGraw-Hill Book Company, New York, 1967.
63. Wylie, C. R.: "Advanced Engineering Mathematics," McGraw-Hill Book Company, New York, 1966.
64. Yang, C. Y., and R. Toland: A Random Walk Model in Random Vibration, *Dept. Civil Eng. Tech. Rep.*, University of Delaware, 1969.

12
Operational Techniques for Random Models

This chapter provides an introduction to operational (transform) techniques and their application to symbolic models. Section 12-1 defines the transforms known as the *generating* and *characteristic functions*. These transforms are used for sums of independent random variables. Sections 12-2 and 12-3 exploit these transforms for sums of fixed and random numbers of independent random variables and provide insights into the random processes. Section 12-4 defines the *Mellin transform* and illustrates its use for products of independent random variables. Extensions to quotients, powers, and linear combinations of random variables are indicated. Several applications of transform techniques are mentioned. However, most civil-engineering-oriented research utilizing them is still in early stages.

12-1 GENERATING AND CHARACTERISTIC FUNCTIONS

Generating and characteristic functions are ways to represent probability functions. Consider the sequence of probabilities $p_0, p_1, \ldots$ for the events that the random variable $X = 0, 1, \ldots$, respectively. The *generating function* is defined by

$$G(s) = \sum_{k=0}^{\infty} p_k s^k \tag{1}$$

where s is the arbitrary transform variable. Since s is arbitrary, it is convenient to restrict it to the unit interval, $0 \leqslant s \leqslant 1$, to ensure convergence of the series in Eq. (1). Therefore, a generating function will always exist for any sequence of probabilities for nonnegative discrete random variables.

The corresponding *characteristic function* for the same random variable X described by the same probabilities is defined by

$$\phi(u) = \sum_{k=0}^{\infty} p_k e^{iuk} \tag{2'}$$

where u is the transform variable and $i = \sqrt{-1}$. Comparing Eqs. (1) and (2'), one notes that replacing e^{iu} by s changes the characteristic function into the generating function. The reason for two transform functions is that Eq. (2') conveniently generalizes for continuous random variables as

$$\phi(u) = \int_{\text{all } x} e^{iux} f(x) \, dx \tag{2}$$

where $f(x)$ is the density function. Note that Eq. (2) defines the Fourier transform; probabilists have simply renamed it the characteristic function. The generating-function format is inconvenient when X is a continuous random variable and is therefore reserved for integer-valued random variables.

Every generating function is unity for $s = 1$. Similarly, every characteristic function is unity for $u = 0$. Note that generating and characteristic functions can be regarded as expected values of the random variables s^X and e^{iuX}, respectively. That is,

$$E(s^X) = G(s) \quad \text{and} \quad E(e^{iuX}) = \phi(u) \tag{3}$$

For the moment, we shall confine our attention to the generating function, although there are many similarities between the two transforms. Consider a two-valued random variable X described by the sequence of probabilities $p_0, p_1, 0, \ldots$ corresponding to $X = 0, 1, 2, \ldots$. Clearly, $p_0 + p_1 = 1$ and the generating function is

$$G(s) = p_0 + p_1 s$$

Next, consider the sequence of probabilities $p_0 = e^{-\nu}, p_1 = \nu e^{-\nu}, p_2 = (\nu^2/2!) e^{-\nu}, \ldots$, that is, the Poisson law. The generating function, according to Eq. (1), is

$$G(s) = \sum_{k=0}^{\infty} \frac{\nu^k}{k!} e^{-\nu} s^k = e^{-\nu} \sum_{k=0}^{\infty} \frac{(\nu s)^k}{k!} = e^{\nu(s-1)}$$

Table 12-1 Generating functions

Probability function	Definition and range	Generating function
Binomial	$\binom{n}{k} p^k q^{n-k} \quad k = 0, 1, \ldots$	$(q + ps)^n$
Poisson	$\dfrac{v^k}{k!} e^{-v} \quad k = 0, 1, \ldots$	$e^{v(s-1)}$
Geometric	$pq^k \quad k = 0, 1, 2, \ldots$	$p(1 - qs)^{-1}$
Negative binomial	$\binom{r + k - 1}{k} p^r q^k \quad k = 0, 1, \ldots \left(\dfrac{p}{1 - qs}\right)^r$	

The generating functions in Table 12-1 have been derived in this fashion. Problems 12-1 and 12-2 call for the calculation of several generating functions.

The correspondence between the probability sequence and its generating function is unique. This ensures, for example, that $e^{v(s-1)}$ is a generating function for a Poisson law with parameter v and that only a Poisson law can lead to that generating function. However, suppose that one has a generating function not listed in Table 12-1. How are the probabilities determined? By expanding the generating function in a Maclaurin series, as in Eq. (1), the coefficients of the powers of s are the desired probabilities. This process is called *inversion*.

Generating functions serve three important purposes. First, they are used in the solution of difference and differential equations (see Appendix 5). Second, they are a convenient source of moments of the random variable. Third, they possess a *convolution property*, to be defined shortly.

Differentiation of Eq. (1) with respect to s is permissible since the summation is with respect to k, that is,

$$\frac{dG(s)}{ds} = \sum_{k=0}^{\infty} k p_k s^{k-1}$$

Setting $s = 1$ yields the expected value of X, that is,

$$\left.\frac{dG(s)}{ds}\right|_{s \to 1} = \sum_{k=0}^{\infty} k p_k = E(X) \tag{4}$$

In other words, *the derivative of the generating function evaluated at $s = 1$ is the mean.* A second differentiation yields

$$\frac{d^2 G(s)}{ds^2} = \sum_{k=0}^{\infty} k(k - 1) p_k s^{k-2}$$

and for $s = 1$,

$$\frac{d^2 G(s)}{ds^2}\bigg|_{s\to 1} = \sum_{k=0}^{\infty} k(k-1)p_k = E[X(X-1)] = E(X^2) - E(X)$$

The variance (Sec. 8-6) is given by

$$\text{Var}(X) = \left\{\frac{d^2 G(s)}{ds^2} + \frac{dG(s)}{ds} - \left[\frac{dG(s)}{ds}\right]^2\right\}\bigg|_{s\to 1} \tag{5}$$

For example, for the Poisson law

$$G(s) = e^{v(s-1)}$$
$$G'(s) = v e^{v(s-1)}$$
$$G''(s) = v^2 e^{v(s-1)}$$

where the primes denote differentiation with respect to s. Using Eqs. (4) and (5) for the Poisson law yields $E(X) = \text{var}(X) = v$, in accord with the results in Chap. 8. The expectations corresponding to the probability functions in Table 12-1 can be calculated in this manner and verified with the calculations in Chap. 8. Next, consider our primary justification for using generating functions, namely, convolution properties for sums of independent random variables.

Let Y be the sum of two independent discrete-valued random variables, X_1 and X_2, that is, $Y = X_1 + X_2$. Let $a_0, a_1, \ldots$ and $b_0, b_1, \ldots$ be the sequence of probabilities for $X_1 = 0, 1, \ldots$ and $X_2 = 0, 1, \ldots$, respectively. Using the techniques in Chap. 9 for symbolic models, the sequence of probabilities $c_0, c_1, \ldots$ for $Y = 0, 1, \ldots$ can be determined. Specifically, the probability that Y assumes a value k is the union of events $\{x_1 = 0, x_2 = k\}$, $\{x_1 = 1, x_2 = k - 1\}, \ldots, \{x_1 = k, x_2 = 0\}$:

$$P\{y = k\} = c_k = \sum_{j=0}^{k} P\{x_1 = j \text{ and } x_2 = k - j\}$$

$$= \sum_{j=0}^{k} P\{x_1 = j\} P\{x_2 = k - j\}$$

$$= a_0 b_k + a_1 b_{k-1} + \cdots + a_{k-1} b_1 + a_k b_0$$

for $k = 0, 1, \ldots$. Note that the independence and mutually exclusive properties of the events have been used.

Now let the generating functions $A(s)$ and $B(s)$ correspond to the probabilities $a_0, a_1, \ldots$ and $b_0, b_1, \ldots$, respectively. Consider the product

$$A(s) B(s) = (a_0 + a_1 s + \cdots)(b_0 + b_1 s + \cdots)$$

Carrying out the series product, the coefficient of s^k is

$$a_0 b_k + a_1 b_{k-1} + \cdots + a_{k-1} b_1 + a_k b_0$$

This is exactly c_k, the probability that the sum $Y = X_1 + X_2$ assumes the value $k, k = 0, 1, \ldots$. Letting $C(s)$ denote the generating function for the sequence of probabilities $c_0, c_1, \ldots$, we express the convolution property by

$$C(s) = A(s)\, B(s) \tag{6}$$

The convolution property significantly extends the applications of probability, and the topics of this chapter depend upon it.

In Chap. 9 we concluded that the sum of two independent Poisson variables with parameters ν_1 and ν_2 is also a Poisson variable with parameter $\nu_1 + \nu_2$. Using Eq. (6), the proof is trivial:

$$e^{\nu_1(s-1)}\, e^{\nu_2(s-1)} = e^{(\nu_1+\nu_2)\,(s-1)}$$

which is a Poisson generating function because of the uniqueness property. A similar result holds for the binomial law. Problems 12-1 to 12-5 serve as exercises.

The previous result can be generalized to the sum of any fixed number of independent integer-valued random variables. Thus the sum Y_n,

$$Y_n = X_1 + X_2 + \cdots + X_n \tag{7}$$

where $X_1, \ldots, X_n$ are independent random variables with associated generating functions $A_1(s), A_2(s), \ldots, A_n(s)$, has the associated generating function $C(s)$, given by

$$C(s) = A_1(s)\, A_2(s)\, \cdots\, A_n(s) \tag{8}$$

To see this, imagine that Eq. (7) is written $Y_n = X_n + Y_{n-1}$, where $Y_{n-1} = X_1 + \cdots + X_{n-1}$. The generating function for Y_n is the product of $A_n(s)$ and the generating function for Y_{n-1}. But Y_{n-1} can be written as $X_{n-1} + Y_{n-2} = X_1 + \cdots + X_{n-2}$. Its generating function is $A_{n-1}(s)$ times the generating function for Y_{n-2}, and so on, to yield Eq. (8).

In addition to the need for generating functions in applications, they furnish a deeper insight into random phenomena and the probability functions which describe them. For example, from Eq. (8) one concludes by inspection that the sum of any number n of independent Poisson variables with parameters $\nu_1, \nu_2, \ldots, \nu_n$ is also a Poisson variable with parameter $\nu_1 + \nu_2 + \cdots + \nu_n$. Consider the binomial law, which describes the outcome of n independent and identical Bernoulli trials (experiments). This can be described by the sum, Eq. (7), of n zero-one random variables with respective trial probabilities q and p. The one-trial generating function, by Eq. (1), is $(q + ps)$ and the n-fold convolution is $(q + ps)^n$, which is the generating function for the binomial law (see Table 12-1).

Example 12-1 Maintaining an automatic toll facility An automatic toll facility operates properly from day to day with probability p.

With probability q it fails to operate and requires repair. Assume that daily operation is an independent random variable and that a repaired facility can be considered as new. The random time T before the first failure is described by the geometric law, that is,

$$p_k = P\{T = k\} = p^k q \qquad k = 0, 1, \ldots$$

and the generating function is

$$G_1(s) = \frac{q}{1 - ps}$$

The generating function for the random time of successful operation before the second failure, using Eq. (6), is

$$G_2(s) = \left(\frac{q}{1 - ps}\right)^2 = q^2 + 2q^2 ps + 3q^2 p^2 s^2 + \cdots$$

The term $(1 - ps)^{-1}$ is regarded as the sum of the geometric series $1 + ps + (ps)^2 + \cdots$. The coefficients of $s^0, s^1, s^2, \ldots$ are the respective probabilities of $0, 1, 2, \ldots$ days of proper operation prior to the second failure.

Generalizing, the generating function for the random number of days of proper operation prior to the rth failure is

$$G_r(s) = \left(\frac{q}{1 - ps}\right)^r$$

This is the generating function for the negative-binomial law. Thus the negative-binomial law describes a model for the discrete waiting time to the rth failure, $r = 1, 2, \ldots$. Note the distinction between the negative-binomial and binomial laws. For the latter, the number of trials is fixed and the number of failures is random; whereas for the former, the number of failures is fixed and the number of trials is random.

Example 12-2 Truncation errors In storing decimals in computer memory, a truncation is made without rounding. For example, $2/3 = 0.66666 \cdots$ is stored as 0.66666666 for eight-place limits. Thus, in adding two decimals, an eighth-place error of zero, one, or two units is possible as a result of the truncation. The probabilities associated with these errors are easily found using generating functions. Let the ninth-place digit be $X_1 = 0, 1, \ldots, 9$ with equal probability. Similarly, for the second decimal, let X_2 be the ninth-place digit.

We adopt the convention that the eighth-place error Y is

$$Y = \begin{cases} 0 & \text{if } X_1 + X_2 = 0 \text{ or } 1 \text{ or } 2 \text{ or } 3 \text{ or } 4 \\ 1 & \text{if } X_1 + X_2 = 5 \text{ or } 6 \text{ or} \cdots \text{ or } 14 \\ 2 & \text{if } X_1 + X_2 = 15 \text{ or } \cdots \text{ or } 18 \end{cases}$$

The generating functions for X_1 and X_2 are identical, namely,

$$\tfrac{1}{10}(s^0 + s^1 + \cdots + s^9)$$

The generating function for their sum, $X_1 + X_2$, by Eq. (6), is

$$(\tfrac{1}{10})^2 (s^0 + s^1 + \cdots + s^9)^2$$

Carrying out the square operation, the sum of the coefficients of s^0, s^1, s^2, s^3, and s^4 divided by 100 is the probability that $Y = 0$, and so on. In this way, the propagation of errors in numerical computations can be studied.

Now consider the characteristic function, defined by Eq. (2). Table 12-2 provides a listing for some well-known probability laws. To illustrate the calculation, consider the uniform law

$$f(x) = 1 \qquad 0 \leqslant x \leqslant 1$$

Its characteristic function is

$$\phi(u) = \int_0^1 e^{iux}\, dx = \frac{e^{iu} - 1}{iu}$$

Similarly, for the exponential law,

$$e(x) = \lambda e^{-\lambda x} \qquad x > 0$$

we have

$$\phi(u) = \int_0^\infty \lambda e^{iux} e^{-\lambda x}\, dx = \frac{\lambda}{iu - \lambda}$$

and so on.

Expected values are obtained from derivatives of characteristic functions in a manner similar to that for generating functions. Specifically,

$$\frac{d\phi(u)}{du} = \frac{d}{du} \int_{\text{all } x} e^{iux} f(x)\, dx = i \int xe^{iux} f(x)\, dx$$

$$\frac{d^2 \phi(u)}{du^2} = - \int_{\text{all } x} x^2 e^{iux} f(x)\, dx$$

Evaluating these derivatives at $u = 0$ yields the mean

$$E(X) = \frac{1}{i} \frac{d\phi(u)}{du}\bigg|_{u=0} \tag{9}$$

and variance

$$\text{Var}(X) = \left\{ -\frac{d^2 \phi(u)}{du^2} + \left[\frac{d\phi(u)}{du}\right]^2 \right\}_{u=0} \tag{10}$$

The reader should verify these formulas.

Table 12-2 Characteristic functions

Probability function	Definition and range	Characteristic function
Rectangular law	$r(x;a,b) = \dfrac{1}{b-a} \qquad a \leqslant x \leqslant b$	$\dfrac{e^{iub} - e^{iua}}{iu(b-a)}$
Normal law	$n(x;\mu,\sigma) = \dfrac{1}{\sqrt{2\pi}\sigma} e^{-(x-\mu)^2/2\sigma^2}$ $-\infty < x < \infty$	$\exp\left(iu\mu - \dfrac{\sigma^2 u^2}{2}\right)$
Exponential law	$e(x;\lambda) = \lambda e^{-\lambda x} \qquad x > 0$	$\left(1 - \dfrac{iu}{\lambda}\right)^{-1}$
Gamma law	$ga(x;\lambda,\alpha) = \dfrac{\lambda}{\Gamma(\alpha)} (\lambda x)^\alpha e^{-\lambda x}$ $x > 0; \; \alpha, \lambda > 0$	$\left(1 - \dfrac{iu}{\lambda}\right)^{-\alpha}$
Chi-square	$chi(x;n) = \dfrac{1}{2^{n/2}\,\Gamma(n/2)} x^{(n/2)-1} e^{-x/2} \qquad x > 0$	$(1 - 2iu)^{-n/2}$

The characteristic function possesses the same uniqueness property and the same convolution property for sums of independent random variables that the generating function possesses.   To illustrate the convolution property, let $Y = X_1 + X_2$, where X_1 and X_2 are independent random variables with respective density functions $f_1(x_1)$ and $f_2(x_2)$, $-\infty < x_1, x_2 < \infty$, and characteristic functions $\phi_1(u)$ and $\phi_2(u)$.   Let $g(y)$ be the density function for Y. Using the techniques of Chap. 9 for symbolic models, we have

$$q_1(y|x_2) = f_1(y - x_2) \qquad -\infty < y, x_2 < \infty$$

and

$$q_2(y,x_2) = f_1(y - x_2) f_2(x_2)$$

whence

$$q(y) = \int_{-\infty}^{\infty} f_1(y - x_2) f_2(x_2)\, dx_2$$

Multiplying both members of the last expression by e^{iuy} and integrating over y yields

$$\phi(u) = \int_{-\infty}^{\infty} e^{iuy} q(y)\, dy = \int_{-\infty}^{\infty} e^{iuy}\, dy \int_{-\infty}^{\infty} f_1(y - x_2) f_2(x_2)\, dx_2$$

$$= \int_{-\infty}^{\infty} \int_{-\infty}^{\infty} e^{iuy} f_1(y - x_2) f_2(x_2)\, dx_2\, dy$$

$$= \int_{-\infty}^{\infty} e^{iux} f_1(x_1)\, dx_1 \int_{-\infty}^{\infty} e^{iux} f_2(x_2)\, dx_2$$

$$= \phi_1(u)\, \phi_2(u)$$

as asserted. An alternative proof follows from an earlier remark that the characteristic function can be regarded as an expected value. Thus

$$\phi(u) = E(e^{iuY}) = E(e^{iu(X_1+X_2)}) = E(e^{iuX_1} e^{iuX_2})$$

$$= E(e^{iuX_1}) E(e^{iuX_2}) = \phi_1(u) \phi_2(u)$$

The result can be generalized to the sum of n independent random variables,

$$\phi(u) = \phi_1(u) \phi_2(u) \cdots \phi_n(u) \tag{11}$$

Example 12-3   Sum and difference of normal variables From Table 12-2, the characteristic function for a random variable with mean μ and variance σ^2 described by a normal law is

$$\phi(u) = \exp\left(i\mu u - \frac{\sigma^2 u^2}{2}\right)$$

For two normal variables with means μ_1, μ_2 and variances σ_1^2, σ_2^2, respectively, their sum has the characteristic function

$$\phi(u) = \exp\left(i\mu_1 u - \frac{\sigma_1^2 u^2}{2}\right)\exp\left(i\mu_2 u - \frac{\sigma_2^2 u^2}{2}\right)$$

$$= \exp\left[i(\mu_1 + \mu_2)u - \frac{\sigma_1^2 + \sigma_2^2}{2} u^2\right]$$

As in Prob. 9-14, we conclude that the sum of two independent normal variables is also a normal variable with mean $\mu_1 + \mu_2$ and variance $\sigma_1^2 + \sigma_2^2$. The result generalizes for the sum of any number of normal random variables.

Consider the difference of two random variables, $Y = X_1 - X_2$. The characteristic function for Y, $\phi(u)$, is

$$\phi(u) = E(e^{iuY}) = E(e^{iu(X_1-X_2)}) = E(e^{iuX_1}) E(e^{i(-u)X_2}) = \phi_1(u) \phi_2(-u)$$

In words, to find the characteristic function for the negative of a random variable, one simply replaces the transform variable by its negative. In the case of the two normal variables, we have

$$\phi(u) = \exp\left[i(\mu_1 - \mu_2)u - \frac{\sigma_1^2 + \sigma_2^2}{2} u^2\right]$$

The difference between two independent normal variables is also a normal variable with mean $\mu_1 - \mu_2$ and variance $\sigma_1^2 + \sigma_2^2$. This result is frequently used in structural reliability for the *margin of safety*. The margin of safety Q is defined as the difference between the random load L and the random resistance R, that is, $Q = L - R$. Random loads and resistances described by the normal law lead to a random safety margin also described by a normal law.

Using Eqs. (1) and (2), we can obtain the generating and characteristic functions from the probability functions. The reverse process, called *inversion*, is also important. For the generating function, we have mentioned that if the probability law is not apparent by inspection, one need only expand it in a Maclaurin series. Unfortunately, inversion of characteristic functions is not as simple as for generating functions. If there were an exhaustive table of characteristic functions, the inversion could be achieved by "looking it up." Otherwise, inversion can be accomplished by the complex integration,

$$f(x) = \frac{1}{2\pi} \int_{-\infty}^{\infty} e^{-iux} \phi(u)\, du$$

Fortunately, computer programs, so-called "fast Fourier transforms," are available to accomplish inversions numerically. Derivations and uniqueness of the inversion integral are beyond our scope.

12-2 SUMS OF FIXED NUMBERS OF INDEPENDENT RANDOM VARIABLES

In the last section we introduced generating and characteristic functions and illustrated the efficiency with which they enable one to treat sums of independent random variables $X_j, j = 1, \ldots, n$, as

$$Y = X_1 + X_2 + \cdots + X_n \tag{7}$$

For example, suppose that several pipelines empty into a main line and that the random flows X_j in the subsidiary lines arise from sources with known, or conveniently obtainable, probability functions. For the design of the main line, it is useful to have the probability function for the total flow Y, which is the sum of the flows in the subsidiary lines. In other applications, Y is the observed variable with known probability function, and insights are sought for the underlying processes described by the X_j's which give rise to it.

Summarizing results from Sec. 12-1, for integer-valued variables the generating function for Y in Eq. (7) is, as Eq. (8),

$$G(s) = \prod_{j=1}^{n} G_j(s)$$

where $G_j(s)$ is the generating function for X_j. For continuous as well as discrete random variables, the characteristic function for Y is

$$\phi(u) = \prod_{j=1}^{n} \phi_j(u) \tag{11}$$

In the special case where the X_j have identical probability functions, these relations become

$$G(s) = [G_j(s)]^n \quad \text{and} \quad \phi(u) = [\phi_j(u)]^n$$

respectively.

Linear combinations of independent random variables such as

$$Y = a_1 X_1 + a_2 X_2 + \cdots + a_n X_n \tag{12}$$

where $a_1, a_2, \ldots, a_n$ are constants, are easily handled. The characteristic function for Y is

$$\phi(u) = \prod_{j=1}^{n} \phi_j(a_j u) \tag{13}$$

That is, one simply uses Eq. (11), replacing u by $a_j u$ in the characteristic function for X_j. An easy way to see this result is to regard the characteristic function as the expectation

$$\phi_Y(u) = E(e^{iu(a_1 X_1 + \cdots + a_n X_n)})$$

$$= E\left(\prod_{j=1}^{n} e^{iu(a_j X_j)}\right)$$

$$= \prod_{j=1}^{n} E(e^{i(ua_j)X_j})$$

$$= \prod_{j=1}^{n} \phi_j(a_j u)$$

Since the random variables are independent, the interchange of the expectation and product operations is permitted.

Equation (12) is a useful generalization of Eq. (7). For example, $X_1, \ldots, X_n$ might be random variables which describe the (anticipated) dollar value of maintenance required by a structure over an n-year design life. The total dollar expenditure is given by Y in Eq. (7). However, sound engineering design of long-term facilities includes provision for the time value of money. The present-worth expenditure is correctly given by Eq. (12) with $a_j = \rho^j$, where ρ is the discount factor (Sec. 1-5). Thus, the characteristic function for the present worth of the future costs, Eq. (13), enables us to more meaningfully compare alternative designs. Another example of Eq. (12) might be random loads $X_1, \ldots, X_n$ at fixed positions $a_1, \ldots, a_n$ so that Y describes their random moment; or the $a_1, \ldots, a_n$ might be direction cosines of the random loads so that Y is the component total in a fixed direction. Equation (13), with X_j as the number of repetitions of load a_i, $i = 1, \ldots, n$, describes the total fatigue damage Y, using Miner's rule, which assumes linearly additive damage. Birnbaum and Saunders [2] have used Eqs. (7) and (13) to describe the total crack length at the end of n load cycles, and so on.

The mean and variance are obtained by differentiation in accordance with Eqs. (4) and (5). The calculations in the last section suggested that the sums of independent binomial, Poisson, and normal variables are also binomial, Poisson, and normal variables, respectively. Not very many known probability laws have this *regenerative property*. Other sums are well known, although they lack the regenerative property. For example, the sum of independent exponential variables is described by the gamma law, as mentioned in Chaps. 9 and 11. The discrete analog is that the sum of independent random variables, each described by the geometric law, is described by the negative-binomial law, as noted in the last section. Naturally, these results can also be derived by the methods of Chap. 9.

Example 12-4 Number of cars in collisions

Suppose that auto collisions are classified by the number of autos involved [6]. That is, let X_1 be the number of collisions involving a single car, X_2 the number of two-car collisions, and so on. By choosing $a_1 = 1$, $a_2 = 2$, etc., Y in Eq. (12) describes the total number of autos involved in all collisions. The characteristic function is

$$\phi(u) = \phi_1(u)\,\phi_2(2u)\,\cdots\,\phi_n(nu)$$

In this instance, the variables X_j are integers, so that Y is also an integer. For such instances a generating-function analog to Eq. (13) is sometimes preferred. Indeed, the characteristic function is easily obtained from the generating function by replacing s by e^{iu}, or vice versa, for integer-valued random variables. This means that e^{2iu} is replaced by $s^2, \ldots, e^{niu}$ by s^n, so that

$$G(s) = G_1(s)\,G_2(s^2)\,\cdots\,G_n(s^n)$$

Suppose that data support the assumption that the number of cars in each classification can be described by a Poisson law. Specifically, let the probability of X_j j-car collisions during a time t be a Poisson law with parameter $\lambda_j t, j = 1, 2, \ldots$. Using the last expression,

$$G(s) = e^{\lambda_1 t(s-1)}\, e^{\lambda_2 t(s^2-1)}\, \cdots$$

Let $\lambda = \lambda_1 + \lambda_2 + \cdots$, so that

$$\frac{\lambda_1}{\lambda} + \frac{\lambda_2}{\lambda} + \cdots = 1$$

Clearly,

$$G(s) = e^{\lambda t[h(s)-1]}$$

where $h(s)$ is the generating function for the sequence

$$0, \frac{\lambda_1}{\lambda}, \frac{\lambda_2}{\lambda}, \ldots$$

and hence

$$h(s) = \frac{\lambda_1}{\lambda} s + \frac{\lambda_2}{\lambda} s^2 + \cdots$$

Note that we have used the generating-function concept for a sequence of numbers which are not probabilities. However, since the sequence was chosen so that its sum is unity, convergence is ensured. Note also that the generating function is of the Poisson type with s replaced by $h(s)$. This is called a *generalized Poisson model*. The special case $h(s) = s$ corresponds to a sequence $0, 1, 0, 0, \ldots$, which, in turn, corresponds to considering only single-car collisions.

Generating functions are convenient for exploring limiting properties of probability functions. For example, consider the Poisson approximation to the binomial law, as in Sec. 8-5. First, the binomial generating function can be written $(q + ps)^n = [1 + p(s - 1)]^n$. We seek the limit for "rare" events, that is, $n \to \infty$, $p \to 0$, and $np \to \lambda$. Substituting, we have

$$\left[1 + \frac{v(s-1)}{n}\right]^n \stackrel{n \to \infty}{\longrightarrow} e^{v(s-1)}$$

which is the Poisson generating function. We are assuming, of course, that the limiting property of the generating function implies a similar limiting property for the probability law. A proof is beyond our scope, and the interested reader may consult texts such as Feller [6] and Gnedenko [9].

12-3 SUMS OF RANDOM NUMBERS OF INDEPENDENT RANDOM VARIABLES

Consider the sum

$$Y = X_1 + X_2 + \cdots + X_N \tag{14}$$

where the X_j are independent random variables whose number N is also a random variable. Such models are called *compound*. Their analyses are convenient because of operational techniques, and they lead to a variety of applications. As examples, the total damage Y in the linear accumulation model used by Crandall and Mark [4] is the sum of the random damages $X_1, X_2, \ldots$ at successive load applications; the number of contracts Y that a firm wins in a particular period is the sum of a random number of variables X_j with unit value if the jth contract is won and zero otherwise; the waiting time Y of an arrival when there are N units in the queue; the random total live load on a bridge where X_j is the load contributed by the jth vehicle; the random number Y of vehicles leaving a turnpike exit, where X_j is unity if the jth vehicle exists and zero otherwise and where N is the random number of approaching vehicles.

To derive the generating function $G(s)$ for Y in Eq. (14), observe that

$$P\{Y = k\} = \sum_{n=0}^{\infty} P\{Y = k, N = n\} = \sum_{n=0}^{\infty} P\{Y = k \mid N = n\} P\{N = n\} \ldots$$

$$k = 0, 1, \ldots$$

and multiply both sides of the equation by s^k and sum over k:

$$G(s) = \sum_{k=0}^{\infty} P\{Y = k\} s^k = \sum_{k=0}^{\infty} \sum_{k=0}^{\infty} P\{Y = k \mid N = n\} P\{N = n\} s^k$$

$$= \sum_{n=0}^{\infty} P\{N = n\} \sum_{k=0}^{\infty} P\{Y = k \mid N = n\} s^k$$

where the order of summation has been interchanged. Suppose that the X_j have a common generating function $G_j(s)$, all j. Therefore, the sum

$$\sum_{k=0}^{\infty} P\{Y = k \mid N = n\} s^k$$

is simply the generating function for the fixed number of random variables $N = n$. Using the convolution property, this sum can be replaced by

$$[G_j(s)]^n$$

and the generating function for Y becomes

$$G(s) = \sum_{n=0}^{\infty} [G_j(s)]^n P\{N = n\}$$

$$= p_0 + p_1 G_j(s) + p_2 [G_j(s)]^2 + \cdots$$

$$= G_N(G_j(s))$$

(15)

where $p_0, p_1, \ldots$ is the sequence of probabilities for the integer-valued variable N and $G_N(s)$ is its generating function. Thus we have the important result that the *generating function for the sum of a random number of independent identically distributed random variables is the compound function formed by replacing the argument in the generating function for the number of variables by the common generating function for the terms of the sum.*

Consider vehicles approaching an exit, and let q be the probability that the vehicle exits and $p(=1 - q)$ the probability that it remains in the main stream. Thus $q + ps$ is the common generating function for each approaching vehicle under the conditions cited, that is, $G_j(s) = q + ps$ for all j. Suppose that the probability for the number of approaching vehicles in a time t is Poisson with parameter λt, an observation which has been well documented for many classes of traffic [10]. From Eq. (15), the generating function for the number of vehicles remaining in the traffic stream, Y, is

$$G(s) = e^{\lambda t[(q+ps)-1]}$$

$$= e^{\lambda t p(s-1)}$$

This remarkable result asserts that the sum of a Poisson random number of binomial variables is also a Poisson variable. This is called the *preservation of the Poisson law under random selection*, and it helps to account for the many traffic studies which conclude traffic to be Poisson [17]. Note that not only does the main-road traffic remain Poisson (with a new parameter) but also the exit traffic is Poisson.

Using characteristic and generating function techniques, it is not difficult to illustrate an important preservation property of the exponential law. Recall that the exponential law often describes the service time in a queueing system. The total service time for a fixed number of services, provided service is continuously going on, is given by the sum of a fixed number of exponential variables. This sum is described by the gamma law, as we have noted. However, consider the time to complete a random number of services. For a single-server steady-state queue with Poisson arrivals, the probabilities for the number in the system, N, immediately after we arrive are given by the geometric law, Eq. (36) in Sec. 11-4,

$$P_n = \rho^n(1-\rho) \qquad n = 0, 1, 2, \ldots$$

where $\rho = \lambda/\mu$ is the traffic intensity and

$$G_N(s) = \frac{(1-\rho)s}{1-\rho s}$$

is the generating function. Now consider the total time T for the single server to complete the N services when he works according to an exponential law, $\mu e^{-\mu t}$, with characteristic function $(1 - iu/\mu)^{-1}$. Using Eq. (15), the characteristic function for T is

$$\phi(u) = \frac{(1-\rho)(1-iu/\mu)^{-1}}{1-\rho(1-iu/\mu)^{-1}} = \left(1 - \frac{iu}{\mu-\lambda}\right)^{-1}$$

which is also a characteristic function for an exponential law. Thus the sum of a random number of independent exponential variables with common parameter μ, when the random number is described by a geometric law with parameter $(1 - \rho)$, is also an exponential law with parameter $\mu(1 - \rho)$. This preservation property under random selection cannot be assumed to hold for other probability functions without verification.

Before considering more general compound processes, consider the mean and variance. By differentiating Eq. (15), we have the derivatives

$$\frac{dG(s)}{ds} = \frac{dG_N(G_j(s))}{dGj(s)} \frac{dG_j(s)}{ds}$$

$$\frac{d^2 G(s)}{ds^2} = \frac{d^2 G_N(G_j(s))}{d^2 G_j(s)} \left(\frac{dG_j(s)}{ds}\right)^2 + \frac{dG_N(G_j(s))}{dG_j(s)} \frac{d^2 G_j(s)}{ds^2}$$

Setting $s = 1$ and remembering the relationships in Sec. 11-1, we have

$$E(Y) = E(N)E(X_j) \tag{16}$$

and

$$\text{Var}(Y) = \text{var}(X_j)E(N) + \text{var}(N)[E(X_j)]^2 \tag{17}$$

These expressions are especially useful when the probability functions are not available. Equations (16) and (17) can serve as a basis for design. Crandall and Mark [4] used Eq. (16) in random vibration studies, and Yang et al. [20] have recently used Eqs. (16) and (17) in other damage models.

Example 12-5 Mean and variance of random damage Let d_j be the random damage due to the jth load cycle and $D(T)$ the total random damage due to a random number of load cycles in a time T, that is, $N(T)$. Thus,

$$D(T) = d_1 + d_2 + \cdots + d_{N(T)}$$

Clearly, from Eq. (16),

$$E[D(T)] = E[N(T)]E(d)$$

when the damages at each load cycle have a common distribution with mean $E(d)$ and variance $\text{var}(d)$. We are assuming that damage cycles are independent, i.e., that the action causing damage subsides between cycles. Also, from Eq. (17),

$$\text{Var}[D(T)] = \text{var}(d)E[N(T)] + \text{var}[N(T)](E[d])^2$$

A simple assumption is that the number $n(a)$ of load cycles of amplitude a to produce failure is given by

$$n(a) = \frac{c}{a^b}$$

where b and c are constants [4]. The damage due to a single load application of amplitude a, $d(a)$, is

$$d(a) = \frac{1}{n(a)} = \frac{a^b}{c}$$

For random amplitude, the cycle damage is also a random variable. The Rayleigh probability law,

$$ra(x;\sigma) = \frac{x}{\sigma^2}\exp\left(-\frac{x^2}{2\sigma^2}\right) \qquad x \geqslant 0$$

is often chosen to describe the random amplitude. The expected cycle damage is given by

$$E(d) = \frac{(\sqrt{2}\sigma)^b}{c}\,\Gamma\left(1 + \frac{b}{2}\right)$$

where σ is the parameter of the Rayleigh law. Also, the expected number of cycles might be assumed proportional to the duration T, that is,

$$E[N(T)] = \lambda_0 T$$

where λ_0 is a constant. Further details, including motivations for the assumptions, appear in references cited.

Example 12-6   Branching processes   Branching processes furnish an interesting use of generating functions for sums of random numbers of random variables. A population begins with a single member called the *zeroth generation*, that is, $Z_0 = 1$. The single member simultaneously gives rise to a random number of offspring Z_1, who comprise the first generation. The number in the second generation is the sum of the random numbers of offspring from each member of the first generation; that is, $Z_2 = X_1 + \cdots + X_{Z_1}$, where X_j is the random number of simultaneous offspring from the jth member of the immediately preceding generation. In this way, the branching process develops. These models have been extensively used to describe such phenomena as nuclear fission ([6], [14]). Clearly, generalizations are suggested, but often the accompanying analysis is difficult. A recent book by Harris [11] considers many aspects, but it is of an advanced character.

Consider the simplest case, in which the offspring are identical and independent within and among generations. Let $p_0, p_1, \ldots$ be the probabilities for the random numbers of offspring from any parent in any generation. We seek the probability generating functions for the numbers in successive generations and, in particular, the probability that the population eventually dies out. Even for this simple case, the analysis is not simple. The main results are:

1. The generating function for the number in the nth generation is $G_n(s) = G_{n-1}(G(s)) = G(G_{n-1}(s))$, where $G(s)$ is the generating function for the sequence $p_0, p_1, \ldots$.
2. The probability of eventual extinction is the smallest positive root of the equation $\alpha = G(\alpha)$. For $\mu \leqslant 1$, that root is unity; while for $\mu > 1$,

there is a unique root less than unity. Here, μ is the average number of offspring from any parent.

3. The expected number in the nth generation is μ^n.

Proofs of these assertions are left for the problems.

POISSON PROCESSES

Next we indicate some aspects of the model of Eq. (14) when the random variable N is governed by a Poisson law: these are the so-called *Poisson processes*. We proceed heuristically to illustrate the power of transform techniques. The Poisson law for the number of arrivals in a time t has the characteristic function

$$\phi_y(u) = e^{\lambda t(e^{iu}-1)}$$

where $i = \sqrt{-1}$, as before, and λ is the Poisson intensity, the mean number of arrivals per unit time. To anticipate more general circumstances, one might express the intensity as a function of time, $\lambda(t)$, so that the last characteristic function describes the special case $\lambda(t) = \lambda$. The general case corresponds to an arrival rate which changes in time and has the characteristic function

$$e^{\int_0^t \lambda(t')\,dt'(e^{iu}-1)} = e^{m(t)(e^{iu}-1)} \tag{18}$$

where $m(t) = \int_0^t \lambda(t')\,dt'$ is a nondecreasing function of t. Now, observe the term e^{iu} in the exponent. This is actually the characteristic function for a random variable which takes the value 1 with probability 1. Equation (18) describes a Poisson process with single arrivals. Suppose that the process is integer-valued, in the sense that arrivals may occur in groups of n, where n is a nonnegative integer-valued random variable with probabilities $p_1, p_2, \ldots$ for $n = 1, 2, \ldots$. This corresponds to a situation in which an arrival brings a random number of items for service. If $\phi(u)$ denotes the characteristic function for this random number, the preceding characteristic function is revised to read

$$\phi_y(u) = e^{m(t)[\phi(u)-1]} \tag{19}$$

the characteristic function for a *generalized Poisson process*. Actually, there is no restriction that $\phi(u)$ describe an integer-valued random variable. When $\phi(u)$ describes a continuous random variable, the process is called *compound Poisson*. A proof for the result in Eq. (19) is given in books on stochastic processes, such as Parzen [13].

Recently, Hasofer [12] has used the model of Eq. (14) to describe the live-load fluctuations in buildings. The live load on a designated area of the building is taken to be a random variable. Loads on non-overlapping equal areas are assumed to act independently with a common probability law. Using Poisson assumptions, the probability that a point load arises in a small area ΔA is $\lambda \Delta A$, where λ is the load density. The probability of more than a single point load in ΔA is assumed negligible. The number N_A of point loads in an area A is consequently given by the Poisson law

$$P\{N_A = k\} = \frac{(\lambda A)^k}{k!} e^{-\lambda A} \qquad k = 0, 1, \ldots$$

If the point loads are independent random variables X_j, with common characteristic function $\phi_j(u)$, $j = 1, 2, \ldots$, the characteristic function for the total load on the area A is

$$\phi(u) = e^{\lambda A[\phi_j(u) - 1]}$$

the generalized Poisson process of Eq. (19). For the point loads X_j, a Pareto probability law was used [12]; i.e., the density

$$pa(x;\alpha,r) = (r - 1)\,\alpha^{r-1}\,x^{-r} \qquad x \geqslant \alpha$$

where α and r are positive parameters.

We have thus far assumed that the random value associated with an occurrence (load, degree of damage, etc.) is time-independent. Suppose that the model of Eq. (14) is replaced by

$$Y = \omega(t,\tau_1,X_1) + \omega(t,\tau_2,X_2) + \cdots + \omega(t,\tau_N,X_N) \tag{20}$$

where X_j has been replaced by a function of X_j, the cumulative time t, and the time at which X_j occurred, τ_j. A typical *response function* might be $\omega(t,\tau_j,X_j) = \omega(t - \tau_j, X_j)$; that is, the response function depends upon the elapsed time since the occurrence of X_j at time τ_j. This model, Eq. (20), seems apt to describe the vibration amplitude at time t due to several random blasts of amplitudes $X_1, X_2, \ldots$ which occurred at times $\tau_1, \tau_2, \ldots$. Specific response functions for this case might be

$$\omega(t - \tau_j, X_j) = \begin{cases} 1 & 0 \leqslant t - \tau_j < X_j \\ 0 & \text{otherwise} \end{cases}$$

or

$$\omega(t - \tau_j, X_j) = \begin{cases} X_j - (t - \tau_j) & 0 < t - \tau_j < X_j \\ 0 & \text{otherwise} \end{cases}$$

The characteristic function corresponding to the model of Eq. (20) is

$$\phi(u) = \exp\left[\int_0^t E(e^{iu\omega(t,\tau_j,X_j)} - 1)\frac{dm(t)}{dt}\,dt\right] \tag{21}$$

This is called a *filtered Poisson process*. The model suggests an important variety of applications, as noted by Benjamin and Cornell [1].

Proofs of these remarks appear in Parzen [13]. As an example, we cite Tung's works ([18] and [19]), which describe the response of highway bridges to random vehicle loads using a filtered Poisson process. The number of vehicles to arrive in a period $(0,t)$, $N(t)$ is taken as Poisson:

$$P\{N(t) = n\} = \frac{(\lambda t)^n}{n!} e^{-\lambda t} \qquad t > 0$$

where λ is the mean arrival rate per unit time. The response at time t is described by the stationary filtered Poisson process

$$Y(t) = \sum_{j=0}^{N(t)} X(t - \tau_j)$$

where $X(t - \tau_j)$ is the influence function for the system's response at time t to the jth vehicle which passed at τ_j. The vehicles are assumed to be identical, and the bridge is considered to be a linearly damped system. The probability density function for the response and various expectations were obtained. More general considerations and further details appear in the references.

12-4 PRODUCTS OF INDEPENDENT RANDOM VARIABLES

Models for products of independent random variables are less well known than those for sums. This brief discussion suggests their promise for engineering applications. Consider the product model

$$Y = X_0 X_1 \cdots X_n \tag{22}$$

where $X_0, X_1, \ldots, X_n$ are independent random variables. Generally, for given probability functions of the independent random variables $X_0, X_1, \ldots, X_n$, the derived techniques of Chap. 9 can be used to obtain the probability function for Y. In this section transform techniques are used.

The model of Eq. (22) is apt when X_0 is an initial quantity and subsequent attenuations (magnifications) reduce (increase) X_0 by the successive fractional amounts X_1, X_2, etc. This helps to account for the use of products in describing hydrologic phenomena where, for example, the quantity of water changes by "percentages" due to evaporation or runoff, where "head" decreases proportionately, or where sediment is transported in streams. In breakage and collision processes, successive volumes and speeds are proportional to the values in the preceding state [1].

Equation (22) is a special case of the model

$$Y = X_0{}^a X_1{}^b \cdots X_n{}^m \tag{23}$$

where $a, b, \ldots, m$ are constants. If $a = b = \cdots = m = 1/(n + 1)$ in Eq. (23), then Y is the geometric mean of $X_0, X_1, \ldots, X_n$. Equations (22) and (23) are more versatile than they appear at first sight. For example, "increment" models,

$$Y_n - Y_{n-1} = Z_n\, Y_{n-1} \tag{24}$$

where Z_n is the random increment factor, or equivalently,

$$Y_n = (1 + Z_n)\, Y_{n-1}$$

and more generally,

$$Y_n = g(Z_n)\, Y_{n-1} \tag{25}$$

where $g(Z_n)$ is an arbitrary function, offer interesting possibilities. The model of Eq. (25), for example, has been used for fatigue studies, and the model of Eq. (24) describes the return on an investment of Y_{n-1} dollars at a rate Z_n. These ideas lead to a "multiplicative" type of branching process, in which every member of a generation has the same random number of offspring.

The *Mellin transform* has the same relation to products of independent random variables as the characteristic and generating functions do to sums. The Mellin transform corresponding to a positive-valued random variable X with density $f(x)$ is defined by

$$M(v) = \int_0^\infty x^{v-1} f(x)\, dx \tag{26}$$

where v is the transform variable. The restriction to nonnegative random variables is convenient but not essential [15]. Note that the Mellin transform can be regarded as the expected value of X^{v-1}, that is, $E(X^{v-1})$. The essential

Table 12-3   Mellin transforms

Probability function	Definition and range	Mellin transform
Rectangular law	$r(x) = 1 \qquad 0 \leqslant x \leqslant 1$	$\dfrac{1}{v}$
Log-normal law	$\dfrac{1}{\sqrt{2\pi}\sigma x} \exp\left[-\dfrac{(\ln x - m)^2}{2\sigma^2} \right] \qquad x > 0$	$\exp\left[m(v-1) + \tfrac{1}{2}\sigma^2 (v-1)^2 \right]$
Gamma law	$\dfrac{\lambda}{\Gamma(\alpha)} (\lambda x)^\alpha e^{-\lambda x} \qquad x > 0;\ \alpha, \lambda > 0$	$\dfrac{\Gamma(\alpha + v - 1)}{\Gamma(\alpha)}$ for $\lambda = 1$
Beta law	$\dfrac{\Gamma(\alpha + \beta + 2)}{\Gamma(\alpha + 1)\,\Gamma(\beta + 1)} x^\alpha (1 - x)^\beta$ $\alpha, \beta > -1;\ 0 \leqslant x \leqslant 1$	$\dfrac{\Gamma(\alpha + \beta + 2)\,\Gamma(\alpha + v)}{\Gamma(\alpha + \beta + v + 1)\,\Gamma(\alpha + 1)}$
Exponential law	$\lambda e^{-\lambda x} \qquad \lambda, x > 0$	$\lambda^{-1}\, \Gamma(v)$

difference is that here the random variable is the base and the transform variable the exponent, whereas for generating and characteristic functions the reverse is true. The Mellin transform conveniently yields the moments of $f(x)$ by successively setting $v = 2, 3, \ldots$. A brief listing of Mellin transforms appears in Table 12-3.

The Mellin transform derives its importance from the convolution property. Let X_1 and X_2 be independent nonnegative random variables with associated Mellin transforms $M_1(v)$ and $M_2(v)$. The Mellin transform for the product $Y = X_1 X_2$ is

$$M(v) = M_1(v) M_2(v)$$

A proof is not difficult [15]. An easy way to see the result is to use the expectation notation:

$$M(v) = E(Y^{v-1}) = E(X_1^{v-1} X_2^{v-1}) = E(X_1^{v-1}) E(X_2^{v-1}) = M_1(v) M_2(v)$$

A more detailed proof for discrete random variables is suggested in Prob. 12-17. As in the case of sums, generalizations follow for an arbitrarily fixed number of independent random variables, as in Eq. (22), to give

$$M(v) = M_1(v) M_2(v) \cdots M_n(v) \tag{27}$$

An argument similar to the one for sums can be used to conclude that for the product of a random number N of random variables, one has

$$M(v) = p_0 + p_1 M_1(v) + p_2 M_1(v) M_2(v) + \cdots$$

where $p_0, p_1, \ldots$ are the probabilities corresponding to $N = 0, 1, \ldots$. For the case where the X_j are identically distributed, $j = 1, 2, \ldots$, one can write

$$M(v) = G(M_j(v)) \tag{28}$$

where $G(s)$ is the generating function for the probabilities of the number of terms in the product, that is, $p_0, p_1, \ldots$, with the argument replaced by the common Mellin transform for the X_j, $i = 1, 2, \ldots$.

The log-normal law (see Table 12-3) has the same regenerative property for products as the binomial, Poisson, and normal laws do in the case of sums of independent random variables. That is, the product of n log-normal variables with parameters m_i and σ_i^2, $i = 1, 2, \ldots, n$, is also a log-normal variable with corresponding parameters $m_1 + m_2 + \cdots + m_n$ and $\sigma_1^2 + \sigma_2^2 + \cdots + \sigma_n^2$.

To illustrate the Mellin transform for models of Eq. (23), consider the term X_1^b and the expectation

$$E[(X_1^b)^{v-1}] = E(X_1^{b(v-1)+1-1}) = E(X_1^{v'-1})$$

where $v' = b(v - 1) + 1$. We conclude that the Mellin transform for the random variable $X_1{}^b$ is the Mellin transform for X_1 with v replaced by $v' = b(v - 1) + 1$. It follows that for the model of Eq. (23),

$$M(v) = M_0(a(v - 1) + 1) M_1(b(v - 1) + 1) \cdots M_n(m(v - 1) + 1) \qquad (29)$$

For example, a random mass M moving with a random velocity S has the random kinetic energy $Y = MS^2/2$. The Mellin transform for Y can be written immediately in terms of the transforms corresponding to M and S:

$$M(v) = (1/2)^{v-1} M_M(v) M_s(2v - 1)$$

The Mellin transform for the safety factor $\eta = R/S$, where R is the random resistance and S the random load, has been written [8]

$$M_\eta(v) = M_R(v) M_S(-v + 2)$$

Thus it is explicit that the model of Eq. (23) includes quotients as well as products.

While the product models of Eqs. (22) to (25) are both interesting and useful, they are limited because they make no provision for sums (and differences). Specifically, consider linear combinations of independent random variables such as

$$Y = X_{11} X_{12} + X_{21} X_{22} + \cdots + X_{n1} X_{n2} \qquad (30)$$

To treat this model by transform techniques, we use the Mellin transform for the products $X_{11} X_{12}, X_{21} X_{22}, \ldots, X_{n1} X_{n2}$ and the characteristic function for the sums. To do this, a relation between the Mellin transform and the characteristic function is needed. The Maclaurin expansion for the exponential function furnishes the key:

$$e^{iuX} = 1 + (iu) X + \frac{(iu)^2}{2!} X^2 + \cdots$$

$$= \frac{(iu)^0}{0!} X^0 + \frac{(iu)^1}{1!} X^1 + \cdots$$

Taking the expected value of both members (regarding X as the random variable) yields

$$E(e^{iuX}) = \sum_{v=1}^{\infty} \frac{(iu)^{v-1}}{(v - 1)!} E(X^{v-1})$$

or

$$\phi(u) = \sum_{v=1}^{\infty} \frac{(iu)^{v-1}}{(v - 1)!} M(v) \qquad (31)$$

While the expressions are not pleasing, and the inversions less so, we can formally write for the model of Eq. (30),

$$\phi(u) = \prod_{j=1}^{n} \sum_{v=1}^{\infty} \frac{(iu)^{v-1}}{(v-1)!} M_{j1}(v) M_{j2}(v) \tag{32}$$

Generalizations of Eq. (30) to include terms such as those of Eq. (23) can easily be achieved.

Consider possible applications of Eq. (30). The random forces $X_{11}, X_{21}, \ldots, X_{n1}$ may be acting at the random positions $X_{12}, X_{22}, \ldots, X_{n2}$ to yield the total moment Y; or Y may be the total reliability of a redundant system with independent components whose reliabilities are random variables; or perhaps Y is the random number of vehicles which pass through a series of traffic signals without stopping for a red signal, as suggested in Prob. 12-19. It is easy to derive transform expressions for the scalar and vector products of vectors [16].

Example 12-7   Scalar and vector products   In the case of the scalar product, one uses the model of Eq. (30) with $n = 3$ corresponding to the vectors $\mathbf{A} = X_{11}\,\boldsymbol{\epsilon}_1 + X_{21}\,\boldsymbol{\epsilon}_2 + X_{31}\,\boldsymbol{\epsilon}_3$ and $\mathbf{B} = X_{12}\,\boldsymbol{\epsilon}_1 + X_{22}\,\boldsymbol{\epsilon}_2 + X_{32}\,\boldsymbol{\epsilon}_3$, where $\boldsymbol{\epsilon}_1$, $\boldsymbol{\epsilon}_2$, and $\boldsymbol{\epsilon}_3$ are the unit vectors.   The scalar product $\mathbf{A} \cdot \mathbf{B}$ is Eq. (30) and has the characteristic function of Eq. (32) for $n = 3$.   In a similar manner, one concludes that the characteristic function for the component of the vector product $\mathbf{A} \times \mathbf{B}$ along $\boldsymbol{\epsilon}_k$ is

$$\phi_k(u) = \phi_{\psi(k+)}(u)\phi_{\psi(k-)}(-u)$$

where $\psi(k\pm) = X_{k\pm1} Y_{k\pm2}$ and

$$\phi_{\psi(k\pm)}(u) = \sum_{v=1}^{\infty} \frac{(iu)^{v-1}}{(v-1)!} M_{k\pm1}(v) M_{k\pm2}(v)$$

where k is the cyclic variable

Again, inversion techniques are generally needed to obtain the probability functions.   The inversion formula for the Mellin transform is

$$f(x) = \frac{1}{2\pi i} \int_{c-i\infty}^{c+i\infty} x^{-v} M(v) \, dv$$

as given in [5].

SUMMARY

This chapter treated more advanced techniques for developing random models. In Sec. 12-1, generating and characteristic functions were introduced and examples were provided to indicate their use. Sections 12-2 and 12-3 continued the development of random models comprised of sums of independent random variables. Section 12-4 briefly developed an operational technique, the Mellin transform, which is suitable for the development of random models that involve products of independent random variables.

PROBLEMS

12-1. Verify the generating functions for the discrete-valued probability laws in Table 12-1.

12-2. Let X be an integer-valued random variable with generating function $G(s)$. Calculate the generating functions for the sequence of probabilities corresponding to the:

    (a) Throw of a fair die
    (b) Random variable $X + 1$
    (c) Random variable $2X$ ◆

12-3. Verify the characteristic functions for the probability laws in Table 12-2.

12-4. Using characteristic functions, reconsider Probs. 9-10 and 9-11.

12-5. Use a limiting characteristic function argument to show that the Poisson law is an approximation to the normal law.

12-6. Show that a linear combination of normal variables is also a normal variable. ◆

12-7. Bernoulli trials with probabilities that change at each trial are known as Poisson trials. In a series of n trials, let $p_1, p_2, \ldots, p_n$ be the probabilities for "success" and $q_1, q_2, \ldots, q_n$ the corresponding probabilities for "failure," with $q_i = 1 - p_i$, $i = 1, 2, \ldots, n$. Write the generating function for Poisson trials without any calculations.

12-8. Derive the generating function for the steady-state probabilities of the queue in Prob. 11-27 for $c = 1$.

12-9. Derive the generating function for the probabilities corresponding to the random variable Z_n which describes the number of arrivals during a service time in Prob. 11-39.

12-10. Let a_n be the probability that n Bernoulli trials result in an even number of successes. Write a recursion relation for a_n. Show that the generating function is

$$S(s) = \sum_{n=0}^{\infty} a_n s^n = \frac{1 - s + ps}{(1 - s)[1 - (q - p)s]}$$

where p is the trial probability [6].

12-11. The number of automobile accidents in time t is a Poisson variable with mean λt. The damage per accident (rounded to the nearest dollar) is also random, and the probability of damage amounting to n dollars is denoted by p_n ($n = 0, 1, \ldots$). Find the generating function corresponding to the total dollar damage due to collisions in a time t.

12-12. Consider the "average bidder" of Sec. 10-2, and let $\phi(u)$ be the characteristic function for the win probability. Suppose that the number of bidders is a random variable described by the Poisson law. Without calculation, write the characteristic function for the win probability.

12-13. A branching process starts with one individual at $n = 0$. At $n = 1$, this individual has offspring whose number has the generating function $f(s)$. These offspring bear further offspring independently, at $n = 2$, each with generating function $g(s)$. They continue in this way, using $f(s)$ at odd n and $g(s)$ at even n. If $G_m(s)$ is the generating function for the population size at time $n = m$, express it in terms of $f(s)$ and $g(s)$.

12-14. (*a*) A traffic stream is described by the number of vehicles passing a given point in a time interval t and is found to be Poisson. Write the generating function.

(*b*) Closer examination indicates that the stream is made up of three types of vehicles, each arising according to a Poisson law with intensities λ_1, λ_2, and λ_3, respectively. Write the generating function for the total number of vehicles.

(*c*) The traffic stream is nearing an exit located immediately before a bridge. The probability that a vehicle of the first type leaves the stream is p_1, etc. Find the generating function for the number of vehicles of all types that remain in the traffic stream.

(*d*) Vehicles of the first type weigh w_1 tons, etc. Find the generating function for the total vehicle weight on the bridge assuming that it takes each vehicle approximately 2 min to cross.

12-15. The transform techniques of this chapter are limited to sums and products of *independent* random variables. Generalizations for sums of *dependent* or *independent* variables are possible. For example, let X_1 and X_2 be two dependent and discrete random variables with the joint probability p_{jk} that $X_1 = j$ and $X_2 = k$. The bivariate generating function is defined by

$$E(s_1{}^{X_1} s_2{}^{X_2}) = \sum_j \sum_k p_{jk} s_1{}^j s_2{}^k$$

where s_1 and s_2 are the transform variables.

When X_1 and X_2 are continuous dependent random variables with the joint density $f(x_1, x_2)$, a bivariate characteristic function is defined by

$$E(e^{i(u_1 X_1 + u_2 X_2)}) = \phi(u_1, u_2) = \int_{x_1} \int_{x_2} e^{i(u_1 x_1 + u_2 x_2)} f(x_1, x_2) \, dx_1 \, dx_2$$

where u_1 and u_2 are the transform variables.

Similarly, a bivariate Mellin transform is defined by

$$E(X_1{}^{v_1-1} X_2{}^{v_2-1}) = M(v_1, v_2) = \int_{x_1} \int_{x_2} x_1{}^{v_1-1} x_2{}^{v_2-1} f(x_1, x_2) \, dx_1 \, dx_2$$

where v_1 and v_2 are the transform variables.

Show that by setting $s_1 = s_2$ (or $u_1 = u_2$), one obtains the generating (or characteristic) function for the sum $X_1 + X_2$. Similarly, show that by setting $v_1 = v_2$, one obtains the Mellin transform for the product $X_1 X_2$. For further observations concerning bivariate generating functions, consult Feller [6].

12-16. Using Mellin transforms, show that the product of two independent rectangular random variables on the intervals $(0, a)$ and $(0, b)$ is governed by a logarithmic law with density

$$f(x) = c^{-1} \ln \frac{c}{x}$$

where $c = ab$.

12-17. Let $p_0 \delta_0^v + \sum_{x=1}^{\infty} x^{v-1} p_x$ define the Mellin transform for the discrete random variable $X = 0, 1, \ldots$ with respective probabilities $p_0, p_1, \ldots$, where δ_0^v is the Kronecker delta. Show that this Mellin transform possesses the convolution property for the product of two independent discrete variables.

12-18. Prove the convolution property for the product of two independent continuous nonnegative random variables.

12-19. Use the product model $Y = X_{11} X_{12} X_{13} + X_{21} X_{22} X_{23} + \cdots + X_{n1} X_{n2} X_{n3}$ to describe the number of vehicles which proceed through three signalized intersections without stopping for a red light. Let X_{ij} be zero if the light is red at the jth intersection, $j = 1,2,3$, for the ith car, $i = 1,\ldots,n$, and unity if it is green. Find the characteristic function for Y using probabilities p_{ij} for $X_{ij} = 1$ and $1 - p_{ij} = q_{ij}$ for $X_{ij} = 0$. Study degenerate cases.

12-20. Solve Prob. 10-15 using transform techniques.

12-21. For the branching process of Example 12-6, show that
$$G_n(s) = G_{n-1}(G(s)) = G(G_{n-1}(s)).$$

12-22. Let α_i be the probability that the branching process terminates at or before the ith generation. Show that the sequence of α_i increases monotonically to a limit α and satisfies the equation $\alpha = G(\alpha)$. Also conclude that α_i tends to the smallest positive root of this equation.

12-23. Use a graphical argument to show that the smallest positive root in Prob. 12-22 is unity for $\mu = G'(s)|_{s\to1} \leq 1$ and that there is a unique root less than unity when $\mu > 1$.

12-24. Generalize Eq. (16) to prove the last assertion in Example 12-6.

REFERENCES

1. Benjamin, J. R., and C. A. Cornell: "Probability, Statistics, and Decision for Civil Engineers," McGraw-Hill Book Company, New York, 1970.
2. Birnbaum, Z. W., and S. C. Saunders: A Probabilistic Interpretation of Miner's Rule, *SIAM J. Appl. Math.*, vol. 16, no. 3, May, 1968.
3. Cornell, C. A.: Stochastic Process Models in Structural Engineering, *Stanford Univ. Tech. Rep.* 34, 1964.
4. Crandall, S. H., and W. D. Mark: "Random Vibration in Mechanical Systems," Academic Press, Inc., New York, 1963.
5. Epstein, B.: Some Applications of the Mellin Transform in Statistics, *Ann. Math. Statist.*, vol. 19, 1948.
6. Feller, W.: "An Introduction to Probability Theory and Its Applications," vol. I, John Wiley & Sons, Inc., New York, 1968.
7. Feller, W.: "An Introduction to Probability Theory and Its Applications," vol. II, John Wiley & Sons, Inc., New York, 1966.
8. Freudenthal, A. M.: Safety, Reliability, and Structural Safety, *J. Struct. Div. ASCE*, March, 1961.
9. Gnedenko, V. V.: "An Introduction to Probability," Chelsea Publishing Company, New York, 1962.
10. Haight, F. A.: "Mathematical Theories of Traffic Flow," Academic Press, Inc., New York, 1963.
11. Harris, T. E.: "The Theory of Branching Processes," Springer-Verlag OHG, Berlin, 1963.
12. Hasofer, A. M.: Statistical Model for Live Floor Loads, *J. Struct. Div. ASCE*, vol. 94, pp. 2183–2196, October, 1968.
13. Parzen, E.: "Stochastic Processes," Holden-Day, Inc., Publishers, San Francisco, 1962.
14. Schroedinger, E.: Probability Problems in Nuclear Chemistry, *Proc. Roy. Irish Acad., Sec. A*, vol. 51, 1945.

15. Springer, M. D., and W. E. Thompson: The Distribution of Products of Independent Random Variables, *J. SIAM Appl. Math.*, vol. 14, May, 1966.
16. Stark, R. M.: Transform Techniques for Random Scalar and Vector Products, *Univ. Delaware Tech. Rep.*, August, 1969.
17. Stephenson, H. K.: Highway Bridge Live Loads Based on Laws of Chance, *Proc. ASCE*, vol. 83, no. ST4, 1957.
18. Tung, C. C.: Random Response of Highway Bridges to Vehicle Loads, *J. Eng. Mech. Div. ASCE*, vol. 93, pp. 79–94, October, 1967.
19. Tung, C. C.: Response of Highway Bridges to Renewal Traffic Loads, *J. Eng. Mech. Div. ASCE*, vol. 95, pp. 41–57, February, 1969.
20. Yang, C. Y., R. M. Stark, and C. Hsu: Fatigue of Non-linear structures in Non-stationary Random Vibration, *Proc. 1st Specialty Conf. Probability Eng.*, Purdue University, November, 1969.

Appendix 1
Curve Fitting

To summarize data analytically, i.e., to fit a curve, one chooses an *analytic form* and a *criterion of fit*. For example, measurements of the force y and corresponding elongation x of a simple spring of constant k, within the elastic range, are summarized by the analytic form $y = kx$. The analytic form may be linear, exponential, a higher-degree polynomial, etc. The criterion of fit may, for example, be to minimize the sum of the absolute deviations of the data from the curve, or perhaps to minimize the sum of the squares of the deviations.

If the unknown function described by the data is assumed analytic, a Taylor expansion exists. When discontinuities are suspected, other expansions are suggested. Generally, increasing the *degree* of the chosen polynomial (or truncated Taylor series) improves the accuracy of fit for the chosen criterion. The criterion of fit is chosen by considering the context in which the data originated and the techniques available for implementation. For example, a line which minimizes the sum of the deviations is undesirable because any number of lines may have a minimum total deviation and not pass close to the data points.

492

A more desirable criterion is to minimize the sum of the squares of the deviations, i.e., to obtain a *least-squares fit*.   Besides statistical justification, least squares is desirable because it is relatively easy to implement.   The least-squares criterion, however, tends to give undue weight to "bad points" since the error is measured by the square of the deviation.   If one is using "temperamental" equipment, for example, a least-squares criterion tends to be more sensitive to "bad" points than is desirable.   Also, a least-squares criterion equally weights equal deviations above and below the curve.   Such weighting is more appropriate for phenomenological data than for design data.   The cost of underdesign, predicted by the resulting line, may differ from that for overdesign.

Another criterion is to minimize the sum of the *absolute deviations* from the curve.   This seems like a reasonable criterion for practical purposes, although it is not widely used.   A probable reason is that only recently have convenient techniques for implementations become available.   We briefly describe techniques to fit least-squares and minimum absolute-deviation curves to the n measurements $(x_1, y_1), \ldots, (x_n, y_n)$.

LEAST-SQUARES CRITERION

The constants of the line $y = ax + b$ are sought so that the total square deviation is a minimum.   The deviation (error) in the ith measurement is $(y_i - ax_i - b)$, and the total square error E_s is

$$E_s = \sum_{i=1}^{n} (y_i - ax_i - b)^2 \tag{1}$$

The minimization of Eq. (1) requires that

$$\frac{\partial E_s}{\partial a} = \frac{\partial E_s}{\partial b} = 0$$

which yields

$$a = \frac{\sum x_i \sum y_i - n \sum x_i y_i}{(\sum x_i)^2 - n \sum x_i^2} \tag{2}$$

$$b = \frac{\sum x_i \sum x_i y_i - \sum y_i \sum x_i^2}{(\sum x_i)^2 - n \sum x_i^2} \tag{3}$$

Computer routines for least-squares fit are widely available.

The technique of least squares is applicable to polynomials of higher degree.   For example, consider

$$y = a_0 + a_1 x + a_2 x^2 + \cdots + a_n x^n \tag{4}$$

and the total square deviation

$$E_s = \sum_{i=1}^{n} (y_i - a_0 x_i - \cdots - a_n x_i^n)^2 \tag{5}$$

This is a linear function of the unknowns $a_0, a_1, \ldots, a_n$. They are determined by setting the partial derivatives of E_s in Eq. (5) equal to zero and solving simultaneously.

When data are of variable creditability, individual observations can be weighted. For example, 4 of 10 measurements are in a region where the measuring instrument is erratic. A possible set of weights is 0.80 for each point in the erratic region and 1.13 for each of the remaining six points, giving a weight total of 10. This means that the squares of the deviations for the temperamental points are multiplied by 0.80 and added to the other deviations multiplied by 1.13. In symbols, let $w_1, \ldots, w_n$ be the weights associated with the n data points such that $\sum_{i=1}^{n} w_i = n$ and $w_i \geqslant 0$ all i. The weighted least-squares deviation, analogous to Eq. (1), is

$$E_{ws} = \sum_{i=1}^{n} w_i (y_i - a x_i - b)^2 \tag{1'}$$

ABSOLUTE-DEVIATION CRITERION

The total absolute deviation E_{ad} is

$$E_{ad} = \sum_{i=1}^{n} |y_i - a x_i - b| = \sum_{i=1}^{n} [(y_i - a x_i - b) \, \mathcal{U}(y_i - a x_i - b)$$
$$+ (a x_i + b - y_i) \, \mathcal{U}(a x_i + b - y_i)] \tag{6}$$

where the step function $\mathcal{U}(y - c)$ is defined by

$$\mathcal{U}(y - c) = \begin{cases} 0 & y < c \\ 1 & y \geqslant c \end{cases}$$

The transformation, considered in Sec. 5-6,

$$y - c = u - v \begin{cases} u = 0 \text{ for } y < c \\ v = 0 \text{ for } y \geqslant c \end{cases} \quad u, v \geqslant 0$$

enables one to rewrite Eq. (6) as the linear objective

$$\text{Min:} \quad E_{ad} = \sum_{i=1}^{n} (u_i + v_i) \tag{7}$$

subject to the n linear constraints

$$u_i - v_i + a x_i + b = y_i \qquad i = 1, \ldots, n$$

and

$$a, b, u_i, v_i \geqslant 0$$

Equations (7) form the standard linear-programming form (Sec. 2-1).   Solutions are easily derived.   This technique can also be extended to higher-degree polynomials.

Individual measurements can also be weighted with an absolute-deviation criterion.   In addition, asymmetric weighting within the measurement, difficult with least squares, is easily accomplished here.   Let w_i' and w_i'' be asymmetric weights for deviations of the ith measurement above and below the curve.   The absolute deviation is

$$E_{wad} = \sum_{i=1}^{n} [w_i'(y_i - ax_i - b)\,\mathcal{U}(y_i - ax_i - b)$$

$$+ w_i''(ax_i + b - y_i)\,\mathcal{U}(ax_i + b - y_i)]$$

Using the above transformation yields

$$\text{Min:} \quad E_{wad} = \sum_{i=1}^{n} (w_i' u_i + w_i'' v_i)$$

with the constraints in Eq. (7) unchanged.   Problems 5-16 and 5-17 are exercises in curve fitting.

Appendix 2
Mathematical Induction

Propositions are formal statements of truth to be demonstrated.   Propositions can be general or particular.   Examples of general propositions are:

1.   All even numbers are divisible by 2.

2.   The sum of the first n integers is $\dfrac{n(n+1)}{2}$.

3.   The difference equation $f(x) = 2f(x-1)\cos\theta - f(x-2)$, $x \geqslant 3$, has the solution $f(x) = \cos x\theta$, $x = 1, 2, \ldots$.

Corresponding particular propositions are:

1'.   Fourteen is divisible by two.

2'.   The sum of the integers to $n = 5$ is given by $\dfrac{n(n+1)}{2} = \dfrac{5(6)}{2} = 15$.

3′. The difference equation $f(3) = 2f(2)\cos\theta - f(1)$ has the solution $f(3) = \cos 3\theta$.

Transitions from general propositions to particular ones are called *deductions*. Progressing from particular propositions to general ones is called *induction*. The second general proposition, for example, asserts that

$$1 = \frac{1(1+1)}{2} = 1 \qquad 1+2 = \frac{2(2+1)}{2} = 3 \qquad 1+2+3 = \frac{3(3+1)}{2} = 6$$

$$1+2+3+4 = \frac{(4)(4+1)}{2} = 10 \qquad 1+2+3+4+5 = \frac{5(5+1)}{2} = 15$$

These suggest the corresponding general proposition, which happens to be true, as we shall prove. Not all generalizations from particulars can be valid. For example, the quadratic expression $x^2 + x + 1$ was used by the mathematician Euler to generate prime numbers, i.e., numbers integrally divisible only by themselves and unity. For $x = 0, 1, \ldots, 39$, the expression generates primes; but for $x = 40$, $(40)^2 + 40 + 1 = 1{,}641$, which is no longer prime. Yet it is not feasible to study all particular cases. A method of reasoning called *mathematical induction* is a useful guide for some mathematical generalizations.

Mathematical induction is based upon the logical principle that a proposition is true for every $n = 2, 3, \ldots$ if it is true (1) for $n = 1$ and (2), assuming it is true for arbitrary n, for $n + 1$. A proof by mathematical induction requires proof of each of the following theorems.

Theorem 1   *The proposition is true for $n = 1$.*

Theorem 2   *The proposition is true for $n + 1$ if it is true for n, $n = 2, 3, \ldots$.*

For example, consider proposition 2 for sums of the positive integers. Theorem 1 holds since $[1(1 + 1)]/2 = 1$. To prove Theorem 2, given that $1 + 2 + \cdots + n = n(n + 1)/2$, we note that

$$1 + 2 + \cdots + n + (n + 1) = \frac{n(n + 1)}{2} + (n + 1)$$

This is also

$$\frac{(n + 1)(n + 2)}{2}$$

which proves Theorem 2 since the formula holds when n is replaced by $n + 1$. The reader can show that general proposition 3 is also true.

Proof by mathematical induction requires proof of Theorems 1 and 2. For example, if the proof of Theorem 1 is ignored, it is easy to conclude that every integer is equal to every other one. The hypothesis of Theorem 2 is $n = n + 1$. Adding unity to each member gives $n + 1 = n + 2$, and Theorem 2 is proved. The fallacy is that Theorem 1 has not been proved. To illustrate another fallacy, consider the sum

$$\frac{1}{1 \cdot 2} + \frac{1}{2 \cdot 3} + \cdots + \frac{1}{n(n+1)}$$

and assume it to be represented by

$$\frac{n+1}{3n+1}$$

For $n = 1$, we have

$$\frac{1}{1 \cdot 2} = \frac{1+1}{3(1)+1}$$

and Theorem 1 is proved. To prove Theorem 2, we assume the result is true for n. If the result is to be true for $n + 1$, we must have that

$$\frac{n+1}{3n+1} + \frac{1}{(n+1)(n+2)}$$

equals

$$\frac{(n+1)+1}{3(n+1)+1}$$

This is false; Theorem 2 cannot be proved, and thus the proposition cannot be true for every $n = 1, 2, \ldots$. Theorem 1 provides the entry, or particular proposition, and Theorem 2 provides the unlimited generalization of the proposition.

Many times in the preceding chapters we have cited mathematical induction to generalize particular propositions. We conclude by illustrating two of them. In the tandem design of Example 6-8, we had $H_1(c) = c$ and $H_2(c) = (c/2)^2$. Thus, Theorem 1 is proved. To prove Theorem 2, assume $H_n(c) = (c/n)^n$. Next,

$$H_{n+1}(c) = \max_{0 \leqslant c_{n+1} \leqslant c} [c_{n+1} H_n(c - c_{n+1})]$$

$$= \max_{0 \leqslant c_{n+1} \leqslant c} \left[c_{n+1} \left(\frac{c - c_{n+1}}{n} \right)^n \right]$$

Differentiating with respect to c_{n+1} yields the maximizing condition $c_{n+1} = c/(n + 1)$ and

$$H_{n+1}(c) = \left(\frac{c}{n + 1}\right)^{n+1}$$

Theorem 2 is proved, and the result holds for the positive integers.

The difference equation (35) in Sec. 11-4,

$$P_n = \rho P_{n-1} \qquad n = 1, 2, \ldots$$

gives $P_1 = \rho P_0$, so Theorem 1 is proved.   Assume that

$$P_n = \rho^n P_0$$

Substituting into the difference equation gives

$$P_{n+1} = \rho P_n = \rho^{n+1} P_0$$

so Theorem 2 is proved and the result holds for $n = 1, 2, \ldots$.

Further details appear in "The Method of Mathematical Induction," by I. S. Sominskii, Blaisdell Publishing Company, Waltham, Mass., 1961.

Appendix 3
Discrete Rate-of-return Factors[1]

$$\text{spcaf} = (l + i)^n \qquad \text{crf} = \frac{i(l + i)^n - l}{i}$$

$$\text{sppwf} = (l + i)^{-n} \qquad \text{uscaf} = \frac{(l + i)^n - l}{i}$$

$$\text{sfdf} = i[(l + i)^n - l] \qquad \text{uspwf} = \frac{(l + i)^n - l}{i(l + i)^n}$$

[1] These tables are adapted from G. A. Taylor, "Managerial and Engineering Economy," D. Van Nostrand Company, Inc., Princeton, N.J., 1964.

At 3% return

n	spcaf	sppwf	sfdf	crf	uscaf	uspwf
1	1.030	0.9709	1.00000	1.03000	1.000	0.971
2	1.061	0.9426	0.49261	0.52261	2.030	1.913
3	1.093	0.9151	0.32353	0.35353	3.091	2.829
4	1.126	0.8885	0.23903	0.26903	4.184	3.717
5	1.159	0.8626	0.18835	0.21835	5.309	4.580
6	1.194	0.8375	0.15460	0.18460	6.468	5.417
7	1.230	0.8131	0.13051	0.16051	7.662	6.230
8	1.267	0.7894	0.11246	0.14246	8.892	7.020
9	1.305	0.7664	0.09843	0.12843	10.159	7.786
10	1.344	0.7441	0.08723	0.11723	11.464	8.530
12	1.426	0.7014	0.07046	0.10046	14.192	9.954
15	1.558	0.6419	0.05377	0.08377	18.599	11.938
20	1.806	0.5537	0.03722	0.06722	26.870	14.877
25	2.094	0.4776	0.02743	0.05743	36.459	17.413
30	2.427	0.4120	0.02102	0.05102	47.575	19.600
40	3.262	0.3066	0.01326	0.04326	75.401	23.115
50	4.384	0.2281	0.00887	0.03887	112.797	25.730
∞	∞	∞	0	0	0.03000	∞	33.333

At 4% return

n	spcaf	sppwf	sfdf	crf	uscaf	uspwf
1	1.040	0.9615	1.00000	1.04000	1.000	0.962
2	1.082	0.9246	0.49020	0.53020	2.040	1.886
3	1.125	0.8890	0.32035	0.36035	3.122	2.775
4	1.170	0.8548	0.23549	0.27549	4.246	3.630
5	1.217	0.8219	0.18463	0.22463	5.416	4.452
6	1.265	0.7903	0.15076	0.19076	6.633	5.242
7	1.316	0.7599	0.12661	0.16661	7.898	6.002
8	1.369	0.7307	0.10853	0.14853	9.214	6.733
9	1.423	0.7026	0.09449	0.13449	10.583	7.435
10	1.480	0.6756	0.08329	0.12329	12.006	8.111
12	1.601	0.6246	0.06655	0.10655	15.026	9.385
15	1.801	0.5553	0.04994	0.08994	20.024	11.118
20	2.191	0.4564	0.03358	0.07358	29.778	13.590
25	2.666	0.3751	0.02401	0.06401	41.646	15.622
30	3.243	0.3083	0.01783	0.05783	56.085	17.292
40	4.801	0.2083	0.01052	0.05052	95.026	19.793
50	7.107	0.1407	0.00655	0.04655	152.667	21.482
∞	∞	0	0	0.04000	∞	25.000

At 5% return

n	spcaf	sppwf	sfdf	crf	uscaf	uspwf
1	1.050	0.9524	1.00000	1.05000	1.000	0.952
2	1.103	0.9070	0.48780	0.53780	2.050	1.859
3	1.158	0.8638	0.31721	0.36721	3.153	2.723
4	1.216	0.8227	0.23201	0.28201	4.310	3.546
5	1.276	0.7835	0.18097	0.23097	5.526	4.329
6	1.340	0.7462	0.14702	0.19702	6.802	5.076
7	1.407	0.7107	0.12282	0.17282	8.142	5.786
8	1.477	0.6768	0.10472	0.15472	9.549	6.463
9	1.551	0.6446	0.09069	0.14069	11.027	7.108
10	1.629	0.6139	0.07950	0.12950	12.578	7.722
12	1.796	0.5568	0.06283	0.11283	15.917	8.863
15	2.079	0.4810	0.04634	0.09634	21.579	10.380
20	2.653	0.3769	0.03024	0.08024	33.066	12.462
25	3.386	0.2953	0.02095	0.07095	47.727	14.094
30	4.322	0.2314	0.01505	0.06505	66.439	15.372
40	7.040	0.1420	0.00828	0.05828	120.800	17.159
50	11.467	0.0872	0.00478	0.05478	209.348	18.256
∞	∞	0	0	0.05000	∞	20.000

At 6% return

n	spcaf	sppwf	sfdf	crf	uscaf	uspwf
1	1.060	0.9434	1.00000	1.06000	1.000	0.943
2	1.124	0.8900	0.49544	0.54544	2.060	1.833
3	1.191	0.8396	0.31411	0.37411	3.184	2.673
4	1.262	0.7921	0.22859	0.22859	4.375	3.465
5	1.338	0.7473	0.17740	0.23740	5.637	4.212
6	1.419	0.7050	0.14336	0.20336	6.975	4.917
7	1.504	0.6651	0.11914	0.17914	8.394	5.582
8	1.594	0.6274	0.10104	0.16104	9.897	6.210
9	1.689	0.5919	0.08702	0.14702	11.491	6.802
10	1.791	0.5584	0.07584	0.13587	13.181	7.360
12	2.012	0.4970	0.05928	0.11928	16.870	8.384
15	2.397	0.4173	0.04296	0.10296	23.276	9.712
20	3.207	0.3118	0.02718	0.08718	36.786	11.470
25	4.292	0.2330	0.01823	0.07823	54.865	12.783
30	5.743	0.1741	0.01265	0.07265	79.058	13.765
40	10.286	0.0972	0.00646	0.06646	154.762	15.046
50	18.420	0.0543	0.00344	0.06344	290.336	15.762
∞	∞	0	0	0.06000	∞	16.667

At 8% return

n	spcaf	sppwf	sfdf	crf	uscaf	uspwf
1	1.080	0.9259	1.00000	1.08000	1.000	0.926
2	1.166	0.8573	0.48077	0.56077	2.080	1.783
3	1.260	0.7938	0.30803	0.38803	3.246	2.577
4	1.360	0.7350	0.22192	0.30192	4.506	3.312
5	1.469	0.6806	0.17046	0.25046	5.867	3.993
6	1.587	0.6302	0.13632	0.21632	7.336	4.623
7	1.714	0.5835	0.11207	0.19207	8.923	5.206
8	1.851	0.5403	0.09401	0.17401	10.637	5.747
9	1.999	0.5002	0.01008	0.16008	12.488	6.247
10	2.159	0.4632	0.06903	0.14903	14.487	6.710
12	2.518	0.3971	0.05270	0.13270	18.977	7.536
15	3.172	0.3152	0.03683	0.11683	27.152	8.559
20	4.661	0.2145	0.02185	0.10185	45.762	9.818
25	6.848	0.1460	0.01368	0.09368	73.106	10.675
30	10.063	0.0994	0.00883	0.08883	113.283	11.258
40	21.725	0.0460	0.00386	0.08386	259.057	11.925
50	46.902	0.0213	0.00174	0.08174	573.770	12.233
∞	∞	0	0	0.08000	∞	12.500

At 10% return

n	spcaf	sppwf	sfdf	crf	uscaf	uspwf
1	1.100	0.9091	1.00000	1.10000	1.000	0.909
2	1.210	0.8264	0.47619	0.57619	2.100	1.736
3	1.331	0.7513	0.30211	0.40311	3.310	2.487
4	1.464	0.6830	0.21547	0.31547	4.641	3.170
5	1.611	0.6209	0.16380	0.26380	6.105	3.791
6	1.772	0.5645	0.12961	0.22961	7.716	4.355
7	1.949	0.5132	0.10541	0.20541	9.487	4.868
8	2.144	0.4665	0.08744	0.18744	11.436	5.335
9	2.358	0.4241	0.07364	0.17364	13.579	5.759
10	2.594	0.3855	0.06275	0.16275	15.937	6.144
12	3.138	0.3186	0.04676	0.14676	21.384	6.814
15	4.177	0.2394	0.03147	0.13147	31.772	7.606
20	6.727	0.1486	0.01746	0.11746	57.275	8.514
25	10.835	0.0923	0.01017	0.11017	98.347	9.077
30	17.449	0.0573	0.00608	0.10608	164.494	9.427
40	45.259	0.0221	0.00226	0.10226	442.593	9.779
50	117.391	0.0085	0.00086	0.10086	1163.909	9.915
∞	∞	0	0	0.10000	∞	10.000

At 12% return

n	spcaf	sppwf	sfdf	crf	uscaf	uspwf
1	1.120	0.8929	1.00000	1.12000	1.000	0.893
2	1.254	0.7972	0.47170	0.59170	2.120	1.690
3	1.405	0.7118	0.29635	0.41635	3.374	2.402
4	1.574	0.6355	0.20923	0.32023	4.779	3.037
5	1.762	0.5674	0.15741	0.27741	6.353	3.605
6	1.974	0.5066	0.12323	0.24323	8.115	4.111
7	2.211	0.4523	0.09912	0.21012	10.089	4.564
8	2.476	0.4039	0.08130	0.20130	12.300	4.968
9	2.773	0.3606	0.06768	0.18768	14.776	5.328
10	3.106	0.3220	0.05698	0.17698	17.549	5.650
12	3.896	0.2567	0.04144	0.16144	24.133	6.194
15	5.474	0.1827	0.02682	0.14682	37.280	6.811
20	9.646	0.1037	0.01388	0.13388	72.052	7.469
25	17.000	0.0588	0.00750	0.12750	133.334	7.843
30	29.960	0.0334	0.00414	0.12414	241.333	8.055
40	93.051	0.0107	0.00130	0.12130	767.091	8.244
50	289.002	0.0035	0.00042	0.12042	2400.018	8.305
∞	∞	0	0	0.12000	∞	8.333

At 15% return

n	spcaf	sppwf	sfdf	crf	uscaf	uspwf
1	1.150	0.8696	1.00000	1.15000	1.000	0.870
2	1.322	0.7561	0.46512	0.61512	2.150	1.626
3	1.521	0.6575	0.28798	0.43798	3.472	2.283
4	1.749	0.5718	0.20027	0.35027	4.993	2.855
5	2.011	0.4972	0.14832	0.29832	6.742	3.352
6	2.313	0.4323	0.11424	0.26424	8.754	3.784
7	2.660	0.3759	0.09036	0.24036	11.067	4.160
8	3.059	0.3269	0.07285	0.22285	13.727	4.487
9	3.518	0.2843	0.05957	0.20957	16.786	4.772
10	4.046	0.2472	0.04925	0.19925	20.304	5.019
12	5.350	0.1869	0.02448	0.18448	29.002	5.421
15	8.137	0.1229	0.02102	0.17102	47.580	5.847
20	16.367	0.0611	0.00976	0.15976	102.444	6.259
25	32.919	0.0304	0.00470	0.15470	212.793	6.464
30	66.212	0.0151	0.00230	0.15230	434.745	6.566
40	267.863	0.0037	0.00056	0.15056	1779.090	6.642
50	1083.657	0.0009	0.00014	0.15014	7217.716	6.661
∞	∞	0	0	0.15000	∞	6.667

At 20% return

n	spcaf	sppwf	sfdf	crf	uscaf	uspwf
1	1.200	0.8333	1.00000	1.20000	1.000	0.833
2	1.440	0.6944	0.45455	0.65455	2.200	1.528
3	1.728	0.5787	0.27473	0.47473	3.640	2.106
4	2.074	0.4823	0.18629	0.38629	5.368	2.589
5	2.488	0.4019	0.13438	0.33438	7.442	2.991
6	2.986	0.3349	0.10071	0.30071	9.930	3.326
7	3.583	0.2791	0.07742	0.27742	12.916	3.605
8	4.300	0.2326	0.06061	0.26061	16.499	3.837
9	5.160	0.1938	0.04808	0.24808	20.799	4.031
10	6.192	0.1615	0.03852	0.23852	25.959	4.192
12	8.916	0.1122	0.02526	0.22526	39.581	4.439
15	15.407	0.0649	0.01388	0.21388	72.035	4.675
20	38.338	0.0261	0.00536	0.20536	186.688	4.870
25	95.396	0.0105	0.00212	0.20212	471.981	4.948
30	237.376	0.0042	0.00085	0.20085	1181.881	4.979
40	1469.772	0.0007	0.00014	0.20014	7343.858	4.997
50	9100.427	0.0001	0.00002	0.20002	45497.191	4.999
∞	∞	0	0	0.20000	∞	5.000

Appendix 4
Probability Tables

Random numbers[1]

09 73 25 33	76 53 01 35 86	34 67 35 48 76	80 95 90 90 17	39 29 27 49
54 20 48 05	64 89 47 42 96	24 80 52 40 37	20 63 61 04 02	00 82 29 16
42 26 89 53	19 64 50 93 03	23 20 90 25 60	15 95 33 47 64	35 08 03 36
01 90 25 29	09 37 67 07 15	38 31 13 11 65	88 67 67 43 97	04 43 62 76
80 79 99 70	80 15 73 61 47	64 03 23 66 53	98 95 11 68 77	12 17 17 68
06 57 47 17	34 07 27 68 50	36 69 73 61 70	65 81 33 98 85	11 19 92 91
06 01 08 05	45 57 18 24 06	35 30 34 26 14	86 79 90 74 39	23 40 30 97
26 97 76 02	02 05 16 56 92	68 66 57 48 18	73 05 38 52 47	18 62 38 85
57 33 21 35	05 32 54 70 48	90 55 35 75 48	28 46 82 87 09	82 49 12 56
79 64 57 53	03 52 96 47 78	35 80 83 42 82	60 93 52 03 44	35 27 38 84
52 01 77 67	14 90 56 86 07	22 10 94 05 58	60 97 09 34 33	50 50 07 39
80 50 54 31	39 80 82 77 32	50 72 56 82 48	29 40 52 42 01	52 77 56 78
45 29 96 34	06 28 89 80 83	13 74 67 00 78	18 47 54 06 10	68 71 17 78
68 34 02 00	86 50 75 84 01	36 76 66 79 51	90 36 47 64 93	29 60 91 01
59 46 73 48	87 51 76 49 69	91 82 60 89 28	93 78 56 13 68	23 47 83 41
48 11 76 74	17 46 85 09 50	58 04 77 69 74	73 03 95 71 86	40 21 81 65
12 43 56 35	17 72 70 80 15	45 31 82 83 74	21 11 57 82 53	14 38 55 37
35 09 98 17	77 40 27 72 14	43 23 60 02 01	45 52 16 42 37	96 28 60 26
91 62 68 03	66 25 22 91 48	36 93 68 72 03	76 62 11 39 90	94 40 05 64
89 32 05 05	14 22 56 85 14	46 42 75 67 88	96 29 77 88 22	54 38 21 45
49 91 45 23	68 47 92 76 86	46 16 28 35 54	94 75 08 99 23	37 08 92 00
33 69 45 98	26 94 03 68 58	70 29 73 41 35	53 14 03 33 40	42 05 08 23
10 48 19 49	85 15 74 79 54	32 97 92 65 75	57 60 04 08 81	22 22 20 64
55 07 37 42	11 10 00 20 40	12 86 07 46 97	96 64 48 94 39	28 70 72 58
60 64 93 29	16 50 53 44 84	40 21 95 25 63	43 65 17 70 82	07 20 73 17
19 69 04 46	26 45 74 77 74	51 92 43 37 29	65 39 45 95 93	42 58 26 05
47 44 52 66	95 27 07 99 53	59 36 78 38 48	82 39 61 01 18	33 21 15 94
55 72 85 73	67 89 75 43 87	54 62 24 44 31	91 19 04 25 92	92 92 74 59
48 11 62 13	97 34 40 87 21	16 86 84 87 67	02 07 11 20 59	25 70 14 66
52 37 83 17	73 20 88 98 37	68 93 59 14 16	26 25 22 96 63	05 52 28 25
49 35 24 94	75 24 63 38 24	45 86 25 10 25	61 96 27 93 35	65 33 71 24
54 99 76 54	64 05 18 81 59	96 11 96 38 96	54 69 28 23 91	23 28 72 95
96 31 53 07	26 89 80 93 54	33 35 13 54 62	77 97 45 00 24	90 10 33 93
80 80 83 91	45 42 72 68 42	83 60 94 97 00	13 02 12 48 92	78 56 52 01
05 88 52 36	01 39 09 22 86	77 28 14 40 77	93 91 08 36 47	70 61 74 29
17 90 02 97	87 37 92 52 41	05 56 70 70 07	86 74 31 71 57	85 39 41 18
23 46 14 06	20 11 74 52 04	15 95 66 00 00	18 74 39 24 23	97 11 89 63
56 54 14 30	01 75 87 53 79	40 41 92 15 85	66 67 43 68 06	84 96 28 52
15 51 49 38	19 47 60 72 46	43 66 79 45 43	59 04 79 00 33	20 82 66 85
86 43 19 94	36 16 81 08 51	34 88 88 15 53	01 54 03 54 56	05 01 45 11

[1] Reproduced from the RAND Corporation, "A Million Random Digits with 100,000 Normal Deviates," Glencoe Press, The Macmillan Company, New York, 1955.

Random normal numbers[1]
$\mu = 0$, $\sigma = 1$

	(1)	(2)	(3)	(4)	(5)	(6)	(7)
1	0 464	0.137	2.455	−0.323	−0.068	0.296	−0.288
2	0.060	−2.526	−0.531	−1.940	0.543	−1.558	0.187
3	1.486	−0.354	−0.634	0.697	0.926	1.375	0.785
4	1.022	−0.472	1.279	3.521	0.571	−1.851	0.194
5	1.394	−0.555	0.046	0.321	2.945	1.974	−0.258
6	0.906	−0.513	−0.525	0.595	0.881	−0.934	1.579
7	1.179	−1.055	0.007	0.769	0.971	0.712	1.090
8	−1.501	−0.488	−0.162	−0.136	1.033	0.203	0.448
9	−0.690	0.756	−1.618	−0.445	−0.511	−2.051	−0.457
10	1.372	0.225	0.378	0.761	0.181	−0.736	0.960
11	−0.482	1.677	−0.057	−1.229	−0.486	0.856	−0.491
12	−1.376	−0.150	1.356	−0.561	−0.256	0.212	0.219
13	−1.010	0.598	−0.918	1.598	0.065	0.415	−0.169
14	−0.005	−0.899	0.012	−0.725	1.147	−0.121	−0.096
15	1.393	−1.163	−0.911	1.231	−0.199	−0.246	1.239
16	−1.787	−0.261	1.237	1.046	−0.508	−1.630	−0.146
17	−0.105	−0.357	−1.384	0.360	−0.992	−0.116	−1.698
18	−1.339	1.827	−0.959	0.424	0.969	−1.141	−1.041
19	1.041	0.535	0.731	1.377	0.983	−1.330	1.620
20	0.279	−2.056	0.717	−0.873	−1.096	−1.396	1.047
21	−1.805	−2.008	−1.633	0.542	0.250	0.166	0.032
22	−1.186	1.180	1.114	0.882	1.265	−0.202	0.151
23	0.658	−1.141	1.151	−1.210	−0.927	0.425	0.290
24	−0.439	0.358	−1.939	0.891	−0.227	0.602	0.973
25	1.398	−0.230	0.385	−0.649	−0.577	0.237	−0.289
26	0.199	0.208	−1.083	−0.219	−0.291	1.221	1.119
27	0.159	0.272	−0.313	0.084	−2.828	−0.439	−0.792
28	2.273	0.606	0.606	−0.747	0.247	1.291	0.063
29	0.041	−0.307	0.121	0.790	−0.584	0.541	0.484
30	−1.132	−2.098	0.921	0.145	0.446	−2.661	1.045
31	0.768	0.079	−1.473	0.034	−2.127	0.665	0.084
32	0.375	−1.658	−0.851	0.234	−0.656	0.340	−0.086
33	−0.513	−0.344	0.210	−0.736	1.041	0.008	0.427
34	0.292	−0.521	1.266	−1.206	−0.899	0.110	−0.528
35	1.026	2.990	−0.574	−0.491	−1.114	1.297	−1.433
36	−1.334	1.278	−0.568	−0.109	−0.515	−0.566	2.923
37	−0.287	−0.144	−0.254	0.574	−0.451	−1.181	−1.190
38	0.161	−0.886	−0.921	−0.509	1.410	−0.518	0.192
39	−1.346	0.193	−1.202	0.394	−1.045	0.843	0.942
40	1.250	−0.199	−0.288	1.810	1.378	0.584	1.216

[1] Reproduced from the RAND Corporation, "A Million Random Digits and 100,000 Normal Deviates," Glencoe Press, The Macmillan Company, New York, 1955.

Unit normal table[1]

$n(z) = \dfrac{1}{\sqrt{2\pi}} e^{-\frac{1}{2}z^2}$ $-\infty < z < \infty$	$n(z)$	z	z	$-z$ z	$-z$ z
z	$n(z)$	$N(z)$	$R(z) = \displaystyle\int_z^\infty n(z)\,dz$	$2R(z)$	$1 - 2R(z)$
0.0	0.3989	0.5000	0.5000	1.0000	0.0
0.1	0.3970	0.5398	0.4602	0.9203	0.0797
0.2	0.3910	0.5793	0.4207	0.8415	0.1585
0.3	0.3814	0.6179	0.3821	0.7642	0.2358
0.4	0.3683	0.6554	0.3446	0.6892	0.3108
0.5	0.3521	0.6915	0.3085	0.6171	0.3829
0.6	0.3332	0.7257	0.2743	0.5485	0.4515
0.7	0.3123	0.7580	0.2420	0.4839	0.5161
0.8	0.2897	0.7881	0.2119	0.4237	0.5763
0.9	0.2661	0.8159	0.1841	0.3681	0.6319
1.0	0.2420	0.8413	0.1587	0.3173	0.6827
1.1	0.2179	0.8643	0.1357	0.2713	0.7287
1.2	0.1942	0.8849	0.1151	0.2301	0.7699
1.3	0.1714	0.9032	0.0968	0.1936	0.8064
1.4	0.1497	0.9192	0.0808	0.1615	0.8385
1.5	0.1295	0.9332	0.0668	0.1336	0.8664
1.6	0.1109	0.9452	0.0548	0.1096	0.8904
1.7	0.0940	0.9554	0.0446	0.0891	0.9109
1.8	0.0790	0.9641	0.0359	0.0719	0.9281
1.9	0.0656	0.9713	0.0287	0.0574	0.9426
2.0	0.0540	0.9772	0.0228	0.0455	0.9545
2.1	0.0440	0.9821	0.0179	0.0357	0.9643
2.2	0.0355	0.9861	0.0139	0.0278	0.9722
2.3	0.0283	0.9893	0.0107	0.0214	0.9786
2.4	0.0224	0.9918	0.0082	0.0164	0.9836
2.5	0.0175	0.9938	0.0062	0.0124	0.9876
2.6	0.0136	0.9953	0.0047	0.0093	0.9907
2.7	0.0104	0.9965	0.0035	0.0069	0.9931
2.8	0.0079	0.9974	0.0026	0.0051	0.9949
2.9	0.0060	0.9981	0.0019	0.0037	0.9963
3.0	0.0044	0.9987	0.0013	0.0027	0.9973
Fractiles					
1.2816	0.1755	0.9000	0.1000	0.2000	0.8000
1.6449	0.1031	0.9500	0.0500	0.1000	0.9000
1.9600	0.0584	0.9750	0.0250	0.0500	0.9500
2.0537	0.0484	0.9800	0.0200	0.0400	0.9600
2.3263	0.0267	0.9900	0.0100	0.0200	0.9800
2.5758	0.0145	0.9950	0.0050	0.0100	0.9900

[1] Adapted from G. A. Wadsworth and J. G. Bryan, "Introduction to Probability and Random Variables," McGraw-Hill Book Company, New York, 1962.

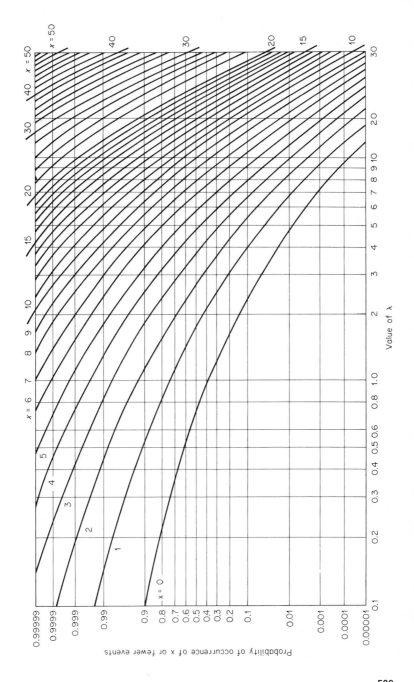

Probability of occurrence of x or fewer events

Value of λ

DISCRETE PROBABILITY FUNCTIONS[1]

Binomial

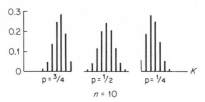

$$b(k;p,m) = \binom{n}{k} p^k q^{n-k} \qquad k = 0, 1, \ldots, n$$

$$0 \leqslant p \leqslant 1; q = 1 - p$$

$$E(X) = np \qquad \mathrm{var}(X) = npq$$

$$\phi(u) = (pe^{iu} + q)^n$$

Geometric

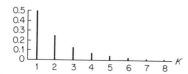

$$ge(k;q) = pq^k \qquad k = 0, 1, \ldots$$

$$0 \leqslant q \leqslant 1; p = 1 - q$$

$$E(X) = \frac{1-q}{p} \qquad \mathrm{var}(X) = \frac{q}{p^2}$$

$$\phi(u) = \frac{p}{1 - qe^{iu}}$$

[1] The figures, intended for qualitative purposes, are adapted from G. J. Hahn and S. S. Shapiro, "Statistical Models in Engineering," John Wiley & Sons, Inc., New York, 1967.

Hypergeometric

$$hy(k;r,m,n) = \frac{\binom{m}{k}\binom{n-m}{r-k}}{\binom{n}{r}} \qquad k = 0, 1, \ldots, r$$

$$r, m, n, \geqslant 0; \; r, m \leqslant n$$

Negative Binomial and Pascal

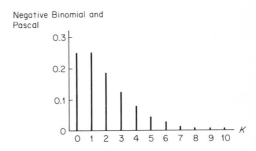

$$nb(k;q,r) = \binom{r+k-1}{k} p^r q^k \qquad k = 0, 1, \ldots$$

$$0 \leqslant q \leqslant 1; \; p = 1 - q; \; r = 1, 2, \ldots$$

$$E(X) = rqp^{-1} \qquad \text{var}(X) = rqp^{-2}$$

$$\phi(u) = \left(\frac{p}{1 - qe^{iu}}\right)^r$$

Poisson

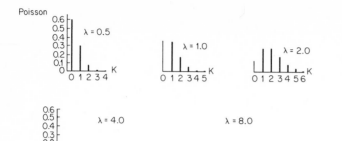

$$p(k;\nu) = \frac{\nu^k}{k!}e^{-\nu} \qquad k = 0, 1, \ldots$$

$$\nu > 0$$

$$E(X) = \text{var}(X) = \nu$$

$$\phi(u) = e^{\nu(e^{iu}-1)}$$

Uniform law

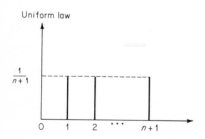

$$un(k;n) = \frac{1}{n+1} \qquad k = 0, 1, \ldots, n$$

$$n = 0, 1, \ldots$$

$$E[X] = \frac{n}{2} \qquad \text{var}[X] = \frac{n^2}{12} + \frac{n}{6}$$

$$\phi(u) = \frac{1 - e^{iu(n+1)}}{(n+1)(1 - e^{iu})}$$

PROBABILITY DENSITY FUNCTIONS[2]

Beta

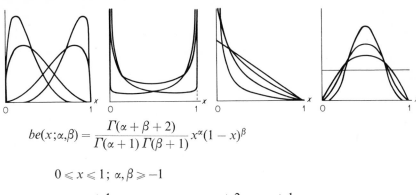

$$be(x;\alpha,\beta) = \frac{\Gamma(\alpha + \beta + 2)}{\Gamma(\alpha + 1)\,\Gamma(\beta + 1)}x^{\alpha}(1 - x)^{\beta}$$

$$0 \leqslant x \leqslant 1;\ \alpha, \beta \geqslant -1$$

$$E[X] = \frac{\alpha + 1}{\alpha + \beta + 2} \qquad \text{var}[X] = \frac{\alpha + 2}{\alpha + \beta + 3}\frac{\alpha + 1}{\alpha + \beta + 2}$$

$$M(v) = \frac{\Gamma(\alpha + \beta + 2)\,\Gamma(\alpha + v)}{\Gamma(\alpha + \beta + v + 1)\,\Gamma(\alpha + 1)}$$

Cauchy

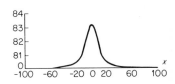

$$ca(x;\alpha) = \frac{\alpha}{\pi}\frac{1}{\alpha^2 + x^2} \qquad -\infty < x < \infty$$

$$\alpha > 0$$

$$E[X] \rightarrow \text{undefined}$$

$$\phi(u) = e^{-\alpha|u|}$$

$$\text{chi}\,(x;n) = \frac{1}{2^{n/2}\,\Gamma\left|\dfrac{n}{2}\right|}x^{(n/2)-1}\,e^{-x/2}$$

$$x > 0$$

[2] The figures, intended for qualitative purposes, are adapted from G. J. Hahn and S. S. Shapiro, "Statistical Models in Engineering," John Wiley & Sons, Inc., New York, 1967.

Exponential

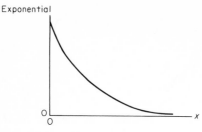

$$e(x;\lambda) = \lambda e^{-\lambda x} \qquad x > 0$$

$$\lambda > 0$$

$$E(X) = \lambda^{-1} \qquad \text{var}(X) = \lambda^{-2}$$

$$\phi(u) = \left(1 - \frac{iu}{\lambda}\right)^{-1}$$

$$M(v) = \lambda^{-1}$$

Gamma (Erlang)

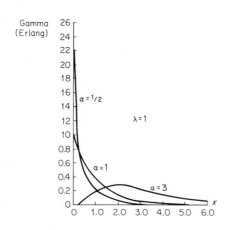
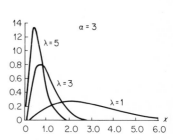

$$ga(x;\lambda,\alpha) = \frac{\lambda}{\Gamma(\alpha)} (\lambda x)^{\alpha-1} e^{-\lambda x}$$

$$x > 0; \ \lambda, \alpha > 0$$

$$E(X) = \frac{\alpha}{\lambda} \qquad \text{var}(X) = \frac{\alpha}{\lambda^2}$$

$$\phi(u) = \left(1 - \frac{iu}{\lambda}\right)^{-\alpha}$$

$$M(v) = \frac{\Gamma(\alpha + v - 1)}{\Gamma(\alpha)} \qquad \text{for } \lambda = 1$$

Log - Normal

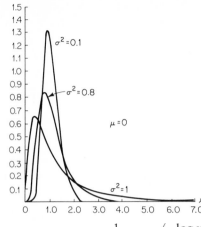

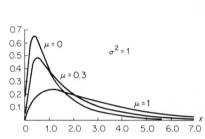

$$\lg{n}\,(x;m,\sigma) = \frac{1}{\sqrt{2\pi}\sigma x}\exp\left(-\frac{\log x - m}{2\sigma^2}\right)$$

$$x > 0;\ -\infty < m < \infty;\ \sigma > 0$$

$$E[X] = \exp\left(\frac{m + \sigma^2}{2}\right)\qquad \text{var}\,[X] = m^2(e^{\sigma^2} - 1)$$

$$M(v) = \exp\left[m(v-1) + \tfrac{1}{2}\sigma^2(v-1)^2\right]$$

Normal

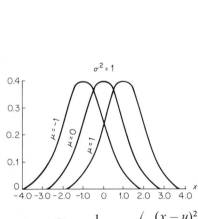

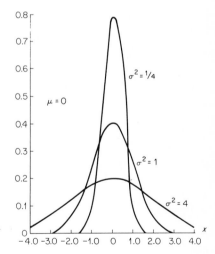

$$n(x;\mu,\sigma^2) = \frac{1}{\sqrt{2\pi}\sigma}\exp\left(-\frac{(x - u)^2}{2\sigma^2}\right)$$

$$-\infty < x < \infty;\ -\infty < \mu < \infty,\ \sigma > 0$$

$$E[X] = \mu\qquad \text{var}\,[X] = \sigma^2$$

$$\phi(u) = \exp\left(iu\mu - \tfrac{1}{2}u^2\sigma^2\right)$$

Rectangular

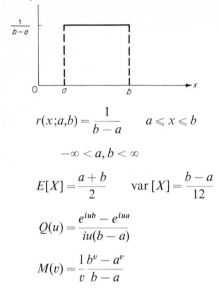

$$r(x;a,b) = \frac{1}{b-a} \qquad a \leqslant x \leqslant b$$

$$-\infty < a, b < \infty$$

$$E[X] = \frac{a+b}{2} \qquad \text{var}\,[X] = \frac{b-a}{12}$$

$$Q(u) = \frac{e^{iub} - e^{iua}}{iu(b-a)}$$

$$M(v) = \frac{1}{v}\frac{b^v - a^v}{b-a}$$

Weibull

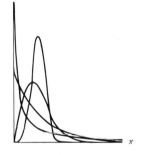

$$wy(x;\lambda,k) = \lambda^k \exp\left(-\frac{x^{k+1}}{k+1}\right)$$

$$x > 0;\ \lambda > 0;\ k = 0, 1, \ldots$$

Appendix 5
Difference Equations

Difference equations are discrete analogs of differential equations. They arise in discrete representations or models. Fortunately, the solution techniques for many difference equations parallel those for differential equations. In this appendix, we consider a few techniques appropriate to the equations which have arisen in the text. The discussion makes no particular attempt at completeness.

CONSTANT COEFFICIENTS

The solutions of homogeneous difference equations with constant coefficients are combinations of exponential functions, just as they are for differential equations. For example, consider the second-order equation

$$y_{n+2} - a y_n = 0 \qquad n = 0, 1, \ldots$$

where a is a constant. Assume a solution of the form $y_n = \lambda^n$, and substitute to get the *indicial equation*

$$\lambda^2 - a = 0$$

The roots are $\lambda = \pm\sqrt{a}$, and the *general (complementary) solution* is

$$y_n = c_1(\sqrt{a})^n + c_2(-\sqrt{a})^n$$

where c_1 and c_2 are arbitrary constants which are evaluated using boundary conditions.

Generalizing, the linear homogeneous difference equation with constant coefficients

$$y_n + a_{n-1} y_{n-1} + \cdots + a_1 y_1 + a_0 y_0 = 0 \tag{1}$$

possesses solutions of the form λ^n. Substituting, one obtains the indicial equation

$$\lambda^n + a_{n-1} \lambda^{n-1} + \cdots + a_1 \lambda + a_0 = 0 \tag{2}$$

Suppose that Eq. (1) has n distinct roots $\lambda_1, \lambda_2, \ldots, \lambda_n$. The general solution is

$$y_n = c_1 \lambda_1^n + c_2 \lambda_2^n + \cdots + c_n y_n^n \tag{3}$$

The roots $\lambda_1, \ldots, \lambda_n$ need not be distinct. The solution in that case is formed by replacing the constant coefficient of the multiple root by a polynomial whose degree is one less than the multiplicity, exactly as for differential equations. For example, consider the difference equation

$$y_{n+3} - (2p + q) y_{n+2} - 2p(p + q) y_{n+1} - p^2 q y_n = 0$$

where p and q are constants. The indicial equation is

$$\lambda^3 - (qp - q) \lambda^2 - 2p(p + q) \lambda - p^2 q = 0$$

The roots are $\lambda_1 = \lambda_2 = p$ and $\lambda_3 = q \neq p$. Since p^n and q^n are independent solutions, we have the general solution

$$y_n = (c_1 + c_2 n) p^n + c_3 q^n \qquad n = 0, 1, \ldots$$

where c_1, c_2, c_3 are arbitrary constants. If $p = q$, then $y_n = (c_1 + c_2 n + c_3 n^2) p^n$, $n = 0, 1, \ldots$.

PARTICULAR SOLUTIONS

The discussion has been limited to homogeneous equations so that the general and complementary solutions coincide. We consider a few simple procedures for obtaining *particular solutions* which, when added to the complementary solution, complete the general solution.

When a particular solution is not apparent by trial and error, one can proceed by writing the difference equation in *operator form*.   Recall that differences are defined by

$$\Delta y_n = y_{n+1} - y_n$$
$$\Delta^2 y_n = \Delta(\Delta y_n) = (y_{n+2} - y_{n+1}) - (y_{n+1} - y_n)$$
$$= y_{n+2} - 2y_{n+1} + y_n$$

so that $y_{n+1} = y_n + \Delta y_n$, $y_{n+2} = \Delta^2 y_n + 2\Delta y_n + y_n$, etc.   Using this difference notation, the nonhomogeneous equation

$$y_{n+2} - ay_{n+1} + by_n = g_n$$

can be written in operator form:

$$L(\Delta y_n) = [\Delta^2 + (2 - a)\Delta + (1 - a + b)]y_n = g_n$$

where a and b are constants and g_n is a polynomial.   A simple procedure for obtaining a particular solution is to expand the reciprocal $1/L(\Delta)$ in a power series in Δ and apply it to $g(n)$.   Formally, the solution y_n is

$$y_n = \frac{1}{L(\Delta)} g_n \tag{4}$$

For example, with $a = b = -1$ and $g(n) = 4n^2 + 2n + 1$, the equations are

$$y_{n+2} + y_{n+1} - y_n = 4n^2 + 2n + 1$$

or

$$(\Delta^2 + 3\Delta + 1)y_n = 4n^2 + 2n + 1$$

Expanding the reciprocal of the operator,

$$(\Delta^2 + 3\Delta + 1)^{-1} = (1 - 3\Delta + 8\Delta^2 - \cdots)$$

and a little calculation yields

$$\frac{1}{L(\Delta)} g_n = (1 - 3\Delta + 8\Delta^2 - \cdots)(4n^2 + 2n + 1) = 4n^2 - 22n + 47$$

which is a particular solution.   The indicial equation, that is, $g(n) = 0$, has the distinct roots $(-3 \pm \sqrt{5})/2$.   Hence the general solution is

$$y_n = c_1 \frac{-3 + \sqrt{5}^n}{2} + c_2 \frac{-3 - \sqrt{5}^n}{2} + 4n^2 - 22n + 47$$

Note that the series expansion of $1/L(\Delta)$ was carried only to second order since higher-order differences of the polynomial are zero.

The foregoing procedure is also effective when the inhomogeneous term g_n has an exponential factor.   For example, suppose $g_n = c^n h_n$, where c is a constant and h_n is a polynomial.   By setting $y_n = c^n u_n$, one obtains a difference equation of the above type in u_n. Trigonometric functions can be expressed as exponentials, so that the transformation is also effective in that instance. The methods of "undetermined coefficients" and "variation of parameters," usually studied in differential equations, are easily adapted to finding particular solutions to difference equations.

LINEAR EQUATIONS WITH VARIABLE COEFFICIENTS

Consider the first-order linear difference equation with variable coefficients,

$$y_{n+1} - a_n y_n = b_n \tag{5}$$

where a_n and b_n are known functions of n and a_n never vanishes. This equation can be reduced to one with constant coefficients by dividing each term by the

product $\prod_{i=1}^{n} a_i$. It is easily seen that Eq. (5) can be replaced by

$$u_{n+2} - u_n = d_n \tag{6}$$

where

$$u_n = \frac{y_n}{\prod\limits_{i=1}^{n} a_n} \quad \text{and} \quad d_n = \frac{b_n}{\prod\limits_{i=1}^{n} a_n}$$

Hence, the techniques for constant coefficients are applicable. Unfortunately, a statement of comparable generality cannot be made for higher-order equations although many can be solved readily.

Consider the general linear second-order equation

$$y_{n+2} + a_n y_{n+1} + b_n y_n = c_n$$

where a_n, b_n, and c_n are known functions. Suppose that a particular solution, p_n, of the homogeneous equation has been found. It can be used to generate the general solution as follows:

1. Let $y_n = p_n e_n$, where e_n is an (as yet) unspecified function of n.
2. Substituting y_n from step 1 into the difference equation, one obtains
   $$e_{n+2} p_{n+2} + a_n e_{n+1} p_{n+1} + b_n e_n p_n = c_n$$
3. By hypothesis,

   $$p_{n+2} + a_n p_{n+1} + b_n p_n = 0$$

   Multiplying by e_{n+1} and subtracting yields

   $$(\Delta e_{n+1}) p_{n+1} - (\Delta e_n) b_n p_n = c_n$$

   This is a linear first-order equation whose solution, (Δe_n), is obtained by the preceding methods. Note that (Δe_n) will contain an arbitrary constant.

4. Next, solve the linear first-order equation in e_n. Note that a second arbitrary constant is introduced.
5. Finally, since p_n is known, a solution to the original equation, the general solution, is the product $e_n p_n$.

For example, the equation

$$y_{n+2} + (n^2 + 1) y_{n+1} + n^2 y_n = 0$$

has a particular solution $p_n = (-1)^n$. Corresponding to step 3, we obtain

$$(-1)^n (\Delta e_{n+1}) - n^2 (-1)^n (\Delta e_n) = 0$$

whose general solution is

$$e_n = c_1 \prod_{i=1}^{n-1} i = e_{n+1} - e_n$$

where c_1 is an arbitrary constant. Corresponding to step 4, the complementary solution is unity and the particular solution, using an earlier result, is

$$e_n = \sum_{i=1}^{n-1} \left(c_1 \prod_{j=1}^{i-1} j^2 \right)$$

The general solution to the last difference equation is

$$e_n = c_2 + c_1 \sum_{i=1}^{n-1} \left(\prod_{j=1}^{i-1} j^2 \right)$$

where c_2 is an arbitrary constant. From step 5, the general solution to the original equation is

$$y_n = c_2 (-1)^n + c_1 (-1)^n \sum_{i=1}^{n-1} \left(\prod_{j=1}^{i-1} j^2 \right)$$

This technique can also be used to reduce the order of an equation by unity.
Another technique for solving difference equations with constant or variable coefficients uses the generating functions of Chap. 12. For example, consider the Bernoulli trial model, Eq. (2) in Chap. 9:

$$b(x;n) = (1 - p) b(x; n - 1) + p b(x - 1; n - 1) \qquad x = 0, 1, \ldots, n;$$
$$n = 1, 2, \ldots$$

The notation differs, but this is a difference equation in two variables, i.e., a *partial difference equation*. From the point of view of solving equations, no distinction is made because x is a random variable whereas n is not.
The generating function $g_n(s)$ is defined by

$$g_n(s) = \sum_{x=0}^{\infty} b(x;n) s^x$$

where s is the transform variable.   Multiplying each term of the difference equation by s^x and summing over x gives

$$g_n(s) = (1 - p)g_{n-1}(s) + psg_{n-1}(s)$$
$$= [(1 - p) + ps]g_{n-1}(s)$$

The partial difference equation has been transformed into a difference equation in a single variable, n.   The solution is clearly

$$g_n(s) = [(1 - p) + ps]^n$$

and the solutions $b(x;n)$ are the coefficients in the binomial expansion of $g_n(s)$.

Equation (33) in Chap. 11 with $\lambda_n = \lambda$ and $\mu_n = n\mu$ is a difference equation with variable coefficients,

$$p_n - \frac{\rho}{n}p_{n-1} = 0 \qquad n = 1, 2, \ldots$$

where $\rho = \lambda/\mu$.   This is equivalent to Eq. (5) with $a_n = \rho/n$ and $b_n = 0$.   Since $\prod_{i=1}^{n} a_i = \rho^n/n!$, the substitution $u_n = n!p_n/\rho^n$ reduces the original difference equation to

$$u_n - u_{n-1} = 0$$

whose solution is $u_n = c_1$, where c_1 is an arbitrary constant.   Thus

$$p_n = \frac{\rho^n}{n!}c_1 \qquad n = 0, 1, \ldots$$

and, since the sum of the p_n's must be unity, the constant c_1 is $e^{-\rho}$.   This is Eq. (39) in Chap. 11.   The equation can also be solved using generating functions.   Write the difference equation as

$$np_n - \rho p_{n-1} = 0 \qquad n = 1, 2, \ldots$$

Multiplying by s^n and summing over n gives

$$\sum_{n=0}^{\infty} np_n s^n - \rho \sum_{n=0}^{\infty} p_{n-1} s^n = 0$$

The factor n in the first summand suggests the derivative of the generating function

$$G(s) = \sum_{n=0}^{\infty} p_n s^n$$

Thus,

$$\sum_{n=0}^{\infty} np_n s^n = s \sum_{n=0}^{\infty} np_n s^{n-1} = sG'(s)$$

where the prime denotes differentiation with respect to s.   The second summand is written

$$\sum_{n=0}^{\infty} p_{n-1} s^n = s \sum_{n=1}^{\infty} p_{n-1} s^{n-1} = sG(s)$$

Therefore, the difference equation is replaced by the differential equation

$$sG'(s) - sG(s) = 0 \qquad s \neq 0$$

whose solution agrees with that previously obtained.

Generating functions can also be used to solve difference-differential equations.   For example, in Prob. 11-31 paired arrivals are served singly and the probabilities satisfy the steady-state equations

$$-\lambda p_0 + \mu p_1 = 0$$
$$-(\lambda + \mu) p_1 + \mu p_2 = 0$$
$$-(\lambda + \mu) p_n + \lambda p_{n-2} + \mu p_{n+1} = 0 \qquad n \geqslant 2$$

Multiplying the first equation by s^0, the second by s^1, etc., and tabulating, we get

	p_0	p_1	p_2	p_3	p_4	p_5	p_6	$\cdots$
s^0	$-\lambda$	μ						
s^1		$-(\lambda+\mu)$	μ					
s^2	λ		$-(\lambda+\mu)$	μ				
s^3		λ		$-(\lambda+\mu)$	μ			
s^4			λ		$-(\lambda+\mu)$	μ		
s^5				λ		$-(\lambda+\mu)$	μ	
s^6					λ		$-(\lambda+\mu)$	$\cdots$
$\cdot$						$\cdots$	$\cdots$	$\cdots$
$\cdot$							$\cdots$	$\cdots$
$\cdot$								$\cdots$

Multiplying and adding,

$$-\lambda p_0 - (\lambda + \mu)(p_1 s^1 + p_2 s^2 + \cdots) + \mu s^{-1}(p_1 s^1 + p_2 s^2 + \cdots)$$
$$+ s(p_0 s^0 + p_1 s^1 + p_2 s^2 + \cdots)$$

Letting $G(s) = \sum_{n=0}^{\infty} p_n s^n$, this is written

$$-\lambda p_0 - (\lambda + \mu)[G(s) - p_0] + \mu s^{-1}[G(s) - p_0] + \lambda s^2 G(s) = 0$$

which yields

$$G(s) = \frac{\mu(1 - s) p_0}{\mu - (\lambda + \mu)s + \lambda s^3}$$

The solutions, of course, are the coefficients of the Maclaurin expansion.

Difference equations have attracted attention in recent years because of their aptness for automatic computation. The reader can consult many references including "Introduction to Difference Equations," by S. Goldberg, John Wiley & Sons, Inc., New York, 1961, or "Numerical Methods for Science and Engineering," by R. G. Stanton, and "Numerical Methods in Engineering," by M. G. Salvadori and M. L. Baron, both published by Prentice-Hall, Inc., Englewood Cliffs, N.J., in 1961.

Solutions to Selected Problems

CHAPTER 1

1-6. Since similar tracts are available in the future, we choose a 12-year study period.

$$PW_A = 300,000 + 25,000 \text{ uspwf } (15\%, 12 \text{ years}) - 60,000 \text{ sppwf } (15,12)$$
$$= \$424,000$$

$$PW_B = 450,000 \text{ crf } (15,20) \text{ uspwf } (15,12) + 20,000 \text{ uspwf } (15,20)$$
$$-30,000 \text{ sppwf } (15,20)$$
$$= \$497,000$$

Choose tract A.

Note that the same study period was maintained for both alternatives by converting the 20-year investment cost for tract B into an equivalent annual cost (crf) and then taking the present worth of only the first 12 years (uspwf) of annual cost.

CHAPTER 2

2-6. The standard form is

$$\text{Min:} \quad z = -3x_1 - 2x_2 - x_3$$

$$\text{Subject to:} \quad 4x_1 + x_2 + x_3 + x_4 = 8$$

$$3x_1 + 3x_2 + 2x_3 + x_5 = 9$$

$$X_i \geqslant 0 \qquad i = 1,\ldots,5$$

The artificial objective function is

$$\text{Min:} \quad w = x_4 + x_5 = 17 - 7x_1 - 4x_2 - 3x_3$$

The Phase 1 Routine yields

		x_1	x_2	x_3	x_4	x_5
	8	④	1	1	1	0
	9	3	3	2	0	1
$z =$	0	-3	-2	-1	0	0
$-w = -17$		-7	-4	-3		
	2	1	1/4	1/4	1/4	0
	3	0	⑨/4	5/4	$-3/4$	1
	6	0	$-5/4$	$-1/4$	3/4	0
	-3	0	$-9/4$	$-5/4$		
	5/3	1	0	1/9	1/3	$-1/9$
	4/3	0	1	5/9	$-1/3$	4/9
	23/3	0	0	4/9	1/3	5/9
$-w =$	0	0				

$$x_1 = 5/3, \ x_2 = 4/3, \ x_3 = 0, \ z = 23/3$$

CHAPTER 3

3-4. Corresponding to an interest rate of 8%, $\rho = 0.926$,

$$\text{Max:} \quad z' = \sum_{m=1}^{4} \sum_{j=1}^{3} \rho^j a_{jm} x_m = (0.926 \times 2.5 \times 10^5 + 0.926^2 \times 10^5) x_1$$

$$+ (0.926 \times 5 \times 10^3 + 0.926^2 \times 3 \times 10^4) x_2 + (0.926^2 \times 500$$

$$+ 0.926^3 \times 1{,}300) x_3 + 0.926^3 \times 400 x_4 = 317{,}300 x_1 + 30{,}430 x_2$$

$$+ 1{,}461 x_3 + 318 x_4$$

Subject to: $400,000x_1 + 30,000x_2 + 1,800x_3 + 300x_4 \leqslant \$750,000$

(bid)

$$0.80 \leqslant x_1 \leqslant 1.80$$
$$6.00 \leqslant x_2 \leqslant 11.00$$
$$6.00 \leqslant x_3 \leqslant 12.00 \quad \text{(bounds)}$$
$$20.00 \leqslant x_4 \leqslant 35.00$$

Solution:

$x_1 = \$0.97 \qquad x_2 = \$11.00 \qquad x_3 = \$12.00 \qquad x_4 = \$35.00$

$z' = \$679,000$

CHAPTER 4
4-1.

25			10	35
0	700	800	400	
15	15			30
0	100	200	600	
5		5		10
0	300	400	700	
30	15	20	10	75

The dummy column balances this transportation problem. Using the "minimum cost rule," the first assignment (15) is made in cell (22), and is entered in the upper left corner of the cell. The table shows the initial assignments which designate the six basic variables $(4 + 3 - 1 = 6)$. Empty cells constitute the nonbasic variables $(12 - 6 = 6)$.

Appropriate loops and the corresponding unit penalties are

Nonbasic cell	*Loop*	*Associated unit penalty*
(1,2)	(1,2) (1,1) (3,1) (3,3) (2,3) (2,2) (1,2)	$700 - 400 + 200 - 100 = 400$
(1,3)	(1,3) (1,1) (3,1) (3,3) (1,3)	$800 - 400 = 400$
(2,1)	(2,1) (3,1) (3,3) (2,3) (2,1)	$400 - 200 = 200$
(2,4)	(2,4) (1,4) (1,1) (3,1) (3,3) (2,3) (2,4)	$600 - 400 + 400 - 200 = 400$
(2,2)	(3,2) (3,3) (2,3) (2,2) (3,2)	$300 - 400 + 200 - 100 = 0$
(3,4)	(3,4) (3,4) (1,4) (1,1) (3,1) (3,4)	$700 - 400 = 300$

Since all unit penalties are positive, the assignments constitute an optimal solution.   The zero unit penalty for cell (3,2) indicates that alternate optima exit.   If C_M is the shipping cost per mile, the minimum total shipping cost is

$$[15(100) + 15(200) + 10(400) + 5(400)]\,C_M = 10{,}500C_M$$

An alternative solution is $C1 = 10$, $A2 = 10$, $B2 = 20$, $A3 = 5$

4-7.   The reduced matrix is

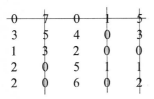

4 lines, 5 × 5 matrix: no immediate optimal solution.

The smallest unlined element is unity at (5,2).   Subtracting one from each unlined element and adding it to each element at the intersection of two lines yields

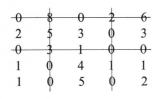

4 lines, 5 × 5 matrix: no immediate optimal solution.

Repeating the procedure,

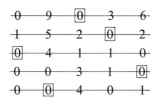

4 lines, 5 × 5 matrix: no immediate optimal solution.

And again,

$$\begin{array}{ccccc}
\cancel{0} & 9 & \boxed{0} & 3 & 6 \\
1 & 5 & 2 & \boxed{0} & 2 \\
\boxed{0} & 4 & 1 & 1 & 0 \\
0 & 0 & 3 & 1 & \boxed{0} \\
0 & \boxed{0} & 4 & 0 & 1
\end{array}$$

5 lines, 5 × 5 matrix: ∴ optimal solution.

Optimal assignment

Engineers	Projects
1	3
2	4
3	1
4	5
5	2

4-8. (a) Converting the problem into the standard "symmetric dual" form,

Max: $3X_1 + 6X_2$

Subject to: $-3X_1 + 3X_2 \leqslant 2$

$4X_1 + 2X_2 \leqslant 4$

$X_1, X_2 \geqslant 0$

The dual problem is

Min: $2Y_1 + 4Y_2$

Subject to: $-3Y_1 + 4Y_2 \geqslant 3$

$3Y_1 + 2Y_2 \geqslant 6$

$Y_1, Y_2 \geqslant 0$

The simplex tableaus become

		Y_1	Y_2	Y_3	Y_4	Y_5	Y_6
	3	-3	④	-1		1	
	6	3	2		-1		1
$-z =$	0	2	4				
$-w =$	-9		-6	1	1		
	3/4	$-3/4$	1	$-1/4$		1/4	
	9/2	⑨/2		1/2	-1	$-1/2$	1
$-z =$	-3	5		1		-1	
$-w =$	$-9/2$	$-9/2$		$-1/2$	1	3/2	
	3/2		1	$-1/6$	$-1/6$	1/6	1/6
	1	1		1/9	$-2/9$	$-1/9$	2/9
$-z =$	-8			4/9	10/9	$-4/9$	$-10/9$
$-w =$	0					1	1

The optimal solution is $Y_1 = 1$, $Y_2 = 3/2$. From the duality theorem, since both dual variables are positive, the corresponding primal constraints are equalities. Solving them simultaneously yields $X_1 = 4/9$ and $X_2 = 10/9$. The same result is obtained from the last dual simplex tableau. The objective coefficient X_1 of the excess variable y_3, corresponding to the first dual constraint, is $4/9$. Similarly $X_2 = 10/9$.

The same result can be obtained graphically.

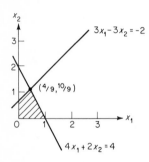

4-10.   Let x_i = amount of aggregate i in concrete C_1

$\qquad\qquad$ y_i = amount of aggregate i in concrete C_2

The total amounts of C_1 and C_2 are therefore $x_1 + x_2$ and $y_1 + y_2$ with associated costs $25x_1 + 20x_2$ and $25y_1 + 20y_2$, respectively. The optimization is

Max: $z = 35(x_1 + x_2) + 38(y_1 + y_2) - 25(x_1 + y_1) - 20(x_2 + y_2)$
$\qquad = 10x_1 + 15x_2 + 13y_1 + 18y_2$

Subject to:

(demand)	$x_1 +$	x_2	$+$	$y_1 +$	y_2	$\leqslant 100$
(availability)	x_1		$+$	y_1		$\leqslant 40$
(production)	$x_1 +$	x_2				$\leqslant 50$
(gradation)	$2x_1 -$	x_2				$\leqslant 0$
(gradation)			$-$	$y_1 +$	$2y_2$	$\leqslant 0$

Decomposing, $l = 2$, and

$$A_1 = \begin{bmatrix} 1 & 1 \\ 1 & 0 \end{bmatrix} \qquad A_2 = \begin{bmatrix} 1 & 1 \\ 1 & 0 \end{bmatrix} \qquad \beta_1 = \begin{bmatrix} 1 & 1 \\ 2 & -1 \end{bmatrix} \qquad \beta_2 = [-1,2]$$

and

$$C_1 = [10,15] \qquad C_2 = [13,18]$$

Consider the subsidiary convex sets, that is,

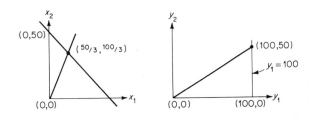

and

$$\mathbf{X} = \begin{bmatrix} 0 \\ 0 \end{bmatrix} \mu_{11} + \begin{bmatrix} 0 \\ 50 \end{bmatrix} \mu_{12} + \begin{bmatrix} 50/3 \\ 100/3 \end{bmatrix} \mu_{13} \qquad \mathbf{y} = \begin{bmatrix} 0 \\ 0 \end{bmatrix} \mu_{21} + \begin{bmatrix} 100 \\ 0 \end{bmatrix} \mu_{22}$$
$$+ \begin{bmatrix} 100 \\ 50 \end{bmatrix} \mu_{23}$$

A decomposed (equivalent) linear program is

	μ_{11}	μ_{12}	μ_{13}	μ_{21}	μ_{22}	μ_{23}	a_1	b_2	$\mathbf{b}$
	0	50	50	0	100	150	100		100
	0	0	50/3	0	100	⑩⓪		100	40
	1	1	1						1
				1	1	1			1
Min $- z/100 =$		−7.5	−20/3		−13	$\boxed{-22}$			0
	0	①/②	1/4	0	−1/2	0	1	−3/2	2/5
	0	0	1/6	0	1	1	0	1	2/5
	1	1	1	0	0	0	0	0	1
	0	0	−1/6	1	0	0	0	−1	3/5
		$\boxed{-7.5}$	−3		9	0		22	44/5
	0	1	1/2	0	−1	0	2	−3	4/5
	0	0	1/6	0	1	1	0	1	2/5
	1	0	1/2	0	1	0	−2	③	1/5
	0	0	−1/6	1	0	0	0	−1	3/5
	0	.75		1.5			15	$\boxed{-.5}$	74/5
	1	1	1	0	0	0	0	0	1
	−1/3	0	0	0	2/3	1	2/3	0	5/15
	1/3	0	1/6	0	1/5	0	−2/3	1	1/15
	1/3	0	0	1	1/3	0	−2/3	0	10/15
	1/6	10/12		10/6			14 2/3	0	89/6

$$\mu_{11} = 0 \qquad \mu_{12} = 1 \qquad \mu_{13} = 0$$
$$\mu_{21} = 2/3 \qquad \mu_{22} = 0 \qquad \mu_{23} = 1/3$$

$$X = \begin{bmatrix} x_1 \\ x_2 \end{bmatrix} = \begin{bmatrix} 0 \\ 50 \end{bmatrix} \times 1 = \begin{bmatrix} 0 \\ 50 \end{bmatrix}$$

$$55\lambda = \begin{bmatrix} y_1 \\ y_2 \end{bmatrix} = \begin{bmatrix} 0 \\ 0 \end{bmatrix} \times 2/3 + \begin{bmatrix} 100 \\ 50 \end{bmatrix} \times 1/3 = \begin{bmatrix} 100/3 \\ 50/3 \end{bmatrix} \qquad z = \frac{\$8,900}{6}$$

CHAPTER 5

5-1. Applying geometric programming techniques, the dual becomes

$$\text{Max:} \quad d(\mu) = \left[\frac{8}{\mu_{01}}\right]^{\mu_{01}} \left[\frac{814}{\mu_{02}}\right]^{\mu_{02}} \left[\frac{5(\mu_{11} + \mu_{12})}{\mu_{11}}\right]^{\mu_{11}} \left[\frac{2(\mu_{11} + \mu_{12})}{\mu_{12}}\right]^{\mu_{12}}$$

Subject to:
$$\mu_{01} + \mu_{02} \qquad\qquad = 1 \qquad \text{(normality condition)}$$
$$\mu_{01} - \mu_{02} - \mu_{12} = 0 \qquad \text{(orthogonality condition for } x_1\text{)}$$
$$-\mu_{02} + \mu_{11} - \mu_{12} = 0 \qquad \text{(orthogonality condition for } x_2\text{)}$$
$$\mu_{ij} \geqslant 0 \qquad i = 0, 1, j = 1, 2$$

Since the problem has one degree of difficulty, the solutions to the dual constraints are written in terms of μ_{01}.   Thus

$$\mu_{02} = 1 - \mu_{01}$$
$$\mu_{11} = \mu_{01}$$
$$\mu_{12} = 2\mu_{01} - 1$$

Substituting in the dual objective, we have

$$d(\mu_{01}) = \left[\frac{8}{\mu_{01}}\right]^{\mu_{01}} \left[\frac{814}{1 - \mu_{01}}\right]^{1-\mu_{01}} \left[\frac{5(3\mu_{01} - 1)}{\mu_{01}}\right]^{\mu_{01}} \left[\frac{2(3\mu_{01} - 1)}{2\mu_{01} - 1}\right]^{2\mu_{01}-1}$$

To obtain the best value of μ_{01}, set $\dfrac{d\ln d(\mu_{01})}{d\mu_{01}} = 0$

Hence

$$\ln\left[\frac{8}{\mu_{01}}\right] - 1 - \ln\left[\frac{814}{1 - \mu_{01}}\right] + 1 + \ln\left[\frac{5(3\mu_{01} - 1)}{\mu_{01}}\right]$$

$$+ \frac{1}{3\mu_{01} - 1} + 2\ln\left[\frac{2(3\mu_{01} - 1)}{2\mu_{01} - 1}\right] - \left[\frac{1}{3\mu_{01} - 1}\right] = 0$$

From which

$$\left[\frac{8}{\mu_{01}}\right]\left[\frac{5(3\mu_{01} - 1)}{\mu_{01}}\right]\left[\frac{2(3\mu_{01} - 1)}{2\mu_{01} - 1}\right]^2 = \frac{814}{1 - \mu_{01}}$$

The solution is $\mu_{01} = 0.7$, and therefore, $\mu_{02} = 1 - \mu_{01} = 0.3$, $\mu_{11} = 0.7$, and $\mu_{12} = 1.4 - 1 = 0.4$. The maximum of the dual function is given by

$$d(\boldsymbol{\mu})_{max} = \left[\frac{8}{0.7}\right]^{0.7}\left[\frac{814}{0.3}\right]^{0.3}\left[\frac{5(0.7 + 0.4)}{0.7}\right]^{0.7}\left[\frac{2(0.7 + 0.4)}{0.4}\right]^{0.4}$$

$$= 492$$

The primal variables can be obtained from any of the following relations:

$$8x_1 = 0.7(492)$$

$$\frac{814}{x_1 x_2} = 0.3(492)$$

$$5x_2 = \frac{0.7}{0.7 + 0.4}$$

$$\frac{2}{x_1 x_2} = \frac{0.4}{0.7 + 0.4}$$

$$x_1 = 43.2 \qquad x_2 = 0.127$$

5-6. We seek the minimum of $(-y)$ subject to the given constraint. The Lagrangian function is $L = -100x_1 - 4 \times 10^3/x_1 x_2 - 50x_2 + \lambda(x_1 - 2x_1 x_2 + x_2)$.

Using Kuhn-Tucker's optimality conditions

(a) if $x_1 > 0$, then $\dfrac{\partial L}{\partial x_1} = 0$, that is, $-100 + \dfrac{4 \times 10^3}{x_1^2 x_2} + \lambda - 2x_2\lambda = 0$

(b) if $x_2 > 0$, then $\dfrac{\partial L}{\partial x_2} = 0$, that is, $\dfrac{4 \times 10^3}{x_1 x_2^2} - 50 - 2x_1\lambda + \lambda = 0$

(c) if $x_1 = 0$, then $\dfrac{\partial L}{\partial x_1} \geqslant 0$, that is, $-100 + \dfrac{4 \times 10^3}{x_1^2 x_2} + \lambda - 2x_2\lambda \geqslant 0$

(d) if $x_2 = 0$, then $\dfrac{\partial L}{\partial x_2} \geqslant 0$, that is, $\dfrac{4 \times 10^3}{x_1 x_2^2} - 50 - 2x_1\lambda + \lambda \geqslant 0$

(e) if $\lambda > 0$, then $\dfrac{\partial L}{\partial \lambda} = 0$, that is, $x_1 - 2x_1 x_2 + x_2 = 0$

(f) if $\lambda = 0$, then $\dfrac{\partial L}{\partial \lambda} \leqslant 0$, that is, $x_1 - 2x_1 x_2 + x_2 \leqslant 0$

As a first trial solution let $x_1, x_2 > 0$, $\lambda = 0$. Then x_1 and x_2 are obtained from the following equations:

$$-100 + \frac{4 \times 10^3}{x_1^2 x_2} = 0$$

$$\frac{4 \times 10^3}{x_1 x_2^2} - 50 = 0$$

Hence, $x_1 = 2.72$, $x_2 = 5.4$. Check the constraint to determine if $\lambda \neq 0$.

$$2.72 - 2(2.72)(5.4) + 5.4 = -21.28 < 0$$

Therefore this solution is optimal.

5-15.   Only the first iteration is indicated in each instance:

(a) $z = x_1^2 + x_1(1 + x_2) + 2x_2^2$

$$\partial z / \partial x_1 = 2x_1 + 1 + x_2 \qquad \partial z / \partial x_2 = x_1 + 4x_2$$

Starting from $(2,-1)$, by Eq. (37),

$$z = [2 - v(2x_1 + 1 + x_2)_i]^2 + [2 - v(2x_1 + 1 + x_2)_i]$$
$$\{1 + [-1 - v(x_1 + 4x_2)_i]\} + 2[-1 - v(x_1 + 4x_2)_i]^2$$
$$= (2 - 4v)^2 + (2 - 4v)(2v) + 2(-1 + 2v)^2$$
$$= 16v^2 - 20v + 6$$
$$\partial z / \partial v = 32v - 20 = 0 \qquad \text{and} \qquad v = 5/8$$

Since $\partial^2 z / \partial v^2$ is positive, this value of v tends to minimize z.   By Eq. (36),

$$x_{1,2} = 2 - 5/8(4) = -1/2$$
$$x_{2,2} = -1 - 5/8(-2) = 1/4$$

(b) $z = (x_1 - x_2)^2 + (x_2 - 1)^2 - x_1^2 - 2x_1 x_2 + 3x_2^2 - 4x_2 + 2$

$$\partial z / \partial x_1 = 2x_1 - 2x_2, \ \partial z / \partial x_2 = -2x_1 + 6x_2 - 4$$
$$z = (2 - 6v)^2 - 2(2 - 6v)(-1 + 14v) + 3(-1 + 14v)^2 - 4(-1 + 14v) + 2$$
$$= 792v^2 - 232v + 17$$
$$\partial z / \partial v = 1584v - 232 = 0$$
$$v = 29/198$$
$$x_{1,2} = 2 - (29/198)6 = 37/33$$
$$x_{2,2} = -1 - (29/198)(-14) = -302/99$$

5-19. Volume of cone $= 1/3$ base $\times$ altitude; surface $= 1/2$ circumference $\times$ slant ht.

$$\text{Min:} \quad z = C_{\text{piles}} + C_{\text{rim}} + C_{\text{cone}} + C_{\text{cylinder}}$$
$$= 200{,}000 + 3(10^7/D) + 1{,}800\,D + 4\pi D(D^2/2 + H^2)^{1/2}$$
$$+ 4{,}000(200 - H)$$

$$\text{Subject to:} \quad \frac{\pi D^2}{4}\left(\frac{H}{3}\right) = 1{,}405{,}000 \text{ ft}^3 \quad \text{or} \quad H = \frac{16{,}860{,}000}{\pi D^2} \leqslant 150$$

$$\therefore \ D^2 \geqslant 35{,}700 \quad \text{or} \quad D \geqslant 188 \text{ ft}$$

The Lagrangian function is

$$L = 1 \times 10^6 + 3 \times 10^7/D + 1{,}800\,D + 4\pi D(D^2/2 + 28.8 \times 10^{12}/D^4)^{1/2}$$
$$- 21.45 \times 10^9/D^2 + \lambda(-D + 188)$$

From the Kuhn-Tucker conditions, for $D > 0$, $\partial L/\partial D = 0$,

$$-3 \times 10^7 \ D^{-2} + 1{,}800 + 4\pi \left(\frac{D^6 + 57.6 \times 10^{12}}{2D^4}\right)^{1/2}$$

$$+ 4\pi D(1/2)\left(\frac{D^6 + 57.6 \times 10^{12}}{2D^4}\right)^{-1/2}$$

$$\left[\frac{2D^4(6D)^5 - (D^6 + 57.6 \times 10^{12})(8D^3)}{4D^8}\right]$$

$$+ 42.9 \times 10^9\, D^{-3} - \lambda = 0 \quad (1)$$

If $\lambda > 0$, $\partial L/\partial \lambda = 0$; $-D + 188 = 0$

If $\lambda = 0$, $\partial L/\partial \lambda \leqslant 0$; $-D + 188 \leqslant 0$

As a first trial, assume $\lambda \geqslant 0$, for which $D = 188$ ft. Substituting into Eq. (1) and simplifying,

$$-\frac{3 \times 10^7}{188^2} + 1{,}800 + 4\pi \left(\frac{188^6 + 57.6 \times 10^{12}}{2 \times 188^4}\right)^{1/2}$$

$$+ 2\pi D \left(\frac{188^2}{2} + \frac{28.8 \times 10^{12}}{188^4}\right)^{-1/2} (188 - 115.2 \times 10^{12}/188^5)$$

$$+ \frac{42.9 \times 10^9}{188^3} > 0$$

The inequality is satisfied. Therefore, $D = 188$ ft, and

$$H = \frac{16{,}860{,}000}{\pi D^2} = 150 \text{ ft}$$

CHAPTER 6

6-4. Let x_i be the length of the ith segment. The problem can be formulated as

$$\text{Max:} \quad z = \prod_{i=1}^{n} x_i$$

$$\text{Subject to:} \quad \sum_{i=1}^{n} x_i = L \quad \text{and} \quad x_i \geqslant 0, \; i = 1,\ldots,n$$

Let $f_n(L)$ be the maximum value of z when the segment of length L is divided into n subsegments.

For $n = 1$, clearly, $f_1(L) = L$ and $x_1 = L$. For $n = 2$, using recursion and the optimality principle,

$$f_2(L) = \max_{0 \leqslant x_2 \leqslant L} \{x_2 f_1(L - x_2)\}$$

$$= \max_{0 \leqslant x_2 \leqslant L} \{x_2(L - x_2)\} = \left(\frac{L}{2}\right)^2$$

with

$$x_1 = x_2 = \frac{L}{2}.$$

A similar calculation for $n = 3$ yields

$$f_3(L) = \max_{0 \leqslant x_3 \leqslant L} \{x_3 f_2(L - x_3)\} = \max_{0 \leqslant x_3 \leqslant L} \left\{x_3 \left(\frac{L - x_3}{2}\right)^2\right\} = \left(\frac{L}{3}\right)^3$$

with

$$x_1 = x_2 = x_3 = \frac{L}{3}$$

An inductive argument (see Appendix 2) can be used to conclude that

$$f_n(L) = \left(\frac{L}{n}\right)^n$$

with

$$x_1 = x_2 = \cdots = x_n = \frac{L}{n} \quad \text{for} \quad n = 1, 2,\ldots$$

Incidentally, the problem can also be solved using Lagrange multiplier techniques (Chap. 5).

6-9. Let $f_n^*(r)$ represent the minimum of the first n terms of the objective function with resources limit r.

For Stage 1

$$f_1^*(r) = \min[c_1 x_1^2] = c_1(r/a_1)^2$$

$$(r/a_1) \leqslant x_1 \leqslant \infty$$

For Stage 2

$$f_2^*(r) = f_2^*(b) = \min[c_2 x_2^2 + f_1(b - a_2 x_2)]$$
$$0 \leqslant x_2 \leqslant \infty$$

$$= \min[c_2 x_2^2 + (c_1/a_1^2)(b - a_2 x_2)^2]$$
$$0 \leqslant x_2 \leqslant \infty$$

$$= \min\left[\left(c_2 + c_1 \frac{a_2^2}{a_1^2}\right)x_2^2 - 2\frac{c_1 a_2 b}{a_1^2}x_2 + \frac{c_1}{a_1^2}b^2\right]$$
$$0 \leqslant x_2 \leqslant \infty$$

To find the minimum set the first derivative to zero; hence

$$x_2 = \frac{c_1 a_2 b}{c_2 a_1^2 + c_1 a_2^2}$$

The second derivative with respect to x_2 is positive, and thus a minimum is obtained:

$$z^* = f_2^*(b) = \left[\frac{c_1 c_2 b}{c_2 a_1^2 + c_1 a_2^2}\right]^2 \left(\frac{a_2^2}{c_2} + \frac{a_1^2}{c_1}\right)$$

and therefore

$$x_1 = \frac{c_2 a_1 b}{c_2 a_1^2 + c_1 a_2^2}$$

CHAPTER 7

7-8. By Steps 1–3 of Sec. 7.6,

Activity	Duration	LST	EFT	LFT	LST	F	Critical path	Resource req'mt P.	Resource req'mt L.	Time 0	5	10	15	20
1-2	3	0	3	3	0	0	X	1	0					
1-3	6	0	6	12	6	6		1	3					
1-4	4	0	4	13	9	9		2	3					
2-4	8	3	11	13	5	2		3	4					
2-5	7	3	10	10	3	0	X	7	1					
3-6	2	6	8	14	12	6		3	5					
4-7	9	11	20	22	13	2		1	2					
5-6	4	10	14	14	10	0	X	0	2					
5-7	5	10	15	22	17	17		2	4					
6-7	8	14	22	22	14	0	X	2	3					

P. 11   4 ⑬ 11 ⑬ 10 5 3   5 3   2
L. 9   6 ⑪ 8 ⑩ 5 ⑩ 8   9 5   3

Total available resources   Total req'd resources

Revised   P. 4   10 11 10   3 4 5   3 2
        L. 6   7 8 5   6 9 9   5 3

CHAPTER 8

8-3. All the set relations can be verified using Venn diagrams. Here we use a symbolic argument.

$$(a) \ (A \cup B)' = I - (A \cup B) = I - (A + B - AB) = (1 - A)(1 - B)$$
$$= A'B'$$

$$(c) \ (A \cup A) = A + A - AA = A(1 + A') = A + AA' = A = AA$$

$$(e) \ (A \cup B) - AB = A + B - AB - AB = A + B - 2AB$$
$$AB' \cup A'B = AB' + A'B - ABB'A' = A(1 - B) + B(1 - A)$$
$$= A - 2AB + B$$

$$(g) \ (A \cup B)C = (A + B - AB)C = AC + BC - ABC = AC + BC$$
$$-ABCC = AC \cup BC$$

8-5. (a) $AB'C'$ (c) ABC (e) $AB \cup AC \cup BC$

(g) $ABC' \cup AB'C \cup A'BC = (AB \cup AC \cup BC) - ABC$

(i) $(ABC)'$

8-9. From Prob. 8d,

$$(1 + u)^n = 1 + \binom{n}{1}u + \binom{n}{2}u^2 + \cdots + \binom{n}{n-1}u^{n-1} + u^n$$

and

$$(1 + u)^m = 1 + \binom{m}{1}u + \binom{m}{2}u^2 + \cdots + u^m$$

Similarly,

$$(1 + u)^{m+n} = 1 + \binom{m+n}{1}u + \binom{m+n}{2}u^2 + \cdots + u^{m+n}$$

Multiply the first two expressions term by term and equate to the preceding expression. Comparing coefficients of like powers of u, one obtains the desired result:

$$\binom{n+m}{1} = \binom{m}{1} + \binom{n}{1}$$

$$\binom{n+m}{2} = \binom{n}{2} + \binom{m}{1}\binom{n}{1} + \binom{m}{2}$$

$$\binom{n+m}{i} = \binom{n}{0}\binom{m}{i} + \cdots + \binom{n}{i}\binom{m}{0} \qquad i = 0, 1, 2, \ldots, n + m$$

8-22. We standardize the variable (and its limits) and use the unit normal.

$$\int_{u-\sigma}^{u+\sigma} n(x;\mu,\sigma)\,dx = \int_{-1}^{1} n(z,0,1) = 0.68$$

Similarly:

$$\int_{u-2\sigma}^{u+2\sigma} n(x;\mu,\sigma) = \int_{-2}^{2} n(z,0,1) = 0.95$$

and

$$\int_{u-3\sigma}^{u+3\sigma} n(x;\mu,\sigma) = \int_{-3}^{3} n(z,0,1) = 0.99$$

8-24. The graph of the function $y = e^{-x}$ is plotted as shown. The integral $\int_0^1 e^{-x}\,dx$ is simply the area under the curve. Using the table of random numbers in Appendix 4, select pairs of random decimals to represent the sample values of x and y shown in the following table.

	x	y
1	0.73	0.53
2	0.89	0.30
3	0.38	0.54
4	0.48	0.49
5	0.76	0.16
6	0.33	0.53
7	0.99	0.70
8	0.80	0.79
9	0.26	0.29
10	0.42	0.20

A quick estimate of area, after plotting these points, is 0.7 for 10 observations. (This is higher than the actual value of 0.63). For more accuracy, more trials are needed.

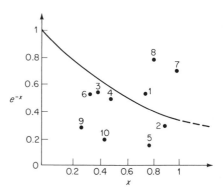

8-26. Let

A = event that two balls are red and white

U_i = event that the drawing took place in urn i, $i = 1, 2$

$$P(U_1|A) = \frac{P(U_1\,A)}{P(A)} = \frac{P(A|U_1)(P|U_1)}{P(AU_1) + P(AU_2)}$$

$$= \frac{P(A|U_1)P(U_1)}{P(A|U_1)P(U_1) + P(A|U_2)P(U_2)}$$

where

$$P(U_1) = P(U_2) = \tfrac{1}{2}, \text{ since each urn is equally likely to be chosen.}$$

And

$$P(A|U_i) = P\{\text{1st ball drawn is white and 2d drawn is red } \cup \\ \text{1st ball drawn is red and 2d drawn is white}\}$$

$$= \frac{w_i}{w_i + b_i + r_i} \frac{r_i}{(w_i + b_i + r_i) - 1} + \frac{r_i}{w_i + b_i + r_i}$$

$$\frac{w_i}{(w_i + b_i + r_i) - 1} \qquad i = 1, 2$$

since the two events in brackets are mutually exclusive.

CHAPTER 9

9-6. The marginal distribution of X is

$$f_1(x) = \int_0^1 6xy(2 - x - y)\,dy = 4x - 3x^2 \qquad 0 \leqslant x \leqslant 1$$

and the conditional density of Y given X, $\phi(y|x)$, is

$$\phi(y|x) = \frac{f(x,y)}{f_1(x)} = \frac{6y(2 - x - y)}{4 - 3x} \qquad 0 \leqslant x, y \leqslant 1$$

As Y varies between 0 and 1, the function $Z = X + Y$ varies from X to $X + 1$, and therefore the conditional density for Z, $\theta(z|x)$, is

$$\theta(z|x) = \phi[(z - x)|x]\frac{dy}{dz} = \frac{6(z - x)(2 - z)}{4 - 3x} \qquad \begin{matrix} x \leqslant z \leqslant x + 1 \\ 0 \leqslant x \leqslant 1 \end{matrix}$$

and

$$g_1(z,x) = f_1(x)\,\theta(z|x) = 6x(2 - z)(z - x) \qquad \begin{matrix} x \leqslant z \leqslant x + 1 \\ 0 \leqslant x \leqslant 1 \end{matrix}$$

For the marginal distribution of an integration on X is needed. The shaded rhombus indicates the admissible region.

$$g_1(z) = \int_0^z 6x(2-z)(z-x)\,dx = z^3(2-z) \quad 0 \leqslant z \leqslant 1$$

$$g_2(z) = \int_{z-1}^1 6x(2-z)(z-x)\,dx$$
$$= (2-z)^2(z^2+2z-2) \qquad 1 \leqslant z \leqslant 2$$

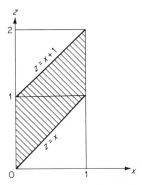

9-9. The probabilities for the number of rejects in either lot are binomial since we have repeated experiments with constant trial probabilities and only two outcomes—that is

$$P\{x_i = k\} = \binom{n_i}{k} p^k q^{n_i - k}$$

Let $Y = X_1 + X_2$. Is the sum binomial?
Fixing X_2,

$$P\{Y = k \mid X_2\} = P\{X_1 = k - X_2 \mid X_2\} = \binom{n_1}{k - x_2} p^{k - x_2} q^{n_1 - k + x_2}$$

$$P\{Y, X_2\} \quad = \binom{n_1}{k - x_2} p^{k - x_2} q^{n_1 - k + x_2} \binom{n_2}{x_2} p^{x_2} q^{n - x_2}$$

$$= \binom{n_1}{k - x_2}\binom{n_2}{x_2} p^k q^{n_1 + n_2 - k}$$

$$P(Y = k) \quad = \sum_{x_2 = 0}^{k} \binom{n_1}{k - x_2}\binom{n_2}{x_2} p^k q^{n-k} = \binom{n}{k} p^k q^{n-k}$$

where

$$n = n_1 + n_2$$

and since

$$\sum_{i=0}^{k} \binom{a}{i}\binom{b}{k-i} = \binom{a+b}{k}$$

CHAPTER 10

10-5. Let Y and X be the random demands in the first and second weeks, respectively, and S the amount on hand at the start of the first week plus the order quantity. Note that a decision on S does not affect costs in the first week. Two cases arise immediately: $S \geqslant Y$ and $S < Y$. These cases correspond to whether or not the second week begins with a positive or negative inventory.

If $S < Y$, then the second week begins with negative inventory, that is, a backlog. The shortage is increased by an amount $(X + Y) - S$. The expected cost of the second week in this instance is

$$\int_0^\infty \int_s^\infty C_s(x + y - S) f(y) f(x) dy \, dx$$

The integration limits are chosen to that $Y > S$ and X can take any nonnegative value.

If $S > Y$, then the second week begins with a positive inventory. However, the second week can end with either a positive or negative inventory depending upon the demand X.

If the second week ends with a positive inventory, say $S - (X + Y)$, only holding costs have been incurred so that the expected cost is

$$\int_0^s \int_0^{s-y} C_h(S - x - g) f(x) f(y) \, dx \, dy$$

The integration limits on X are chosen so that it does not exceed $S - Y$ in order to maintain a positive inventory and the limits on Y chosen so that the first week ends with a nonnegative inventory.

If the second week ends with negative inventory, say $X + Y - S$, then the expected cost is

$$\int_0^s \int_{s-y}^\infty C_s(x + y - S) f(x) f(y) \, dx \, dy$$

Again, integration limits are chosen using a similar logic.

The total expected cost is the sum of these expressions.

If the derivative (using Leibnitz' rule) of the total expected cost expression (with respect to S) is equated to zero, after some careful manipulation the expression in the problem statement is obtained.

10-14. For two contracts, $n = 2$, we have four contingencies:

1. win first and lose second
2. win second and lose first
3. win both
4. win neither

The expected profit function can be written

$$z = E(P_1(b_1), P_2(b_2)) = (b_1 - c_1)\,\alpha_1(b_1)\,[1 - \alpha_2(b_2)]$$
$$+ (b_2 - c_2)\,\alpha_2(b_2)\,[1 - \alpha_1(b_1)]$$
$$+ [(b_1 - c_{1,2}) + (b_2 - c_{2,1})]\,\alpha_1(b_1)\,\alpha_2(b_2)$$

where $P_1(b_1)$ and $P_2(b_2)$ are the random profit functions for the two contracts at the respective bids. For the given data

$$z = (b_1 - 2)\,\alpha_1(b_1)\,[1 - \alpha_2(b_2)] + (b_2 - 1)\,\alpha_2(b_2)\,[1 - \alpha_1(b_1)]$$
$$+ [b_1 + b_2 - 2.25]\,\alpha_1(b_1)\,\alpha_2(b_2)$$

$$\alpha_1(b_1) = \int_{b_1/c_1}^{\infty} 4\gamma_1 e^{-2\gamma_1}\,d\gamma_1 = 4e^{-2\gamma_1}\left[\frac{\gamma_1}{-2} - 1/4\right]_{b_1/2}^{\infty}$$
$$= b_1 e^{-b_1} + e^{-b_1} = (b_1 + 1)\,e^{-b_1}$$

$$\alpha_2(b_2) = \int_{b_2/c_2}^{\infty} \tfrac{1}{2}\,d\gamma_2 = \tfrac{1}{2}\int_{b_2/c_2}^{3} d\gamma_2 = 3/2 - b_2/2 = \frac{3 - b_2}{2}$$

Substituting

Max: $z' = (b_1 - 2)(b_1 + 1)\,e^{-b_1}[b_2/2 - \tfrac{1}{2}] + (b_2 - 1)\,[e^{b_1} - b_1 - 1]$
$$e^{-b_1}[3/2 - b_2/2] + [b_1 + b_2 - 2.25](b + 1)\,e^{-b_1}[3/2 - b_2/2]$$

Setting the derivative to zero yields the bids

$$b_1 \approx \$294{,}000$$
$$b_2 \approx \$192{,}000$$

for a maximum expected profit of $77,695.

Actually, we should recognize the possibility that it may be more profitable to bid only a single contract. In this instance the expected profits are

$$E(P_1(b_1)) \text{ yields } (b_1 - c_1)\,\alpha_1(b_1) \rightarrow \$20{,}615 \text{ with a bid of } \$330{,}000$$
$$(b_1/c_1 = 1.65)$$

$$E(P_2(b_2)) \text{ yields } (b_2 - c_2)\,\alpha_2(b_2) \rightarrow \$50{,}000 \text{ with a bid of } \$200{,}000$$
$$(b_2/c_2 = 2.0)$$

Hence, bid both contracts as indicated.

10-24.

$$L(N) = \frac{P + \sum \rho^n C(n) - S(n)}{N}$$

(a) neglecting interest, $\rho = 1$

Machine 1, P = $6,000

n	$C_1(n)$	$C_i(n)$	$S_1(n)$	$nL_1(n)$	$L_i(n)$
1	$1,800	$ 1,800	$4,500	$ 3,300	$3,300
2	2,200	4,000	4,000	6,000	3,000
3	2,400	6,400	3,500	8,900	2,967
4	2,800	9,200	3,000	12,200	3,050
5	3,200	12,400	2,500	15,900	3,180

Economic life = 3 years, $L_1(3)$ = $2,967.

Machine 2, P = $10,000

n	$C_2(n)$	$C_2(n)$	$S_2(n)$	$nL_2(n)$	$L_2(n)$
1	$1,000	$1,000	$9,600	$1,400	$1,400
2	1,200	2,200	9,200	3,000	1,500
3	1,600	3,800	8,800	5,000	1,667

Economic life = 1 year, $L_2(1)$ = $1,400.

The present machine should be replaced by the new machine whenever the yearly cost of the former exceeds $14,000, that is, now.

(b) Interest rate = 5%, $\rho = \dfrac{1.00}{1.05} - 0.952$

Machine 1

n	ρ^n	$\rho^n C_1(n)$	$\rho^n C_1(n)$	$\rho^n S_1(n)$	$nL_i(n)$	$L_i(n)$
1	0.952	$1,715	$ 1,715	$4,290	$ 3,425	$3,425
2	0.907	1,995	3,710	3,630	6,080	3,040
3	0.864	2,070	5,780	3,020	8,760	2,920
4	.823	2,300	8,080	2,465	11,615	2,904
5	.785	2,510	10.590	1,960	14,630	2,926

Economic life = 4 years, $L_1(4)$ = $2,904.

Machine 2

n	ρ^n	$\rho^n C_2(n)$	$\rho^n C_2(n)$	$\rho^n S_2(n)$	$nL_2(n)$	$L_2(n)$
1	0.952	\$ 952	\$ 952	\$9,150	\$1,802	\$1,802
2	0.907	1,088	2,040	8,350	3,690	1,845
3	0.864	1,380	3,420	7,600	5,820	1,940

Economic life = 1 year, $L_2(1) = \$1,802$.

Replace when the cost for an additional year of production exceeds $1,802. In the first year, the cost of retaining the first machine is $1,715 + $660 = \$2,375 (cost of operation and depreciation); therefore, it would be optimal to replace immediately.

CHAPTER 11

11-1. Since

$$f'(t) + \frac{h^2(t) - h'(t)}{h(t)} f(t) = 0$$

and

$$h(t) = \lambda_0 - \lambda t \qquad 0 < t \leqslant \frac{\lambda_0}{\lambda}$$

$$f'(t) + \frac{(\lambda_0 + \lambda t)^2 + \lambda}{\lambda_0 - \lambda t} f(t) = 0$$

Multiplying by the integrating factor

$$\exp \int \left(\lambda_0 - \lambda t + \frac{\lambda}{\lambda_0 - \lambda t} \right) dt$$

Therefore

$$\{ (\lambda_0 - \lambda t)^{-1} e^{(\lambda_0 t - \lambda t^2/2)} f(t) \}' = 0$$

Integrating, rearranging, and completing the square yields

$$\exp - \left(\lambda_0 t - \frac{\lambda t^2}{2} \right) = \exp + \frac{(\lambda_0 - \lambda t)^2 - \lambda_0^2}{2\lambda}$$

and integrating again,

$$\int_0^{\lambda_0/\lambda} f(t) dt = c_1 e^{-(\lambda_0^2)/2\lambda} \int_0^{\lambda_0/\lambda} (\lambda_0 - \lambda t) e^{(\lambda_0 - \lambda t)^2/2\lambda} dt$$

Let

$$\mu = \frac{(\lambda_0 - \lambda t)^2}{2\lambda}$$

$$= -c_2 \int_{\lambda_0{}^2/2\lambda}^{0} e^u \, du = -c_2(1 - e^{\lambda_0{}^2/2\lambda}) = 1$$

where

$$c_2 = 2c_1 e^{-(\lambda_0{}^2)/2\lambda}$$

therefore

$$f(t) = \frac{(\lambda_0 - \lambda t)e^{(\lambda_0 - \lambda t)^2/2\lambda}}{2(e^{(\lambda_0{}^2/2\lambda)} - 1)}$$

11-12. In Eq. (15) simply replace b by $2b$ and x by $2x$ to yield

$$\Omega'(x) = \begin{cases} \dfrac{(q/p)^{2b} - (q/p)^{2x}}{(q/p)^{2b} - 1} & q \neq p \\[2mm] 1 - \dfrac{x}{b} & q = p = \tfrac{1}{2} \end{cases}$$

Clearly

$$\Omega'(x) = \frac{(q/p)^{2b} - (q/p)^{2x}}{(q/p)^{2b} - 1} = \frac{(q/p)^b - (p/q)^x}{(q/p)^b - 1} \cdot \frac{(q/p)^b + (q/p)^x}{(q/p)^b + 1}$$

$$\Omega(x) \frac{(q/p)^b + (q/p)^x}{(q/p)^b + 1}$$

If the game is unfavorable, that is, $q > p$, then

$$\frac{(q/p)^b + (q/p)^x}{(q/p)^b + 1} > 1$$

so that the probability of our eventual ruin is increased as a consequence of the smaller stakes.

11-34. (a) $\lambda_n = \lambda = 1$; all n

$$\mu_n = \begin{cases} n\mu = 18/24n & n > 0 \\ 0 & n = 0 \end{cases}$$

From Eq. (33)

$$P_n = \frac{\rho^n}{n!} P_0 = \frac{\rho_n}{n!} e^{-\rho}$$

Since

$$\rho = \lambda/\mu = 4/3 \quad \text{and} \quad \sum P_n = 1$$

(b) $E(v) = \lambda^{-1} E(n) = \lambda^{-1} \sum_{n=0}^{\infty} n \frac{P_n}{n!} e^{-\rho} = \frac{\rho e^{-\rho}}{\lambda} \sum_{n=1}^{\infty} \frac{\rho^{n-1}}{(n-1)!} = \frac{\rho}{\lambda} = \frac{4}{3}$

CHAPTER 12

12-2.   Let $G(S)$ be the probability generating function for X.

(a) $P_x(k) = \frac{1}{6} \quad k = 1, 2, \ldots, 6$

$G(S) = \frac{1}{6}S + \frac{1}{6}S^2 + \cdots + \frac{1}{6}S^6$

$= \frac{1}{6} \frac{S + S^6}{1 - S} = \frac{S(1 - S^6)}{6 \ 1 - S}$

(b) $P\{x + 1 = k\} = P\{x = k - 1\} = P_{k-1} \quad k = 1, 2, \ldots$

$= p_0 S^1 + p_1 S^2 + \cdots = SG(S)$

(c) $P\{2x = 2k\} = P\{x = k\} = p_k \quad k = 0, 1, 2, \ldots$

$G_{2x}(S) \quad = p_0 + p_1 S^2 + p_2 S^4 + \cdots$

$= \sum_{k=0}^{\infty} p_k S^{2k} = \sum_{k=0}^{\infty} p_k (S^2)^k = G(S^2)$

12-6.   Let X_1 and X_2 be independent normally distributed random variables with parameters μ_1, σ_2 and μ_2, σ_2 respectively, and

$$Y_2 = X_1 + X_2$$

therefore

$$\Phi_Y(u) = \Phi_{X_1}(u) \Phi_{X_2}(u)$$

$$= \exp\left\{ iu\mu_1 - \frac{\sigma_1^2 u^2}{2} \right\} \exp\left\{ iu\mu_2 - \frac{\sigma_2^2 u^2}{2} \right\}$$

$$= \exp\left\{ iu(\mu_1 + \mu_2) - \left(\frac{\sigma_1^2 + \sigma_2^2}{2} \right) u^2 \right\}$$

which, because of the uniqueness property of characteristic functions, is the characteristic function of a normal variable mean $\mu_1 + \mu_2$ and variance $\sigma_1^2 + \sigma_2^2$.

The result easily generalizes for $n = 3, 4, \ldots$

Index

Index